QUALITATIVE ANALYSIS AND ELECTROLYTIC SOLUTIONS

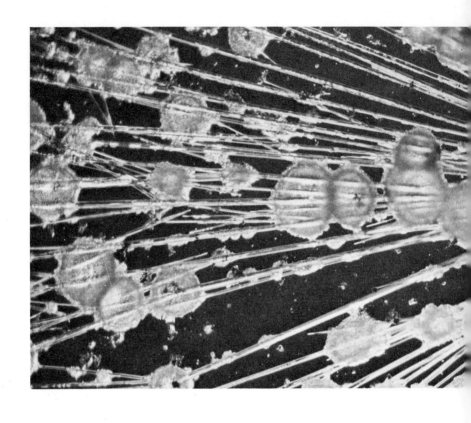

UNDER THE GENERAL EDITORSHIP OF *Larkin H. Farinholt*

Qualitative
Analysis
and
Electrolytic
Solutions

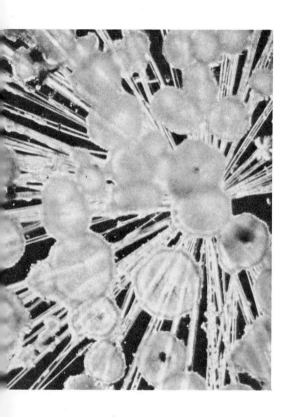

EDWARD J. KING

Barnard College,
Columbia University

HARCOURT, BRACE & WORLD, INC.   NEW YORK AND BURLINGAME

Illustrations by Tom Morgan

*Cover illustration is the boric acid crystal (see Fig. 2-4).
Title-page illustration is a photomicrograph of copper
carbonate (rods) and calcium carbonate (granules) by
L. C. Massopust, Marquette University.*

To
G. W. K.
and
A. W. K.

Preface

There is perhaps no other course in chemistry that has been the subject of more discussion than the course in qualitative analysis. Many teachers have labored mightily in recent years to defend it and to maintain its place in the curriculum. Like many of these I believe that qualitative analysis provides a remarkably appropriate setting for the presentation of chemical principles. This book has been written to express certain convictions of mine about the presentation of these principles and their integration with the laboratory work.

It is my conviction, for example, that the field of electrolytic solutions must be depicted as it is now, full both of new developments and of old problems still unsolved, an active, ever-expanding area of research. Accordingly, certain outmoded concepts such as "the apparent extent of ionization" have been eliminated, and in their place subjects of current interest have been presented, e.g., the structure of liquid water and the effect of ions on it. Any discussion of electrolytic solutions must bring out the difficulties of determining the structural units of solutes, both in the solid state and in solution. Reference is therefore made to such recent studies as, for example, those of sulfurous and carbonic acids. Moreover, I have thought it important to indicate now and again that there are many subjects on which authorities still disagree. In short, I have tried to write a textbook which is *not* a cemetery of old theories and experimental results.

It is also my conviction that a textbook of qualitative analysis should deal with the subject in some depth. For many students, e.g., those in biology and engineering, this course may be the last opportunity to acquire more insight into chemical principles. For prospective chemistry majors it must provide a thorough grounding for quantitative analysis and physical chemistry. At the same time, I have tried to design the book in such a way that each teacher can feel at liberty to lead his class in only to that depth which he considers to be safe. Each chapter is divided into sections; those that present more advanced material are self-contained units that can be assigned to the whole class, suggested as further reading to the better students, or omitted entirely.

The establishment of structural units in solids and solutions and the interpretation of their interactions are two central themes of this book. The point of view is largely based on simple electrostatics modified when necessary by polarization or formation of partially covalent bonds. The current revival of interest in the crystal field theory justifies discussion of bonding in complexes from the electrostatic point of view; the covalent, hybrid orbital theory would take an inordinate amount of space to develop properly. The treatment of interionic forces in solution has been scattered over several chapters (Secs. 5-13 to 5-15, 7-16, 8-7, 10-14 to 10-16, 11-13, and 12-5) in the belief that it is more digestible in small doses.

I also believe that problems and other exercises are an integral part of a course in qualitative analysis. More than 100 numerical problems are worked out in the text. The instructor can select problems for outside assignments from the more than 300 in the exercises at the ends of the chapters. To facilitate self-help, answers to all numerical problems are given in Appendix A. For general review there are also 75 problems, of varying types and levels of difficulty, in Appendix B. In addition to numerical problems, the text provides a large number of exercises that require qualitative discussion or explanation. Most of these are designed to make the student apply, rather than merely repeat, the knowledge acquired by study of the chapter. Frequently these take the form of quoting data and asking the student to supply an interpretation. Other exercises ask the student to prove various relations, for it is important that he gain skill in simple algebraic manipulations before undertaking the use of calculus in physical chemistry.

The approach to problem-solving taken in this text stresses careful analysis, development of a plan of attack, and recognition of simplifying assumptions. Certain perennial student problems are met head on. How do we solve quadratic equations? Why double and then square? How many figures should we carry in calculations? When can we neglect the hydrogen ion concentration? How do we handle negative logarithms? How do we extract roots and solve quadratic equations with a slide rule? The principles of electroneutrality (Sec. 4-12) and material balance (Sec. 4-13) are introduced to aid in understanding the simplifying assumptions that are customarily made in solving equilibrium problems and to provide a sound basis for the treatment of complex equilibria. I have not found these principles too difficult for freshmen to comprehend, but those sections in which they are put to extensive use, e.g., Secs. 10-7 and 11-12 and Chapter 13, are separate units and can be omitted in brief courses. Mastery of the principles makes it possible for a student to judge for himself when approximations are valid and to be free from reliance on a store of memorized formulas which hold only in limited ranges of concentration and equilibrium constants.

Each instructor must decide for himself which aspects of the first fifteen chapters to cover, for to a large extent this will depend on the preparation of his students. For a sophomore course that follows a good full-year course in general chemistry, Chapters 1 to 4 will be largely review and can be passed over rapidly; time will then be available for the more advanced material of later chapters. When qualitative analysis is given with the second term of general chemistry, it is suggested that sections marked with asterisks in the table of contents be omitted. It is my hope that the organization of the book is sufficiently flexible to make it adaptable to almost any type of course in qualitative analysis.

Chapters 16 to 25 are concerned with the laboratory practice of qualitative analysis; they also include extended discussions of the descriptive chemistry of the ions. In all cases a structural basis is sought for the behavior of ions and periodic relations are stressed. The anions, for example, are treated in Chapter 22 according to the position of the nonmetals in the Periodic Table, rather than grouped according to the relatively trivial ability or inability to form precipitates with certain cations. Extensive cross references are given to the first fifteen chapters so the laboratory and lecture material can be seen as intimately related. For convenience the table of atomic weights, the periodic chart, and the table of common logarithms have been inserted between Chapters 15 and 16.

The principal justification for the laboratory work in qualitative analysis is the demonstration that it provides of the triumphs as well as the limitations of our theoretical insights into the behavior of electrolytic solutions and precipitates. It is my conviction that conventional qualitative procedures are of proved pedagogical value when used intelligently and flexibly. Experienced teachers will therefore find little that is novel in the laboratory procedures. The anions are largely detected by individual tests, but a semisystematic procedure is given for classifying some of them into groups and for detecting the halide ions in the presence of each other. This is an adaptation of the scheme of Belcher and Weisz (*Mikrochim. Acta*, **1956**, 1847; **1958**, 571) for the eighteen most popular anions and can readily be expanded to include seventeen more if the instructor so desires.

Eight years of experience have convinced me that thioacetamide, far from being simply an acceptable substitute for hydrogen sulfide, is superior to it in many respects. The procedures in this text are accordingly based on the use of thioacetamide, although with a few slight modifications indicated in the text, hydrogen sulfide gas can be substituted if the instructor prefers. The elimination of evil-smelling, poisonous hydrogen sulfide is the foremost advantage of thioacetamide; it has the further advantages of giving purer, more crystalline precipitates and of precipitating arsenic(V) without special treatment. The lack of success in using thioacetamide reported by some teachers appears to be largely the consequence of trying to apply it on too large a scale. It works best on samples of 10-25 mg and volumes up to 3 ml. On this true semimicro scale precipitation is almost invariably complete within five minutes. The sample must be heated in vigorously boiling water, and it is advisable to use a fairly concentrated solution of thioacetamide. These precautions are more effective when the sample is kept small.

It is sometimes objected that we do not know enough about the action of thioacetamide to justify its use in a beginning course. In point of fact little is known after all these years about the detailed mechanism of precipitation of sulfides by hydrogen sulfide gas. Thanks to the pioneering work of Professors E. H. Swift and T. I. Taylor, we are now beginning to learn something about the kinetics of reaction of thioacetamide. Here then is a frontier area under active investigation in which the boundaries of our understanding are gradually being pushed back before the student's eyes. What better illustration can there be that qualitative analysis is not a moribund subject but one that derives fresh stimulus from current work? We can capitalize further on what has been learned about thioacetamide in recent years and use its behavior to illustrate the principles of homogeneous kinetics, hydrogen ion catalysis, and precipitation from homogeneous medium. At the same time, the use of classical equilibrium considerations is still valid as long as the rate of precipitation of sulfides is governed by the rate of hydrolysis of thioacetamide. The advantages of this reagent thus far outweigh its disadvantages.

The scheduling of the laboratory work will depend markedly on the hours available and the relative emphasis given to introductory experiments, group unknowns, and general unknowns. I have attempted to devise interesting and challenging introductory experiments for the cations and to avoid experiments which are purely routine verification of statements in the text. It is my conviction that introductory experiments should be kept to a minimum in order that more time can be devoted to analysis. The cation groups are presented in the normal sequence (Chapters 17 to 21) in order that students may not become confused about the general plan of cation analysis. A good case can be made, however, for starting with the simpler chemistry and techniques of Cation Group 5 (Chapter 21). Before the analysis of the first known and unknown solutions is made, it is advisable to perform the introductory experiments of Chapter 21 in order to acquire the necessary practice in techniques. (If the instructor prefers to start with Cation Group 1, he will find the directions and references in Chapter 17 sufficiently detailed.) After Cation Group 5 any one of several sequences can be followed. One which leads the students from simple to more complex chemistry and from easy to more difficult techniques is as follows: Cation Group 4 (Chapter 20), Anions (Chapters 22 and 23), Cation Group 1 (Chapter 17), Cation Group 2 (Chapter 18), Cation Group 3 (Chapter 19), and Special Methods (Chapter 25). If more time is available, one or more simple salts or general unknowns can be analyzed (Chapter 24). Chapter 25, which deals with spot testing, chromatography, and other special methods, makes a stimulating climax to the work of the term.

This book would hardly have been written were it not for the introduction to recent research on electrolytes that I received under the tutelage of Professors H. S. Harned and B. B. Owen. The theories and experimental results summarized in their classic monograph, *The Physical Chemistry of Electrolytic Solutions*, have been invaluable guides; any errors in simplifying them for first and second year college students are mine. Professor Owen and Dr. Marshall Alpert kindly made available their data on the ionization of the dihydrogen phosphate ion in sodium chloride solutions for use in Fig. 11-2. This text owes much also to the well-known books of MacInnes, Ricci, and Robinson and Stokes, and to numerous original articles. If I have cited only a few of the latter, perhaps their authors will understand that a book at this level cannot be burdened too heavily with scholarly annotations. Professor Martin Paul, Dr. Gloria Toralballa, and Miss Lenore Meadows used preliminary versions of this book and were most generous with helpful advice. Professor Larkin H. Farinholt's editorial advice was extremely helpful, as were the readings given the manuscript by Professors Ralph H. Petrucci and Richard Bersohn and the galley proofs by Professor John E. Cavelti. Professor Helen R. Downes gave me every encouragement to forge ahead and valiantly read several chapters in proof. My students over the past years are perhaps not aware of the extent to which they too have contributed to this book. I am particularly indebted to Misses Betty Freiman, Lorraine Gold, Susan Rubin, and Jane Weissman for helping me with various aspects of the work. My wife, Dr. Grace W. King, has sustained me in the struggle and has made one of the most important contributions, the index. Finally, the character of this book owes much to Mrs. Judy (Weitzman) Meyer of Harcourt, Brace and Company, who before her untimely death patiently guided me through countless difficulties in the preparation of the manuscript.

EDWARD J. KING

New York, N.Y.
February 1959

Contents

* Sections preceded by an asterisk may be omitted at the instructor's discretion.

xiii

Appendixes 595

Index 623

QUALITATIVE ANALYSIS AND ELECTROLYTIC SOLUTIONS

CHAPTER ONE

Water

1-1. A Familiar but Extraordinary Liquid. It is appropriate to begin the study of qualitative analysis and electrolytic solutions with an examination of the properties of water. Almost all the analytical reactions occur in this solvent, and its peculiar nature is responsible for the participation of ions in these reactions. Ions can exist in water to an extent that far surpasses that in any other common solvent. Like many familiar, seemingly simple things, water is extraordinary in its behavior and complex in its structure.

Some of these peculiarities are common knowledge. Water has the rare ability to float its own solid form, ice. Because of this, lakes freeze first at the surface, and pipes containing water may burst as the water freezes. When heated above its melting point, water contracts until it attains its maximum density at 4°C. Above this temperature it expands when heated as most liquids do. The specific heat of water—that is, the heat required to raise the temperature of a gram of it one degree—is greater than that of other common liquids. Thus large bodies of water can absorb or give off a considerable amount of heat without much change in temperature, and they help to maintain a uniform climate in adjacent lands.

1-2. Some Less Familiar Peculiarities of Water. Though composed of simple, light molecules, water has a remarkably high melting point and boiling point. Its heat of vaporization—the energy required to vaporize a gram of water at its boiling point—is also unusually large. These and other properties of water are compared in Table 1-1 with those of ammonia and hydrogen fluoride, the hydrides of elements on either side of oxygen in the Periodic Table. The boiling point of water is shown in Fig. 1-1 in comparison with those of hydrogen sulfide, hydrogen selenide, and hydrogen telluride, the hydrides of the other elements in Group VIB of the Periodic Table. For comparison the boiling points of the hydrides of the elements in Group IVB are also given. Starting with the second compound the hydrides of the two series show a parallel increase in boiling point with increase in number of electrons per molecule. But water, instead of boiling at about −110°, as we would expect if methane were a reliable guide, boils at +100°.

TABLE 1-1.

Some Properties of Water and Related Liquids

	NH₃	H₂O	HF
Molecular weight	17	18	20
Melting point, °C	−78	0	−83
Boiling point, °C	−33	100	20
Heat of vaporization, cal/g	327	540	360
Dielectric constant at 0°	19.6	88.0	83.6

1-3. The High Dielectric Constant of Water, Another Peculiarity. Water is differentiated from all but a few other liquids by its high *dielectric constant*. The significance of this property is most readily understood by reference to *Coulomb's law*. Suppose two particles bearing charges q_1 and q_2 are separated

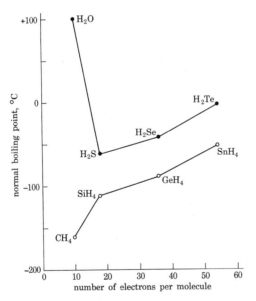

FIG. 1-1. The boiling points of some hydrides.

by a distance d that is large in comparison with the size of the particles. The force between the particles varies directly as the product of the charges and inversely as the square of the distance between them. But the same charges separated to the same extent act on each other with less force when they are immersed in alcohol than when they are in air and with still less force when they are immersed in water. To express this effect of the medium a factor D, the dielectric constant of the medium, is introduced into Coulomb's law, which then takes the form

$$\text{Force} = \frac{q_1 q_2}{D d^2} \qquad \qquad 1$$

Another version of Coulomb's law gives the work required to move two charges further apart. Either the force or the work varies inversely with the dielectric constant. The work required to increase by the same amount the distance between each pair of charges shown in Fig. 1-2 will be $\frac{1}{80}$ as much

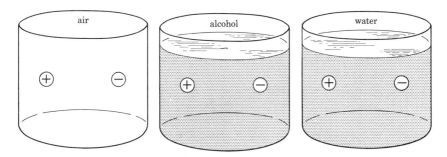

FIG. 1-2. Interaction between charges.

in water as in air, and $\frac{1}{24}$ as much in alcohol as in air. The numbers 1, 24, and 80 are the approximate dielectric constants of air, alcohol, and water at room temperature. Furthermore

$$\frac{\text{Work required in water}}{\text{Work required in alcohol}} = \frac{\text{dielectric constant of alcohol}}{\text{dielectric constant of water}} = \frac{24}{80}$$

or only 30% as much work is required to move the charges further apart in water as in alcohol. Because the force between ions is comparatively weak in water, ions can exist with extraordinary freedom in this solvent.

The dielectric constants of representative liquids are given in Table 1-2. For an evacuated space the dielectric constant is taken to be 1.0000 and that of air is close to unity. Many organic solvents have dielectric constants between 2 and 10. Dioxane, benzene, diethyl ether, and ethyl acetate are typical of such liquids. Others, particularly the alcohols, have dielectric constants between 20 and 35. Only a few liquids have dielectric constants larger than that of water. The values in the table are those of the liquids at 25°. The dielectric constants decrease as the temperature is raised. For water at 0° the value is 88.0, at 25° it is 78.5, and at 100°, 55.3. Thus the work required to move charged particles further apart is greater at higher temperatures.

TABLE 1-2.

Dielectric Constants of Some Liquids at 25°

	Formula	Dielectric constant
Dioxane	$C_4H_8O_2$	2.213
Benzene	C_6H_6	2.275
Diethyl ether	$C_4H_{10}O$	4.23
Ethyl acetate	$C_4H_8O_2$	6.02
Acetone	C_3H_6O	20.7
Ethyl alcohol	C_2H_5OH	24.30
Methyl alcohol	CH_3OH	32.63
Water	H_2O	78.54
Hydrogen sulfate (anhydrous)	H_2SO_4	101
Hydrogen cyanide (anhydrous)	HCN	107

1-4. The Structure of Water Molecules. The extraordinary properties of water arise from the concerted behavior of large communities of water molecules. Before considering this, let us examine the structure of the individual molecules. No single drawing can represent all their significant features. How we picture the water molecule will depend on what aspect of it we need to emphasize. Various useful representations are collected in Fig. 1-3.

Some of these pictures emphasize the size and shape of the molecule. Figure 1-3a shows that the hydrogen and oxygen nuclei do not lie on a straight line but are at the corners of a triangle. We cannot see a water molecule, but we can obtain some idea of its size and shape by the repulsion it exerts on other molecules brought close to it. This is the same method we use to find the shape of a pitch-dark room, except that we usually speak of hitting the wall rather than of being repelled by it. Such a picture of the water molecule is given in Fig. 1-3b. To show that atoms are not little hard balls with their electrons confined to volumes of fixed size, the boundaries of the molecule have been left hazily defined. When we want to show the interactions of water molecules with other particles it is usually sufficient to draw the atoms as small balls and the bonds as sticks, as in Fig. 1-3c, d, e.

Other pictures emphasize the electronic structure and distribution of charge within the molecule. The covalent bonds between the atoms are shown most simply as a pair of electrons shared between each hydrogen nucleus and the oxygen, as in Fig. 1-3f. There are two other *lone pairs* of electrons in the outer shell of the oxygen atom which are not used for bonding. This picture is oversimplified, for the electrons are not in a single plane but so distributed in space as to be concentrated toward the corners of a regular tetrahedron, as shown in Fig. 1-3g. Electrons in a molecule rotate in no fixed orbits and are not confined in any definite volume. They are nevertheless localized in certain regions of the molecule. Such a localized region where the electron spends most of its time is called an *orbital*. There can be at most only two electrons in an orbital. They will have equal energies but opposite spins. In the water molecule the two pairs of bonding electrons and the two lone pairs occupy four lobe-shaped orbitals directed to the corners of a tetrahedron. These orbitals in Fig. 1-3*h* are pictured with definite boundaries so defined that the chance of finding an electron inside is 90%, and only 10% of the time will it be expected to be outside. An important consequence of the arrangement of orbitals in the water molecule is that the molecule is polar.

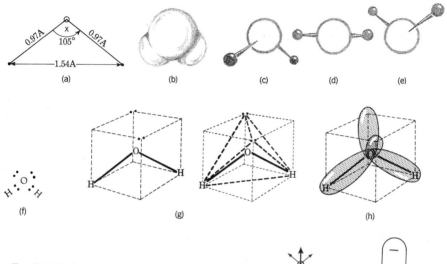

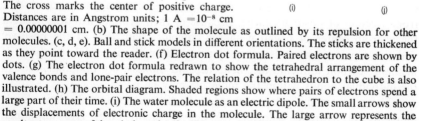

FIG. 1-3. Various representations of a water molecule. (a) The geometry of the molecule. Open circle, oxygen nucleus; closed circles, hydrogen nuclei. The cross marks the center of positive charge. Distances are in Angstrom units; 1 A $=10^{-8}$ cm = 0.00000001 cm. (b) The shape of the molecule as outlined by its repulsion for other molecules. (c, d, e). Ball and stick models in different orientations. The sticks are thickened as they point toward the reader. (f) Electron dot formula. Paired electrons are shown by dots. (g) The electron dot formula redrawn to show the tetrahedral arrangement of the valence bonds and lone-pair electrons. The relation of the tetrahedron to the cube is also illustrated. (h) The orbital diagram. Shaded regions show where pairs of electrons spend a large part of their time. (i) The water molecule as an electric dipole. The small arrows show the displacements of electronic charge in the molecule. The large arrow represents the resultant moment of the whole molecule. The arrow heads point to the negative end of each dipole. (j) A simplified picture of the water dipole.

1-5. Polar Molecules. Particles that contain centers of positive and negative charge in different locations are electric dipoles, and a molecule containing a dipole is called a *polar molecule*. In the water molecule one positive charge resides in each hydrogen nucleus, and eight in the oxygen nucleus. The center of positive charge is thus somewhat below the oxygen nucleus or at the cross in Fig. 1-3*a*. The center of negative charge must be higher for two reasons. First, there is a displacement of electrons in the bonds toward the more electronegative oxygen atom. Each bond is therefore polar. Second, the negative charge carried by the lone-pair electrons is localized largely above the oxygen nucleus as shown in Fig. 1-3*g, h*. The four displacements of charge are represented by small arrows in Fig. 1-3*i*. The heavy arrow stands for the resultant displacement of charge in the molecule as a whole. The simplified picture in Fig. 1-3*j* is a convenient and frequently adequate representation of the water dipole.

A quantitative measure of polarity is provided by the *dipole moment.* Consider a dipole that has two opposite charges of magnitude *q* separated by a distance *d*. The dipole moment *m* is defined as the product of *d* and *q*:

$$m = dq \qquad\qquad\qquad \textbf{2}$$

It is expressed in debye units, which are so scaled that a dipole in which *q* has the magnitude of the charge on the proton or electron and *d* is one angstrom unit or 0.00000001 cm would have a dipole moment of 4.80 debyes.[1] Figure 1-4 gives a schematic picture of the effect of distance and charge on

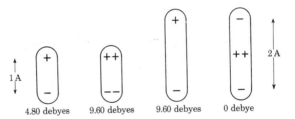

FIG. 1-4. Dipole moment and the debye unit.

dipole moment. In the right-hand picture two negative charges are equidistant from a center of positive charge. Because of their symmetrical arrangement the over-all center of negative charge coincides with that of the positive, and the dipole moment is zero. Symmetrical molecules such as those of methane, carbon tetrachloride, benzene, and dioxane are nonpolar, though the individual bonds within the molecule may be polar.

There are many polar molecules. Some examples with their dipole moments are: hydrogen chloride, 1.08 debyes; diethyl ether, 1.15; ammonia,

[1]The electrostatic unit of charge is defined by means of Coulomb's law (Eq. 1). Force is expressed in dynes, one dyne being required to accelerate a gram by one centimeter per second per second. Two particles bearing equal charges, situated one centimeter apart in an evacuated space ($D=1$), and acting on each other with a force of one dyne are assigned charges of one electrostatic unit (esu) or statcoulomb. One electron bears a charge of -4.80×10^{-10} esu. Three million esu would be required to neutralize the charge on enough silver ions to plate out about one milligram of silver. In Eq. 2 for the dipole moment the charge is usually some fraction of the electronic charge, or about 10^{-10} esu, and the distance is in angstroms or 10^{-8} cm. The dipole moments of most molecules are thus around $10^{-10} \times 10^{-8}$ or 10^{-18} esu-cm. This is one debye unit.

1.3; ethyl alcohol, 1.69; acetic acid, 1.74; ethyl acetate, 1.78; water, 1.84; hydrogen fluoride, 1.91; hydrogen cyanide, 2.95; and the amino acid glycine, 15. The dipole moment of water is seen to be large but not exceptionally so.

A molecule may be expected to be polar if it is made of atoms that differ in electronegativity or attraction for electrons in a covalent bond and if the atoms are not arranged symmetrically. The structures of hydrogen fluoride, water, ammonia, and methane molecules are shown in Fig. 1-5. The dipole

FIG. 1-5. The electronic structure and dipole moment of some simple hydrides. Small arrows show displacements of bonding electrons; heavy arrows stand for the dipole moments of the molecules as a whole. Dots stand for lone pair electrons.

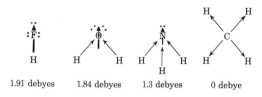

1.91 debyes   1.84 debyes   1.3 debyes   0 debye

moments follow the order of electronegativity of the nonmetal. The fluorine atom is most electronegative and attracts electrons most strongly away from the hydrogen atom. In hydrogen fluoride there are also three lone pairs that contribute to the moment. In methane the symmetrical arrangement of the bonds precludes any dipole moment for the molecule as a whole. In a series of compounds such as the hydrides of Group VIB there is a decrease in electronegativity and increase in size of the nonmetal atom with increasing atomic number. The dipole moments fall from 1.84 for water to 0.92 for hydrogen sulfide and down to 0.24 for hydrogen selenide. The dipole moment of hydrogen telluride is unknown, but it must be considerably less than 0.24. In hydrogen selenide the Se—H bonds are not very polar, so that little displacement of charge occurs. The effect of the lone pairs is also less in the large selenium atom than it is in the smaller atoms of sulfur and oxygen.

1-6. Weak Interactions Between Water Molecules. The simplest organization of water molecules is found in water vapor at high temperatures and low pressures. The molecules are far apart, move at random, and exert little force on each other. The extraordinary character of water is not evident here. As water vapor is cooled and compressed, the molecules move about less rapidly and are closer together on the average. Various interactions between them become important. All molecules when brought sufficiently near each other show a weak attraction caused by mutual distortion of electronic structures. This *van der Waals attraction* increases with the number of electrons in the molecule and is the cause of the steady increase in boiling point from hydrogen sulfide to hydrogen telluride and from methane to stannane (SnH_4) shown in Fig. 1-1. This weak attraction changes to repulsion when the molecules approach each other so closely that their electron shells begin to overlap. Water molecules are subject to these attractive and repulsive forces, but the attraction is stronger than that between two non-polar molecules. This is a result of the interaction between the dipoles, as shown in Fig. 1-6. Water vapor is thus more readily condensible than vapor composed of nonpolar molecules like nitrogen. Even so, the behavior of water vapor does not give much insight into the peculiar nature of the liquid.

FIG. 1-6. Interactions between dipoles.

The structure of ice, a more highly organized community of water molecules, will provide the necessary clues.

1-7. The Structure of Ice.   Like all crystals, ice is built of particles arranged in an orderly pattern or lattice, which can be established by the technique of x-ray diffraction (see Sec. 2-4). Each water molecule in the crystal is surrounded by four others, as shown in Fig. 1-7. The distance

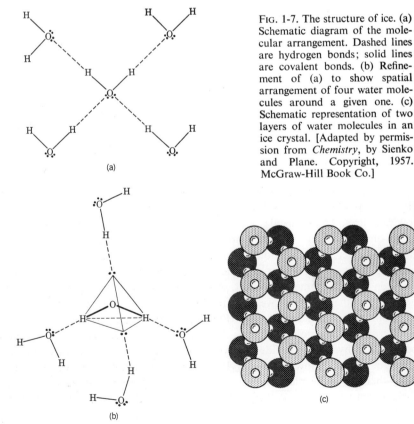

FIG. 1-7. The structure of ice. (a) Schematic diagram of the molecular arrangement. Dashed lines are hydrogen bonds; solid lines are covalent bonds. (b) Refinement of (a) to show spatial arrangement of four water molecules around a given one. (c) Schematic representation of two layers of water molecules in an ice crystal. [Adapted by permission from *Chemistry*, by Sienko and Plane. Copyright, 1957. McGraw-Hill Book Co.]

between nearest oxygen nuclei is 2.76 A. The packing of the molecules in a small fragment of an ice crystal is illustrated in Fig. 1-7c. The crystal lattice is seen to have large holes in it. This is consistent with the low density of ice. If ice were made up of spheres of diameter 2.76 A closely packed together, one gram of ice would occupy 0.50 ml. Since its specific volume is actually 1.09 ml/g or more than twice as large, the molecules must be loosely packed. The close packing of argon atoms in the lattice of that substance is shown in Fig. 1-8 for comparison.

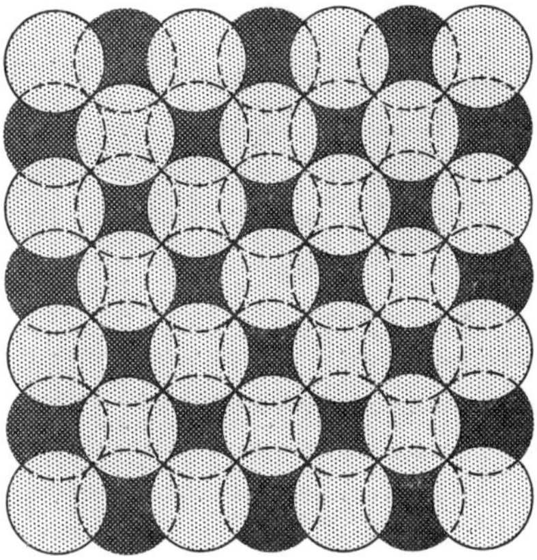

FIG. 1-8. Two layers of closely packed atoms in a crystal of argon.

1-8. Strong Interactions Between Water Molecules. The forces that hold water molecules in the ice lattice are a special type called *hydrogen bonds* or hydrogen bridges. They are represented in Fig. 1-7 by dashed lines. Hydrogen bonds are less than one-tenth as strong as covalent bonds such as those that join oxygen and hydrogen atoms within a molecule. They are nevertheless much stronger than van der Waals and dipole-dipole forces. Solid hydrogen sulfide, in which the molecules are held together only by these weak forces, melts at $-86°$, while ice must be heated to $0°$ before thermal agitation of the molecules overcomes the stronger hydrogen bonds and causes a breakdown of the crystal.

A second feature of hydrogen bonds is evident from their role in ice: they are confined to certain directions. In this respect they resemble covalent bonds and differ from van der Waals forces or the action of charges which extend in all directions. All O—H $\cdots\cdots$ O bridges in ice are linear. It is this requirement that causes the molecules to spread out to give the open lattice of ice.

1-9. The Structure of Liquid Water. Liquid water can best be described as partially broken-down ice. As ice melts, the hydrogen bonds bend and some of them break. The open framework of the crystal collapses so that a more closely packed structure of higher density results for the liquid, as illustrated in Fig. 1-9. Each water molecule is still bound to several others, but somewhat more than four other molecules are now packed around it. Patches of highly organized molecules persist as the temperature is increased.

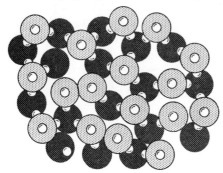

FIG. 1-9. Schematic representation of the structure of liquid water. [Adapted by permission from *Chemistry*, by Sienko and Plane. Copyright, 1957. McGraw-Hill Book Co.]

At 4°, the temperature of maximum density, the collapse of the ice structure has its maximum effect. From here to the boiling point the density of the liquid decreases as increasing thermal agitation causes the molecules to move away from each other. Hydrogen bonding still persists in liquid water at 100°, as shown by its abnormally high heat of vaporization and boiling point.

1-10. Hydrogen Bonding in Other Liquids. The existence of hydrogen bonds is inferred from abnormally high boiling points, dielectric constants, heats of sublimation or vaporization; from abnormalities in the spectrum of the liquid; and from the results of diffraction experiments. By these tests hydrogen bonds are formed by ammonia, hydrogen fluoride, the alcohols, and many acids and basic hydroxides. Almost all biological processes, from the construction of proteins within a living cell to the attachment of dirt to the skin, involve hydrogen bonds.

Though the existence of this special bond cannot be doubted, its exact nature is still in dispute. The hydrogen atom is always between two electronegative atoms, usually nitrogen, oxygen, or fluorine. This suggests that the bond is partly electrostatic in nature. Thus in the bridge $O_A^- - H^+ \cdots \cdot^- O_B$ there is an attraction between the right-hand oxygen atom (O_B) and the positive hydrogen atom. A covalent contribution results from some delocalization of the electrons of O_B, so that they spend part of their time around H and O_A. A third, ever-present attraction is the van der Waals interaction. Opposing these three attractive forces is a repulsion caused by the proximity of the oxygen atoms O_A and O_B. The success of hydrogen in forming such a stable bridge is attributed to its small size and lack of inner closed electron shells. This makes it possible for the positive charge of the hydrogen nucleus to get very close to the negative charges on other atoms. Other electropositive atoms such as those of lithium or sodium do not form bridges because the repulsion between their inner shells and those of the electronegative atoms is too strong.

Many substances form hydrogen bonds, but those of water are unique. Ammonia and hydrogen fluoride molecules, though they contain the same number of electrons as do water molecules, cannot build up elaborate networks in space as the water molecules do in ice. The ammonia molecule (Fig. 1-5) has three hydrogen atoms that can form bonds with other molecules, but it has only one lone pair of electrons to attract a hydrogen. Ammonia has plenty of money, so to speak, and not enough places to spend it. Hydrogen fluoride has three lone pairs of electrons but only one hydrogen. Its molecules associate to give rings and chains, not lattices. The water molecule has two hydrogen atoms to form bonds and two lone pairs to attract hydrogen atoms from other molecules. It is this balance of money and places to spend it that makes possible the special structure of ice.

1-11. The Relation Between Dipole Moment and Dielectric Constant. Because the water molecule is polar we expect its dielectric constant to be somewhat higher than those of nonpolar liquids such as benzene or carbon tetrachloride. But the dipole moment, which is a property of a single water molecule, is not abnormally high whereas the dielectric constant, which is a property of a large collection of molecules, is unusually large. There must be cooperation between water molecules to account for this, and hydrogen bonding makes this cooperation possible. Hydrogen bonding is responsible for the very high dielectric constant of water. We shall return to this point again after considering the relation between the dielectric constant of a liquid and the polarity of its molecules.

The connection between dielectric constant and dipole moment is most readily observed in the behavior of electrical capacitors (formerly called condensers). A simple capacitor is made of two separate, parallel metal plates connected to a battery, as shown in Fig. 1-10a. The battery, by doing electrical work, can pull electrons off one plate, leaving it positively charged, and push them onto the other, making it negatively charged. The flow of electrons from one plate to another through the wires and battery will quickly stop because the pile-up of charge on the plates opposes further transfer. The higher the voltage applied by the battery to the plates, the greater the charge that can be put on them. The *capacitance* of the capacitor is defined as the ratio of the charge built up on either plate to the applied voltage. A charged particle such as an ion inserted in the space between the plates is subjected to an electrical force because of the *electric field*. This force, which draws the ion to the oppositely charged plate, is proportional to the charge per unit area of plate.

The capacitance of the capacitor is increased when the space between the plates is filled with a liquid. Suppose that the liquid is made up of polar molecules. Before the plates are charged, the dipoles lie every which way (Fig. 1-10b). As the capacitor is charged, the dipoles turn so that their charged ends point to the oppositely charged plates. The continual thermal agitation of the molecules prevents this lining-up from being perfect (Fig. 1-10c). In effect, the line-up of the dipoles produces layers of positive and

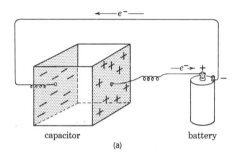

FIG. 1-10. Polar liquid in a capacitor. (a) Charging the capacitor. (b) Random orientation of polar molecules between uncharged plates. (c) Partial line-up of molecules between charged plates. Arrows show direction of rotation of some of the molecules. (d) Effective distribution of charge caused by orientation of polar molecules.

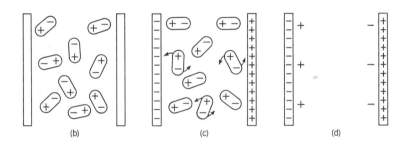

negative charge at the surfaces of the liquid next to the plates (Fig. 1-10d). This decreases the electric field between the plates, because the charge on them which causes the field is partially neutralized by the charges at the surfaces of the liquid, but the battery restores the field to its original value by transferring more charge to the plates. Thus the capacitance of the capacitor is increased by filling the space between the plates with liquid. The greater the dipole moment of the liquid molecules, the greater the increase in charge and capacitance.

Coulomb's law leads us to expect the force acting on an ion between the plates of a capacitor to vary directly with the charge per unit area of plate and inversely with the dielectric constant of the liquid. The larger the dielectric constant, the greater the charge required to maintain a given force on the ion. If we take the dielectric constant of empty space to be unity, the dielectric constant of the liquid can be expressed as

Dielectric constant of the liquid

$$= \frac{\text{capacitance of capacitor filled with liquid}}{\text{capacitance of empty capacitor}} \qquad 3$$

The capacitance of a capacitor filled with water is thus about 80 times that of an empty one.

Nonpolar liquids also have dielectric constants greater than unity. This comes about because the field induces a temporary displacement of charge within the molecules. The electrons in the molecules are so displaced that the centers of positive and negative charge no longer coincide. The molecule is said to be *polarized* by the field and has an induced dipole moment. This occurs too with polar molecules, but the effect of the induced moment is small in comparison with that of the permanent moment. The dielectric constants of nonpolar liquids are low—only about twice that of an evacuated space.

The dielectric constants of hydrogen-bonded liquids are abnormally large. The hydrogen bonds tie together molecules into large aggregates with a total dipole moment many times that of a simple molecule. This is particularly true for water, which contains large three-dimensional networks of molecules, and for hydrogen fluoride and hydrogen cyanide, which contain chains of molecules. In ammonia, hydrogen bonding cannot build up large aggregates (Sec. 1-10), and the dielectric constant of liquid ammonia is considerably lower than that of water or hydrogen fluoride (Table 1-1).

1-12. The Ionization of Water. Pure water is a very poor conductor of electricity. The feeble conductance is caused by the presence of very small amounts of two charged particles: the hydronium or oxonium ion, H_3O^+, and the hydroxide ion, OH^-. These are formed by the reaction

$$H_2O + H_2O \rightarrow H_3O^+ + OH^-$$

A molecular picture of this reaction is given in Fig. 1-11. There is a shift of a hydrogen nucleus, or proton, from one molecule to another.

The feeble conductance of water results from the motion of the ions in the electric field. The positive hydronium ion travels toward the negative electrode, the negative hydroxide ion toward the positive electrode. The migration is in part like the motion of a submarine: the ion pushes water aside as it moves toward the electrode. Yet the positive and negative charges actually move more than five times as rapidly as one might expect for submarine-like motion. To account for this speed it is assumed that the charge is carried mostly by a series of proton shifts similar to those that occur in ionization (Fig. 1-12). The proton shift itself requires about 0.00000000000001 or 10^{-14} second, but the shift cannot occur until the next water molecule is lined up to receive it. By way of analogy, consider a field so densely crowded with people that a man carrying a football across the field makes very slow progress because he has to push people aside. If the football is handed from one person to another it gets across the field faster, but if people are moving around at random and have to turn to receive the ball, its passage is delayed. It has been calculated that a proton remains on a particular water molecule at least 25 times as long as the time required for the shift. Since protons spend

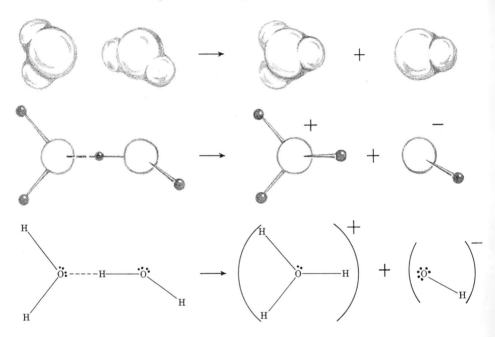

FIG. 1-11. The ionization of water

more time attached to a water molecule than they do in shifting, it is proper to treat the hydronium ion as an entity, though any one such ion persists for only a very short time.

The addition of another proton to the lone pair of electrons in a hydronium ion, to give the H_4O^{++} ion, and the loss of a proton by a hydroxide ion, to give the oxide ion, O^{--}, are conceivable, but neither occurs to a detectable extent in water. Nor does water contain an appreciable amount of free, unhydrated protons. The proton is an exceptionally concentrated positive charge unscreened by orbital electrons. If a 1-mm dot on the blackboard is taken to represent the comparative size of a proton, a sodium ion would have a radius of about 100 feet. The nuclear charge in a sodium ion can be brought nowhere as close to the electrons of a water molecule as a proton can. The bond between proton and water molecule in the hydronium ion is comparatively strong.

If ionization is possible by simple, rapid transfer of protons, and if in addition the water-proton bond is strong, it is only natural to ask why only a minute fraction of the water ionizes. There are a number of reasons. The O—H bond in the hydronium ion, though strong, is weaker than that in the water molecule because the positive charge becomes distributed over all three

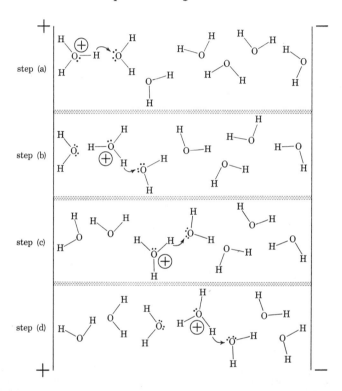

Fig. 1-12. The conduction of positive charge through water by proton jumps. The initial jump in step (a) is followed in succession by further jumps in steps (b) to (d).

hydrogen atoms and they repel each other. Furthermore, work is required to separate a positive proton from the negative hydroxide ion. Finally, water in the neighborhood of the ions becomes subject to restraints on its motion because of the attraction of the charges on the ions for water dipoles. Though the hydronium and hydroxide ions do not differ greatly in size from the original water molecules, they alter the structure of the surrounding water, as shown in Fig. 1-13. The three molecules of water immediately surrounding the hydronium ion are said to be in its *primary hydration shell*. Recent experimental work shows that in the primary hydration shell of the hydroxide ion there are six water molecules. The restraints on water molecules in the primary hydration shell are much like those on water molecules between the plates of a capacitor (Sec. 1-11). Chemical systems, like some people, prefer maximum freedom from restraints, so that regimentation of water into hydration shells about the ions makes the ionized state an undesirable one.

The ionization of water is so feeble that in one liter at room temperature there are only about 0.0000001 or 10^{-7} moles of each ion. This relation of 10^{-7} out of 1 liter corresponds to about one person out of the entire population of China.

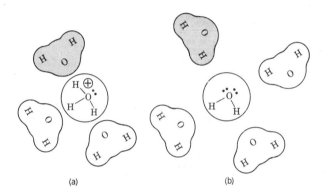

(a)   (b)

FIG. 1-13. Orientation of water dipoles about a hydronium ion. For comparison the orientation about a water molecule is also shown. The positive charge pulls the hydration layer in closer to the ion. The shaded water molecule is oriented differently in the two hydration layers.

SUPPLEMENTARY READING

Easier references are given first. References to journal articles are given in standard form: author, title of article, name of journal in standard abbreviated form, volume number, page numbers, and year.

A. M. BUSWELL and W. H. RODEBUSH, "Water," *Sci. American*, **194**, 77–89 (1956). A readable, semipopular account of the extraordinary properties and structure of water, with excellent illustrations.

M. SIENKO and R. PLANE, *Chemistry*, McGraw-Hill, New York, 1957, pp. 323–25. An excellent discussion of structure and properties of water in a general chemistry text. The electronic structure of molecules is discussed in Chapter 4.

L. PAULING, *College Chemistry*, Freeman, San Francisco, 1955, pp. 356–67. A brief, elementary treatment of water, its properties, van der Waals forces, the hydrogen bond, dipole moment, and dielectric constant. Molecular structure is discussed in Chapter 11.

T. R. Hogness and W. C. Johnson, *Qualitative Analysis and Chemical Equilibrium*, 4th ed., Holt, New York, 1954, pp. 8–11. A good discussion of polar molecules and dielectric constant.

O. K. Rice, *Electronic Structure and Chemical Binding*, McGraw-Hill, New York, 1940, pp. 392–98.

L. Pauling, *The Nature of the Chemical Bond*, Cornell University Press, Ithaca, 1939, pp. 284–96. A classic account of the hydrogen bond.

R. A. Robinson and R. H. Stokes, *Electrolyte Solutions*, Academic Press, New York, 1955, pp. 1–6.

M. L. Huggins, " Hydrogen Bonding in High Polymers and Inclusion Compounds," *J. Chem. Educ.*, **34**, 480 (1957).

M. Gorman, " Some Aspects of Hydrogen Bonding in Inorganic Chemistry," *J. Chem. Educ.*, **33**, 468 (1956).

EXERCISES

Answers to numerical problems are given in Appendix A.

1-1. Give an interpretation based on the arrangement and interaction of water molecules for each of the following observations:

(a) At 0° liquid water is more dense than ice.

(b) Liquid water has a temperature of maximum density a few degrees above its melting point.

(c) The heat of vaporization of water is larger than that of hydrogen sulfide.

(d) The melting point of water is higher than that of hydrogen fluoride.

(e) The dielectric constant of water is higher than that of ammonia.

1-2. If only van der Waals forces operated between molecules, which substance in each set would you expect to have the highest boiling point, and which the lowest?

(a) AsH_3, NH_3, PH_3.   (b) SiH_4, H_2S, HCl.

1-3. A sodium and a chloride ion are 50 A apart. Compare the force between them when (a) they are immersed in water and then in dioxane at 25°; (b) they are immersed in water at 0° and then in water at 100°.

1-4. Draw pictures of the water molecule to show (a) the polar character; (b) the approximate shape; (c) the arrangement of bonding and lone-pair electrons.

1-5. Draw pictures similar to those in Fig. 1-3*b*, *c*, and *f* for hydrogen fluoride and hydrogen selenide, and compare with those for water.

1-6. What is meant by "orbital"? Draw an orbital picture of the ammonia molecule.

1-7. Account for the fact that a water molecule is polar.

1-8. A glycine molecule has a dipole moment of 15 debyes. It contains charges $+q$ and $-q$ equal in magnitude to those on the proton or electron. Calculate the distance of separation of the charges.

1-9. The dipole moment of molecular $HgCl_2$ is zero, but there is a displacement of electrons toward the chlorine end of each Hg—Cl bond. Is the molecule bent, like that of water, or linear? Explain.

1-10. The dipole moments of Br_2, BrCl, and BrF are, respectively, 0, 0.57, and 1.29 debyes. Account for the differences.

1-11. The dipole moment of arsenic trichloride, $AsCl_3$, is 1.59 debyes. Is the molecule planar with the arsenic atom in the center of a triangle formed by the three chlorine atoms, or is it pyramidal with the arsenic atom at the apex?

1-12. Arrange the following in order of increasing dipole moment and account for the differences: AsH_3, SbH_3, PH_3, NH_3.

1-13. How does a hydrogen bond between two water molecules differ from dipole-dipole interaction?

1-14. It has been found that helium gas, but not nitrogen, will pass through a thin disk of ice. Suggest an explanation.

1-15. Explain why hydrogen sulfide, unlike water, does not form hydrogen bonds. Cite evidence to support this statement.

1-16. If one hydrogen atom of a water molecule is replaced by a methyl group, methyl alcohol, CH_3OH, is the result. If only van der Waals forces were responsible for holding molecules of methyl alcohol or water in the liquid state, which would you expect to have the higher boiling point? Actually both molecules form hydrogen bonds using the hydrogen atoms attached to oxygen but not those attached to carbon. Why then does water boil at the higher temperature?

1-17. Seven different forces or bonds between atoms, molecules, or ions were mentioned in this chapter. List them and give an example of each. Which is particularly weak?

1-18. Suppose that water between the plates of a charged capacitor is heated. What happens to the capacitance of the capacitor? Why does the dielectric constant of the water decrease?

1-19. Show how proton transfers occur in (a) the ionization of water; (b) the conduction of electricity by hydroxide ions.

1-20. If there are 6.02×10^{23} ions in a mole of ions (Avogadro's number), find the number of hydronium ions in a drop of water (0.05 ml) at room temperature.

1-21. In a hydrogen chloride molecule the two nuclei are 1.27 A apart. If the bonding electrons were shared equally between hydrogen and chlorine, we would expect the dipole moment to be zero. Suppose the chlorine captured complete control of the electrons so that the molecule became an ion-pair, H^+Cl^-. Calculate the dipole moment of the ion-pair. The measured dipole moment of hydrogen chloride is 1.08 debyes. The ratio of this measured value to that calculated for the ion-pair was used by Pauling as the fractional ionic character of the hydrogen-chlorine bond.

1-22. The dielectric constants of some liquids are given in Tables 1-1 and 1-2 and the dipole moments are given in Sec. 1-5. (a) Make a graph of dielectric constant against dipole moment. (b) Read and report on the discussion by Pauling, *The Nature of the Chemical Bond*, pp. 292–96.

CHAPTER TWO

An Introduction to Solutes and Solutions

2-1. Introduction.   Reactions between substances in aqueous solution—those we use in qualitative analysis, those that occur in a living cell, or those applied on an industrial scale—are of paramount importance. In Chapter 1 the common solvent, water, was considered. In this chapter we examine the structure and properties of some solutes and their aqueous solutions. We particularly need to know in later work what the structural units are in the pure solute and in its solution. The experimental study of solutions is also illustrated in this chapter by discussion of the results of conductance measurements and determination of the effect of solutes on the freezing point of water.

2-2. Molecules in Gases.   In a gas the structural units are molecules. These are in rapid motion, and the average distance between molecules is generally large in comparison with the size of the molecules themselves. The formula of gas molecules is conveniently established by finding the weight of a molar volume. At 0° and 1 atm the weight of 22.4 liters of hydrogen chloride is about 36.5 g. This is the sum of the gram-atomic weights of hydrogen and chlorine, and the gas, therefore, contains HCl molecules. Iodine vaporizes readily to give a beautiful violet gas. The weight of 61.8 liters of this gas, a molar volume at 480° and 1 atm, is about 253 g, or approximately double the gram-atomic weight. Iodine vapor thus contains I_2 molecules. A molar volume of sodium chloride vapor at 2000° and 1 atm weighs about 59 g. Since the sum of the gram-atomic weights of sodium and chlorine is 58.46 g, the vapor contains simple NaCl units at this high temperature. These molecules are believed to be essentially two ions held together by a bond that is largely electrostatic, i.e., (Na^+) (Cl^-).

The formula is not the only property of a molecule that is of interest. It is also important to know the shape of the molecule and the strength of the bond that cements the atoms together. This information can be found by studying the absorption spectrum of the gas. When white light is passed through iodine vapor, certain wave lengths are absorbed by the iodine molecule and violet light is transmitted. The method of ascertaining the amount of light absorbed at each wave length is indicated in Fig. 2-1. From a study of the infrared spectrum, we learn that the two iodine nuclei in the

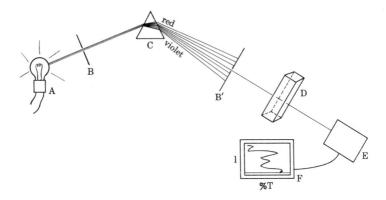

FIG. 2-1. Determination of an absorption spectrum. Light from source *A* is defined into a narrow beam of parallel rays by various mirrors and a slit represented schematically by *B*. This pencil of light is resolved into its component wave lengths by the prism *C*, and a narrow range of wave lengths is passed through another slit *B* and through the cell *D* containing the sample under examination. Some of the light is absorbed by the sample; the part that is transmitted falls on the detector *E*, usually a photoelectric cell. The latter is often connected to a recorder *F* in which a pen traces on moving paper a record of the percentage of the light transmitted (%T) against the wave length (*l*) of the light sent through the cell.

molecule are 2.67 A apart. It is from a study of the spectrum of water vapor that we obtain the information pictured in Fig. 1-3.

CRYSTALS

2-3. Types of Crystals.   Crystalline solids contain particles arranged in a geometrical pattern or lattice. Because of this, crystals have plane faces and the angles between the faces are the same regardless of the size of the crystal or its method of preparation. If the structural units of which the crystal is built are molecules, whether these molecules are held together by van der Waals forces (iodine) or by hydrogen bonds (boric acid), a *molecular crystal* results. In *ionic crystals,* such as those of sodium chloride, the structural units are charged particles. *Metallic crystals* contain atoms held together by loosely bound, rapidly moving outer electrons. Finally, some crystals are single giant molecules made of many atoms covalently bound together. Diamonds are an illustration of such *valence crystals.* These four classes of crystals are really ideal types, and there are many crystals of intermediate character. Cadmium iodide crystals have properties in between ionic and molecular. The fool's gold luster of iron pyrites indicates that this crystal has some metallic, as well as ionic, character.

2-4. The Investigation of Crystal Structures. The most powerful technique for establishing the structure of crystals is that of x-ray diffraction. In one version of this method a beam of x-rays is reflected from the surface layers of a crystal to give an arrangement of spots on photographic film (Fig. 2-2).

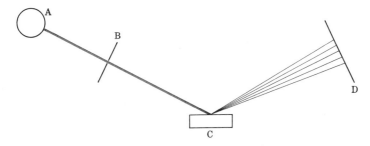

Fig. 2-2. X-ray diffraction in a Bragg spectrometer. A beam of x-rays from the tube *A* is passed through slit *B* onto the surface of crystal *C*. The diffracted rays are detected at *D* either photographically or electronically.

From a mathematical analysis of the positions and intensities of these spots, it is possible to deduce the geometrical pattern of the lattice and the nature of the structural units. (The location of hydrogen atoms in a crystal is not given by x-ray diffraction. Such information can be obtained if a beam of neutrons is used in place of the x-rays.)

2-5. Molecular Crystals. A crystal of argon was pictured in Fig. 1-8. The structural units, atoms for this inert gas, are packed together as tightly as possible. In crystalline iodine (Fig. 2-3) the molecules are also closely packed, but the pattern is no longer the simple cubic one of the argon crystal because the molecules are not spheres. In the crystal some iodine nuclei are 2.70 A apart, while others are separated by 3.54 A. The first distance is only slightly larger than that between nuclei in the vapor molecule (Sec. 2-2). The virtual identity of the molecule in crystal and vapor is thus established. The larger distance quoted above is that between nuclei in different molecules. Many other crystals contain molecular units, e.g., those of nitrogen, carbon dioxide, mercury(II) chloride, and tin(IV) chloride.[1]

In other crystals the simple molecular units are bound into more complex structures by hydrogen bonds. The three-dimensional network of the ice

[1]The Roman numeral is used to indicate the oxidation state ("valence") of the metal; the old names for these two compounds are mercuric chloride and stannic chloride. This use of Roman numerals was suggested by A. Stock and is a feature of the rules for nomenclature of inorganic compounds proposed by a committee of the International Union of Pure and Applied Chemistry.

crystal was pictured in Fig. 1-7. Crystalline boric acid consists of stacks of
sheets, such as the one shown in Fig. 2-4. The simple molecular units, H_3BO_3
or rather $B(OH)_3$, are held within the sheet by hydrogen bonds. The slippery
nature of boric acid comes about because the sheets can slide over each other.
Hydrogen bonding is important in crystals of other water-free oxygen acids.

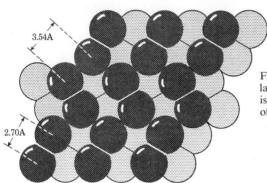

3.54A

2.70A

Fig. 2-3. The iodine crystal. A
layer of close packed molecules
is shown together with a portion
of the layer underneath it.

Molecular crystals have low melting points, e.g., argon, $-189°$; tin(IV)
chloride, $-30°$; ice, $0°$; acetic acid, $16.6°$; iodine, $113.5°$; mercury(II)
chloride, $277°$. This is what we should expect of crystals held together by
comparatively weak forces.

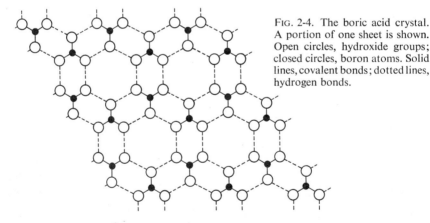

Fig. 2-4. The boric acid crystal.
A portion of one sheet is shown.
Open circles, hydroxide groups;
closed circles, boron atoms. Solid
lines, covalent bonds; dotted lines,
hydrogen bonds.

2-6. Ionic Crystals.   Although sodium chloride vapor contains NaCl
molecules (or ion-pairs), these units are not found in the crystal. If they were,
a crystal of salt would be constructed much like one of iodine: a sodium atom
would be close to one chlorine atom, and other chlorine atoms would be
further away. In a sodium chloride crystal each sodium is surrounded by six
equidistant chloride particles, and each chloride is likewise surrounded by

six sodium particles. There are no molecules of sodium chloride in the solid. The crystal structure of sodium chloride has a simple cubic pattern, as shown in Fig. 2-5.

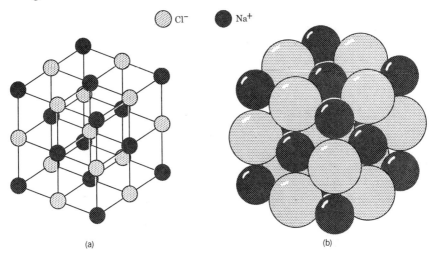

(a) (b)

FIG. 2-5. The crystal structure of sodium chloride. In (a) the centers of the ions are shown; in (b) the ions have been given their correct sizes.

The structural units of the sodium chloride crystal are charged particles: sodium and chloride ions. The sodium ion is equivalent to an atom of sodium that has lost its outermost electron. Since the ion has a nuclear charge of $+11$ and has only ten electrons, it bears a net single positive charge. The chloride ion is equivalent to an atom of chlorine that has gained an electron and is negatively charged. Both ions have complete octets of electrons in their outer shells, the stable electronic structures of the inert gases neon and argon.

The most direct evidence for the existence of ions in crystalline sodium chloride comes from x-ray diffraction measurements. These give the electron density, or average number of electrons, at the sodium positions of the crystal lattice as 9.98, and the electron density at the chloride positions as 17.72. These are close to the expected numbers 10 and 18 for the ions. Other properties of sodium chloride are consistent with the presence of ions, e.g., its appreciable conductivity near the melting point and the still greater conductivity of the molten salt. Furthermore, the strong forces between the ions bind the crystal together tightly and make its melting point high ($800°$) and its vapor pressure low compared with those of molecular crystals.

It is perhaps difficult to conceive of the strength of attraction between positive and negative ions because the charge borne by each ion is so small. Suppose all the sodium ions in a mole (58.5 g) of sodium chloride could be sorted into one pile and all the chloride ions into another. Let one pile be placed on the North Pole and the other on the South Pole. Though about 8000 miles apart, they would still attract each other with a force of more than five tons. This is indeed long-range attraction. By way of contrast it may be noted that the gravitational attraction and the van der Waals force between 23 g of sodium ions and 35.5 g of chloride ions 8000 miles apart are virtually nil. The very strength of the electrostatic forces really makes it impossible to separate the sodium chloride into two such piles. Nor would a pile of ions all of the same charge stay together, for the strong repulsion between like charges would make them fly apart. In a sodium chloride crystal it is the balance between the attraction of unlike charges and the repulsion of like that maintains the ions as separate units.

The crystals of many other salts are composed of ions. Silver chloride has a structure very similar to that of sodium chloride. The silver and chloride ions are arranged in a cubic pattern with six chloride ions about a silver ion and six silver ions about a chloride. The term *coordination number* is used for the number of nearest neighbors to a given ion in a crystal and is six for both ions in sodium chloride and silver chloride. Calcium fluoride has twice as many negative ions as positive ones and forms crystals of a different pattern, as shown in Fig. 2-6b. The rutile, or titanium dioxide, and the cesium chloride structures also represented in Fig. 2-6 are other typical patterns for ionic crystals.

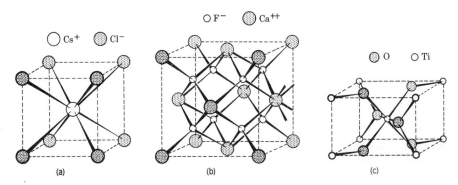

FIG. 2-6. The structure of other ionic crystals (a) Cesium chloride, CsCl. (b) Fluorite, CaF_2. (c) Rutile, TiO_2. [Adapted by permission from *Structural Inorganic Chemistry* by A. F. Wells, 2nd ed. Copyright 1950, by the Clarendon Press, Oxford.]

The formulas of ionic substances no longer stand for molecules but only for the simplest ratio of the ions. It is perhaps not apparent from Fig. 2-5 that there are equal numbers of sodium and chloride ions in a crystal of sodium chloride, but only a small section of a crystal is shown. If we imagine the cube to be continued in all directions, the eight sodium ions at the corners are each only $\frac{1}{8}$ in the cube and the six sodium ions in the middle of the faces only half belong to the original cube. There is then the equivalent of only four sodium ions in the cube. Similarly, the twelve chloride ions on the edges are only $\frac{1}{4}$ in the cube, and these together with the one in the center make a total of four chloride ions to match the four sodium ions. The formula NaCl shows that the crystal contains equal numbers of the two ions.

2-7. The Electronic Structures of Ions. The simplest ions are formed from atoms either by loss of one to three electrons or by gain of one or two. These ions can be divided into four classes.

1. Ions with inert gas structures. The Li^+, Be^{++}, and H^- ions have two electrons, the helium structure. The other ions have eight electrons in their outer shells. They are listed below according to the group in the Periodic Table to which they belong.

> Group IA: Na^+, K^+, Rb^+, Cs^+, Fr^+
> Group IIA: Mg^{++}, Ca^{++}, Sr^{++}, Ba^{++}, Ra^{++}
> Group III: Al^{+++}, Sc^{+++}, Y^{+++}, La^{+++}, Ac^{+++}
> Group VIB: O^{--}, S^{--}, Se^{--}, Te^{--}
> Group VIIB: F^-, Cl^-, Br^-, I^-, At^-

2. Ions with outer shells of 18 electrons.

> Group IB: Cu^+ and Ag^+
> Group IIB: Zn^{++}, Cd^{++}, Hg^{++}
> Group IIIB: Ga^{+++}, In^{+++}, Tl^{+++}

3. Ions with two electrons in addition to a shell of 18. The extra two electrons have been dubbed by Sidgwick the "inert pair" because of the difficulty with which they are lost or shared.

> Group IIIB: In^+ and Tl^+
> Group IVB: Sn^{++} and Pb^{++}
> Group VB: Sb^{+++} and Bi^{+++}

4. Ions with other structures. These are formed by the transition metals in Groups IVA to IB. Some familiar examples, with the number of electrons in their outer shells are: Cr^{+++}, 12; Fe^{+++}, 13; Fe^{++}, 14; and Ni^{++}, 16.

A more detailed discussion of the electronic structures of a number of these cations is given with the chemistry of the cation groups.

2-8. The Size of Ions. An isolated atom or ion has no fixed size, for there are no bounds on the location of its electrons. There is indeed a chance, though an exceedingly small one, that the electrons of an atom could at some instant be as far away as the moon. Only when two atoms or ions are brought close together does the concept of size take on meaning. As they are pushed together, their inner closed shells of electrons begin to overlap and the ions repel each other strongly. At ordinary pressures the ions will settle into positions such that the repulsion and attraction are balanced. It is convenient to regard the ions as spheres in contact and treat the equilibrium distance d as the sum of *ionic radii*, $r_c + r_a$, as in Fig. 2-7a.

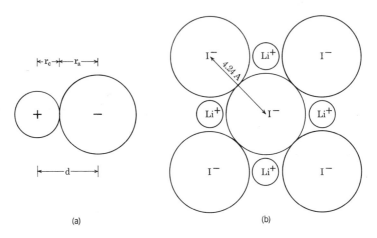

(a)   (b)

FIG. 2-7. Ionic radii.

The concept of an ionic radius is useful largely because the size of an ion is found to be approximately the same in all crystals as long as the coordination number of the ion is unchanged. Some evidence to support this assertion is collected in Table 2-1. The internuclear distances given in the table were obtained from x-ray diffraction measurements. If the radius of the lithium ion is the same in lithium chloride and lithium bromide, the difference between the internuclear distances of the two salts will be the difference in radii of the bromide and chloride ions. The data in the table show that the difference in radii is about the same regardless of the cation. Similarly, the difference in radii of the potassium and sodium ions is almost independent of which anion is present. It is then reasonable to assume that each ion will have about the same radius in most crystals.

There are several ways of dividing the internuclear distance into two ionic radii. The x-ray measurements by themselves give only sums or differences of the radii, and an assumption is required to obtain a single radius. The generally accepted values of the radii are those proposed by Goldschmidt or by Pauling. An earlier, simpler method of Landé gives about the same results and will illustrate the principle of substitution. Landé assumed that in a lithium iodide crystal the large iodide ions were in contact with each other (Fig. 2-7b). The ionic radius of the iodide ion is then simply half the smallest distance between iodide ions in the crystal, that is $\frac{1}{2}(4.24)$ or 2.12 A. Once the radius of one ion has been established, the other radii can be obtained by substitution in the internuclear distances. For example, if the I—K distance in potassium iodide is 3.53 A, the radius of the potassium ion must be $3.53 - 2.12$ or 1.41 A. Next, the radius of the fluoride ion can be obtained by subtracting the radius of the potassium ion from the internuclear

TABLE 2-1.

Constancy of Ionic Radii

Salt	Internuclear distance, A	$r_{Br^-} - r_{Cl^-}$	Salt	Internuclear distance, A	$r_{K^+} - r_{Na^+}$
LiBr	2.75	0.18	KF	2.67	0.36
LiCl	2.57		NaF	2.31	
NaBr	2.98	0.17	KCl	3.14	0.33
NaCl	2.81		NaCl	2.81	
KBr	3.29	0.15	KBr	3.29	0.31
KCl	3.14		NaBr	2.98	
RbBr	3.43	0.15	KI	3.53	0.30
RbCl	3.28		NaI	3.23	

distance in potassium fluoride. By continued substitution a complete set of ionic radii can be obtained. Several values of the radius of an ion will be found by different substitutions. These must be compared and averaged to obtain a self-consistent set.

The assumption that the radius of an ion is the same in all crystals is no more than a rough, if useful, approximation. The size of an ion depends, for example, on its coordination number. The radius of a sodium ion in contact with a single chloride ion in the vapor molecule is 0.79 A, or almost 0.2 A less than it is in the salt crystal, where it is surrounded by six chloride ions. As more chloride ions crowd about a sodium ion, their mutual repulsions force them away from the sodium ion. Values of the ionic radii are usually tabulated for a coordination number of six. There are a number of other causes of variations in the radius of an ion. Values of the radii given by various authorities often differ by as much as 0.1 A. We must not for that reason attach much significance to variations in radii of a few hundredths of an Angstrom unit. Despite these reservations we shall find the ionic radius to be a key to the understanding of such properties as hydration, solubility, acid strength, and similarity in crystal forms.

In our subsequent discussions it is helpful to remember some relations between ionic radius and position of the element in the Periodic Table.

Rule 1. Cations are smaller than anions of the same electronic structure. For example,

Ion	Mg^{++}	Na^+	F^-	O^{--}
Radius in A	0.65	0.98	1.33	1.40
Atomic number	12	11	9	8

Each of these four ions has ten electrons. They differ in nuclear charge. The larger the nuclear charge, the more closely the electrons are bound and the smaller is the radius.

Rule 2. The radius of cations decreases from left to right in a Period, i.e., with increase in atomic number. For example,[2]

Ion	Na^+	Mg^{++}	Al^{+++}	(Si^{+4})	(P^{+5})	(S^{+6})
Radius in A	0.98	0.65	0.50	(0.38)	(0.35)	(0.29)
Atomic number	11	12	13	(14)	(15)	(16)

All these ions have the same electronic structure, and the decrease in radius is again caused by the increase in nuclear charge. On the other hand, the series of ions Mn^{++}, Fe^{++}, Co^{++}, Ni^{++}, Cu^{++}, and Zn^{++} of the transition metals in the first long Period all have radii between 0.7 and 0.8 A. These ions differ in nuclear charge and in the number of electrons in their outer shells. The addition of electrons in passing from left to right merely thickens the density of charge in the outer shell without expanding it.

Rule 3. Of two cations of the same element, the one with the higher charge is smaller. For example, the radius of the Fe^{++} ion is 0.75 A, that of the Fe^{+++} ion is 0.67. The more highly charged ion has fewer electrons, and these are held more tightly by the same nuclear charge.

Rule 4. In a group or family of the Periodic Table the radius increases from top to bottom with the increase in number of electron shells.

EXAMPLE 1. The alkali metals.

Ion	Li^+	Na^+	K^+	Rb^+	Cs^+	Fr^+
Radius in A	0.68	0.98	1.33	1.48	1.67	(1.75)
Number of shells	1	2	3	4	5	6

EXAMPLE 2. The halogens.

Ion	F^-	Cl^-	Br^-	I^-	At^-
Radius in A	1.33	1.81	1.96	2.19	(2.27)
Number of shells	2	3	4	5	6

EXAMPLE 3. Group IIB.

Ion	Zn^{++}	Cd^{++}	Hg^{++}
Radius in A	0.79	0.97	1.10
Number of shells	3	4	5

[2]The ions enclosed in parentheses are hypothetical ones. Their radii are obtained by theoretical calculations.

The average distance of an electron from the nucleus depends on the shell it is in; electrons in the third shell are farther from the nucleus than those in the second shell. Some of the cations in the middle of the third long Period are abnormally small as a result of the presence of the lanthanide series in that Period.

2-9. Complex Ions in Crystals. Polyatomic ions, such as sulfate or carbonate, are found in many crystals. Calcite, a form of calcium carbonate, has a lattice derived from that of sodium chloride by distortion to accommodate the flat, triangular carbonate ion (Fig. 2-8a). Other crystals contain anions so closely crowded around a metal ion as to constitute a complex ion. The structural units of potassium hexachloroplatinate, K_2PtCl_6, are K^+ and $PtCl_6^{--}$ ions (Fig. 2-8c). Crystals of potassium ferrocyanide contain the $Fe(CN)_6^{----}$ complex ion.

Other complex ions in crystals can be formed by association of metal ions with neutral molecules such as water or ammonia. In blue vitriol, $CuSO_4 \cdot 5H_2O$, the structural units are $[Cu(H_2O)_4^{++}]$ and SO_4^{--} ions or

The fifth water molecule fits into a hole in the lattice and is bonded through its hydrogen atoms to two sulfate ions and through its lone-pair electrons to two water molecules attached to the cupric ion. Many other crystals contain hydrated ions; e.g., alum has $[Al(H_2O)_6]^{+++}$; and $HClO_4 \cdot H_2O$ has H_3O^+ or $H(H_2O)^+$. The deep blue crystals of the salt $CuSO_4 \cdot 4NH_3 \cdot H_2O$ contain the $[Cu(NH_3)_4]^{++}$ complex; and the complex ion $[Co(NH_3)_6]^{+++}$ is found in crystals of $CoCl_3 \cdot 6NH_3$. The existence of complex ions in crystals is common and well established.

2-10. Crystals with Layer Lattices. Many crystals have structures intermediate in character between molecular and ionic. The cadmium iodide crystal can be described as a stack of sandwiches. Two layers of closely packed iodine ions constitute the bread, and the cadmium ions are the filling (Fig. 2-9a). The hydroxides of some divalent metals, e.g., $Ca(OH)_2$, $Mg(OH)_2$, $Cd(OH)_2$, $Fe(OH)_2$, and $Ni(OH)_2$, have a similar structure. In crystalline aluminum hydroxide each Al^{+++} ion is surrounded by six hydroxide ions; some of the hydroxide ions are shared with other Al^{+++} ions, and others are hydrogen-bonded to hydroxide ions in the next layer. The structure of

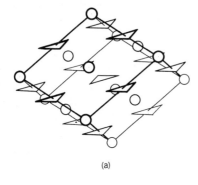

(a)

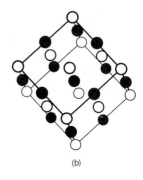

(b)

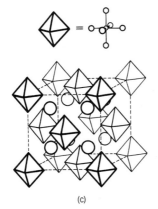

(c)

FIG. 2-8. Crystal structures containing complex ions. (a) Calcite, $CaCO_3$. Small circles, Ca^{++}; triangles, CO_3^{--}. (b) Sodium chloride crystal oriented in same way. Note that the calcite structure is spread out horizontally to accommodate the carbonate ions. (c) Potassium hexachloroplatinate, K_2PtCl_6. Circles, K^+; octahedra, $PtCl_6^{--}$. [Adapted by permission from *The Nature of Crystals* by A. G. Ward. Copyright, 1939, by Blackie and Son Ltd. and *Structural Inorganic Chemistry* by A. F. Wells, 2nd ed. Copyright, 1950, by the Clarendon Press, Oxford.]

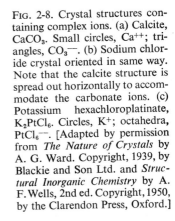

aluminum hydroxide differs from that of magnesium hydroxide in the way the sandwiches are stacked together (Fig. 2-9*b*).

2-11. A Summary.   The gist of the foregoing discussion of solutes is this. Crystals of most salts are built of ions. The formula of the salt shows the simplest ratio of positive to negative ions in the crystal and is not to be interpreted literally as standing for a molecule. It is convenient to regard many ions in crystals as spheres in contact with each other and to assign to each an ionic radius which is roughly the same in all crystals containing that ion. Complex ions consisting of a simple positive ion associated with neutral molecules or anions into a single structural unit are found in many crystals. Molecules are the units in crystals of anhydrous acids and nonelectrolytes. A large number of substances have crystals of complex structure, e.g., layer lattices or lattices containing molecules bound by hydrogen bonds into sheets, chains, or space-filling frameworks.

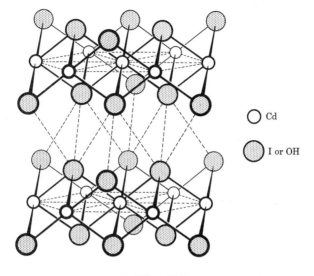

O Cd

◉ I or OH

(a) CdI$_2$ or Cd(OH)$_2$

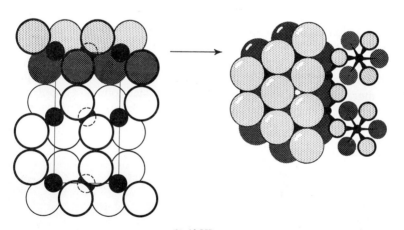

(b) Al(OH)$_3$

FIG. 2-9. Crystals with layer lattices. (a) Cadmium iodide or cadmium hydroxide. Small circles, Cd^{++} ions; large circles, I$^-$ or OH$^-$ ions. (b) Aluminum hydroxide. Small circles, Al^{+++} ions; large circles, OH$^-$ ions. The packing of layers is shown at the left. A simplified version of the single layer is shown at the right; some of the ions are shown with reduced size to indicate bonding within a layer. [Adapted by permission from *Structural Inorganic Chemistry* by A. F. Wells, 2nd ed. Copyright, 1950, by the Clarendon Press, Oxford.]

SOLUTIONS

2-12. The Nature of Solutions. Solutions are produced by dispersal of one substance in another to give a homogeneous mixture. Some pairs of substances are miscible in all proportions. More commonly, a limited amount of one substance, the solute, can be dissolved by a given amount of the other, the solvent. So long as the concentration of the solute is low, the physical properties of the solution are those of the solvent slightly modified by the presence of the solute. We have seen in Chapter 1 that water, the principal solvent, is a very peculiar liquid, and it is thus of interest to find how the structure and properties of water are affected by solutes.

Liquid water was described as being more densely packed but less organized than ice. Molecules in the liquid have some freedom of movement, though at any instant they may be bonded to as many as four others. Foreign molecules can be accommodated in this structure in several ways. If the molecule is small, it fits into holes or gaps in the water structure. Some solute molecules of favorable size and shape, e.g., methane or argon, can induce the water molecules to assemble about them into a cagelike structure somewhat like a ball of ice about a pebble.   Larger molecules of solute must push aside water to make room for themselves and can disorganize the structure of the liquid. Generally, nonpolar molecules such as those of carbon tetrachloride, methane, and iodine are not very soluble in water, for they have little attraction for water molecules and are squeezed out of solution by the strong interactions of water molecules with each other.

Polar molecules, especially those containing nitrogen, oxygen, and fluorine atoms which can form hydrogen bonds with water, are frequently much more soluble in water than are the nonpolar solutes. The interaction with water of acetone and of ethyl alcohol, which mix with it in any proportion, is represented by

2-13. Ionization of Molecular Solutes.   Anhydrous acids and bases are molecular substances that often form hydrogen bonds with water. The attraction between water and solute molecules is followed by a shift of the proton or hydrogen nucleus from the acid molecule to water or from water to the base molecule. The ionization of molecular hydrogen chloride, ammonia, and formic acid by proton transfer is represented by

Water is used as a proton acceptor in the first and last reactions and as a proton donor in the second.

2-14. The Detection of Ions by Conductance Measurements.   The ability of ions to carry electric charge through a solution is the basis for a particularly sensitive method of detecting their presence. Consider the apparatus shown in Fig. 2-10. A cubical cell, one centimeter on a side, is fitted with electrodes on opposite faces. When a solution is placed in the cell, current will be carried between the electrodes by the ions. The motion of positive ions toward the negative electrode carries positive charge in that direction, and the motion of the anions carries negative charge in the opposite direction. Charge is transferred between solution and electrodes by chemical changes with electron transfer. In hydrochloric acid, for example, the electrode reactions are principally

$$2H_3O^+ + 2e^- \rightarrow H_2 + 2H_2O \text{ (cathode)}$$
$$2Cl^- \rightarrow Cl_2 + 2e^- \text{ (anode)}$$

Current is carried through the wires of the external circuit by electrons.

The electric current through the cell is the quantity of charge flowing through the cell in unit time. This is determined by the voltage applied to the cell and the conductance of the solution.[3] For a fixed voltage the current through the cell, as indicated crudely by the brightness of the light in the circuit, is proportional to the conductance of the solution. The conductance of the centimeter cube is called the *specific conductance*.[4] It depends on (1) the number of ions per cubic centimeter and (2) the mobility of these ions.

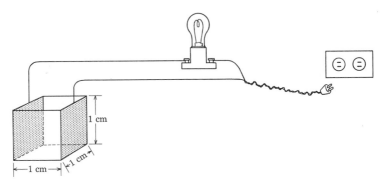

FIG. 2-10. Demonstration of electrolytic conductance.

Motion of the ions is not completely free because they must push aside water molecules to move and because the attraction of other ions exerts a drag on them that interferes with their motion. Even the hydronium and hydroxide ions, the most mobile of all, are not completely free to move (Sec. 1-12). The mobility of ions increases with rising temperature, so that the conductance of solutions likewise increases. The conductance of current in metals by electrons goes down with rising temperature.

2-15. Nonelectrolytes. Strong and Weak Electrolytes. Water itself is a very poor conductor (Sec. 1-12), for it contains very low concentrations of ions. Its specific conductance ranges from about 0.000001 or 1×10^{-6} for ordinary distilled water, which contains dissolved carbon dioxide, to 0.00000004 or 4×10^{-8} for the purest water. A large number of solutes called *nonelectrolytes* cause no change in the conductance of water. These include such substances as alcohol, acetone, sugar, urea, and thioacetamide, which do not give ions in aqueous solution. Solutions of acids, bases, and salts are much better conductors than water; these solutes are called *electrolytes*. The specific conductance of 0.05 M hydrochloric acid is 20×10^{-3} or 0.020 or

---

[3] The current and conductance also vary directly with the area of the electrodes and inversely with the distance between them. We are interested in the solution in the cell and not the cell itself, and therefore we take electrodes of fixed area separated by a fixed distance to keep these variables constant.

[4] The specific conductance is the reciprocal of the specific resistance and is expressed in reciprocal ohm-centimeters. It is a common whimsey to write mho for reciprocal ohm.

about 500,000 times that of the purest water. The specific conductances of 0.05 M solutions of ammonia and formic acid are a good deal less than that of hydrochloric acid (respectively, 0.25×10^{-3} and 1.25×10^{-3}), but they are still much larger than that of water.

It is convenient to separate electrolytes into those with large specific conductance, *strong electrolytes*, and those with low specific conductance, *weak electrolytes*. Hydrochloric acid is a typical strong electrolyte, and its high specific conductance is an indication that its ionization reaction (Sec. 2-13) goes to a large extent. We cannot detect in 0.05 M solution any hydrogen chloride molecules, though we must recognize that traces of molecules are much harder to find than traces of ions. Ammonia and formic acid are typical weak electrolytes. Their ionization reactions proceed only to a small extent before a balance is reached between the formation of ions and their recombination.

In using specific-conductance data to classify substances as strong or weak electrolytes we must be careful to make comparisons at the same molar concentration. The specific conductance of 0.0005 M hydrochloric acid is 0.21×10^{-3}, or less than that of 0.05 M ammonia or formic acid. But this is what we should expect: at 0.0005 M concentration there are one-hundredth as many ions per cubic centimeter as there are in 0.05 M hydrochloric acid, and hence there is about one-hundredth the conductance. It must also be noted that there is no minimum specific conductance for strong electrolytes or maximum value for weak electrolytes. The two classes are not sharply divided. Some electrolytes, e.g., oxalic acid, might with reason be classed as either strong or weak. Nature stubbornly resists being confined to only two man-made categories.

2-16. The Reversibility of Proton Transfer.   The ionization of molecular acids and bases is generally reversible, and their solutions may contain both ions and molecules. The presence of molecules in concentrated solutions of hydrochloric acid, ammonia, and formic acid is indicated by the distinctive odor of each, for it is the molecules, not the ions, that vaporize and reach our nostrils. In dilute solutions fewer molecules are present, and they are difficult to detect because molecules rarely possess a specific and sensitive property, whereas conductivity is useful for detecting ions. Sometimes molecules are colored and the ions have a different color. The absorption spectrum can then be used to discover the presence of molecules. Acid-base indicators are examples of electrolytes that can be studied in this way.

The presence or absence of molecules is usually decided by indirect methods. In dilute solutions of hydrochloric acid (6 M or less) all the properties of the solution can be accounted for by the presence of ions. There are no residual properties or discrepancies of behavior that require the presence of molecules for an explanation. Hence we customarily assume that hydrochloric acid is completely ionized in such solutions. This is not to imply that minute numbers of molecules may not be present. Our argument is merely that the number of such molecules is too small to have any effect on the properties of the solution which we can detect by our most sensitive measurements.

Ions and molecules, when they occur together, are at equilibrium. The equilibrium in ammonia solution ("ammonium hydroxide") is that represented by

$$NH_3 + H_2O \rightleftharpoons NH_4^+ + OH^-$$

Ions are being produced by the reaction of ammonia with water as fast as they are recombining to give back the molecules. The forward and reverse reactions go on continuously and simultaneously.

Changes in conditions will affect the extent to which the electrolyte is broken up into ions. Dilution of the solution with more water increases the extent of ionization. This can be given a simple kinetic interpretation. In all but very concentrated solutions of ammonia, the ammonia molecules are completely surrounded by water molecules. The addition of more water cannot materially alter the chance of proton transfer from water to ammonia. It does reduce the chance of recombination of the ions because in the more dilute solution the ions are further apart and are less likely to come close enough to each other for reaction to occur. In a brief time after dilution and before the new equilibrium is established, ionization will occur more rapidly than recombination. When a balance of the two reactions is again achieved, more of the electrolyte is in the form of ions. The rate of ionization may be compared with the speed of a squirrel running counter to the revolution of a wheel cage. If the cage is suddenly rotated more slowly (just as the rate of recombination of ions is decreased by addition of water), the squirrel will be higher up in the wheel than before by the time he responds to the change.

An important way of decreasing the extent of ionization is by the *common ion effect*. The ionization of ammonia is repressed by the addition to the solution of any substance that supplies an excess of either ammonium ions or hydroxide ions, e.g., ammonium chloride or sodium hydroxide. If the number of ammonium ions per unit volume is increased, the chance of recombination of ammonium and hydroxide ions is increased. At the new equilibrium that is soon established, the concentration of hydroxide ions will be less than it was before the addition of ammonium chloride. By the same argument the addition of sodium hydroxide to aqueous ammonia will lower the concentration of ammonium ions and raise that of ammonia. The common ion effect is extensively used in qualitative analysis and will be treated in more detail later.

2-17. The Study of Electrolytes by Measurement of Freezing Point Depression. The existence of ions in solution can be inferred from their influence on the properties of the solvent. Solutes (whether ionized or molecular) lower the vapor pressure of water, raise its boiling point (if the solute is not volatile), depress its freezing point, and produce an osmotic pressure. In dilute solutions all four of these properties depend primarily on the relative number of solute and solvent particles. Because of this common feature they are called *colligative* properties after the Latin word *colligatus*, meaning "bound together." Depression of the freezing point as a typical colligative property is singled out for discussion here.

Ice first begins to freeze out of solutions only when the temperature is brought below 0°. In dilute solutions of nonelectrolytes the lowering of the freezing point, ΔT,[5] is proportional to the molality of solute, m:

$$\Delta T = K_f m \qquad \qquad 1$$

The molality (moles of solute per 1000 g of solvent) is an appropriate expression for the relative number of solute and solvent particles in solutions of nonelectrolytes. The proportionality constant K_f is characteristic of the solvent, irrespective of the solute, and has the value 1.860 for water. If the freezing point depressions of various solutions of methyl alcohol in water are determined, 1.860 is the average value of $\Delta T/m$ calculated from these measurements (Fig. 2-11). It is customary to regard the behavior expressed in Eq. 1 as standard or *ideal* and use it as a standard of comparison in dealing with solutions of electrolytes.

The freezing point of an electrolytic solution is lower than that of a nonelectrolyte at the same molality. One mole of hydrogen chloride produces two moles of ions, one of hydronium and one of chloride. It therefore has almost twice the effect on the freezing point of water as a mole of methyl alcohol in the same weight of water. Let i, the van't Hoff mole number, be defined by the equation

$$i = \frac{\text{observed freezing point depression}}{\text{ideal freezing point depression}} = \frac{\Delta T}{K_f m} \qquad \qquad 2$$

The mole number indicates the approximate number of particles per formula. It is 1.00 for the nonelectrolyte methyl alcohol, almost 2 for hydrochloric acid, and only slightly larger than 1 for the weakly ionized ammonia and formic acid. For hydrochloric acid i decreases slightly as the concentration of acid increases (Fig. 2-11). This is attributed to interionic forces which become more effective as the ions move closer together. For strong electrolytes in general the mole number is somewhat less than the number of ions per formula but approaches this value in very dilute solutions.

2-18. Dissolving an Ionic Crystal. The Effect of Dielectric Constant. We have seen that ions are found in crystals of many salts. Yet when the crystal is heated sufficiently to break it apart and vaporize the salt, the ions do not

[5] The Greek letter delta is used to indicate a change; ΔT stands for a change in temperature.

persist in the vapor but unite to give molecules. Now solutions of salts in water are good conductors of electricity and have values of i that are close to 2, 3, or even larger whole numbers. Ions must be present in these solutions. We must explain how ions can remain as separate units in solution but not in the vapor. There are two causes: the high dielectric constant of water and the stabilization of free ions by hydration.

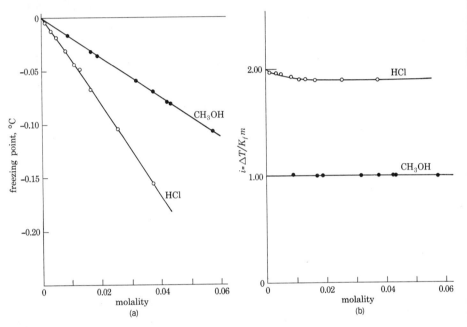

Fig. 2-11. The freezing points and mole numbers of methyl alcohol and hydrochloric acid solutions. Circles represent experimental points. In (a) the distance from $0°$ down to a point is the freezing point depression, ΔT. The slope of the line for methyl alcohol or $\Delta T/m$ is $1.860°$.

The electrical forces between ions are greatly decreased when they are separated by water. Because water has a dielectric constant of about 80 at room temperature (Sec. 1-3), the work required to move two ions further apart is only $\frac{1}{80}$ as much in water as it is when the two ions are in the vapor state. Other common solvents such as benzene, acetone, the alcohols, and carbon tetrachloride have much lower dielectric constants, and forces between ions in these solvents are much stronger. Even hydrogen chloride is a weak electrolyte when dissolved in benzene. These solvents are much less effective in dissolving ionic crystals than water is. Such ions as do go into solution in benzene or acetone tend to associate. A positive ion and a negative ion can join to give an *ion-pair* held together by strong electrical attraction. The two ions may still be separated by a solvent molecule, whereas in the molecules of salt that occur in the gaseous state they are in contact with each other. Formation of ion-pairs will occur even in aqueous solution if the attraction between ions is sufficiently strong, i.e., when the ions bear high charges or are very close together, as they are in concentrated solutions. Some typical examples are $[K^+Fe(CN)_6^{----}]$ in solutions of $K_4Fe(CN)_6$ and $[Co^{++}SO_4^{--}]$ in solutions of $CoSO_4$.

2-19. Dissolving an Ionic Crystal.   The Formation of Hydrated Ions.   The existence of hydrated ions in crystals (Sec. 2-9) shows that water dipoles can be attracted by positive and negative ions. An ion should in principle exert an attraction on every water molecule in solution, but it is customary to ignore its effect on all but the very nearest ones. The existence of primary hydration shells about hydronium and hydroxide ions was discussed in Sec. 1-12. The orientation of water molecules in the primary hydration shells of cations and anions is shown in Fig. 2-12.

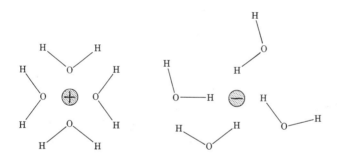

FIG. 2-12. Orientation of water molecules about ions.

The number of water molecules about a metal ion in crystals is fixed, e.g., four about each Cu^{++} ion in $CuSO_4 \cdot 5H_2O$, and six about each Al^{+++} ion in $KAl(SO_4)_2 \cdot 12H_2O$. Water molecules and ions in solution are in constant motion and, because the attraction between them is weak, the number of water molecules next to a metal ion is usually variable. There are various ingenious, indirect methods of estimating the *hydration number* or the average number of water molecules bound to a metal ion, and the results of the different methods agree fairly well. Cations that are small and highly charged exert the strongest attraction on water molecules and have the highest hydration numbers. Thus the hydration number of Li^+ ion, crystal radius 0.68 A, is about 4; while that of K^+ ion, crystal radius 1.33 A, is only 2. The Mg^{++} ion, crystal radius 0.65 A, has a much higher average hydration number, namely 10, because of its double charge. The hydration number of the small fluoride ion is between 2 and 4; the larger halide ions have hydration numbers of about 1.

The hold of some metal ions on water has been studied with water containing abnormally large amounts of heavy oxygen, as H_2O^{18}. To a solution of a metal perchlorate, $Me(ClO_4)_3$, in ordinary water was added the labeled water, which we write as H_2O^*. Samples of the mixture were taken out at various times after mixing and some of the water was removed by distillation and analyzed for its content of O^{18}. If water molecules are only loosely held by the metal ion, they will rapidly exchange places with other, nearby water molecules:

$$Me(H_2O)_x{}^{+++} + H_2O^* \rightarrow Me(H_2O)_{x-1}(H_2O^*)^{+++} + H_2O$$

The percentage of O^{18} in the solvent will then rapidly decrease. For many metal ions, e.g., Fe^{+++} and Al^{+++}, this exchange was found to be complete in a few thousandths of a second, indicating that these ions do hold the water molecules only loosely; but for Cr^{+++} ion the exchange was only half finished in 40 hours. Taube of the University of Chicago, who did this work, concluded further that six water molecules were attached to the Cr^{+++} ion in solution just as they are in solid $KCr(SO_4)_2 \cdot 12H_2O$. Even so, the behavior of Cr^{+++} ion is exceptional, and other ions do not hold water molecules as tightly or in fixed numbers.

As anhydrous salts dissolve in water, their ions become hydrated. A small contraction in volume and a release of energy as heat are associated with the hydration. The contraction occurs because the attraction between ion and water dipoles pulls in the solvent about the ion. The volume of a salt solution is usually less than the combined volume of water and salt used in its preparation and is sometimes actually less than the volume of the water itself. Exactly 1000.0 ml of 2% zinc sulfate solution can be made by mixing 5.45 ml of solid zinc sulfate with 1000.4 ml of water. The attraction between ion and water also causes the release of energy. Therefore, the energy of the hydrated ions is lower than that of the unhydrated ions and they are more stable.[6] Conversely, energy must be absorbed (i.e., work is required) to pull the ions and water molecules apart against this attraction.

The excellent solvent power of water for many salts and the very existence of ions in aqueous solution are consequences of (1) the high dielectric constant of water which results in weak interionic attraction and (2) the formation of hydrated ions which are stabilized by a release of energy. It is the combination of the two effects that makes water such a good solvent. Other solvents with high dielectric constant, e.g., hydrogen cyanide, do not solvate ions readily. Occasionally liquids of low dielectric constant will be good solvents for certain salts. Ether, for example, dissolves iron(III) chloride and cobalt(II) thiocyanate, but it is not a good solvent for salts in general. Such

---

[6]Stabilization by release of energy is counteracted to some extent by the increased restraints on the motion of the water molecules bound to the ions. See Sec. 1-12.

specific solvation effects, just because they are so unusual, are very useful in separating iron and cobalt from other metals.

2-20. A Summary of How Ions Get into Solution.   We have seen in Secs. 2-13 and 2-15 that substances such as hydrogen chloride, ammonia, and formic acid form ions by a proton transfer reaction with water. These anhydrous solutes are molecular. If transfer of protons is complete, as it is in dilute solutions of hydrochloric acid, essentially no molecules are left and the substance is a strong electrolyte. More commonly the transfer of protons is incomplete and some molecules remain in equilibrium with the ions of the weak electrolyte.

The crystals of most salts, unlike those of acids and bases, already contain ions. To bring the ions into solution the force of attraction between them must be weakened and the separate ions stabilized by hydration. There are no molecules of such salts as sodium chloride or calcium nitrate in solution. Some salts, such as silver chloride or barium sulfate, are not very soluble in water, but this is not inconsistent with the preceding statements. A saturated solution of silver chloride actually has a higher specific conductance than a solution of sodium chloride of the same concentration, namely 1.84×10^{-6} as against 1.67×10^{-6}. By this test silver chloride is a strong electrolyte. Its crystals also contain ions (Sec. 2-6), but the forces that bind them in the crystal are so strong that it is difficult to bring the ions into solution. It is not correct to regard slightly soluble salts as weakly ionized, for this implies the existence of an equilibrium between molecules and ions. Crystals and solutions of most salts contain no molecules.

A few salts, such as $HgCl_2$ and $AsCl_3$, are molecular in the crystalline state. When these dissolve in water, ions are probably formed by a stepwise displacement of the anion by water, a hydration process

$$HgCl_2 + H_2O \rightleftharpoons Hg(OH_2)Cl^+ + Cl^-$$
$$Hg(OH_2)Cl^+ + H_2O \rightleftharpoons Hg(OH_2)_2{}^{++} + Cl^-$$

Simultaneously, there may be a proton transfer

$$Hg(OH_2)Cl^+ + H_2O \rightleftharpoons Hg(OH)Cl + H_3O^+$$

This is an example of a *hydrolysis* reaction. For this salt these reactions go to only a slight extent, and it is therefore a weak electrolyte. The conductance measurements confirm this; the specific conductance of $0.05\ M\ HgCl_2$ is only 0.0001, much less than the value 0.0102 for $0.05\ M\ CaCl_2$.

2-21. The Nature of Acids in Aqueous Solution.   There are relatively few strong acids. The more common ones are hydrochloric, hydrobromic, hydriodic, nitric, chloric, perchloric, and sulfuric acids. All but sulfuric acid lose a single proton, and the ionization is complete at acid concentrations below 0.1 mole per liter, e.g.,

$$HNO_3 + H_2O \rightarrow H_3O^+ + NO_3^-$$

In concentrated solutions of several of these acids molecules have been detected. In 10 M hydrochloric acid, for example, about 0.3% of the acid is in the molecular form according to an estimate based on the pressure of hydrogen chloride gas above the solution. Molecules of hydrogen nitrate, HNO_3, can be detected by spectral measurements. In 6 M nitric acid, the so-called "dilute" acid, three out of four molecules have ionized, whereas in the 16 M acid 9 out of 10 are un-ionized. At concentrations of sulfuric acid below 14 M the loss of the first proton is complete:

$$H_2SO_4 + H_2O \rightarrow H_3O^+ + HSO_4^-$$

It is more difficult to remove the second proton,

$$HSO_4^- + H_2O \rightleftharpoons H_3O^+ + SO_4^{--}$$

because it must be pulled away from the double negative charge of the sulfate and because the superfluity of hydronium ions from the first ionization step represses by the common ion effect the formation of more. The second step in the ionization goes to completion only in very dilute solutions. The maximum concentration of sulfate ion in any solution of sulfuric acid is about 1.8 M at room temperature. In 3 M sulfuric acid about two-thirds of the sulfur is in the form of HSO_4^-, and the rest is in simple SO_4^{--} ions. Concentrated sulfuric acid contains about 2 to 4% water and is almost entirely molecular H_2SO_4.

Most acids are weakly ionized. They include hydroacids such as hydrofluoric (HF) and hydrosulfuric (H_2S) and oxyacids containing a nonmetal in a low oxidation state, such as hypochlorous acid (HClO) or sulfurous acid (H_2SO_3). Acetic acid ($HC_2H_3O_2$) is the most familiar of a large number of weak organic acids; two others are oxalic acid ($H_2C_2O_4$) and benzoic acid ($HC_7H_5O_2$).

The molecular formulas of some acids in solution are not always well defined because of uncertainties as to the extent of hydration. Arsenious acid is written $HAsO_2$ by some authors, H_3AsO_3 by others. You will note that the second formula is a hydrated version of the first; i.e., $HAsO_2 + H_2O \rightarrow H_3AsO_3$. Telluric acid, it is now believed, occurs as $Te(OH)_6$, the equivalent of $H_2TeO_4 + 2H_2O$. The absorption spectrum of the borate ion in solution is more consistent with the formula $B(OH)_4^-$ than with the older forms $H_2BO_3^-$ or BO_2^-, and this in spite of the fact that the crystal contains H_3BO_3 molecules (Sec. 2-5). Similar measurements on solutions of silicates indicate that the formula of the silicate ion is probably $H_2SiO_4^{--}$ and not SiO_3^{--}. With many acids there is as yet no experimental evidence that can be used to decide between various degrees of hydration in writing formulas.

Carbonic and sulfurous acids present another problem. They exist only in solution and are extensively decomposed into the acidic oxide, e.g.,

$$H_2CO_3 \rightleftharpoons H_2O + CO_2$$

Only about one molecule of carbon dioxide out of every 400 is hydrated to carbonic acid, according to recent measurements. The only reason for calling such solutions "carbonic acid" is force of habit. The extent of hydration of sulfur dioxide to sulfurous acid is less than 3%.

Phosphoric acid (H_3PO_4), oxalic acid ($H_2C_2O_4$), sulfamic acid (HNH_2SO_3), and hydrogen sulfate ion (HSO_4^-) are ionized to a moderate extent and cannot be classified as strong or weak except by arbitrary rule. There is, as we noted before, no sharp division of electrolytes into those that are strong and those that are weak.

2-22. The Nature of Bases in Aqueous Solution. The strong basic hydroxides include those of the alkali metals (Periodic Group IA) and those of calcium, strontium, and barium (Periodic Group IIA). All are completely ionized, but association between hydroxide ions and the doubly charged cations Ca^{++}, Sr^{++}, and Ba^{++} occurs to an appreciable extent. It has been estimated that in a saturated solution of calcium hydroxide as much as 25% of the calcium is in the form of $[Ca^{++}(OH^-)]^+$ and the rest is free Ca^{++} ion.

Most bases, like most acids, are weakly ionized. Ammonia solution or "ammonium hydroxide" is the most familar. The molecular condition of ammonia in water is difficult to determine experimentally. There is some evidence of definite association between ammonia and water molecules which could be represented either as $NH_3 \cdot H_2O$ or as NH_4OH according to taste. In this text the simple, unhydrated formula NH_3 is used.

Other important weak bases can be derived from ammonia by replacing one or more of its hydrogen atoms by organic radicals, e.g.,

CH$_3$NH$_2$
methylamine

(C$_2$H$_5$)$_2$NH
diethylamine

(C$_2$H$_4$OH)$_3$N
triethanolamine

$$C_6H_5NH_2$$
aniline

$$C_5H_5N$$
pyridine

They remove protons from water in the same way that ammonia does:

$$NH_3 + H_2O \rightleftharpoons NH_4^+ + OH^-$$

$$CH_3NH_2 + H_2O \rightleftharpoons CH_3NH_3^+ + OH^-$$

$$(C_2H_5)_2NH + H_2O \rightleftharpoons (C_2H_5)_2NH_2^+ + OH^-$$

$$C_5H_5N + H_2O \rightleftharpoons C_5H_5NH^+ + OH^-$$

A large number of metal hydroxides are very sparingly soluble, e.g., $Mg(OH)_2$, $Al(OH)_3$, and $Cu(OH)_2$. Their saturated solutions contain such minute amounts of solute that it is difficult to determine directly the extent to which they are dissociated into hydroxide and simple metal ions. The crystalline hydroxides form layer lattices (Sec. 2-10) in which there are strong metal ion to hydroxide ion bonds. Complexes between metal and hydroxide ions are also known to occur in solutions of the metal salts. Solutions of iron(III) salts, for example, contain $FeOH^{++}$ and $Fe_2(OH)_2^{++++}$ ions. It is probable that complexes such as these occur in saturated solutions of the metal hydroxides.

2-23. The Nature of Salts in Aqueous Solution. Almost all salts, unlike acids and bases, are strong electrolytes. It is worth emphasizing again that the small amount of a sparingly soluble salt like silver chloride which goes into solution is usually completely ionized (Sec. 2-20).

All experimental evidence points to complete ionization of the halides and perchlorates of the alkali and alkaline earth metals in aqueous solution. Complete ionization is generally assumed for most other salts, although reliable data are usually lacking; for some salts the evidence is not clear cut and the authorities disagree. It is clear that mercury(II) chloride, $HgCl_2$, is weakly ionized. Mercury(II) cyanide, lead acetate, and the chloride, bromide, and iodide of cadmium are often considered to be weak electrolytes.

The behavior of most salts in concentrated solutions and in solvents of low dielectric constant such as the alcohols is complicated by ion-pair formation (Sec. 2-18). In dilute solutions the ion-pairs are extensively dissociated unless the two ions are highly charged. Therefore, dilute solutions of salts such as sodium sulfate, potassium ferrocyanide, and lead nitrate are still much better conductors than equimolar solutions of weak acids or mercury(II) chloride. Because of this and because, for all too many salts, insufficient data are available to enable us to decide the extent of ion-pair formation, we shall ignore it in writing formulas and shall represent salts as completely broken up into ions, e.g.,

$$2Na^+ + SO_4^{--} \text{ and } 4K^+ + Fe(CN)_6^{----}, \text{ but } HgCl_2$$

SUPPLEMENTARY READING

General references:

M. SIENKO and R. PLANE, *Chemistry*, McGraw-Hill, New York, 1957, pp. 137–39 (molar volumes), 170–77 (crystals), 194–97 (solutions), 197–200 (depression of the freezing point), and 200–04 (electrolytes).

L. PAULING, *College Chemistry*, Freeman, San Francisco, 1955, pp. 185–90 (molar volumes), 198–202 (ionic radii), 381–83 (depression of the freezing point), 365–69 (water as a solvent).

J. TIMM, *General Chemistry*, 3rd ed. McGraw-Hill, New York, 1956, Chapter 22 (electrolytes).

A. W. LAUBENGAYER, *General Chemistry*, rev. ed. Rinehart, New York, 1957, Chapter 11 (crystals), Chapter 16 (electrolytes).

T. R. HOGNESS and W. C. JOHNSON, *Qualitative Analysis and Chemical Equilibrium*, 4th ed. Holt, New York, 1954, Chapter 2 (electrolytes and nonelectrolytes).

More detailed discussions of crystal structure and x-ray diffraction:

L. PAULING, *General Chemistry*, 2nd ed. Freeman, San Francisco, 1953, Chapters 2 and 3.

G. I. BROWN, *A Simple Guide to Modern Valency Theory*, Longmans, Green, London, 1953, pp. 45–49 (electronic structure of ions), pp. 116–26 (x-ray and electron diffraction and spectroscopy), pp. 130–33 (ionic radii).

E. S. GOULD, *Inorganic Reactions and Structures*, Holt, New York, 1955, Chapters 12 and 20.

A. F. WELLS, *Structural Inorganic Chemistry*, 2nd ed. Clarendon Press, Oxford, 1950, Chapters 3 and 6.

K. LONSDALE, *Crystals and X-Rays*, Van Nostrand, New York, 1949.

W. H. BRAGG and W. L. BRAGG, *X-Rays and Crystal Structure*, Harcourt, Brace, New York, 1924.

EXERCISES

2-1. The density of aluminum chloride vapor at 200°C and 740 mm pressure is about 6.8 g/l. Find the weight of a molar volume and the correct formula for the vapor.

2-2. At 1468° and 1 atm a molar volume of iodine vapor weighs only 147 g. Suggest an explanation.

2-3. In crystals of $HgCl_2$ the linear Cl—Hg—Cl molecules pack together in each layer just as iodine molecules do. Draw a sketch to show this close packing. These molecules are longer than those of iodine. What effect will this have on the shape of the layer?

2-4. In a calcium fluoride crystal (Fig. 2-6) what is the coordination number of each kind of ion? Verify the formula CaF_2.

2-5. Give the number of electrons in each shell of the following atoms and ions: (a) K atom and K^+ ion, (b) Mg atom and Mg^{++} ion, (c) Cu atom and Cu^{++} ion, (d) Zn atom and Zn^{++} ion, (e) O atom and O^{--} ion, (f) Bi atom and Bi^{+++} ion.

2-6. Arrange the ions in each set in order of increasing size: (a) O^{--}, Te^{--}, S^{--}, Se^{--}, (b) Ce^{+++}, Pr^{+++}, Nd^{+++}, Pm^{+++}, (c) Al^{+++}, In^{+++}, Ga^{+++}, Tl^{+++}, (d) Se^{--}, Sr^{++}, Br^-, Rb^+, (e) (Mn^{+4}), Mn^{++}, Mn^{+++}, (Mn^{+7}).

2-7. What similarities and differences do you note in the crystal structures of calcium fluoride (Fig. 2-6) and potassium hexachloroplatinate (Fig. 2-8)?

2-8. Show by a diagram the arrangement of ammonia molecules about a Cu^{++} ion in the $Cu(NH_3)_4^{++}$ complex.

2-9. Show by equations similar to those in Sec. 2-13 the ionization of (a) H_2SO_4, (b) CH_3NH_2, (c) HF.

2-10. Describe how an electric current is carried through a solution of $CuBr_2$, copper(II) bromide.

2-11. What is meant by the statement "the specific conductance of 0.1 M HCl is 0.0391"?

2-12. The specific conductance of 0.01 M calcium chloride is 2.3×10^{-3}. Calculate the resistance of a centimeter cube of this solution.

2-13. The specific conductance of 0.05 M HCl is 20.0×10^{-3}; that of 0.1 M HCl is 39.1×10^{-3}. Why is the second value almost, but not quite, twice the first.

2-14. A solvent mixture containing 82% dioxane and 18% water has a dielectric constant of 9.53. The specific conductance of 0.01 M HCl in this mixture is 1.5×10^{-4} as compared with 41.2×10^{-4} for 0.01 M HCl in water. Why is the conductance less in the solvent mixture?

2-15. The specific conductances of 0.02 M solutions of HCl and NaCl are, respectively, 8.14×10^{-3} and 2.32×10^{-3}. Why is hydrochloric acid the better conductor?

2-16. The specific conductance of 0.05 M acetic acid is 3.68×10^{-4}, and that of the 0.025 M acid is 2.59×10^{-4}. Why is the first value considerably less than twice the second?

2-17. The dependence of the specific conductance of sulfuric acid on concentration is shown in Fig. 2-13. Account for (a) the initial rise of the curve and (b) the subsequent falling off as the concentration of acid increases.

2-18. Explain why the extent of ionization of acetic acid increases as a solution of the acid is diluted with water.

2-19. Which solution has the higher concentration of sulfide ion, 0.1 M hydrogen sulfide or a solution which is 0.1 M in hydrogen sulfide and 0.2 M in hydrochloric acid? Explain.

2-20. A solution contains 0.7263 g of mannitol, $C_6H_{14}O_6$, a nonelectrolyte, in 100 g of water. Ice begins to form from this solution at $-0.07430°C$. Calculate the freezing point constant K_f.

2-21. The ratio of freezing point depression to molality ($\Delta T/m$) is 1.86 for a nonelectrolyte in water at low concentrations. The same ratio for $HgCl_2$ is 1.8, for $K_2Fe(CN)_6(NO)$ is 5.2, and for $AgNO_3$ is 3.3. Calculate i for each salt. How many ions per formula does each salt give in solution?

2-22. Compare the work required to separate a sodium and a chloride ion in water at 25° with that required to separate to an equal extent at 25° (a) a sodium and a chloride ion in ethyl alcohol; (b) a magnesium and a sulfate ion in water.

2-23. Picture the arrangement of water molecules about positive and negative ions in solution. Why does formation of hydration layers stabilize ions in solution?

2-24. Comment on the practice in some texts of writing $Fe(H_2O)_6^{+++}$ for the formula of the ferric ion in solution.

2-25. Account for the ready solubility of many ionic crystals in water.

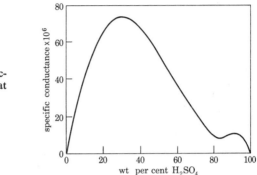

FIG. 2-13. The specific conductance of sulfuric acid solutions at 18°.

2-26. Cite experimental evidence to support the assertion that ions are hydrated in solution.

2-27. Heat is absorbed when $Na_2SO_4 \cdot 10H_2O$ dissolves in water but is evolved when anhydrous Na_2SO_4 dissolves. Suggest an explanation.

2-30. Why is it incorrect to say that sodium chloride ionizes when it dissolves in water?

2-31. Represent by equations the ionization of $AsCl_3$ molecules to give ultimately H_3AsO_3 and the ions of hydrochloric acid. How does this differ from the ionization of HCl and from the dissolving of sodium chloride?

The following exercises are added in the hope that they will stimulate further interest in structural chemistry.

2-32. The measured dipole moment of an isolated sodium chloride molecule is 8.5 debyes. The distance between the sodium and chlorine nuclei is 2.36 A. Calculate the dipole moment, on the assumption that the molecule contains a single positive charge centered on the sodium nucleus and a single negative charge at the position of the chlorine nucleus. The crystal radii of the two ions are given in Sec. 2-8. Compare the sum of these with the observed internuclear distance. What do both of these calculations show about the type of bond between sodium and chlorine in the molecule?

2-33. An early investigation of the ionization of nitric acid used a spectroscopic method [O. Redlich and J. Bigeleisen, *J. Am. Chem. Soc.*, **65**, 1883 (1943)]. Blue light from a mercury arc was passed through solutions containing nitrate ions. Some was absorbed by the ions and re-emitted with altered wave length (the Raman effect). Some of this altered light coming off at right angles to the incident blue light was allowed to fall on a photographic plate. The intensity of darkening was found to be a measure of the concentration of nitrate ion present. In a typical experiment the intensity of this light from a 6.6 M nitric acid solution was found to match that from a 4.46 M sodium nitrate solution. Assume that sodium nitrate is completely ionized and calculate the concentrations of ions and molecules in 6.6 M nitric acid and the percentage ionization of the acid.

2-34. Of the three solutes $C_2H_4(OH)_2$, C_2H_6, and $C_2H_4Cl_2$, one is nonpolar, one is polar, and one is polar and capable of forming hydrogen bonds. Predict their relative solubilities in (a) water, (b) methyl alcohol, and (c) benzene.

2-35. A molar volume of formic acid in the vapor state at low pressures and temperatures weighs about 92 g. Simple molecules of formic acid have a dipole moment; those in the vapor do not. Assume that the forces holding the simple molecules together are hydrogen bonds and draw a diagram of the structure of the vapor molecules which is in accord with these facts.

CHAPTER THREE

Ionic Reactions and Ionic Equations

3-1. Introduction. In the previous chapter the nature of solutes, whether pure or in solution, was considered. The properties of solutes that we are most directly concerned with in qualitative analysis are their chemical reactions. In this chapter we consider mainly the problem of representing such reactions by equations. In Chapter 9 the more fundamental problem of whether or not a reaction will occur is examined. This is treated only sketchily now because our concern must be to acquire sufficient facility in writing equations to cope with the laboratory work.

3-2. The Removal of Ions by Ionic Reactions. When reactions between ions occur, at least one kind of ion is removed from the field of action. Its concentration decreases as the reaction proceeds. Consider as an example the precipitation of silver chloride by addition of hydrochloric acid to some 0.1 M silver nitrate solution. The silver ion concentration decreases from 0.1 at the start to less than 0.00001 mole per liter after a slight excess of chloride has been added. On the other hand, silver chloride will not react to an appreciable extent with dilute nitric acid for the very reason that there is no conceivable reaction between them that will remove ions.

Removal of ions can be brought about in three ways.

1. Formation of a Precipitate. The more insoluble we can make the precipitate by choice of conditions, the more extensively will ions be removed. In precipitating silver chloride, for example, in the analysis of Cation Group 1, it is advantageous to add a slight excess of hydrochloric acid. Because of the common ion effect (Sec. 2-16) an excess of chloride ions drives the reaction farther to the right and removes more silver ions:

$$Ag^+ + NO_3^- + H_3O^+ + Cl^- \rightarrow AgCl \downarrow + H_3O^+ + NO_3^-$$

2. Formation of a Weakly Ionized Substance. The weak electrolyte can be water, a weak acid, a weak base, a weak salt, or a weakly dissociated complex ion. A weak electrolyte such as ammonia allows only low concentrations of

49

its ions at equilibrium. Thus, when sodium hydroxide is added to an ammonium salt in carrying out the test for ammonium ion, molecular ammonia and water are formed by combination of the hydroxide and ammonium ions:

$$NH_4^+ + Cl^- + Na^+ + OH^- \rightarrow NH_3 + H_2O + Na^+ + Cl^-$$

The lower we can make the extent of ionization of the product, the greater the extent of reaction will be. In the example above, to increase the yield of ammonia we use a slight excess of sodium hydroxide which furnishes the common hydroxide ion. If the weak electrolyte is a slightly soluble gas like H_2S, a sparingly soluble solid like H_3BO_3, or an unstable acid like H_2CO_3, H_2SO_3, or HNO_2, the reaction may proceed to virtual completion.

3. Oxidation or Reduction of an Ion.   Sulfide ions, for example, can be removed by oxidizing them to free sulfur. Cupric ions can be eliminated by reducing them to free copper. This method will be dealt with in Secs. 3-10 through 3-14. In the early sections of the chapter we shall concentrate on formation of precipitates and weak electrolytes.

Chemical equations are written to identify the reacting substances and products and to show the ratios in which the ions and molecules react or form. "Ionic equations" are so written as to show removal of ions. To know when to expect reactions to occur and to write proper ionic equations the student must be able to recognize substances as being soluble or insoluble and as being strong or weak electrolytes. The following two sections provide useful summaries of this information.

3-3. A Summary of Solubilities.   A condensed summary of solubilities is given in Table 3-1. It should be memorized. This is not intended as a complete summary, but it gives an adequate background for the early work of the course. During the laboratory work you will learn the solubility rules for other classes of compounds, e.g., chromates and oxalates. The solubilities in the table refer to pure water as the solvent. Many of these substances can be dissolved by chemical reactions with reagents; this is the kind of information you will learn during your laboratory work. The word "insoluble" is used hereafter in its customary sense of "very slightly soluble." In principle, no substance is completely insoluble.

3-4. A Summary of Strong and Weak Electrolytes.   The basis of this classification has been given in Sec. 2-15. The summary in Table 3-2 is a condensation and simplification of the discussion in Secs. 2-21 to 2-23. For the practical purpose of writing formulas and equations it is necessary to simplify. No formula by itself can possibly represent the complicated character of a sodium chloride solution, much less the still more complex nature of a lead nitrate solution. The information in Table 3-2 should be memorized.

TABLE 3-1.

Summary of Solubilities

Rule	Exceptions
1. Nitrates and acetates are generally soluble	No common ones. Silver acetate is moderately insoluble
2. Compounds of the alkali metals and ammonium ion are generally soluble	No common ones. Some moderately insoluble ones are formed in Cation Group 5
3. Chlorides, bromides, and iodides are generally soluble	The halides of Ag, Hg(I), and Pb(II); HgI_2; BiOCl and SbOCl
4. Sulfates are generally soluble	$PbSO_4$, $SrSO_4$, $BaSO_4$; $CaSO_4$ is moderately insoluble
5. Carbonates and sulfites are generally insoluble	Those of the alkali metals and ammonium
6. Sulfides are generally insoluble	Those of the alkali metals and ammonium; sulfides of the alkaline earth metals and Cr_2S_3 and Al_2S_3 are decomposed by water
7. Hydroxides are generally insoluble	Those of the alkali metals and ammonium; the hydroxides of Ba, Sr, and Ca are moderately soluble

TABLE 3-2.

Summary of Strong and Weak Electrolytes

Rule	Exceptions
1. Most acids are weak electrolytes	The common strong acids are HCl, HBr, HI, HNO_3, H_2SO_4, $HClO_3$, and $HClO_4$
2. Most bases are weak electrolytes	The strong basic hydroxides are those of Li, Na, K, Rb, Cs, Ca, Sr, and Ba
3. Most salts are strong electrolytes	The most important weakly ionized salt is $HgCl_2$; sometimes $Hg(CN)_2$, $CdCl_2$, $CdBr_2$, CdI_2, and $Pb(C_2H_3O_2)_2$ are also listed but there is no general agreement on these.

3-5. Rules for Writing Formulas. It is easy to write ionic equations if the formulas are written according to certain rules. These rules too should be memorized.

Rule 1. Ionic formulas are written for strong electrolytes in solution.

EXAMPLES: $Na^+ + Cl^-$ and not NaCl; $2Na^+ + SO_4^{--}$ and not Na_2SO_4, $Na_2^+ + SO_4^{--}$, or $Na_2^{++} + SO_4^{--}$; $2H^+ + SO_4^{--}$ for dilute sulfuric acid; $Na^+ + HCO_3^-$ and not $NaHCO_3$.

COMMENTS: Hydration of ions is not shown; i.e., Cr^{+++} is written instead of $Cr(H_2O)_6^{+++}$. The hydronium ion, H_3O^+, will hereafter be abbreviated to H^+ except when the proton transfer process is being emphasized. Ion-pair formation is shown only in the rare cases when it exerts a decisive influence on the course of a reaction.

Rule 2. Molecular formulas are written for

(a) Elements, gases, solids, and nonelectrolytes.

EXAMPLES: Cl_2, SO_2, Cu, HCl (gas), CH_3CSNH_2, CCl_4, C_2H_5OH.

(b) Weak electrolytes in solution.

EXAMPLES: H_2O, $HC_2H_3O_2$, NH_3, H_2SO_4 (concentrated).

(c) Solid strong electrolytes or precipitates.

EXAMPLES: $AgCl \downarrow$, $BaSO_4 \downarrow$, $CaCO_3 \downarrow$.

COMMENTS: Though ions are present in these solids and a formula such as $Ag^+Cl^- \downarrow$ would show this better, the charges are customarily omitted for simplicity.

3-6. Writing Ionic Equations. General Remarks.   It is helpful in writing ionic equations to ask and answer three questions:

1. What kind of reaction is it: double decomposition or oxidation-reduction?

2. What are the possible products of the reaction?

3. Are any of the possible products or reactants insoluble or weakly ionized?

The answers to the first two questions are related. A consideration of the possible products often may be helpful in deciding the kind of reaction. First, we shall take up double decomposition reactions including those in which protons are transferred. Then we shall consider oxidation-reduction, or "redox," reactions in which electron transfer occurs.

3-7. Double Decomposition Reactions. Formation of Precipitates and Weak Electrolytes.   The principles involved in writing ionic equations are illustrated best by specific examples.

EXAMPLE 1. *Potassium chloride and calcium nitrate.* These substances do not react with each other in dilute solution. The possible products are potassium nitrate and calcium chloride. Both these salts are soluble (Table 3-1) and highly ionized (Table 3-2). No ions are removed by their formation and no reaction will occur unless an ion is removed. Students are sometimes tempted to write

$$2K^+ + 2Cl^- + Ca^{++} + 2NO_3^- \rightarrow 2K^+ + 2NO_3^- + Ca^{++} + 2Cl^-$$

But this only shows the same particles on both sides in different orders, a pointless result. Simply write N.R. (for no reaction).

EXAMPLE 2. *Formation of a precipitate. Silver nitrate and hydrochloric acid.* The possible products are silver chloride and nitric acid. All four substances, products and reactants, are strong electrolytes (Table 3-2), and all are soluble but silver chloride (Table 3-1). We write ionic formulas for the strong electrolytes in solution (Rule 1, Sec. 3-5) and a molecular formula with an arrow pointing down for silver chloride (Rule 2c).

$$Ag^+ + NO_3^- + H^+ + Cl^- \rightarrow AgCl \downarrow + H^+ + NO_3^-$$

This equation shows removal of silver and chloride ions. The other two ions are bystanders and do not take part. We shall make a practice of omitting bystander ions. The essential equation is then

$$Ag^+ + Cl^- \rightarrow AgCl \downarrow$$

EXAMPLE 3. *Formation of a weak electrolyte. Hydrochloric acid and calcium acetate.* The possible products are acetic acid and calcium chloride. All four of these are soluble substances (Table 3-1), and all but acetic acid are strong electrolytes (Table 3-2). The formation of weakly ionized acetic acid with removal of hydrogen (i.e., hydronium) and acetate ions is the essential feature of this reaction. The essential equation is

$$H^+ + C_2H_3O_2^- \rightarrow HC_2H_3O_2$$

The chloride and calcium ions are bystanders and have been omitted.

EXAMPLE 4. *Conversion of one weak electrolyte to another. Acetic acid and sodium hydroxide.* The possible products are sodium acetate and water. Both the products and the reactants are soluble in water (Table 3-1), and sodium hydroxide and sodium acetate are strong electrolytes (Table 3-2). The essential reaction is the transfer of a proton from an acetic acid molecule to the hydroxide ion:

$$HC_2H_3O_2 + OH^- \rightarrow C_2H_3O_2^- + H_2O$$

This reaction can occur because water is more weakly ionized than acetic acid is; thus H^+ and OH^- ions are removed from the field of action. Yet the equation $H^+ + OH^- \rightarrow H_2O$ would not be a good representation of the reaction, for it does not show that the reaction also causes acetic acid to ionize. The heat liberated in the reaction is the sum of the heat of ionization of acetic acid and the heat of neutralization of hydronium ions with hydroxide ions. An essential equation should represent all important features of the reaction.

EXAMPLE 5. *Conversion of one precipitate to another. Lead chloride and sodium sulfate.* The possible products are sodium chloride (strong electrolyte, soluble) and lead sulfate (strong electrolyte, insoluble). The reaction can be thought of as a competition between chloride and sulfate ions for lead ions, a competition that sulfate wins because lead sulfate is more insoluble than lead chloride. The essential equation must show the disappearance of lead chloride as well as the formation of lead sulfate

$$PbCl_2 \downarrow + SO_4^{--} \rightarrow PbSO_4 \downarrow + 2Cl^-$$

Lead ions and sulfate ions are removed from the field of action.

EXAMPLE 6. *Competition between a weak electrolyte and a precipitate. Hydrogen sulfide and Copper(II) nitrate in acid solution.* The possible products are copper(II) sulfide (insoluble) and nitric acid (strong and soluble). Although hydrogen sulfide is very weakly ionized, the solubility of copper(II) sulfide is so low that sulfide ions are removed from equilibrium with the weak acid to give the precipitate:

$$Cu^{++} + H_2S \rightarrow CuS \downarrow + 2H^+$$

The equation $Cu^{++} + S^{--} \rightarrow CuS \downarrow$ is unsatisfactory because it does not show ionization of the hydrogen sulfide and release of hydrogen ions. The precipitation is actually reversible, and, if too high a concentration of acid builds up, precipitation may stop before the reaction has gone to a satisfactory extent.

3-8. Double Decomposition by Proton Transfer. There are many reactions in which protons[1] are transferred from one substance, the proton donor D, to another, the proton acceptor A; passing notice has been taken of some of these reactions already. Such transfers are reversible when the products also include a proton donor and acceptor, as is generally the case. They then conform to the pattern

$$D_1 \rightleftharpoons A_1 + \text{proton}$$

$$\text{proton} + A_2 \rightleftharpoons D_2$$

$$\overline{D_1 + A_2 \rightleftharpoons D_2 + A_1}$$

These reactions are called *protolytic* from Greek words meaning "proton loosening." Examples 3 and 4 of Sec. 3-7 follow this pattern:

$$H_3O^+ + C_2H_3O_2^- \rightleftharpoons HC_2H_3O_2 + H_2O$$

$$HC_2H_3O_2 + OH^- \rightleftharpoons H_2O + C_2H_3O_2^-$$

In both of these the second donor (D_2) is more weakly ionized than the first, and protons are removed from the field of action.

In writing equations to show proton transfer the student should use the formula H_3O^+ for the hydronium ion rather than the abbreviated form H^+.

Proton donors may be molecules of weak acids ($HC_2H_3O_2$), anions containing an acid hydrogen (HCO_3^-), or cations (H_3O^+, NH_4^+). Proton acceptors are molecules or ions that can take up a proton to give back a proton donor ($C_2H_3O_2^-$, CO_3^{--}, HCO_3^-, H_2O, NH_3). It should be noted that some substances such as H_2O and HCO_3^- can be either proton donors or acceptors. How they behave in a particular reaction depends on the other reactant.

Some other protolytic reactions are

	D_1	$+$	A_2	$\rightleftharpoons$	D_2	$+$	A_1
1.	HCO_2H	$+$	H_2O	$\rightleftharpoons$	H_3O^+	$+$	HCO_2^-
2.	H_2O	$+$	NH_3	$\rightleftharpoons$	NH_4^+	$+$	OH^-
3.	HSO_4^-	$+$	CH_3NH_2	$\rightleftharpoons$	$CH_3NH_3^+$	$+$	SO_4^{--}
4.	NH_4^+	$+$	CO_3^{--}	$\rightleftharpoons$	HCO_3^-	$+$	NH_3
5.	H_2O	$+$	S^{--}	$\rightleftharpoons$	HS^-	$+$	OH^-

[1] "Proton" as used here refers to a hydrogen nucleus whether it actually is a proton or is, less commonly, a deuteron or triton.

The first two reactions are usually called "ionization reactions." The third is a "neutralization reaction," the acid being hydrogen sulfate ion and the base methylamine. The fourth shows one equilibrium in an ammonium carbonate solution. The fifth is a "hydrolysis reaction" in a sulfide solution.

3-9. Reactions Involving Precipitates and Complex Ions.   Such reactions can be treated without the introduction of any new principles if we recognize that most complex ions are weakly dissociated.

EXAMPLE 1. *Solution of a precipitate by formation of a complex ion. Silver chloride and ammonia solution.* The precipitate dissolves in ammonia because the concentration of silver ion in equilibrium with the complex is below that required for equilibrium with the precipitate. Silver ions are removed from the field of action:

$$AgCl \downarrow + 2NH_3 \rightarrow Ag(NH_3)_2^+ + Cl^-$$

EXAMPLE 2. *Dissociation of a complex to give a precipitate. Silver ammonia chloride and potassium iodide.* Silver iodide is less soluble than silver chloride and requires a lower concentration of silver ion for equilibrium than the complex does. Silver and iodide ions are removed to form the precipitate, and the complex is dissociated:

$$Ag(NH_3)_2^+ + I^- \rightarrow AgI \downarrow + 2NH_3$$

EXAMPLE 3. *Conversion of one complex to another. Cadmium ammonia sulfate and potassium cyanide.* Cadmium ions are removed from the ammonia complex to give the more weakly dissociated cyanide complex:

$$Cd(NH_3)_4^{++} + 4CN^- \rightarrow Cd(CN)_4^{--} + 4NH_3$$

EXAMPLE 4. *Decomposition of a complex and formation of a precipitate. Silver ammonia chloride and nitric acid.* The reaction is represented by

$$Ag(NH_3)_2^+ + Cl^- + 2H^+ \rightarrow AgCl \downarrow + 2NH_4^+$$

Two changes take place: the ammonia is withdrawn from the complex to form the more weakly dissociated ammonium ion, and the liberated silver ions combine with the chloride ions also present to precipitate silver chloride.

3-10. Oxidation-Reduction. Oxidation Numbers.   In some reactions simple ions suffer an increase or decrease of charge, e.g.,

$$Fe^{+++} + V^{++} \rightarrow V^{+++} + Fe^{++}$$

$$Cl_2 + 2Br^- \rightarrow Br_2 + 2Cl^-$$

Let us define a set of *oxidation numbers* for each element such that

1. The oxidation number of an ion is equal to its charge.

2. The oxidation number of a free or uncombined element is zero.

An increase in oxidation number is then defined as *oxidation* and a decrease in oxidation number as *reduction*. In the examples above V^{++} and Br^- ions are being oxidized and Cl_2 and Fe^{+++} ion are being reduced. These changes are brought about by transfers of electrons. Oxidation is accompanied by loss of electrons, e.g.,

$$V^{++} \rightarrow V^{+++} + e^-$$
$$2Br^- \rightarrow Br_2 + 2e^-$$

Reduction is accompanied by gain of electrons, e.g.,

$$e^- + Fe^{+++} \rightarrow Fe^{++}$$
$$2e^- + Cl_2 \rightarrow 2Cl^-$$

These concepts can be generalized to include molecules and ions containing covalent bonds. Oxidation numbers have no simple structural interpretation with these more complex particles. They are assigned according to certain arbitrary rules. These include the two already given and the following three:

3. The oxidation number of oxygen is usually -2. The principal exceptions are -1 in peroxides and zero in free oxygen.

4. The oxidation number of hydrogen is usually $+1$. In the hydrides of the active metals, e.g., LiH and CaH_2, it is -1.

5. The sum of the oxidation numbers of the elements in an ion must be equal to the net ionic charge, and the sum for a molecule must be zero.

These rules are illustrated by the following examples.

EXAMPLE 1. Find the oxidation number of carbon in $HC_2H_3O_2$. Hence x, the oxidation number of carbon, is zero.	2 C $= 2x$ 4 H $= +4$ 2 O $= -4$ Total $= 0$
EXAMPLE 2. Find the oxidation number of chromium in the dichromate ion, $Cr_2O_7^{--}$. Hence x, the oxidation number of chromium, is $+6$.	2 Cr $= 2x$ 7 O $= -14$ Net charge $= -2$
EXAMPLE 3. Find the oxidation number of iron in its magnetic oxide, Fe_3O_4. Hence x, the average oxidation number of iron, is $+8/3$.	3 Fe $= 3x$ 4 O $= -8$ Total $= 0$

The fractional value of the last result will serve to emphasize that oxidation numbers are formal bookkeeping devices[2] which have simple physical significance only for ions, such as Fe^{++}, V^{+++}, and Cl^-. The assignments we have made are not even unique. For acetic acid it would be perfectly possible to set the oxidation numbers of carbon and hydrogen equal to $+4$ and $+1$, respectively, and then the oxidation number of oxygen would have to be -6. These numbers satisfy the requirement that their sum be zero for the molecule.

[2]It is possible to preserve integral oxidation numbers in Fe_3O_4 by assuming that it contains one Fe^{++} and two Fe^{+++} ions.

In reactions between ions and molecules containing covalent bonds the changes in oxidation number are often associated with electronic changes. There may be a direct transfer of electrons or the electrons may be carried along by other atoms. For the reaction between chlorate and sulfite ions, of which the first step is the reduction of chlorate to chlorite,

$$
\begin{bmatrix} :\ddot{O}: \\ :\ddot{O}:\ddot{Cl}:\ddot{O}: \end{bmatrix}^- + \begin{bmatrix} :\ddot{O}: \\ :\ddot{S}:\ddot{O}: \\ :\ddot{O}: \end{bmatrix}^= \rightarrow \begin{bmatrix} :\ddot{O}: \\ :\ddot{O}:\ddot{Cl}: \end{bmatrix}^- + \begin{bmatrix} :\ddot{O}: \\ :\ddot{O}:\ddot{S}:\ddot{O}: \\ :\ddot{O}: \end{bmatrix}^=
$$

Taube has used chlorate labeled with O^{18} as a tracer to prove that one oxygen atom of the chlorate is transferred to the sulfite. The reaction is one of oxygen atom transfer and not electron transfer.

Our concern at this early stage is with balancing equations for oxidation-reduction reactions. We cannot and need not pursue further these intriguing problems concerning the detailed way in which the reactions occur. For balancing equations this information is not required; we only need to know what the reactants and products are. We also must pass over for the time being the problem of predicting whether or not a given combination of re-agents will react. This is considered in Chapter 9. It is useful, nevertheless, to have in mind the typical behavior of some oxidizing and reducing agents.

3-11. Oxidizing and Reducing Agents. *Reducing agents* are substances that cause reduction of other substances. They themselves are oxidized and can lose electrons. Typical reducing agents include metals, metal ions in a low oxidation state, nonmetal anions, and molecules or ions containing an element in a low oxidation state combined with oxygen. Examples are given in Table 3-3.

TABLE 3-3.

Typical Reducing Agents

Reducing agent	Conditions	Oxidized form	Change in oxidation number
Zn	acid solution	Zn^{++}	0 to $+2$
Al	basic solution	$Al(OH)_4^-$	0 to $+3$
H_2S	acid solution	S	-2 to 0
Sn^{++}	HCl solution	$SnCl_6^{--}$	$+2$ to $+4$
$Sn(OH)_3^-$	basic solution	$Sn(OH)_6^{--}$	$+2$ to $+4$ (Sn)
$S_2O_4^{--}$	basic solution	SO_3^{--}	$+3$ to $+4$ (S)
HNO_2	acid solution	NO_3^-	$+3$ to $+5$ (N)
H_2O_2	acid solution	O_2	-1 to 0 (O)

Oxidizing agents cause oxidation of other substances. They themselves are reduced and can gain electrons. Typical oxidizing agents include metal ions, free nonmetals, and oxy compounds (Table 3-4). It will be noted that some oxidizing agents can be reduced to several different oxidation states. Nitrate and permanganate ions are notorious for the variety of their reduction products. Only the most common of these are given in Table 3-4.

TABLE 3-4.

Typical Oxidizing Agents

Oxidizing agent	Conditions	Reduced form	Change in oxidation number
Cu^{++}		Cu	$+2$ to $\;0$
Fe^{+++}		Fe^{++}	$+3$ to $+2$
Br_2	acid solution	Br^-	0 to -1
$Cr_2O_7^{--}$	acid solution	Cr^{+++}	$+6$ to $+3$ (Cr)
MnO_4^-	acid solution	Mn^{++}	$+7$ to $+2$ (Mn)
MnO_4^-	basic solution	MnO_2	$+7$ to $+4$ (Mn)
NO_3^-	concentrated (16 M) acid	NO_2	$+5$ to $+4$ (N)
NO_3^-	dilute (6 M) acid	NO	$+5$ to $+2$ (N)
NO_3^-	basic solution	NH_3	$+5$ to -3 (N)
ClO_3^-	HNO_3 solution	ClO_2	$+5$ to $+4$ (Cl)
H_2O_2	acid solution	H_2O	-1 to -2 (O)
H_2O_2	basic solution	OH^-	-1 to -2 (O)

3-12. Balancing Equations for Redox Reactions.   There are two convenient methods of balancing equations for oxidation-reduction, or "redox," reactions: the *ion-electron method* and the *oxidation number method*. Because it ignores oxidation numbers, the ion-electron method is more convenient for balancing equations for reactions in which several elements are being oxidized or reduced simultaneously. The partial equations obtained by this method are the electrode reactions of an electric cell that uses the redox reaction as a source of electrical energy. Many chemists prefer the other method because it focuses attention on the changes in oxidation state. Both procedures are primarily recipes for obtaining a balanced equation with a minimum of effort. Neither gives any real indication of the sequence of events that actually takes place, which is frequently far too complex to be shown by a single equation. Both procedures give us an equation which correctly shows the reactants and products in the proper proportions; this is all we require at this time.

3-13. The Ion-Electron Method of Balancing Redox Equations.   There are six steps in the procedure.

1. Write skeleton partial equations showing

Oxidizing agent $\rightarrow$ reduced form

Reducing agent $\rightarrow$ oxidized form

As an example consider the reaction between potassium dichromate and sulfurous acid in acid solution. The skeleton equations are

$$Cr_2O_7^{--} \rightarrow Cr^{+++}$$
$$H_2SO_3 \rightarrow SO_4^{--}$$

2. Equalize the number of atoms on both sides of each partial equation. It is generally best to proceed in the following order.

(a) Balance first the atoms of the elements undergoing changes in oxidation number.

EXAMPLE: $Cr_2O_7^{--} \rightarrow 2Cr^{+++}$

(b) Balance oxygen atoms by application of the following rules. *They should be memorized.*

Rule A: $2H^+ +$ (extra O) $\rightleftharpoons H_2O$ (Acid solution)

Rule B: $H_2O +$ (extra O) $\rightleftharpoons 2OH^-$ (Basic solution)

Note that when read from left to right the rules show how to dispose of an extra oxygen, and, from right to left, how to furnish one.

EXAMPLE: In $Cr_2O_7^{--} \rightarrow 2Cr^{+++}$ there are seven extra oxygen atoms on the left; hence balance with $14H^+$ on the left and $7H_2O$ on the right as specified in Rule A:

$$14H^+ + Cr_2O_7^{--} \rightarrow 2Cr^{+++} + 7H_2O$$

In $H_2SO_3 \rightarrow SO_4^{--}$ there is an extra oxygen atom on the right; add $1H_2O$ to the left and $2H^+$ to the right:

$$H_2O + H_2SO_3 \rightarrow SO_4^{--} + 2H^+$$

Note that hydrogen ions and water are plentiful in acid solution, and it is appropriate to use them for balancing. In basic solution few hydrogen ions are available and it is better to use hydroxide ions and water. It is no more reasonable to use H^+ and OH^- in the same equation than it is to expect six dogs and six cats to live together comfortably in the same room.

(c) If extra hydrogen atoms are still to be disposed of, use Rules C and D.

Rule C: (extra H) $\rightleftharpoons H^+$ (Acid solution)

EXAMPLE: $H_2SO_3 + H_2O \rightarrow SO_4^{--} + 4H^+$

Rule D: $OH^- +$ (extra H) $\rightleftharpoons H_2O$ (Basic solution)

EXAMPLE: $4OH^- + Cr(OH)_4^- \rightarrow CrO_4^{--} + 4H_2O$

3. Balance each partial equation electrically by adding electrons to equalize the *ionic* charges.

EXAMPLES: $14H^+ + Cr_2O_7^{--} + 6e^- \rightarrow 2Cr^{+++} + 7H_2O$

$$\underbrace{\quad+12\quad} \quad \underbrace{-6} \quad = \quad \underbrace{+6}$$

$$H_2O + H_2SO_3 \rightarrow SO_4^{--} + 4H^+ + 2e^-$$

$$\underbrace{\qquad 0 \qquad} \quad = \quad \underbrace{+2} \quad -2$$

The electron changes are found without reference to the oxidation numbers. Only the ionic charges are used. Of course, these must be written correctly or the method will fail. (The number of electrons will correspond to the change in oxidation number; i.e., $2Cr(VI)$ to $2Cr(III)$ is a total change of 6 caused by gain of 6 electrons.)

4. By cross multiplication make the number of electrons lost in one partial equation equal to the number gained in the other.

EXAMPLE: $(H_2SO_3 + H_2O \rightarrow SO_4^{--} + 4H^+ + 2e^-) \times 3$

5. Add the two partial equations and cancel electrons, H^+, H_2O, and OH^- as far as possible. There should be no electrons in the final equation.

EXAMPLE: $2H^+ + Cr_2O_7^{--} + 3H_2SO_3 \rightarrow 2Cr^{+++} + 3SO_4^{--} + 4H_2O$

6. Check the final equation.

(a) The net ionic charges on the two sides should be equal.

EXAMPLE: Left side 0, right side 0.

(b) The number of atoms of each kind must be the same on both sides.

EXAMPLE: Each side has 8H, 3S, 2Cr, and 16O.

3-14. The Oxidation Number Method of Balancing Redox Equations.   There are six steps in this method.

1. Write a skeleton equation showing formulas of reducing and oxidizing agents on the left and their products on the right. Balance immediately atoms other than oxygen or hydrogen. As an example consider the reaction between potassium dichromate and sulfurous acid in acid solution, for which the skeleton equation is

$$Cr_2O_7^{--} + H_2SO_3 \rightarrow 2Cr^{+++} + SO_4^{--}$$

2. Assign oxidation numbers to all atoms and determine which undergo change.

$$\overset{+6\ -2}{Cr_2O_7^{--}} \quad + \quad \overset{+1+4-2}{H_2SO_3} \quad \rightarrow \quad \overset{+3}{2Cr^{+++}} \quad + \quad \overset{+6-2}{SO_4^{--}}$$

3. Determine the number of electrons lost *per formula* of reducing agent and the number gained *per formula* of oxidizing agent.

EXAMPLE: $S(IV) \rightarrow S(VI)$ means loss of $2e^-$
$Cr_2(VI) \rightarrow 2Cr(III)$ means gain of $6e^-$

Note that the change in oxidation number of *two* chromium atoms must be considered; this is fixed by the formula $Cr_2O_7^{--}$.

4. Adjust the coefficients of the formulas to balance the electron transfer. Use the smallest possible coefficients.

EXAMPLE: $Cr_2O_7^{--} + 3H_2SO_3 \rightarrow 3SO_4^{--} + 2Cr^{+++}$

5. Complete the balance of charge and atoms by inserting H^+ and H_2O if the solution is acid and OH^- and H_2O if it is basic. *Under no circumstances are the ratios of coefficients established in Step 4 to be altered.*

EXAMPLE: As the unfinished equation comes from Step 4, the left-hand side has a net ionic charge of -2 and it has 16 oxygen and 6 hydrogen atoms; the right-hand side has an ionic charge of $+6 - 6$ or zero and 12 oxygen atoms. By inspection it is seen that oxygen atoms will balance if $4H_2O$ are inserted on the right and charges and hydrogen atoms will balance if $2H^+$ ions are used on the left:

$$2H^+ + Cr_2O_7^{--} + 3H_2SO_3 \rightarrow 3SO_4^{--} + 2Cr^{+++} + 4H_2O$$

6. Check the final equation.

(a) The net ionic charges on the two sides should be equal.

EXAMPLE: Left side zero, right side zero.

(b) The number of atoms of each kind on the two sides must be the same.

EXAMPLE: Each side has 8H, 3S, 2Cr, and 16O.

SUPPLEMENTARY READING

H. H. BARBER and T. I. TAYLOR, *Semimicro Qualitative Analysis*, rev. ed., Harper, New York, 1953, Chapter 3.
T. R. HOGNESS and W. C. JOHNSON, *Qualitative Analysis and Chemical Equilibrium*, 4th ed., Holt, New York, 1954, Chapter 5.
T. MOELLER, *Qualitative Analysis*, McGraw-Hill, New York, 1958, Chapter 3.

EXERCISES

In all the following exercises you are to assume that a chemical reaction does occur.

3-1. Write an essential ionic equation for the reaction between each pair of reagents, and state which ion or ions are removed from the field of action. Assume dilute solutions of all soluble reagents. (a) silver nitrate and magnesium chloride, (b) iron(II) sulfide and hydrochloric acid, (c) nitrous acid and potassium hydroxide. (d) iron(III) chloride and sodium hydroxide, (e) lead nitrate and potassium chromate, (f) ammonium chloride and calcium hydroxide, (g) calcium carbonate and nitric acid, (h) lead sulfate and ammonium sulfide, (i) barium hydroxide and sulfuric acid, (j) hydrogen sulfide and tin(II) chloride, (k) copper(II) hydroxide and ammonia, (l) acetic acid and potassium cyanide, (m) ammonium carbonate and calcium nitrate, (n) bismuth(III) chloride and ammonia water, (o) silver acetate and potassium iodide, (p) calcium sulfite and perchloric acid, (q) strontium hydroxide and ammonium sulfate, (r) zinc sulfide and hydrochloric acid, (s) aluminum hydroxide and hydrobromic acid, (t) calcium hydroxide and nitric acid.

3-2. Write ionic equations for the following protolytic reactions. Identify the proton donors and acceptors. Write H_3O^+, rather than H^+, for the hydronium ion in these equations. (a) nitric acid and lithium hydroxide, (b) ammonium acetate and hydrochloric acid, (c) hydrogen cyanide gas and water, (d) sodium acetate and water, (e) potassium hydroxide and sodium hydrogen carbonate, (f) methylamine and water, (g) ammonium nitrate and water, (h) sodium dihydrogen phosphate and potassium cyanide, (i) hydrogen chloride gas and water, (j) sodium hydrogen carbonate and acetic acid, (k) sodium hydroxide and oxalic acid, (l) potassium carbonate and water.

3-3. Balance the following either by the ion-electron method or by the oxidation number method.

(a) $NO_3^- + Bi \rightarrow Bi^{+++} + NO_2$ (Acid solution)

(b) $Fe_3O_4 \downarrow + H_2O_2 \rightarrow Fe^{+++} + H_2O$ (Acid solution)

(c) $HClO + Br_2 \rightarrow BrO_3^- + Cl^-$ (Acid solution)

(d) $Cr^{+++} + ClO_3^- \rightarrow ClO_2 + Cr_2O_7^{--}$ (Acid solution)

(e) $H_2O_2 + Co(OH)_2 \downarrow \rightarrow Co_2O_3 \downarrow + H_2O$ (Basic solution)

(f) $Bi(OH)_3 \downarrow + Sn(OH)_3^- \rightarrow Sn(OH)_6^{--} + Bi \downarrow$ (Basic solution)

(g) $MnO_4^- + NO_2^- \rightarrow MnO_2 \downarrow + NO_3^-$ (Basic solution)

(h) $O_2 + H_2O + I^- \rightarrow I_2 + OH^-$ (Basic solution)

(i) $CHCl_3 + MnO_4^- \rightarrow Cl_2 + CO_2 + Mn^{++}$ (Acid solution)

(j) $Cu(NH_3)_4^{++} + CN^- \rightarrow CNO^- + Cu(CN)_3^{--} + NH_3$ (Basic solution)

(k) $H_2O_2 + SCN^- \rightarrow NH_4^+ + H_2O + HCO_3^- + HSO_4^-$ (Acid solution)

(l) $W + NO_3^- \rightarrow WO_3 \downarrow + NO_2$ (Acid solution)

(m) $Cu(NH_3)_4^{++} + S_2O_4^{--} \rightarrow SO_3^{--} + Cu \downarrow + NH_3$ (Basic solution)

(n) $Al + NO_3^- \rightarrow Al(OH)_4^- + NH_3$ (Basic solution)

(o) $Cu^{++} + I^- \rightarrow I_2 + CuI \downarrow$ (Acid solution)

(p) $Cr_2O_7^{--} + C_2H_4O \rightarrow HC_2H_3O_2 + Cr^{+++}$ (Acid solution)

(q) $H_2S + Fe^{+++} \rightarrow Fe^{++} + S \downarrow$ (Acid solution)

(r) $MnO_4^{--} \rightarrow MnO_2 \downarrow + MnO_4^-$ (Acid solution)

(s) $ClO^- \rightarrow Cl^- + ClO_3^-$ (Basic solution)

(t) $Pb \downarrow + PbO_2 \downarrow + SO_4^{--} \rightarrow PbSO_4 \downarrow$ (Acid solution)

(u) $ClO_3^- + As_2S_3 \downarrow \rightarrow Cl^- + H_2AsO_4^- + S \downarrow$ (Acid solution)

(v) $H_2SO_3 + I_2 \rightarrow I^- + SO_4^{--}$ (Acid solution)

(w) $Pb_3O_4 \downarrow + Cl^- \rightarrow PbCl_2 \downarrow + Cl_2$ (Acid solution)

(x) $NO_3^- + Bi_2S_3 \downarrow \rightarrow Bi^{+++} + NO + S \downarrow$ (Acid solution)

(y) $ClO^- + Mn(OH)_2 \downarrow \rightarrow MnO_2 \downarrow + Cl^-$ (Basic solution)

(z) $HO_2^- + Cr(OH)_4^- \rightarrow CrO_4^{--} + OH^-$ (Basic solution)

3-4. Write ionic equations for the following reactions. Some, but not all, are redox reactions and their equations should be balanced by the ion-electron or oxidation number method. Water has been left out of the list of reactants and products.

(a) Manganese(II) sulfide and hydrochloric acid → manganese(II) chloride and hydrogen sulfide

(b) Lead sulfide and dilute nitric acid → lead nitrate, nitric oxide, and sulfur

(c) Silver chloride and hydrogen sulfide → silver sulfide and hydrochloric acid

(d) Barium sulfate and sodium carbonate → barium carbonate and sodium sulfate

(e) Potassium chlorate, nitric acid, and manganese(II) nitrate → chlorine dioxide and manganese(IV) oxide

(f) Oxygen and sodium sulfite → sodium sulfate (basic solution)

(g) Potassium chromate and hydrochloric acid → potassium dichromate

(h) Concentrated nitric acid and arsenious acid → arsenic acid and nitrogen dioxide

(i) Concentrated nitric acid and lithium carbonate → lithium nitrate and carbon dioxide

(j) Iron(II) hydroxide and hydrogen peroxide → iron(III) hydroxide (basic solution)

(k) Carbon dioxide and barium hydroxide → barium carbonate

CHAPTER FOUR

The Concentrations of Substances in Solution

4-1. Introduction. In this chapter we shall review some of the quantitative relationships based on equations and formulas and ways of expressing concentrations of substances in solution.

This is the first chapter in which problem solving is our primary concern and some comments are appropriate. Facility in solving problems, so necessary in advanced work in science, should be cultivated with utmost care. Go beyond the mere grinding out of answers and give some thought to the techniques you use in solving problems. The following discussion is designed to draw your attention to some of these.

In starting to solve a problem, we must first be clear about what we are to find and what we are given. These may perhaps be obvious from the statement of the problem, but it is often helpful to try to rephrase the information. (Suppose, for example, that we are given that a solution is 2% NaCl by weight. What does this mean? Remembering that per cent means parts of something in 100 total parts, we rephrase the information to read: 2 g of NaCl in 100 g of solution or, perhaps, 2 lb of NaCl in 100 lb of solution.) Continuing the analysis, we should consider next what general relations or definitions may be relevant. In the problems of this chapter the basic concepts are those of the mole (or millimole), molarity, the chemical formula, and the chemical equation. Has a similar problem been seen in the text (many sample problems are worked out in this book) or was one done in class that resembles the problem at hand? Even if you have seen no other problem that is of the same type, do you remember one that started with the same data or that had the same unknown? Outline a solution of the problem. After carrying it out, check the answer. Is it reasonable? Or is it a thousand times larger than it can possibly be? Has more material been produced than we started with? Do the units of the various factors combine to give the units of the answer? Looking back over the problem, do you see an easier method of solution?

These are the questions that should be asked in problem solving. Consciously cultivate such patterns of thought if you wish to develop facility. Remember, too, that facility is acquired by practice. Reading *about* problems will not do; you must take pencil and paper in hand and solve as many as possible. If you spend an inordinate amount of time on the problem you work, take the pains to discover why; is it lack of knowledge of principles or faulty technique?

4-2. Formulas and Equations. For a molecular substance such as iodine or carbon tetrachloride, the formula shows the number of atoms of each kind in the molecule. For an ionic substance such as calcium fluoride or potassium sulfate, the formula indicates only the simplest ratio of the different kinds of ions in the crystal, e.g., $1Ca^{++}$ to $2F^-$ or $2K^+$ to $1SO_4^{--}$ (Sec. 2-6). It is convenient to have a name for the group of ions required to make a formula. We call this a *kome* after a Greek word meaning a "mobile group."[1] One Ca^{++} ion and $2F^-$ ions make a kome of calcium fluoride and $3K^+$ ions and $1Fe(CN)_6^{---}$ ion make a kome of potassium ferricyanide. In a chemical equation the formulas can stand for single molecules or ions or komes of ions or any multiple of these. The equation

$$2Ag^+ + 2NO_3^- + H_2S \rightarrow Ag_2S \downarrow + 2H^+ + 2NO_3^-$$

can thus be read as "two komes of silver nitrate with a molecule of hydrogen sulfide give a kome of silver sulfide and two komes of nitric acid." It could also be read as "832 komes of silver nitrate and 416 molecules of hydrogen sulfide give 416 komes of silver sulfide and 832 komes of nitric acid." The number 832 was chosen at random, but the ratios of silver nitrate to hydrogen sulfide to silver sulfide to nitric acid are fixed by the equation and cannot be varied.

4-3. The Mole. In almost all chemical reactions the number of atoms, molecules, or ions involved is enormous, ranging from about 10^{18} to 10^{27}. It is convenient to deal in units of a size in this range just as we do business in dollars rather than pennies, measure distances from city to city in miles rather than inches, and tell our ages in years rather than seconds. The actual size of the unit might be taken as some round number like 10^{24} molecules, but because its definition was originally based on mass rather than number of molecules, it is not a simple number. We define one *mole* of a substance as 6.02×10^{23} atoms, molecules, ions, or komes, whichever may be appropriate.[2] The equation in the preceding section can then be read as "two moles of silver nitrate and a mole of hydrogen sulfide give one mole of silver sulfide and two moles of nitric acid." Two moles of nitric acid correspond to $2 \times 6.02 \times 10^{23}$ komes or $2 \times 6.02 \times 10^{23}$ hydrogen ions and an equal number of nitrate ions.

[1] This useful word was introduced by R. W. Gurney in his book *Ionic Processes in Solution*.

[2] Some authors use gram-ion for 6.02×10^{23} ions, and gram formula weight for 6.02×10^{23} komes of an ionic compound. It is hardly necessary to multiply terms to this extent as long as we recognize that the use of "mole" does not commit us to molecules as the structural units.

In actual practice we obtain a mole of a substance by weighing and not by counting out 6.02×10^{23} molecules. In fact, if we could see molecules and could handle one every second, it would take all the people in the world (about 2×10^9) working night and day a little over two weeks to count out the number of iodine molecules in a microgram, a barely weighable amount. Had Peking man 500,000 years ago started to count the iodine molecules in a mole and passed this chore on to his descendants, we would still be counting today with the end almost ten million years ahead. It is more practical to define a mole in the original way as that quantity of substance which has a mass in grams numerically equal to the atomic weight (for a metal or inert gas), the molecular weight (for a molecular substance), or the formula weight (for an ionic substance). One mole of magnesium weighs 24.32 g and contains 6.02×10^{23} atoms, one mole of carbon dioxide weight 44.01 g and contains 6.02×10^{23} molecules, and one mole of calcium fluoride weighs 78.08 g and contains 6.02×10^{23} komes of calcium and fluoride ions.[3]

It is frequently necessary to find the *number of moles* of a substance in some given quantity of it. This is analogous to finding the number of bricks in a pile if the total weight of the pile and the weight of one brick are known, i.e.,

Number of bricks = (total weight of pile)/(weight of one brick)

Number of moles = (total weight of substance)/(weight of one mole)

Thus in 100 g of sodium chloride (formula weight 58.5) there are

$$\frac{100 \text{ g}}{58.5 \text{ g/mole}} = \frac{100 \text{ g}}{58.5 \text{ g}} \text{moles} = \boxed{1.71 \text{ moles}}$$

Note that the units of 58.5 are g/mole, not moles. Students sometimes confuse the weight of one mole (weight of a brick) with number of moles (number of bricks). Though we often speak of 58.5 g as being a mole of sodium chloride, we actually mean that this is the weight of a mole. The distinction is between calling 20 cents an ice cream soda and saying that an ice cream soda costs 20 cents. Notice that in the calculation of the number of moles of sodium chloride in 100 g the units of the answer on the right match those of the quotient on the left. This is a check on the method of calculation. Had we done the problem incorrectly by multiplying 100 by 58.5, the units of the product would have been g^2/mole and not moles.

The small quantities used in semimicro qualitative analysis make it convenient to use a smaller unit than the mole, namely, the millimole, which is one-thousandth of a mole. The weight of a millimole (abbreviated mmole) is the number of milligrams numerically equal to the atomic, molecular, or

---

[3]The term *gram-atom* must be used for 6.02×10^{23} atoms of elements whose molecules contain more than one atom; e.g., a gram-atom of oxygen weighs 16 g, a mole of it weighs 32 g. The distinction between gram-atom and mole is not important for free metals.

formula weight. The number of mmoles of sodium chloride in 100 g is a thousand times the number of moles:

$$100\,g \times \frac{1000\,mg}{g} \times \frac{mmoles}{58.5\,mg} = \boxed{1710\ \ mmoles}$$

4-4. The Molarity.   The principal concentration unit that we shall use in this course is the *molarity*, or number of moles of substance in one liter of solution. It can also be expressed as the number of *milli*moles of substance in one *milli*liter of solution.

EXAMPLE 1. Find the molarity of calcium nitrate in a solution that contains 10 g of $Ca(NO_3)_2 \cdot 4H_2O$ in 50 ml.

Analysis: We have to find the number of moles of salt per liter. We know how to convert grams to moles (Sec. 4-3). Let us therefore first find the number of grams per liter.

Ca:	40
2 N:	28
10 O:	160
8 H:	8
	236

Step 1:

$$\frac{10\ g}{50\ ml} \times \frac{1000\ ml}{liter} = 200\ g/l$$

Step 2: The number of moles in 200 g is

$$\frac{200\ g}{liter} \times \frac{moles}{236\ g} = 0.85\ moles/l = \boxed{0.85\ M}$$

EXAMPLE 2. Find the molarity of ammonia in an aqueous solution containing 12% NH_3 by weight and having a density of 0.950 g/ml.

Analysis: We want to find the number of moles of ammonia per liter. Let us examine what we are given. The density refers to the number of grams of solution per ml, not to grams of ammonia or water alone. Now 12% NH_3 means 12 grams of ammonia per 100 grams of solution (per cent = parts per hundred). We should be able to combine the density and percentage data to find the weight of ammonia per ml or per liter. The problem is completed by converting grams to moles.

Step 1: The weight of one liter of solution is

$$\frac{0.950\ g\ solution}{ml} \times \frac{1000\ ml}{1} = 950\ g\ solution/l$$

Step 2: Of this 12% is ammonia or

$$\frac{950\ g\ solution}{1} \times \frac{12\ g\ NH_3}{100\ g\ solution} = 114\ g\ NH_3/l$$

Step 3: Converting this to moles we find

$$\frac{114\ g\ NH_3}{1} \times \frac{moles}{17\ g\ NH_3} = \boxed{6.7\,M}$$

1 N:	14
3 H:	3
	17

EXAMPLE 3. Find the molarity of calcium ion in a solution that contains 1 mg of Ca^{++} ion in 10 drops. Assume 20 drops per ml.

Analysis: The small quantities involved make millimoles and milliliters more convenient units than grams and liters. We have to find the number of millimoles per milliliter and can do this if we know the number of milligrams per milliliter.

Step 1: Ten drops corresponds to $\frac{1}{2}$ ml. There are thus 2 mg Ca^{++}/ml.[4]

Step 2: One mmole of Ca^{++} ion weighs 40 mg. Hence

$$\frac{2 \text{ mg } Ca^{++}}{\text{ml}} \times \frac{\text{mmoles}}{40 \text{ mg } Ca^{++}} = \frac{1 \text{ mmole}}{20 \text{ ml}} \text{ or } \boxed{0.05 \ M}$$

EXAMPLE 4. Find the number of millimoles and milligrams of crystalline oxalic acid, $H_2C_2O_4 \cdot 2H_2O$, in 3 ml of 0.10 M solution

Analysis: The volume of solution multiplied by its concentration gives the quantity of solute it contains. Therefore

$$\frac{0.10 \text{ mmoles}}{1 \text{ ml}} \times 3 \text{ ml} = \boxed{0.3 \text{ mmole}}$$

Each millimole weighs 126 mg and 0.3 mmole weighs

$$0.3 \text{ mmole} \times \frac{126 \text{ mg}}{\text{mmole}} = \boxed{38 \text{ mg}}$$

6 H:	6
2 C:	24
6 O:	96
	——
	126

4-5. The Accuracy of Our Calculations.   In the preceding examples, the answers were given to two or three digits. Chemical formulas and equations express the combination of atoms in simple ratios and their indestructibility in all but nuclear reactions. The accuracy of calculations based on equations and formulas is therefore limited only by uncertainties in the atomic weights. Most of these are known to four or five digits so that very accurate calculations are possible. While such accuracy is required in quantitative analysis, we are concerned here with learning to analyze problems and to apply certain principles. To carry the calculations through to four or five digits could so involve us in tedious arithmetic as to make us forget the goals. Many problems in later chapters concern equilibrium conditions, and, with these, certain inherent difficulties in applying the general principles often limit the accuracy of the calculation. It would be pointless to carry five digits in the calculations if the last three have no significance. For these reasons, we shall arbitrarily elect to carry only two or three digits in our calculations.

For such approximate calculations a slide rule is a very convenient tool. Inexpensive slide rules which come with booklets for self-instruction can be obtained. A two- or three-place logarithm table can also be used. But to use

[4]Avoid working out problems in mental arithmetic in elaborate and painful detail. It should not be necessary to write 10/20 = x/1.

long-hand multiplication or division or four- or five-place logarithms would be equivalent to shooting ducks with field artillery.

If data are given to more than three digits (exclusive of zeros required to fix the decimal point), they can be rounded off to three. The following examples will illustrate certain points. Thus 23465 rounds off to 23500 where two zeros fix the decimal point. The zero in 0.03436 does likewise and this rounds off to 0.0344, not 0.034. The number 8.375 is rounded off to 8.38, because the five comes after seven which is an odd number; on the other hand, 8.365 rounds off to 8.36, because the five comes after an even digit. Carry no decimals in the atomic weights except in those of chlorine (35.5), copper (63.5), and rubidium (85.5). The atomic weight of antimony, for example, is rounded off from 121.76 to 122 and that of cadmium from 112.41 to 112. When several factors are used in a calculation, it is best to carry three digits in each and round off the answer to two. If each factor is rounded off first, there may be an accumulation of errors from this source.

Nothing that has been written above should be taken to indicate that carelessly done calculations are acceptable.

4-6. Dilution Problems. The addition of more solvent to a solution does not alter the total quantity of solute but decreases its concentration. The quantity of solute in some specified volume of solution is given by the product of the volume by the concentration; e.g.,

(molarity, or moles per liter) (volume in liters) = moles

(molarity, or mmoles per ml) (volume in ml) = mmoles

(lb per gallon) (volume in gallons)   = lb

EXAMPLE 1. The reagent kit contains 6 M HCl. We need 15 drops of 2 M HCl. How shall we make it?

Analysis: The quantity of HCl is measured by 15 drops $\times$ 2 M. If we let V be the volume of 6 M acid to be taken, the quantity of HCl is also measured by 6 M $\times$ V drops. The condition that dilution leave the quantity of HCl unchanged is then expressed by $15 \times 2 = 6V$ or $V = 15 (2/6)$, or 5 drops. We must mix 5 drops of 6 M HCl with 10 drops of water to get the required solution. A backward glance at this calculation should reveal that, in spelling out the underlying principle we have made the calculation unnecessarily cumbersome. We see now that the final solution is one-third ($\frac{2}{6}$) as concentrated as the original. To give the same quantity of hydrochloric acid, the initial volume of acid must be one-third the final volume, or 5 drops. Note that the volumes have been left in drops and not converted to milliliters or liters. Both volumes must be in the same units, but any convenient unit may be used.

EXAMPLE 2. Find the final concentrations of acetic acid and sodium acetate if 20 ml of 0.60 M acetic acid is mixed with 30 ml of 0.10 M sodium acetate. Assume that the final volume is approximately the sum of the initial volumes, i.e., 50 ml.

Analysis: The millimoles of acetic acid and sodium acetate taken are, respectively, 20 ml × 0.60 M and 30 ml × 0.10 M. Since molarity stands for the number of mmoles/ml, the molarities are found by dividing the number of millimoles by 50 ml. Alternatively, we can note that the final concentration of acetic acid will be $\frac{20}{50}$ the original:

$$0.60 \ M \times (20 \ ml/50 \ ml) = \boxed{0.24 \ M \ \text{acetic acid}}$$

and that of sodium acetate $\frac{30}{50}$ the original:

$$0.10 \ M \times (30 \ ml/50 \ ml) = \boxed{0.06 \ M \ \text{sodium acetate}}$$

4-7. Problems Based on Equations. Because equations show the molar ratios in which substances react, they can also be interpreted, if the concentrations are known, in terms of volumes of solutions that react.

EXAMPLE 1. Find the number of milliliters of 0.50 M silver nitrate solution required to precipitate virtually all of the chromate in 4.0 ml of 0.10 M potassium chromate.

Step 1: We start by writing the equation for the reaction:

$$2Ag^+ + 2NO_3^- + 2K^+ + CrO_4^{--} \rightarrow Ag_2CrO_4 \downarrow + 2K^+ + 2NO_3^-$$

This shows that 2 mmoles of silver nitrate are equivalent to 1 of potassium chromate.

Step 2: Four ml of 0.10 M potassium chromate contain 0.40 mmoles and will require twice this or 0.80 mmoles of silver nitrate. The latter will be contained in (0.80 mmole/0.50 mmole per ml) = $\boxed{1.6 \ ml}$

EXAMPLE 2. Find the number of drops of 3 M nitric acid required to dissolve 50 mg of strontium carbonate.

Step 1: The equation for the reaction is

$$SrCO_3 \downarrow + 2H^+ + 2NO_3^- \rightarrow Sr^{++} + 2NO_3^- + CO_2 \uparrow + H_2O$$

and this shows that 1 mmole of $SrCO_3$ requires 2 mmoles of nitric acid.

Step 2: Fifty mg of $SrCO_3$ contain (50 mg/148 mg per mmole) mmoles.

Step 3: The number of mmoles of nitric acid is twice this or $\frac{100}{148}$, and this must also be given by the product of molarity by volume. Let V be the volume in ml; then $3V = (\frac{100}{148})$, or $V = 100/(148 \times 3)$.

Sr:	88
C:	12
3 O:	48
	———
	148

Step 4: If we assume that 20 drops make a milliliter, the number of drops is given by $20V$ or $20 \times 100/(148 \times 3)$, which is $\boxed{4.5 \ drops}$

EXAMPLE 3. Find the concentrations of acetic acid and sodium acetate in a solution made by mixing 20 ml of 0.50 M sodium acetate with 15 ml of 0.20 M hydrochloric acid.

Step 1: We have to recognize a chemical reaction when we see one. The equation for it is

$$Na^+ + C_2H_3O_2^- + H^+ + Cl^- \rightarrow Na^+ + Cl^- + HC_2H_3O_2$$

and this shows that the formation of each millimole of acetic acid consumes 1 mmole each of sodium acetate and hydrochloric acid.

Step 2: We start with $20 \times 0.50 = 10$ mmoles of sodium acetate and $15 \times 0.20 = 3.0$ mmoles of hydrochloric acid. These 3 mmoles of acid will react with an equal number of millimoles of sodium acetate to yield 3 mmoles of molecular acetic acid. There will be $10 - 3 = 7$ mmoles of sodium acetate left in excess.

Step 3: We know the number of mmoles of each substance and we know that the total volume is approximately $15 + 20 = 35$ ml. The molarities, or number of millimoles per milliliter, are then

$$3 \text{ mmoles/35 ml} = \boxed{0.086 \ M \text{ acetic acid}}$$

$$7 \text{ mmoles/35 ml} = \boxed{0.20 \ M \text{ sodium acetate}}$$

4-8. Other Concentration Units. The first problem in the preceding section can be set up in a simpler fashion. As worked out in Example 1 the solution was in the form

$$n \times 4.0 \text{ ml} \times 0.10 \ M = V \text{ ml AgNO}_3 \times 0.50 \ M$$

where n, the number of univalent silver ions required by the chromate ion, was two. The factor n is called the *combining capacity* of chromate in this reaction; the combining capacity of silver was unity. The combining capacities of various kinds of reagents are summarized in Table 4-1. Let us define a new concentration unit, the *normality*, by the relation

$$\text{Normality} = (\text{molarity}) (\text{combining capacity})$$

The solution to Example 1 of Sec. 4-7 can now be expressed as

$$4.0 \text{ ml} \times 0.20 \ N = V \text{ ml} \times 0.50 \ N$$

Equal volumes of solutions of the same normality always react exactly, if they react at all. For equimolar solutions, equal volumes will react only if the substances combine in a one to one molar ratio.

Let us define one *gram equivalent weight* as that quantity of a substance which has a mass equal to that of a mole divided by the combining capacity. A milliequivalent has a mass equal to that of a millimole divided by the combining capacity. The *normality* can now be expressed as the number of gram equivalent weights per liter of solution or the number of milliequivalents per milliliter. When potassium chromate is used for precipitation reactions, it has a combining capacity of two; one milliequivalent weighs half as much as a millimole, and the normality of its solution is twice the molarity.

We shall make only occasional use of the normality unit in this book, but it is very useful in quantitative analysis. Other concentration units that are sometimes used are (1) per cent by weight, the number of grams of substance in 100 g of solution; (2) per cent by volume, the number of milliliters of substance in 100 ml of solution; (3) parts per million (ppm), the number of grams in a million grams or the number of milligrams per kilogram;

(4) molality (m), the number of moles of solute per kilogram of solvent (Sec. 2-17). In qualitative analysis the concentration of a metal ion is sometimes expressed as the number of milligrams of metal per milliliter. This unit will be illustrated in the next section.

TABLE 4-1.

Combining Capacities

Reagent	Combining capacity	Examples
Acids	Number of protons used per formula	$n = 1$ for H_3PO_4 neutralized to NaH_2PO_4, 2 for neutralization to Na_2HPO_4, and 3 for neutralization to Na_3PO_4
Basic Hydroxides	Number of hydroxide ions used per formula	$n = 1$ for KOH and 2 for $Ca(OH)_2$
Salts	Total oxidation number of positive or negative ions	$n = 6$, or 3×2, for $Al_2(SO_4)_3$
Reducing Agents	Number of electrons lost or total gain in oxidation number per formula	$n = 2$ for $Cu \rightarrow Cu^{++} + 2e^-$ but 1 for $2I^- \rightarrow I_2 + 2e^-$
Oxidizing Agents	Number of electrons gained or total loss of oxidation number per formula	$n = 5$ for $MnO_4^- + 8H^+ + 5e^- \rightarrow Mn^{++} + 4H_2O$ $n = 3$ for $MnO_4^- + 2H_2O + 3e^- \rightarrow MnO_2 + 4OH^-$

4-9. The Quantitative Meaning of Formulas. Since a formula stands for a mole of a substance, it is also the key to the composition of the substance expressed either in moles or in grams. The formula $MgCl_2$ represents 1 mole of magnesium chloride weighing 95.23 g and containing 1 mole of magnesium ions weighing 24.32 g and 2 moles of chloride ions weighing 2×35.457 g.

EXAMPLE 1. Find the number of milligrams of aluminum per milliliter of $0.10\,M$ aluminum sulfate solution. The formula $Al_2(SO_4)_3$ shows that 0.10 mmole of aluminum sulfate contains 0.20 mmole of aluminum. Hence (0.20 mmole Al/ml) × (27 mg Al/mmole) = $\boxed{5.4 \text{ mg Al/ml}}$

EXAMPLE 2. What weight of $Cu(NO_3)_2 \cdot 3H_2O$ shall be taken to give 100 ml of solution containing 5 mg Cu/ml?

Step 1: The formula shows that 1 mmole of the salt weighing 242 mg contains 1 mmole of copper weighing 63.5 mg.

Step 2: The required weight of copper is 100 ~~ml~~ × 5 mg Cu/~~ml~~ or 500 mg of Cu.

Cu:	63.5
2 N:	28
9 O:	144
6 H:	6
	———
	242

Step 3: The required weight of salt is then

$$500 \text{ mg Cu} \times \frac{242 \text{ mg salt}}{63.5 \text{ mg Cu}} = \boxed{1910 \text{ mg or } 1.91 \text{ g}}$$

If a solute is completely dissociated, the formula indicates the number of ions in a kome or the relative number in a mole or in any quantity of the substance.

EXAMPLE 3. Find the concentrations of aluminum and sulfate ions in 0.10 *M* aluminum sulfate solution. Although ion-pair formation between such highly charged ions is undoubtedly important (Sec. 2-18), we shall assume complete dissociation. The formula shows that each kome contains 2 Al^{+++} and 3 SO_4^{--} ions, and the concentration of aluminum ion will be twice the molarity of the salt, or 0.20 *M*, and that of sulfate three times the molarity, or 0.30 *M*.

Students are sometimes tempted, in solving such a problem, to find the percentage of aluminum in aluminum sulfate, then the weight of aluminum in a liter of 0.10 *M* solution of the salt, and finally the number of moles of aluminum per liter. It is always possible to go from New York to San Francisco by way of Rome and New Delhi.

EXAMPLE 4. Find the concentrations of the ions in a mixture of 20 ml of 0.10 *M* magnesium perchlorate and 30 ml of 0.30 *M* sodium perchlorate. Assume complete dissociation and additivity of the volumes.

Analysis: Each kome of $Mg(ClO_4)_2$ contains 1 Mg^{++} and 2 ClO_4^- ions, and each kome of $NaClO_4$ contains 1 Na^+ and 1 ClO_4^- ion. All perchlorate ions are alike, regardless of source, so the concentration of that ion will be the total millimoles of perchlorate per milliliter.

$$\frac{20 \text{ ml} \times 0.10 \text{ } M \text{ } Mg^{++}}{50 \text{ ml}} = \frac{0.040 \text{ mmoles } Mg^{++}}{\text{ml}} = \boxed{0.040 \text{ } M \text{ } Mg^{++}}$$

$$\frac{30 \text{ ml} \times 0.30 \text{ } M \text{ } Na^+}{50 \text{ ml}} = \frac{0.18 \text{ mmoles } Na^+}{\text{ml}} = \boxed{0.18 \text{ } M \text{ } Na^+}$$

$$\frac{[(20 \times 0.10 \times 2) + (30 \times 0.30)] \text{ mmoles } ClO_4^-}{50 \text{ ml}} = \boxed{0.026 \text{ } M \text{ } ClO_4^-}$$

4-10. Solubility. The solubility of a substance can be expressed in various ways, and we must be able to convert from one concentration unit to another.

EXAMPLE 1. At 25° 0.0762 g of lead iodide (PbI_2) dissolves in 100 g of water. Find the molar concentrations of Pb^{++} and I^- ions in the saturated solution.

Step 1: Since the solution is very dilute and the density of water at 25° is close to unity, we may, for approximate calculations, take the solubility to be 0.0762 g in 100 ml of solution or 0.762 g/l.

Pb:	207
2 I:	254
	———
	461

Step 2: The molarity of dissolved salt will be the number of moles of PbI_2 in 0.762 g or

$$\frac{0.762 \text{ g}}{1} \times \frac{\text{moles}}{461 \text{ g}} = 0.00165 = 1.65 \times 10^{-3} \, M$$

Step 3: Suppose that lead iodide is completely dissociated. One kome contains 1 Pb^{++} and 2 I^- ions. Therefore[5]

Concentration of Pb^{++} = concentration of PbI_2 = $\boxed{1.65 \times 10^{-3} M}$

Concentration of I^- = 2 × concentration of PbI_2 = $\boxed{3.30 \times 10^{-3} M}$

EXAMPLE 2. The concentration of silver ion in a saturated solution of silver carbonate in water is found by an electrical method to be $2.3 \times 10^{-4} \, M$. Calculate the solubility of the salt in grams per liter.

Step 1: Each mole of Ag_2CO_3 that dissolves gives 2 moles of Ag^+ ion. The molar concentration of dissolved salt or the number of moles that dissolve to give a liter of solution must be half the molar concentration of Ag^+ ion or 1.15×10^{-4}.

$$\begin{array}{rl} 2\ Ag: & 216 \\ C: & 12 \\ 3\ O: & 48 \\ \hline & 276 \end{array}$$

Step 2: The weight of silver carbonate is found in the usual way

$$\frac{1.15 \times 10^{-4} \text{ moles}}{1} \times \frac{276 \text{ g}}{\text{mole}} = \boxed{0.032 \text{ g/l}}$$

4-11. The Extent of Ionization or Dissociation. In Sec. 4-9 the calculation of the concentrations of the ions in solutions of completely dissociated electrolytes was described. If a substance is weakly ionized, the concentrations of its ions and molecules in solution can still be found if the extent of ionization is known. By *extent of ionization* we mean the fraction out of the total number of moles of substance that ionizes. The *percentage ionization* is one hundred times this. If one molecule out of four ionizes, the extent of ionization is 0.25 or 25%. The term *extent of dissociation* will be used in a similar way for ion-pairs and complex ions.

EXAMPLE 1. Find the concentrations of ions and molecules in 0.10 M acetic acid if it is 1.3% ionized at this concentration. The fraction ionized is 1.3/100. Out of a total of 0.10 mole per liter only $0.10 \times 1.3/100$ or 0.0013 mole ionizes, and the quantity remaining un-ionized is $0.10 - 0.0013$, or the difference between that originally present and that removed by ionization. The ionization reaction is represented most simply by

$$HC_2H_3O_2 \rightleftharpoons H^+ + C_2H_3O_2^-$$

This shows that each mole that ionizes gives a mole of hydrogen ions and a mole of acetate ions. Hence the concentrations of ions and molecules in this solution are 0.0013 M H^+, 0.0013 M $C_2H_3O_2^-$, and 0.0987 M $HC_2H_3O_2$. The last result can be rounded off to 0.099 without serious error.

---

[5]The concentration of free lead ions will actually be somewhat less than this because lead ions are removed by ion-pair formation ($Pb^{++} + I^- \rightleftharpoons [Pb^{++}I^-]$) and by hydrolysis ($Pb^{++} + H_2O \rightleftharpoons PbOH^+ + H^+$). We shall not trouble ourselves further with such subtleties.

EXAMPLE 2. Find the concentrations of the ions in a saturated (0.02 M) solution of calcium hydroxide. The first step in the dissociation is complete (Sec. 2-22):

$$Ca(OH)_2 \rightarrow CaOH^+ + OH^-$$

From 0.02 mole of calcium hydroxide this dissociation produces 0.02 mole of the $CaOH^+$ ion-pair and 0.02 mole of free OH^- ion. The dissociation of the ion-pair then occurs to the extent of 75% in this solution:

$$CaOH^+ \rightleftharpoons Ca^{++} + OH^-$$

In this step $0.02 \times \frac{75}{100}$ or 0.015 mole of $CaOH^+$ dissociates to give 0.015 mole of Ca^{++} ion and 0.015 mole of OH^- ion. The total number of moles of hydroxide ion per liter is the sum of the moles from each step, or $0.020 + 0.015 = 0.035$. The ion-pair is 25% undissociated, so $0.02 \times \frac{25}{100}$ mole of $CaOH^+$ remains. To summarize, the concentrations are: Ca^{++}, 0.015 M; $CaOH^+$, 0.005 M; and OH^-, 0.035 M.

4-12. The Principle of Electroneutrality. So far we have taken concentrations at face value, i.e., as expression of the moles of an ion or molecule per liter. Concentrations can also be used to express other concepts. Perhaps an analogy will make this clear. A certain street has x red houses, y white houses, and z yellow houses. Each red house contains two cats and each white house only one, while each yellow house contains a dog. There are an equal number of dogs and cats on this street. We can most conveniently express this "condition of canine-feline equality" by $2x + y = z$. We use the number of houses to express a condition about dogs and cats. Similarly, we shall use concentrations to express general relations among the ions and molecules in solution.

The first generalization is the *principle of electroneutrality*: every solution is electrically neutral, and none contains a detectable excess of positive or negative charge. Singly charged ions like K^+ and Cl^- bear charges of 1.602×10^{-19} coulomb or 4.80×10^{-10} esu (Sec. 1-5, footnote 1). A mole of these ions may be said to bear a mole of charge or $1.602 \times 10^{-19} \times 6.024 \times 10^{23} = 96,490$ coulombs. This quantity of electrical charge is called one *faraday*. A mole or faraday of negative charge is carried by that quantity of electrons required to plate out a mole of silver ions as silver metal. Expressed in faradays, the principle of electroneutrality requires that in any given volume of solution large enough to be studied in the laboratory

Positive charge in faradays = negative charge in faradays

It is convenient to use ionic concentrations to express charges. To simplify such expressions let us write square brackets around the formulas of substances in solution and use these to represent molar concentrations; e.g., $[Cl^-]$ stands for the molar concentration of chloride ion or the number of moles of chloride per liter. Each chloride bears a single charge, so that the symbol $[Cl^-]$ can also stand for the number of faradays of negative charge per liter. The equation $[K^+] = 0.2\ M$ tells us that, in the solution for which this holds, there is 0.2 mole of K^+ ions per liter and these contribute 0.2 faraday of positive charge per liter.

EXAMPLE 1. Write the electroneutrality (EN) condition for a $0.2\ M$ solution of KCl. We start by listing all ionic species in the solution: K^+ and Cl^- from the salt and H^+ and OH^- from the ionization of water (Sec. 1-12). Hence

$$EN: [K^+] + [H^+] = [Cl^-] + [OH^-]$$

This is actually a general relation for any potassium chloride solution regardless of its concentration. In $0.2\ M$ KCl most of the positive charge is contributed by the potassium ions and most of the negative charge by the chloride ions, because the ionization of water is so feeble. If the actual numerical values of the concentrations are substituted in the general relation, we get

$$0.2 + 0.0000001 = 0.2 + 0.0000001$$

But the original relation can be written down even if we do not know these actual concentrations. All we need to know is what ions are in solution and what charges they bear.[6]

EXAMPLE 2. Write the electroneutrality condition for $0.1\ M$ hydrochloric acid. The ionic species present are H^+, Cl^-, and OH^-. Hence

$$EN: [H^+] = [Cl^-] + [OH^-]$$

This relation is sometimes interpreted to mean that the total hydrogen ion concentration is the sum of contributions from the acid (measured by $[Cl^-]$) and from water (measured by $[OH^-]$). Although this is sometimes a useful approach, it must be realized that there is no possible experimental distinction between hydrogen ions from the two sources. It is not a matter, for example, of one being pink and the other blue. The symbol $[H^+]$ always refers to the total concentration of hydrogen ion (or hydronium ion) in the solution regardless of source. It will occasionally be misleading to attempt to divide the total concentration of an ion into contributions from different substances. As in the previous example, the two anions do not make equal contributions of negative charge per liter, for there are many more chloride ions than hydroxide ions. Let us accept for the time being that the hydroxide ion concentration of this solution is $10^{-13}\ M$ (we shall see later how to determine this value). Then we can use the electroneutrality condition to show that

$$[H^+] = 0.1 + 0.0000000000001$$

We make no appreciable error, then, if we write $[H^+] = 0.1$.

Up to this point we have considered solutions containing only singly charged ions. The extension of the electroneutrality principle to ions of higher charge is easily made. A mole of Cu^{++} ions or of S^{--} ions bears a total charge of two faradays. Twice as much electricity is required to deposit a mole of copper as a mole of silver. The symbol $[Cu^{++}]$ stands for the number of moles of cupric ions per liter, but the number of faradays of positive charge contributed by these ions per liter is $2[Cu^{++}]$.

---

[6] Electroneutrality or equality of charge should not be confused with the term "neutral solution," which refers to solutions having equal concentrations of hydrogen and hydroxide ions. The potassium chloride solution is neutral in this sense too: $[H^+] = [OH^-]$.

EXAMPLE 3. Write the electroneutrality condition for a solution of calcium hydroxide. The ionic species present are Ca^{++}, $CaOH^+$, H^+, and OH^-, and the electroneutrality condition is

$$EN: 2[Ca^{++}] + [CaOH^+] + [H^+] = [OH^-]$$

An analogy may be helpful in understanding this bookkeeping. Suppose we go to the bank with x two-dollar bills and y old, tattered one-dollar bills and ask for z new one-dollar bills in exchange. Evidently $2x + y = z$. Similarly for charge, a calcium ion is worth twice as much as a singly charged positive ion.

It is important to realize that the electroneutrality conditions are balances of charges, not of ions. In the calcium hydroxide solution, for example, the total numbers of positive and negative ions are not equal but the total positive and negative charges are. This is illustrated in Table 4-2 for a saturated solution of calcium hydroxide.

TABLE 4-2.

The Concentrations of Ions and Charges in a Saturated Solution of Calcium Hydroxide

	Ca^{++}	$CaOH^+$	H^+	OH^-	Totals
Positive ions	0.015 M	0.005 M	Negligible		0.020 moles/l
Negative ions				0.035 M	0.035 moles/l
Positive charge	0.030 faradays/l	0.005 faradays/l	Negligible		0.035 faradays/l
Negative charge				0.035 faradays/l	0.035 faradays/l

4-13. The Principle of Material Balance. A second useful relation between the concentrations of substances in solution is based on the law of conservation of mass. Atoms are not created or destroyed in chemical manipulations with stable isotopes. Atoms of a substance that is put into solution must remain there in some form or other unless they escape by precipitation or evaporation. This is the *principle of material balance*.

Material balance can be expressed in mass or mole units. In *mass balance* the atoms are weighed: the mass of substance put into a system is equal to the total mass of substance in all parts of the system.

EXAMPLE 1. Iodine is soluble both in water and in carbon tetrachloride. If 100 mg of iodine is added to 50 ml of CCl_4 and 35 ml of H_2O and the mixture is shaken, the iodine will distribute itself between the two liquids. The mass balance condition (MB) is

$$MB: 100 \text{ mg } \overline{I_2} \text{ input} = \text{mg } I_2 \text{ in } H_2O \text{ layer} + \text{mg } I_2 \text{ in } CCl_4 \text{ layer}$$

EXAMPLE 2. When 0.3 g of solid silver chromate is shaken with water, some of the salt dissolves. The mass balance condition is

MB: 0.3 g input $=$ g Ag_2CrO_4 in solution $+$ g solid left undissolved

A more useful version of material balance for solutions in which chemical reactions occur is *mole balance*. Whereas in mass balance we weigh, in mole balance we count. We can count atoms, ions, or molecules, and the result is expressed using molar concentrations.

EXAMPLE 1. Write the mole balance condition for nitrogen atoms in a solution prepared by dissolving 0.10 mole (5.35 g) of ammonium chloride in enough water to make a liter of solution. Each kome of NH_4Cl contains one nitrogen atom. Hence, 0.10 g-atom of nitrogen has been put into each liter of solution. Because the equilibrium expressed by the equation

$$NH_4^+ \rightleftharpoons NH_3 + H^+$$

is rapidly established in this system, the nitrogen atoms will be divided between those in ammonium ions and those in molecular ammonia. The principle of material balance expresses the fact that nitrogen atoms are not created or destroyed by this reaction

MB (N): 0.10 g-atoms per liter $= [NH_4^+] + [NH_3]$

or

Input $=$ most of the nitrogen $+$ the rest of it

Let us suppose, by way of analogy, that ten apples are selected, and the total weight is found to be 2.5 lb. Take six of these apples, and cut a small slice off each. *Mass* balance requires that the total mass of the four whole apples and the small and large pieces of the other six be 2.5 lb. The equivalent of *mole* balance would be a count such as

Number of apples taken (10)
   $=$ number of whole apples (4) $+$ number of large pieces (6)

or

Number of apples taken (10)
   $=$ number of whole apples (4) $+$ number of small pieces (6)

But note that the number of apples taken (10) is not equal to the total number of whole apples and pieces (16). Similarly, the mole balance for nitrogen in the ammonium chloride solution counts only the ammonium ions (whole apples) and ammonia (large pieces) and does not add on the hydrogen ions (small pieces). We could formulate the mole balance for nitrogen as $0.10 = [NH_4^+] + [H^+]$ were it not for the fact that hydrogen ions come from other sources than ammonium ions, e.g., water itself. This expression is then only approximate, whereas $0.10 = [NH_4^+] + [NH_3]$ is exact.

For molar balance we can often count groups of atoms or radicals if these remain unchanged in the chemical reactions that take place in solution. The acetate radical, for example, preserves its identity in double decomposition reactions.

EXAMPLE 2. Write the material balance condition for acetate in a mixture that contains 0.1 mole of acetic acid and 0.25 mole of barium acetate per liter of solution. The acetate put into solution comes from the acid and from the salt. The former contributes 0.1 moles/l and the latter 2×0.25 mole/l because each kome of $Ba(C_2H_3O_2)_2$ contains two acetate ions. The acetate ions from the two sources are indistinguishable so we must write material balance for total acetate. In solution acetate occurs as the free ion or in molecules of acetic acid. The material balance condition is

$$\text{MB (acetate): } 0.6 = [HC_2H_3O_2] + [C_2H_3O_2^-]$$

EXAMPLE 3. Write the material balance conditions for chlorine, nitrogen, and silver atoms of $0.02\ M\ Ag(NH_3)_2Cl$ solution. The solute is completely dissociated to $Ag(NH_3)_2^+$ and Cl^- ions, but two equilibria must be noted:

$$Ag(NH_3)_2^+ \rightleftharpoons Ag^+ + 2NH_3$$
$$NH_3 + H_2O \rightleftharpoons NH_4^+ + OH^-$$

The material balance condition for chlorine is trivial since chloride ion is the only form in which chlorine occurs in this solution:

$$\text{MB (Cl): } 0.02 = [Cl^-]$$

Silver occurs in the complex and as free silver ion:

$$\text{MB (Ag): } 0.02 = [Ag^+] + [Ag(NH_3)_2^+]$$

In counting nitrogen atoms we must double the concentration of the complex because each one contains two nitrogen atoms:

$$\text{MB (N): } 2 \times 0.02 = [NH_4^+] + [NH_3] + 2[Ag(NH_3)_2^+]$$

SUPPLEMENTARY READING

C. PIERCE and R. N. SMITH, *General Chemistry Workbook*, Freeman, San Francisco, 2nd ed.,1958, pp. 60–63 (formulas), 88–91 (equations) 115–29 (concentrations).

L. J. CURTMAN and S. M. EDMONDS, *Calculations of Qualitative Analysis*, Macmillan, New York, 1940, Chapters 3 (formulas and equations) and 4 (concentrations).

S. W. BENSON, *Chemical Calculations*, Wiley, New York, 1952, Chapters 1 through 4 and 8.

D. SCHAUM, *Theory and Problems of College Chemistry*, 4th ed., Schaum, New York, 1958, Chapters 4, 5, 6, and 11.

G. POLYA, *How to Solve It*, 2nd ed., Doubleday Anchor Book A93, Doubleday, Garden City, N. Y., 1957. This is an excellent discussion of the techniques of problem solving. Though the illustrations are mostly from geometry, the suggestions are equally applicable to the solution of chemical problems.

EXERCISES

4-1. For each of these compounds, calculate the molecular and equivalent weights: (a) $KHSO_4$ used as a source of sulfate ions, (b) H_3PO_4 used to form $CaHPO_4$, (c) Al_2O_3 used to react with HCl, (d) $Ca(OH)_2$ used as a base, (e) $KMnO_4$ used as an oxidizing agent in acid solution, (f) $KMnO_4$ used as an oxidizing agent in basic solution.

4-2. Calculate the required quantity of each substance: (a) the number of millimoles of $BaCl_2$ in 0.416 g of the salt, (b) the number of millimoles of Ca^{++} ion in 100 mg of solid $CaCO_3$, (c) the number of gram-atoms of Cr in 350 mg of $K_2Cr_2O_7$, (d) the number of milligrams of Zn in 72 mg of $ZnSO_4 \cdot 7H_2O$, (e) the number of milligrams of K in 100 mg of $K_2NaCo(NO_2)_6 \cdot 2H_2O$, (f) the maximum number of milliequivalents of H^+ ion supplied by 70 mg of $H_2C_2O_4 \cdot 2H_2O$.

4-3. Calculate the molarity of each solution: (a) a solution containing 200 g of ammonium chloride per liter, (b) a solution containing 30.0 g of Na_2HPO_4 per 250 ml, (c) a saturated solution of silver chloride if it contains 0.192 mg of salt per 100 ml at 25°, (d) a solution containing 5 mg of magnesium per ml, (e) concentrated nitric acid which is 70% HNO_3 by weight and has a density of 1.42 g/ml, (f) concentrated ammonia solution which is 28% NH_3 by weight and has a density of 0.90 g/ml.

4-4. Calculate the normality of each solution: (a) concentrated sulfuric acid which is 98% H_2SO_4 by weight and has a density of 1.84 g/ml, (b) 0.1 M $MgCl_2$ used as a source of Mg^{++}, (c) 0.1 M $Ba(OH)_2$ used as a source of OH^-, (d) 0.1 M $KMnO_4$ used as an oxidizing agent in acid solution.

4-5. Calculate the number of millimoles of each substance. (a) ammonium ion in 100 ml of 0.34 M ammonium chloride, (b) nitrate in 25 ml of 0.20 M nitric acid, (c) barium and chloride ions in 10 ml of 0.1 M barium chloride, (d) nickel and nitrate ions in 2 ml of a solution of $Ni(NO_3)_2$ containing 10 mg Ni/ml, (e) potassium, barium, and chloride ions in 5 drops of a mixture in which both KCl and $BaCl_2$ are at 0.03 M concentration.

4-6. Calculate the number of drops of solution required to give the specified quantity of substance. Assume 20 drops/ml. (a) one millimole of H^+ ion from 6 M HCl, (b) two milligrams of Mn from a solution containing 10 mg Mn/ml, (c) one millimole of H^+ ion from 6 N H_2SO_4, (d) five millimoles of OH^- ion from 0.02 M $Ba(OH)_2$ assuming complete dissociation to Ba^{++} and OH^-, (e) three millimoles of SO_4^{--} ion from 0.15 M $La_2(SO_4)_3$ assuming complete dissociation to La^{+++} and SO_4^{--} ions.

4-7. In the following dilution problems assume 20 drops/ml.

(a) What is the molarity of K_2CrO_4 if 1 ml of 0.5 M solution is diluted to 4 ml?

(b) How many ml of 0.1 M nitric acid can be prepared from one drop of 6 M acid?

(c) How many drops of water should be added to 2 drops of 0.5 M NH_4Cl to make a 0.2 M solution?

(d) What is the final concentration in mg Pb/ml of a solution prepared by diluting one drop of a solution containing 5 mg Pb/ml with 10 drops of water?

(e) We require for an experiment 10 drops of a solution containing 2 mg Ag/ml. How many drops of the stock solution containing 5 mg Ag/ml should be diluted?

(f) What are the molarities of the ions in a mixture prepared by mixing 5 ml of 0.1 M $CuSO_4$ and 20 ml of 0.01 M Na_2SO_4? Assume complete dissociation of the salts and additivity of the volumes.

4-8. A solution used for practice in analysis contains 8.0 g of $Pb(NO_3)_2$, 2.8 g of $Hg_2(NO_3)_2 \cdot 2H_2O$, 4.0 g of $AgNO_3$, and 35 ml of 6 M HNO_3 per liter. Calculate the number of milligrams of Pb^{++}, Hg_2^{++}, and Ag^+ ions per milliliter and the molarity of nitric acid.

4-9. In each of the following, set down the chemical equation before attempting to solve the problem.

(a) How many drops of 3 M HCl are required to precipitate the silver from 0.25 ml of solution containing 2 mg Ag/ml and to leave 1 drop of HCl solution in excess?

(b) How many drops of 0.5 M K_2CrO_4 solution are required to precipitate the barium in 5 drops of 0.02 M $BaCl_2$ solution?

(c) Will 10 drops of 3 M HCl suffice to dissolve 50 mg of alloy and still leave 2 drops of acid in excess? Assume that the alloy is magnesium for the purpose of the calculation.

(d) What is the minimum weight of sodium carbonate in milligrams that must be added to 30 drops of a solution that contains 5 mg each of Ca^{++} and Sr^{++} ions to precipitate them as the carbonates?

(e) How many mg of Cu^{++} ion will be reduced to metallic copper by 10 mg of sodium dithionite ($Na_2S_2O_4$) if the latter is oxidized to sulfite?

(f) If 5 mg of Mn^{++} ion is oxidized to MnO_2 by 150 mg of solid $KClO_3$ in the presence of nitric acid, how much excess $KClO_3$ is left over? Potassium chlorate is reduced to ClO_2.

4-10. Calculate the specified concentrations for each mixture: (a) the concentration of sodium ion in moles per liter in a sodium chloride solution that contains 1 mg Na/ml, (b) the concentrations of La^{+++} and Cl^- ions in a solution that contains 0.49 g of $LaCl_3$ in 250 ml, (c) the concentrations of the ions in a solution that contains 10 g of $Mg(NO_3)_2 \cdot 6H_2O$ per 500 ml, (d) the concentrations of the ions in a solution made by mixing 20 ml of 0.1 M NaCl and 30 ml of 0.02 M $BaCl_2$, (e) the concentrations of potassium and nitrate ions in a solution made by mixing equal volumes of 0.20 M KOH and 0.20 M HNO_3. What is the concentration of hydrogen ion in this mixture? (f) the concentrations of acetate ion and acetic acid in a mixture of 20 ml of 0.2 M NaOH and 80 ml of 0.1 M $HC_2H_3O_2$ (Note that partial neutralization occurs), (g) the concentrations of acetate ion and acetic acid in a mixture of 35 ml of 0.1 M NaOH and 65 ml of 0.2 M $HC_2H_3O_2$, (h) the concentrations of acetate ion and acetic acid in a mixture of 40 ml of 0.1 M HCl and 60 ml of 0.15 M $NaC_2H_3O_2$.

4-11. (a) The solubility of cobalt(II) iodate, $Co(IO_3)_2$, in various solutions is given below. For each solution find the molar concentration of iodate ion and the number of grams of salt in 100 ml of solution. (1) 0.0158 mole/l in 0.145 M NaCl, (2) 0.0010 mole/l in 0.10 M $NaIO_3$, and (3) 0.0093 mole/l in 0.10 M $CoSO_4$.

(b) At 18° the concentration of Pb^{++} ions in a saturated solution of lead(II) thiocyanate, $Pb(SCN)_2$, in water is 0.0137 M. How many milligrams of salt are in each milliliter of this solution?

(c) The hydroxide ion concentration of a saturated solution of silver oxide in water at 25° is 0.00019 M. When silver oxide dissolves, the reaction which occurs is

$$Ag_2O + H_2O \rightleftharpoons 2Ag^+ + 2OH^-$$

Calculate the solubility of silver oxide in grams per liter.

4-12. (a) Calculate the concentrations of hydrogen and nitrate ions and molecular nitric acid in 6 M nitric acid if it is 72% ionized.

(b) Calculate the concentrations of hydrogen and cyanide ions and hydrogen cyanide molecules in 0.1 M HCN if the acid is 0.006% ionized in this solution.

(c) The hydrolysis of sodium carbonate, represented by

$$CO_3^{--} + H_2O \rightleftharpoons HCO_3^- + OH^-$$

occurs to the extent of 3.8% in a 0.1 M solution of the salt. Calculate the concentrations of sodium, carbonate, bicarbonate, and hydroxide ions in this solution.

(d) If lead chloride is completely dissociated to $PbCl^+$ and Cl^- and if $PbCl^+$ is 90% dissociated to Pb^{++} and Cl^- in 0.01 M $PbCl_2$ solution, calculate the concentrations of the Pb^{++}, $PbCl^+$, and Cl^- ions in this solution.

4-13. Express the electroneutrality condition in each of the following solutions in terms of the molar concentrations of the ions: (a) 0.5 M $NaNO_3$, (b) 0.35 M $BaCl_2$, (c) 0.01 M Na_2SO_4, (d) 0.05 M $NaOH$, (e) 0.1 M H_2S, (f) 0.4 M H_3PO_4, (g) a mixture containing 0.01 mole of KNO_3 and 0.1 mole of HNO_3 per liter of solution, (h) a mixture containing 0.5 mole of $HC_2H_3O_2$ and 0.03 mole of $Ca(C_2H_3O_2)_2$ per liter of solution.

4-14. Express the material balance conditions for the following systems. Numerical calculations are not required.

(a) Express the material balance for lactic acid in grams if 0.2 g of the acid in 50 ml of CCl_4 is shaken with 100 ml of water.

(b) One liter of 3.3 M HCl is shaken with excess solid benzoic acid ($HC_7H_5O_2$), and 0.0153 mole of acid dissolves. Express (1) mass balance for benzoic acid in the system and (2) mole balance for the benzoic acid in the solution.

(c) One-tenth of a millimole of solid KH_2PO_4 is added to enough water to make 4 ml of solution. Express the mole balance for phosphate in the solution.

(d) One liter of water at 25° dissolves 2240 ml of H_2S, measured at STP, with virtually no change in volume. Express the material balance for sulfur atoms in this solution.

(e) A solution is prepared by dissolving 0.1 mole of pure H_2SO_4 in enough water to make 250 ml of solution. Write the material balance expression for sulfate.

CHAPTER FIVE

More About Solutes and Solutions

5-1. Introduction. As you perform a qualitative analysis you can hardly fail to be puzzled by many phenomena. Consider silver chloride and sodium chloride: they have virtually the same crystal structure, and yet one precipitates at the beginning of the analysis while the other remains in solution to the end. Sulfides range in color from white to black; the bright yellow color of cadmium sulfide, which serves to identify cadmium, becomes more arresting when we recall that cadmium and sulfide ions form many colorless compounds with other ions. The chlorides, hydroxides, and sulfides of calcium, strontium, and barium are soluble; why then are these metal ions precipitated by carbonate? And why is the carbonate of magnesium too soluble to precipitate with Cation Group 4?

To gain some insight into these phenomena we must consider further the forces between one ion and another and between an ion and water molecules. Ions exert on each other forces of attraction or repulsion that are directly proportional to the product of the ionic charges and inversely proportional to the square of the distance between them and the dielectric constant of the medium in which they are immersed (Sec. 1-3). The discussion of this chapter begins with consideration of the simple interaction between ions in the gaseous state and progresses to their interactions in crystals and solutions. Many aspects of their behavior are shown to be accounted for by their charges and radii as would be expected from Coulomb's law. Yet such striking phenomena as the low solubility of silver chloride and the yellow color of cadmium sulfide cannot be explained without also considering the electronic structures of the ions.

The concluding sections of the chapter deal with interactions between ions in solution. The effects of these are perhaps less spectacular than the behavior of silver chloride or cadmium sulfide but are nonetheless important. The electrolytic conductance of a solution is particularly sensitive to the interionic forces. A theoretical interpretation of the conductance of very dilute solutions can be given.

83

5-2. Stabilization of Ions in Gas Molecules and Crystals. Gaseous sodium and chlorine atoms combine by transfer of electrons

$$Na \rightarrow Na^+ + e^-$$
$$e^- + Cl \rightarrow Cl^-$$
$$\overline{Na + Cl \rightarrow Na^+ + Cl^-}$$

The work required to remove an electron from an atom is called its *ionization potential* (IP). For the removal of the valence electrons of one gram-atom (23.0 g) of sodium atoms it is 118,000 calories or 118 kilogram calories (kcal). This is about the same energy as that required to melt a kilogram of ice and bring the temperature of the water up to body temperature. Some of the energy invested in ionizing the sodium atoms is recouped when the electrons are added to chlorine atoms, but the energy released, which is the *electron affinity* (EA) of chlorine, is only 86 kcal/g-atom. The energy deficit is thus $118 - 86$, or 32 kcal per mole of sodium chloride (Fig. 5-1). The resulting gaseous mixture of separate sodium and chloride ions, because of its higher

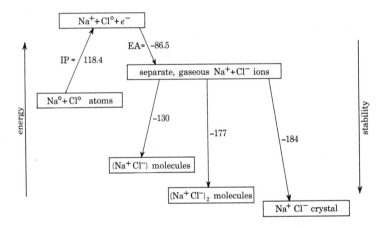

FIG. 5-1. Energy relations in the combination of sodium and chlorine. Numbers are energy changes per 23.0 g of sodium, 35.5 g of chlorine, or 58.5 g of sodium chloride. Positive values indicate energy absorbed; negative values, energy released.

energy, should revert to the more stable original atoms. Yet no trace of sodium atoms can be detected in this gas. The strong attraction between the ions has caused them to associate and release energy.

The simplest association of ions is into Na^+Cl^- pairs, customarily called molecules even though they are composed of ions. The energy released in forming the pair can be estimated by using Coulomb's law in the form

$$E_{CL} = \frac{q(-q)}{d} \qquad \qquad \mathbf{1}$$

where q and $-q$ are the charges on the sodium and chloride ions and d is the equilibrium distance between their nuclei in the molecule (Fig. 5-2). The release of energy is calculated to be 133 kcal/mole, more than enough to stabilize the ions in this form and prevent them from reverting to the atoms.

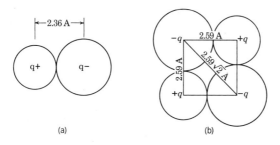

FIG. 5-2. Sodium chloride molecules. (a) The monomer. (b) The dimer. Distortion of electronic structures by polarization is not shown.

Further association of the molecules to double molecules, or dimers, occurs in gaseous sodium chloride. At $750°$ the vapor is 35% (Na^+Cl^-)$_2$. The simplest arrangement of the ions is in a square (Fig. 5-2). By Coulomb's law the energy released is

$$E_{CL} = 4\frac{q(-q)}{d} + \frac{(-q)(-q)}{d\sqrt{2}} + \frac{qq}{d\sqrt{2}} = -2 \times 1.293\frac{q^2}{d} \qquad 2$$

per quartet or two komes. The first term is for attraction between opposite charges and the second and third terms are for repulsion between like charges. A comparison of Eqs. 1 and 2 will reveal that the energy released per kome would be 29.3% higher for the dimer if d were the same.

It is reasonable to expect still more energy to be released when a large number of ions are brought together to give a crystal and this is indeed what happens. The release in energy in forming a crystal containing N komes of ions is, by an extension of Coulomb's law,

$$E_{CL} = \frac{-NAq^2}{d} \qquad 3$$

where A, the Madelung constant, depends only on the geometrical arrange-ment of the ions in the lattice and not upon the kind of ions. It is 1.748 for simple cubic lattices such as those of sodium chloride, potassium iodide, and lead sulfide. Consequently, the formation of a crystal of sodium chloride would release 74.8% more energy per kome than the formation of a gas mole-cule with the same value of d. The crystalline solid is the stable form of sodium chloride at room temperature.

The interaction of the ions in the molecules and crystal is actually more complex than we have supposed in the preceding paragraphs. The energy values in Fig. 5-1 have been corrected for the repulsion that results when closed electron shells of adjacent ions overlap and for a small attraction that results from a distortion or polarization of electronic structures when the ions are close together.

5-3. The Lattice Energy.   The cohesion of the ions in a crystal is measured by the *lattice energy*, the energy released when the crystal is formed by bringing together the separate ions. The lattice energy of sodium chloride is -184 kcal/mole where the negative sign indicates a release of energy. The energy absorbed in tearing a crystal apart into its ions is the lattice energy with changed sign, $+184$ for sodium chloride.

Consider a crystal made up of cations with valence z_c and radius r_c and anions with valence z_a and radius r_a. The lattice energy can be expressed by a generalization of Eq. 3:

$$E_L = \frac{-z_c z_a N A q^2}{r_c + r_a} + E' \qquad\qquad 4$$

where the first term on the right represents the effect of attraction and repulsion between charges predicted by Coulomb's law and E' is the remainder of the lattice energy due to polarization and other interactions. From Eq. 4 we see that if the crystal contains small, highly charged ions, the lattice energy is large and negative, so that much energy is released in forming the crystal. The effects of charge and radius are illustrated by the data in Table 5-1. In the two series of alkali metal halides the crystals with the smallest ions, KF and LiCl, have the largest (most negative) lattice energies. Strontium oxide and lithium chloride have the same internuclear distance, yet because of the double charge on the strontium and oxide ions the lattice energy of that compound is almost four times as large as that of lithium chloride. Strontium oxide is harder and has a much higher melting point (2430°) than lithium chloride (614°) because of the strong cohesion of its ions in the solid. It is also much less soluble in water than lithium chloride is. Hardness, high melting point, and low solubility in water are frequent, but not invariable, consequences of a large, negative lattice energy.

5-4. The Anomalous Behavior of Ions with Noninert Gas Structure.   The influence of size and charge, though major, is not sufficient to account for all variations in lattice energy. One important source of irregular behavior is the electronic structure of the cation. In the examples of the preceding section only cations with inert gas structure were considered. The silver ion with an outer shell of 18 electrons (Sec. 2-7) does not have inert gas structure. It is of interest to compare the lattice energies of the silver and alkali metal halides. Silver chloride and sodium chloride have the same type of crystal lattice and the internuclear distances are about the same, namely 2.81 A for

NaCl and 2.77 for AgCl. The lattice energies are -184 and -216, respectively, so that the lattice energy of silver chloride is larger by 17%. Anomalously large lattice energies are found for the other silver halides and for the halides containing Cu^+ ions (outer shell of 18 electrons) and Tl^+ ions (outer shells of $18 + 2$ electrons).

TABLE 5-1.

The Relation Between Size and Charge of Ions and Lattice Energy

	Compound	Radius sums $r_c + r_a$, angstroms	Lattice energy E_L, kcal/mole
Varying anion size	KF	2.67	-193
	KCl	3.14	-168
	KBr	3.29	-162
	KI	3.52	-152
Varying cation size	LiCl	2.57	-202
	NaCl	2.81	-184
	KCl	3.14	-168
	RbCl	3.27	-163
Varying charge	LiCl	2.57	-202
	SrO	2.57	-784

If it takes more work to tear apart a silver chloride crystal into its ions than it does for a sodium chloride crystal, it should be harder to dissolve silver chloride in water. This is true, but when a salt dissolves not only must the crystal be torn apart, but also the ions must be hydrated (Secs. 2-18, -19). A careful discussion of solubility must include both influences (Sec. 5-7). Here we need only note that for the silver halides as compared with those of the alkali metals the effect of hydration is minor, and the high lattice energies of silver chloride, bromide, and iodide are responsible for their low solubilities.

5-5. Partially Covalent or Polarized Bonds. Two explanations of the abnormally large lattice energies of the silver halides have been proposed. According to the first, the electrons of the chloride ions in silver chloride, for example, are not all localized about the chlorine nucleus, and they may spend a small part of the time about the silver nucleus. Since these electrons are shared to some extent between the two ions, the bond between them is partially covalent though predominantly ionic. This partially covalent bond is stronger than the simple ionic bond in sodium chloride and the lattice energy of silver chloride is larger (more negative). According to the second interpretation, the silver ion polarizes the chloride ion or, in other words, the nucleus of the silver ion distorts the swarming motions of the electrons about the chlorine nucleus so that they spend more time in the direction of the silver ion than away from it (Fig. 5-3). Both explanations describe a loosening of

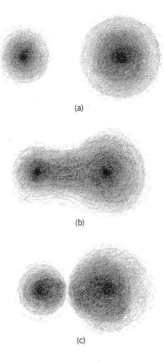

(a)

(b)

(c)

FIG. 5-3. Partially covalent and polarized ionic bonds. (a) Separate ions. (b) Partially covalent bond. (c) Polarized ionic bond.

the electronic structures of the ions but differ in the degree of loosening prescribed. We cannot as yet say which description is right. The former is perhaps more popular, but both are in current use and they lead to the same predictions of behavior of ionic compounds.

The existence of partially covalent or polarized bonds is inferred from various observations. The abnormally large lattice energies of the silver halides have been cited. The standard of comparison can be the lattice energies of compounds in which the bonds are predominantly ionic or it can be a theoretical estimate of the lattice energy. Low solubility has also been mentioned as a frequent, but not invariable, consequence of high lattice energy and partially covalent bonds. Color is often a helpful indication. Visible color is a result of removal of certain wavelengths or component colors from white light as it passes through a substance. A crystal of $CuSO_4 \cdot 5H_2O$, for example, is blue because it absorbs principally red and violet light. Light carries energy, and what is absorbed is used to change temporarily the electronic structure of the ions from which the crystal is built.

The outer electrons of the ions must be held loosely, else the energy carried by visible light will be insufficient to cause any electronic changes. Because the electrons of ions with inert gas structure are held tightly, solids, such as NaCl or CaO, that are built of such ions are colorless. There are many solids that are colored though formed from colorless ions, e.g., yellow AgI, CdS, and PbO; red HgI_2; and black PbS and HgS. The cations of these solids do not have inert gas structure, and the anions have electrons that are readily polarized or loosened by the cations so that they can absorb light energy.

The extent to which electrons about a nucleus become polarized or involved in partial covalent bonds depends on the hold of that nucleus on its electrons and on the distorting force exerted on them by other ions. We must consider then the polarizability of an ion and the polarizing power of the ions about it. Generally we picture the electronic structure of anions as being distorted by nearby cations, for the anions have a surplus of electrons which are less tightly bound to the nucleus than are those of cations. The following generalizations, first proposed in somewhat different form by Fajans, will be useful in subsequent discussions.

Rule 1. The covalent character of cation-anion bonds increases with increase in size of the anion and decrease in size of the cation.

EXAMPLE A. The iodide ion is larger and more polarizable than the chloride ion. Hence the Ag^+—I^- bond has more covalent character than the Ag^+—Cl^- bond. This is revealed in various ways. Both silver halides have anomalously large lattice energies, but the discrepancy is larger for silver iodide. Silver iodide is yellow, whereas the chloride is white. Silver iodide is much less soluble than the chloride. The valence electrons of the iodide are farther from the nucleus than those of the chloride and are more easily shared with other ions.

EXAMPLE B. The sulfide ion is more polarizable than the oxide ion. Sulfides are frequently less soluble and more deeply colored than oxides.

Rule 2. The covalent character of cation-anion bonds increases with increasing charge on either ion.

EXAMPLE A. The oxide ion is more polarizable than fluoride ion. The bonds in metal fluorides are more ionic in character than those in the oxides. The oxides are frequently colored, e.g., red HgO, and the fluorides are colorless, e.g., HgF_2. The two anions have the same number of electrons, but oxide has one less positive charge in its nucleus and thus less control over the electrons. The sulfide ion is likewise more polarizable than the chloride ion.

EXAMPLE B. The polarizing power of Mg^{++} ion is greater than that of Li^+ ion. Thus $Mg(OH)_2$ is more insoluble and covalent than LiOH. Though the two ions are about the same size, the higher charge of the magnesium ion exerts a stronger force on the electrons of hydroxide ions.

Rule 3. The covalent character of cation-anion bonds is greater for cations that do not have inert gas structure.

EXAMPLE. The Ag^+—Cl^- bond is more covalent than the Na^+—Cl^- bond. The consequences of this have already been discussed. The electrons of the inert gas octet in Na^+ frequently penetrate close to the nucleus and are tightly held. The large shell of eighteen electrons in the Ag^+ ion is more loosely held, and the electrons are more readily polarized by anions. Such cations not only polarize anions but are themselves polarized. The latter effect is most pronounced when the cation has a low charge like the Ag^+ ion.

When the cation itself is readily polarizable, Rule 1 does not strictly apply. In the series Zn^{++}, Cd^{++}, Hg^{++} the small Zn^{++} ion has the greatest polarizing power but the large Hg^{++} ion is itself almost as polarizable as Cl^- ion. All three of these ions form bonds with covalent character; those of Hg^{++} ion have the most. This is reflected in the nature of the sulfides: ZnS, white, most soluble; CdS, yellow, precipitated in the presence of 0.3 M HCl; HgS, black, perhaps the most insoluble of all the sulfides we study.

5-6. The Heat of Hydration of Ions.   The attraction of ions for water dipoles was described in Sec. 2-19, and it was noted that a decrease in volume and release of energy was associated with this interaction. When an ionic crystal is dissolved in a large volume of water, heat may be absorbed, cooling the solution (as for ammonium nitrate), or, less frequently, evolved, heating the solution (as for sodium hydroxide or anhydrous sodium sulfate). Let us imagine the process of dissolving the crystal to occur in two steps (Fig. 5-4):

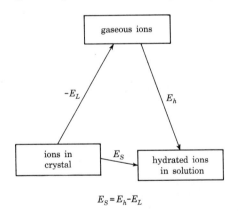

FIG. 5-4. Two ways of dissolving a crystal.

1. Decomposition of the crystal into its separate gaseous ions. The energy absorbed is $-E_L$, or the lattice energy with the sign changed (Sec. 5-3).

2. Hydration of the gaseous ions to give the solution. Let the heat absorbed be E_h, the hydration energy.

The heat of solution of the crystal must be the sum of these separate energy changes, or

$$E_S = E_h - E_L \qquad\qquad \textbf{5}$$

If the heat of solution E_S is measured and if the lattice energy is known, the heat of hydration of the gaseous ions can be calculated from Eq. 5. The heats of hydration of the gaseous ions of some alkali metal fluorides are: LiF, -246; NaF, -218; KF, -199; RbF, -191 kcal/mole, where the negative sign shows that energy is released. These data show, as we should expect, that the smaller cations attract water dipoles more strongly and release more energy upon hydration.

Attempts have been made to divide the total heat of hydration between the two ions, but these are all based on arbitrary assumptions and the heats of hydration of the individual ions so obtained are too uncertain to be of much use. The various estimates do agree on the relation of the heat of hydration of an ion to its structure. Release of energy is largest for small, highly charged ions. The heat of hydration varies approximately with the square of the ionic charge. It is about four times as large for Mg^{++} ion as for Li^+ ion and about nine times as large for La^{+++} as for Na^+, where the comparisons are between ions of the same size. Silver ions, which are both more polarizable and more polarizing than sodium ions, have the higher heat of hydration.

Although release of energy as heat of hydration tends to stabilize ions in solution, this is counteracted in part by the increased restraints on water molecules regimented into hydration shells about the ions (Sec. 1-12). Energies of hydration that have been corrected for the increase in restraints are called *free energies of hydration*. It will be generally assumed in the discussion that follows that this correction has been made.

5-7. The Relation of Solubility to Lattice and Hydration Energies. The tendency of a crystal to dissolve can be judged from the energy of solution. A large, negative energy change corresponds to a release of energy as the crystal dissolves and favors solubility. In Sec. 5-6 we saw that the process of solution could be separated into two steps (Fig. 5-4) and that the energy of solution was the difference between the heat of hydration and the lattice energy (Eq. 5). For soluble salts the heat of hydration is generally larger than the lattice energy, and energy is released in dissolving the salt. This is true of sodium chloride for which the energy of solution is -2.2 kcal/mole and of silver fluoride for which the value is -3.5. For the other silver halides the lattice energies are abnormally large (Sec. 5-4), increasingly so as the halide ion becomes larger and more polarizable, and energy is absorbed, not released, on solution. The hydration energy of the silver ion, though larger than that of the sodium ion, is not large enough to compensate for the increase in lattice energy.

It is difficult to make these predictions quantitative. Both E_L and E_h are large, negative numbers, and E_S is a small difference between them; e.g., for sodium chloride, E_L is -184, E_h is -186, and E_S is only -2, or about 1% of the other values. Minor errors in E_L and E_h then become exaggerated in E_S. The difficulty is somewhat like trying to find the weight of an engineer by weighing the locomotive before and again after he climbs into the cab. Thus we must be content with qualitative explanations and hope that, as better data become available, the discussion can be made more quantitative. Let us examine some observations about solubility and see if they can be given a plausible, if qualitative, interpretation.

Solubility is often strikingly affected by the size of the charges on the ions. Many insoluble compounds, e.g., MgO, $BaSO_4$, $SrCO_3$, CaC_2O_4, and PbS, contain two highly charged ions. The lattice energies of such compounds are large and negative and the crystals are difficult to tear apart and bring into solution. Yet there are some compounds of highly charged ions, e.g., $MgSO_4$, $FeSO_4$, and $ZnSO_4$, that are very soluble. The cations in these salts are small and heavily hydrated in solution, so that the energy of hydration overbalances the lattice energy.

These concepts can be used to interpret the sequence of group separations in qualitative analysis. Cation Group 1 is precipitated as insoluble chlorides by hydrochloric acid. The insolubility of silver chloride has been discussed already. The cations Pb^{++} and Hg_2^{++} are large and have non-inert gas structures. They are only weakly hydrated but very polarizable and are more strongly attracted to chloride ions than to water. Cation Group 2 is precipitated as the sulfides in 0.1 to 0.3 M acid solution. Most of these cations have outer shells of either 18 or $18 + 2$ electrons and have a strong tendency to combine with the very polarizable sulfide ion to give crystals with high lattice energies. The members of Cation Group 3 include several small, bivalent ions, e.g., Zn^{++}, Ni^{++}, Co^{++}, Fe^{++}, and Mn^{++}, that precipitate as sulfides in basic solution. These cations are more heavily hydrated than most of those in Cation Group 2 and require a higher concentration of sulfide ion for precipitation. Cation Group 3 also includes the trivalent Al^{+++} and Cr^{+++} ions which form insoluble hydroxides strongly bound together by hydrogen bonds (Fig. 2-9). Cation Group 4 consists of the alkaline earth metal ions, Ca^{++}, Sr^{++}, and Ba^{++}. These are large, hydrated ions with inert gas structure. They have little polarizing action on sulfide, hydroxide, or chloride ions and are thus not precipitated in previous groups. They can be precipitated here by a doubly charged ion, e.g., CO_3^{--}, which gives a precipitate with a large lattice energy. Cation Group 5 consists of the leftovers: the singly charged NH_4^+, K^+, and Na^+ ions which give soluble crystals with low lattice energies, and the doubly charged, but small, Mg^{++} ion for which the energy of hydration overbalances the effect of the lattice energy.

The effect of ionic radius on solubility, being weaker than that of charge, is often less easy to explain. From one compound to another in a series variations in solubility will often result from a fine interplay between lattice energy, heat of hydration, and restraints on water and the ions. It is not always possible to explain various fluctuations in solubility in a series.

5-8. Evidence for the Existence of Interionic Forces in Solutions.   Since ions bear charges, they must attract and repel other ions. By Coulomb's law (Sec. 1-3) such interactions will be large when the ions bear high charges, when they are close together, and when the solvent has a low dielectric constant. These expectations are confirmed by experimental measurements of many kinds. The studies of freezing point depression and conductance discussed in Chapter 2 are typical examples. The mole number i obtained from freezing point measurements (Sec. 2-17) is usually smaller than the number of ions per formula. For sodium chloride it is less than two and becomes smaller as the concentration of salt increases and the ions come closer together. The mole number of magnesium sulfate is considerably less than that of sodium chloride in equimolal solutions. This is reasonable if we remember that the force between doubly charged magnesium and sulfate ions is four times that between sodium and chloride ions spaced the same distance apart. Increase in concentration does not cause an exactly proportionate increase in specific conductance. If interionic forces did not operate, a 0.1 N solution should have a specific conductance exactly twice that of a 0.05 N solution because it contains twice as much charge per cubic centimeter to carry the current. The actual conductance ratios are less than 2.000; they are 1.922 for NaCl, 1.882 for $CaCl_2$, 1.866 for $LaCl_3$, and 1.713 for $CuSO_4$. The higher the charges, the smaller the ratio. In more dilute solutions the ratio is closer to 2.000; e.g., the specific conductance of 0.001 N NaCl divided by that of 0.0005 N NaCl is 1.987. Abnormal changes in mole number and conductance are more pronounced in ethyl alcohol, a solvent with a lower dielectric constant than water. All these observations are consistent with the hypothesis that the effects are caused by interionic forces.

5-9. The Equivalent Conductance.   The measurement of conductance is an exceptionally sensitive method of studying interionic forces. These electrical measurements can be made with a precision of a few hundredths of a per cent. The principal experimental problem is to prepare solvent and solute in a state of high purity, for the measurements are very sensitive to traces of extraneous ions.

Specific conductance is not a convenient quantity to use in the study of interionic forces, because it depends primarily on the number of charges per cubic centimeter and only secondarily on the interaction between the charges. The conductance ratios quoted in the preceding section illustrate this. All were close to the ideal ratio of 2.000, yet it is the small difference between actual ratio and the ideal value that we are interested in. It will be simpler to study interionic forces if we define a new quantity, *equivalent conductance,* represented by the Greek capital lambda Λ. It may be visualized as the conductance between plane electrodes 1 cm apart and of such area as to contain 1 g equivalent weight of solute between them at any given concentration (Fig. 5-5). By choosing one gram equivalent weight of solute, we keep the

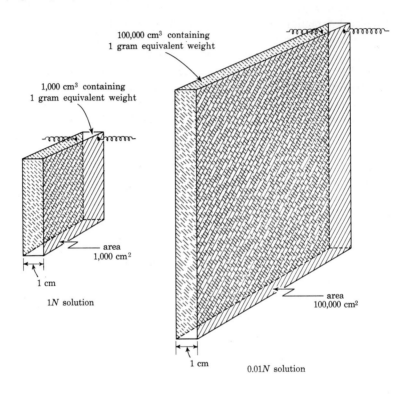

FIG. 5-5. The concept of equivalent conductance.

number of charges between the electrodes constant when the electrolyte is completely ionized. One gram equivalent of sodium nitrate contains a faraday of positive charge and a faraday of negative charge (Sec. 4-12). A mole of barium chloride contains 2 faradays each of positive and negative charge, but a gram equivalent weight, which is half a mole, contains 1 faraday of each. The equivalent conductance of equinormal solutions of sodium nitrate and barium chloride will differ only because of differences in the mobilities of the ions in the two solutions; the number of charges is the same.

The equivalent conductance is never determined directly but is calculated from the specific conductance L. If L is the conductance between electrodes of unit area, the equivalent conductance must be AL, where A is the area of electrodes required to make the cell contain one gram equivalent weight. This area is, numerically, $1000/C$, where C is the normality (Fig. 5-5):

$$\Lambda = 1000\, L/C \qquad\qquad 6$$

5-10. The Results of Conductance Measurements. The conductances of solutions of potassium chloride, a typical strong electrolyte, are given in Table 5-2. The specific conductance increases with increase in concentration of the salt

TABLE 5-2.

Equivalent Conductance of Potassium Chloride Solutions at 25°

C	Λ	C	Λ
0.000032576	149.37	0.00060895	147.56
.00010445	148.95	.00084200	147.27
.00026570	148.42	.00092856	147.11
.00033277	148.23	.0011321	146.80
.00035217	148.16	.0014080	146.50
.00046948	147.93	.0015959	146.30

because of the increase in number of charges per cubic centimeter. The equivalent conductance shows a small decrease. The interionic forces become more effective as the ions move closer together and these forces cause a drag on the motion of the ions. The equivalent conductance is plotted in Fig. 5-6

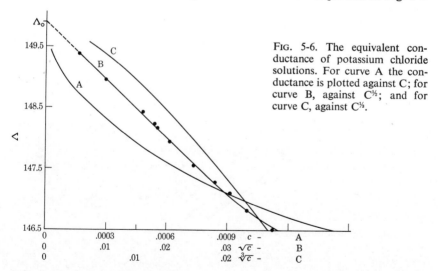

FIG. 5-6. The equivalent conductance of potassium chloride solutions. For curve A the conductance is plotted against C; for curve B, against $C^{1/2}$; and for curve C, against $C^{1/3}$.

against C, $\sqrt{C}$, and $\sqrt[3]{C}$. The simplest graph, a straight line, is obtained with the square root of the concentration. A straight line can always be represented by an equation of the form $y = mx + b$, where m is the slope and b is the value of y at $x = 0$. Let us identify Λ with y and $\sqrt{C}$ with x. Let us write Λ_0 for the intercept b and $-A$ for the slope, where A is a positive number and the minus sign corresponds to the downward slope of the line. Then the equation for the straight line in Fig. 5-6 is

$$\Lambda = \Lambda_0 - A\sqrt{C} \qquad\qquad 7$$

This equation was first developed as an expression of experimental facts by Kohlrausch in the latter part of the nineteenth century, and a satisfactory theoretical interpretation was not given until 1923-27 by Debye, Hückel, and Onsager.

The Kohlrausch equation holds for strong electrolytes in very dilute solutions. It fails, for example, for potassium chloride solutions of normality greater than about 5×10^{-4}. The constants Λ_0 and A are different for different salts and depend also on the temperature and dielectric constant of the solvent. The conductance behavior of several strong electrolytes is shown in Fig. 5-7, and that of several weak electrolytes in Fig. 5-8. The rapid decrease in equivalent conductance of acetic acid with increasing concentration

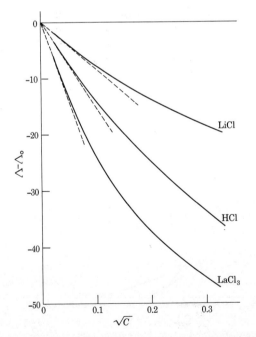

FIG. 5-7. The variation of equivalent conductance of some strong electrolytes with concentration.

is caused by the decrease in extent of ionization. The Kohlrausch equation does not apply to acetic acid at any concentration. Sulfamic acid is much stronger than acetic acid, and its conductance approaches the Kohlrausch line at low concentrations. The behavior of zinc sulfate is typical of electrolytes with highly charged ions that form ion-pairs in concentrated solutions.

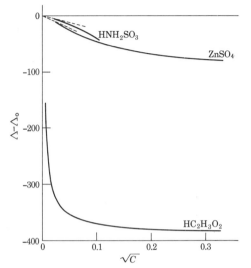

FIG. 5-8. The variation of equivalent conductance of some weak and associated electrolytes with concentration.

5-11. The Limiting Equivalent Conductance. The simple, linear relations such as that expressed by Eq. 7 are always treasured more highly than complex curves. This is partly because their simplicity suggests that there must be a simple explanation, although, in view of the highly mathematical theory of conductance, it cannot be said that this expectation was exactly fulfilled for Eq. 7. A linear relation is also prized because of its usefulness, whether for interpolation of conductances between the measured values or for extrapolation beyond them. Extrapolation, or extension of the line, is used to find the value of the intercept Λ_0, the *limiting equivalent conductance*, of a strong electrolyte.

The limiting equivalent conductance is important for showing how the electrolyte behaves when interionic forces are negligibly small. It is not the conductance of pure water, for, although the solute has been dissolved in an exceedingly large volume of water so that its concentration is virtually zero, the area of the electrodes has been correspondingly (infinitely) increased so that the cell still contains one gram equivalent weight of electrolyte. The ions are so far apart on the average in this exceedingly dilute solution as to exert no effect on each other.

The fact that ions move independently of each other at infinitely high dilution was also discovered by Kohlrausch. The data in Table 5-3 illustrate his law of independent migration. The conductances of pairs of potassium and sodium salts containing a common anion are given. The differences in limiting equivalent conductances of the salts in each pair are seen to be the same regardless of the anion. These differences represent the difference in limiting conductance of the potassium and sodium ions:

$$\Delta = \Lambda_{0\ KX} - \Lambda_{0\ NaX} = \lambda_{0\ K^+} + \lambda_{0\ X^-} - \lambda_{0\ Na^+} - \lambda_{0\ X^-} \qquad 8$$

The conductance of the anion cancels if it is independent of the cation. Equation 8 does not apply at ordinary concentrations, because the ions no longer move independently.

TABLE 5-3.

Kohlrausch's Law of Independent Migration

Substance	Λ_0	$\Delta = \Lambda_{KX} - \Lambda_{NaX}$, at 25°	
		$C = 0$	$C = 0.01$
KCl	149.86 ⎫	23.41	22.76
NaCl	126.45 ⎬		
KI	150.38 ⎫	23.44	22.94
NaI	126.94 ⎬		
K_2SO_4	153.50 ⎫	23.37	20.78
Na_2SO_4	130.13 ⎬		

Kohlrausch's law gives us a method of finding the limiting equivalent conductance of a *weak* electrolyte. This cannot be found by extrapolation because the conductance never approaches the linear behavior of a strong electrolyte (Fig. 5-8). The sum of the limiting ionic conductances of a weak electrolyte is found by combination of the limiting equivalent conductances of three strong electrolytes. Nitric acid, potassium nitrate, and potassium propionate ($KC_3H_5O_2$), for example, are completely ionized; and their limiting equivalent conductances, as found by linear extrapolation, are, respectively, 421.2, 145.0, and 109.3 at 25°. To find the limiting equivalent conductance of propionic acid we use the fact that the conductance of the nitrate ion is the same whether combined with hydrogen or potassium ions and that the conductance of the potassium ion is the same whether combined with nitrate or propionate ions if the solutions are so dilute that the ions are too far apart to have any effect on each other. Then we can write,

$$\Lambda_{0\ HC_3H_5O_2} = \Lambda_{0\ HNO_3} + \Lambda_{0\ KC_3H_5O_2} - \Lambda_{0\ KNO_3}$$

$$= \lambda_{0\ H^+} + \lambda_{0\ NO_3^-} + \lambda_{0\ K^+} + \lambda_{0\ C_3H_5O_2^-} - \lambda_{0\ K^+} - \lambda_{0\ NO_3^-}$$

$$= 421.2 + 109.3 - 145.0 = 385.5$$

5-12. The Extent of Ionization of a Weak Electrolyte from Conductance Measurements. Suppose that the equivalent conductance Λ of a weak electrolyte at some concentration has been measured. Then its extent of ionization α (Greek alpha) is given by

$$\alpha = \frac{\Lambda}{\Lambda_0} \qquad\qquad 9$$

because Λ_0 is the equivalent conductance of the completely ionized electrolyte.

Example. The equivalent conductance of 0.010937 N formic acid is 50.3 units. Find the extent of ionization if the limiting equivalent conductance of this acid is 404.5

$$\alpha = \frac{50.3}{404.5} = 0.12 \text{ or } \boxed{12\%}$$

Such calculations neglect the drag exerted on the ions at ordinary concentrations by interionic forces. In more accurate work this must be taken into account.

5-13. Dilute and Concentrated Solutions.   We turn from these experimental studies to consider the theory of interionic forces. This theory is successful in interpreting the behavior of electrolytes in very dilute solutions, e.g., the changes in conductance described by Eq. 7. It fails for more concentrated solutions. Let us see why the behavior of dilute solutions is easy to interpret and that of concentrated solutions is so difficult.

Were we able to follow a single ion in its wanderings, we would find it subject to many forces. Caged in by some water molecules and buffeted about by others, it pushes its way through the loosely organized network of molecules in liquid water. Since it bears a charge, it will attract or repel other ions. Attractions and repulsions between ions are long range forces that operate even though the ions are not in direct contact. Recall that a mole of sodium ions at the North Pole would attract a mole of chloride ions at the South Pole with a force of more than five tons (Sec. 2-6). Such attractions and repulsions are responsible for the orderly pattern of ions in crystals. In dilute solutions the ions are far apart, and their thermal motion is more important than the electrostatic interaction, so that the arrangement of ions is only slightly different from a completely random one. If the ion we are following is positive, other positive ions as they come close to it in their continual motion through the solution will be repelled and deflected away, but negative ions will swerve toward it (Fig. 5-9). On the average then, any ion will be surrounded more closely by ions of the opposite sign.

In concentrated solutions the ion is subjected to a wider variety of forces. The electrostatic interactions themselves will be stronger because the ions are close together. There will also be van der Waals forces of attraction and the ions will repel each other, even if oppositely charged, when they are so close together that their closed shells of electrons begin to overlap. When the attraction between the ions becomes strong, ion-pairs may form. Lightly solvated ions such as Na^+, K^+, and Ba^{++} are more prone to do this than the highly hydrated ones such as Li^+ and Mg^{++}, which are prevented by their tightly held hydration shells from closely approaching an anion. Cations with non-inert gas structure are prone to attract anions by polarization (Sec. 5-5). Readily polarizable anions such as iodide, acetate, nitrate, oxalate, sulfate, and dihydrogen phosphate have the strongest tendency to form ion-pairs.

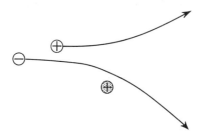

FIG. 5-9. Motion of ions near a positive ion.

The behavior of concentrated solutions is also influenced by the fact that most of the water is in the immediate neighborhood of ions and subject to their spell. A rough estimate of the average separation of potassium and chloride ions in solution gives 44 A when the concentration of salt is 0.01 M, 9.4 A for a 1 M solution, and 4.4 A for 10 M. The sum of the radii of these two ions in crystals is 3.14 A, and the diameter of a water molecule is 2.8 A. Thus in a 1 M solution only about two water molecules intervene between a potassium ion and a chloride ion, and in a 10 M solution less than one water molecule on the average would separate the ions. A saturated solution of potassium chloride is actually only 4.2 M; thus long before this state of affairs is reached the salt crystallizes. The effect of different ions on the structure of water is currently a subject under intensive investigation, and, as this is being written, it is difficult to obtain a clear, general view, for some of the contradictions have not yet been resolved. Some ions, such as K^+ (crystal radius, 1.33 A) or OH^-, are about the same size as water molecules (radius, 1.40 A) and fit into the water structure with minor readjustments. Larger ions, such as Br^- or Cs^+, do not fit in readily, and the arrangement of water molecules near them is less orderly than that in pure water. Small ions, such as Li^+, or highly charged ones, such as Ca^{++}, pull water molecules around them into highly organized hydration shells. The main point is that different ions interact with water in different ways and these specific interactions contribute to the complex behavior of concentrated solutions.

As a concentrated solution is diluted, the weaker interactions such as van der Waals forces fade rapidly in importance. When the distance between ions is far greater than their radii there can be no overlap of electron shells and repulsion. Each ion still interacts with neighboring water molecules, but in dilute solutions the total effect of this interaction is negligible, because only a small fraction of the water is very close to the ions. In very dilute solutions, the only significant interaction between one ion and another is that which results from the charges they bear. Then it matters little to a nitrate ion whether it interacts with K^+, Na^+, Ag^+, or Li^+ ions; all bear the same charge and are indistinguishable at a distance. So too when we see a person far away, we may be able to tell only that it is a man or woman; close at hand, when the special features of the person are obvious, we may recognize an old friend. The interaction of ions at a distance is relatively uncomplicated, and a theory of their behavior has been developed that is successful for very dilute solutions. Concentrated solutions are under active investigation, and we know much more about them today than formerly, but no successful comprehensive theory has yet been developed for the many types of interaction that are important when the ions are close together.

5-14. The Ionic Atmosphere. In Secs. 5-2 and 5-3 we have seen that Coulomb's law is readily applied to the interaction between ions in vapor molecules of sodium chloride and its dimer and in crystalline sodium chloride. It is quite otherwise with interaction between ions in solution, for these ions are in constant motion, and their thermal energy is generally larger than the energy of interaction.

In the preceding section we saw that any ion tends, on the average, to be surrounded by ions of charge opposite to its own. If we were to travel out from a positive ion to some neighboring region of solution, we would be more likely to find a negative than a positive ion. Any instantaneous snapshot of the distribution of ions about a given one will not be useful in interpreting the behavior of solutions, for we need to know the average distribution over a period of time. Let us load a magic camera with color film and take a time exposure while we keep the camera focused on one ion in its wanderings through the solution. Suppose that positive ions are blue and negative ions red. Then, far away from a positive ion, the blue and red tracks made by the ions in the time exposure will smear into a purple blur. Closer to the central positive ion of the picture, the purple blur gradually acquires more of a reddish tinge. This corresponds to the better chance of finding negative ions near a given positive ion. The smeared-out cloud of negative charge (red blur) about the positive ion is called its *ionic atmosphere*. Were we to focus our camera on a negative ion we would find that it too had an ionic atmosphere or a blue blur in our time exposure. An ionic atmosphere surrounds each ion in solution much as the atmosphere of air surrounds the earth.

The theory of interionic attraction proposed by Debye and Hückel in 1923 abbreviates the separate interactions between a given ion and every other ion in solution to an attraction between the ion and its atmosphere. The charge on an atmosphere is equal in size but opposite in sign to that on its ion. In a solution of barium chloride each barium ion is surrounded by an atmosphere that is made up of the other ions, barium and chloride, in the solution; and this atmosphere has a double negative charge to balance the double positive charge on the central barium ion.

5-15. The Theory of Electrolytic Conductance. The concept of the ionic atmosphere was first used to interpret conductance behavior in 1923 by Debye and Hückel. Their treatment was extended and improved by Onsager, whose highly mathematical revision was published in 1927 when he was 23 years old. According to the theory, the drag on the motion of the ions caused by interionic forces is the result of two effects.

The *electrophoretic effect* arises because the ion and its atmosphere move in opposite directions when current is passed through the solution. The ions of the atmosphere are solvated; so as the atmosphere moves, it drags solvent with it. The central ion is then moving against a flow of solvent and ions in the opposite direction. It is subjected to the same sort of drag as a boat going upstream against the current.

The *time lag effect* comes about because an ion moving in an electric field is not surrounded uniformly by its atmosphere. As the central ion moves, the atmosphere does not immediately re-form about it. Because of this time lag, or "time of relaxation" as it is often called, the atmosphere of the ion is no longer centered on it as it moves. This displacement is shown in Fig. 5-10.

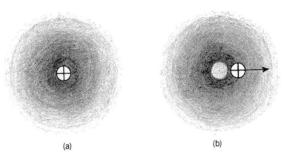

(a)   (b)

FIG. 5-10. The time lag effect. (a) Ion in center of its atmosphere before current is passed. (b) Ion off center when current passes.

The density of charge of the atmosphere is greatest on the side of the ion opposite to its direction of motion. This causes a drag on the ion and reduces its mobility.

These qualitative pictures of the effects causing the drag on the ions would be plausible, perhaps, but not convincing were they unsupported by quantitative predictions. The theory predicts that the equivalent conductance of an electrolyte made up of singly charged ions can be expressed by

$$\Lambda = \Lambda_0 - (a\Lambda_0 + b)\sqrt{C} \qquad \textbf{10}$$

where a and b are constants for a given solvent at some specified temperature and C is the normality of the strong electrolyte or the concentration of the ionized part of a weak electrolyte. This equation is seen to be of the same form as Kohlrausch's relation (Eq. 7) if we identify the constant A of the latter with $(a\Lambda_0 + b)$ in Eq. 10. The numerical value of A found by experiment agrees with that calculated from the theory.

The term $(a\Lambda_0 + b)\sqrt{C}$ on the right side of Eq. 10 is the correction for the drag due to the two effects. The first part, $a\Lambda_0\sqrt{C}$, expresses the time lag effect; it is large when the ions are very mobile (large Λ_0) and when the atmosphere is concentrated about the ion in the center (large C) so that force between ion and atmosphere is strong. The second part, $b\sqrt{C}$, expresses the electrophoretic effect and is large for highly fluid solvents in which the ion has to contend with a strong current. Both a and b get smaller as the dielectric constant and temperature increase; this is to be expected because their increase causes a decrease in interionic forces. Finally, it should be noted that the theory correctly predicts that the conductance varies linearly with the square root of the concentration. Had we assumed that the decrease in conductance with increasing concentration was caused by incomplete ionization, we would have been led to the erroneous conclusion that the conductance should vary with the first power of the concentration.

The theory of conductance is further substantiated by the behavior of electrolytes under extreme conditions. If a high voltage, e.g., 100,000 volts, is applied to the cell, the conductance is found to increase. The increase in voltage boosts the velocity of an ion from a few cm/hr to several m/sec. It whisks through the solution so rapidly that the atmosphere cannot follow it. The time lag effect vanishes, and, with less drag, the conductance increases. This is called the Wien effect. In other experiments the direction of the current is reversed many times per second. The ion oscillates back and forth, faithfully following the reversals of the field, but the atmosphere again fails to keep up, and the time lag effect vanishes. This is called the Debye-Falkenhagen effect.

SUPPLEMENTARY READING

W. B. MELDRUM and A. F. DAGGETT, *A Textbook of Qualitative Analysis*, American Book Co, New York, 1946, pp. 214–25 (conductance).

S. GLASSTONE, *Elements of Physical Chemistry*, Van Nostrand, New York, 1946, pp. 411–20 (conductance).

S. MARON and C. PRUTTON, *Principles of Physical Chemistry*, Macmillan, New York, 1958, pp. 443–58 (conductance).

F. DANIELS and R. ALBERTY, *Physical Chemistry*, Wiley, New York, 1955, pp. 378–87, 400 (conductance).

T. MOELLER, *Inorganic Chemistry*, Wiley, New York, 1952, pp. 178–86 (lattice energy and Born-Haber cycle), pp. 342–43 (solubility).

J. A. A. KETELAAR, *Chemical Constitution*, Elsevier, Houston, Texas, 1953, pp. 34–45 (lattice energy and Born-Haber cycle), pp. 96–102 (solubility, hydration energy, and entropy).

O. K. RICE, *Electronic Structure and Chemical Binding*, McGraw-Hill, New York, 1940, pp. 222–49 (lattice energy and Born-Haber cycle), pp. 398–411 (energy and entropy of solution), pp. 414–18 (solubility).

EXERCISES

5-1. Explain in words why the sodium chloride crystal is the most stable form of that substance at room temperature.

5-2. Draw a diagram for lithium bromide similar to that in Fig. 5-1. The ionization potential of lithium is 124 kcal/g-atom and the electron affinity of bromine is 81.5 kcal/g-atom. There are gaseous monomers (LiBr), dimers $(LiBr)_2$, and trimers $(LiBr)_3$. The heats of dissociation in kcal/mole of LiBr are

$$148 + \text{monomer} \rightarrow \text{separate gaseous ions}$$
$$203 + \text{crystal} \rightarrow \text{separate gaseous ions}$$
$$42 + \text{dimer} \rightarrow 2 \text{ monomers}$$
$$36 + \text{trimer} \rightarrow \text{monomer} + \text{dimer}$$

5-3. It has been proposed that a sodium chloride dimer is a rhombus, not a square, with a distance between two chlorine nuclei equal to $2b$, which is larger than the distance $2a$ between sodium nuclei. Derive an expression for E_{CL} similar to Eq. 2 using these distances a and b. [C. T. O'Konski and W. I. Higuchi, *J. Chem. Phys.*, **23**, 1175 (1955).]

5-4. Account for the difference in lattice energies of the compounds in each pair. Values of the lattice energy are given in parentheses. (a) KI (-152), KBr (-160); (b) MgS (-790), MgO (-913); (c) NaCl (-184), MgO (-913); (d) CuCl (-236), NaCl (-184); (e) AgBr (-212), AgI (-211); (f) NaF (-217), AgCl (-216).

5-5. Which compound in each pair would you expect to have the larger lattice energy? Numbers in parentheses are values of $r_c + r_a$. (a) $MgSO_4$, $BaSO_4$; (b) $(NH_4)_2NaCo(NO_2)_6$, $K_2NaCo(NO_2)_6$ (Hint: The ammonium and potassium ions have about the same radius), (c) CdS (2.32), BaO (2.24); (d) TlI (3.64), CsBr (3.63); (e) Ag_2O, Ag_2S; (f) CuF (2.3), CuS (2.5).

5-6. What is meant by "polarization"? By "partially ionic bond"?

5-7. Which of the following compounds would you expect to be colored? $RaBr_2$, CdO, Tl_2S, Sc_2O_3, LiI, HgF_2, BiI_3, $AlBr_3$, BaO, CuCl, Ag_2S, PbO_2, AgF_2.

5-8. Which bond in each pair would have more covalent character or be more polarized? (a) Tl—Cl, Tl—I; (b) Be—Cl, Mg—Cl; (c) Be—OH, B—OH; (d) Cu—S, Mg—S; (e) Pb—Cl, Pb—S; (f) Hg—I, Zn—I.

5-9. Which ion in each pair would you expect to have the higher heat of hydration? (a) Al^{+++}, La^{+++}; (b) S^{--}, Cl^-; (c) NH_4^+, K^+; (d) Ag^+, Tl^+; (e) Na^+, Ba^{++}; (f) Cr^{+++}, Cr^{++}.

5-10. The lattice energy of potassium chloride is -168 kcal/mole and the initial heat of solution of the solid salt is $+4.4$ kcal/mole. Calculate the total heat of hydration of the gaseous ions of the salt.

5-11. Explain the following observations by reference to lattice and hydration energies.

(a) AgF is very soluble; AgCl is not.

(b) SnS precipitates with Cation Group 2; MgS does not.

(c) $BaCrO_4$ is less soluble than $SrCrO_4$.

(d) BaF_2 is more soluble than SrF_2.

(e) $MgCO_3$ does not precipitate in Cation Group 4; $CaCO_3$ does.

5-12. Account for the similarities or differences in the mole numbers i of the compounds given in each part.

(a) 0.01 molal solutions of NaCl ($i = 1.943$), HCl ($i = 1.941$), and KCl ($i = 1.946$).

(b) 0.01 molal solutions of calcium chloride ($i = 2.75$) and sodium sulfate ($i = 2.72$).

(c) 0.001, 0.01, and 0.1 molal solutions of sodium chloride ($i = 1.973$, 1.943, and 1.875).

(d) 0.01 molal solutions of calcium chloride ($i = 2.75$) and cadmium bromide ($i = 2.41$).

(e) 0.01 molal solutions of sodium chloride ($i = 1.94$) and magnesium sulfate ($i = 1.54$).

5-13. Tabulated below are some very accurate values of i for six alkali halides at two concentrations. For each concentration find the average of the six results and the average deviation. The latter is obtained by adding up the deviations of the six results from the average and dividing by six. Compare the average deviations and account for the difference.

m	KCl	NaCl	LiCl	KBr	NaBr	LiBr
0.001	1.9778	1.9784	1.9752	1.9778	1.9794	1.9786
0.1	1.8532	1.8674	1.8864	1.8586	1.8830	1.9036

5-14. The equivalent conductance of 0.005 N LiCl is 109.40. Calculate its specific conductance and the resistance of this solution when placed between electrodes in a cylinder 100 cm long and with a cross-sectional area of 10 cm^2.

5-15. Why does the specific conductance of potassium chloride decrease as the solution is diluted? Why does the equivalent conductance increase?

5-16. Sketch graphs to show the typical variation of equivalent conductance with concentration for a strong electrolyte, a weak electrolyte, and an electrolyte of intermediate strength. Why is it advantageous to use the square root of the concentration in these graphs?

5-17. Why is the limiting equivalent conductance at infinite dilution obtained? How could it be found for potassium bromide? Why is this method not suitable for finding the limiting equivalent conductance of formic acid?

5-18. Calculate the limiting equivalent conductance of acetic acid from the following limiting conductances HCl, 426.2; NaCl, 126.4; $NaC_2H_3O_2$, 91.0.

5-19. The equivalent conductance of 0.025 N acetic acid is 10.36 units. From this and the data in Ex. 5-18 calculate the extent of ionization of the acid.

5-20. Describe the forces acting on a sodium ion in a saturated solution of sodium nitrate and compare with the forces acting on a sodium ion in 0.0000001 M sodium nitrate.

5-21. Which of the following electrolytes would you expect to form ion-pairs readily in concentrated solutions? (a) calcium sulfate, (b) lithium dihydrogen phosphate, (c) calcium fluoride, (d) cadmium perchlorate, (e) strontium hydroxide, (f) sodium nitrate.

5-22. The following statements concern a solution of potassium nitrate which also contains some sodium chloride. Classify them as true or false.

(a) The ionic atmosphere about the potassium ion extends throughout the solution.

(b) The ionic atmosphere about the nitrate ion has a net $+1$ charge.

(c) The density of charge of the atmosphere about a sodium ion would be decreased by heating the solution.

(d) The atmosphere about a potassium ion consists of nitrate ions.

(e) The force between a potassium ion and its atmosphere will be increased by addition of dioxane to the solution.

5-23. Account for the decrease in mobilities of the potassium and chloride ions as the solution is made more concentrated.

5-24. How would you expect the time lag effects in equinormal solutions of hydrochloric acid and potassium chloride to compare?

5-25. How is the correctness of the Debye-Hückel-Onsager theory tested against experimental data?

CHAPTER SIX

Coordination Compounds

6-1. Introduction. The existence in crystals of complex units, e.g., $Cu(NH_3)_4^{++}$, $PtCl_6^{--}$, and $Al(H_2O)_6^{+++}$, has been established by x-ray diffraction measurements (Sec. 2-9). Such complexes frequently persist when the solid is brought into solution. In analytical chemistry complex formation is useful both for separating and for identifying ions.

In a complex, the neutral molecules or anions are said to be coordinated to the central positive ion. Although the complex is most commonly an ion itself, it may occasionally be a neutral molecule. We use the term *coordination compound* to refer to any substance containing a complex. In its broadest sense this term might be used for such salts as calcium carbonate or trisodium phosphate, but it is not customary to consider the anions of familiar acids as complex ions. A hydrated salt is often fittingly considered to be a coordination compound when it contains a hydrated cation, e.g., $KAl(SO_4)_2 \cdot 12H_2O$, which contains the $Al(H_2O)_6^{+++}$ ion, and $(NH_4)_2Cu(SO_4)_2 \cdot 6H_2O$, which contains the $Cu(H_2O)_6^{++}$ ion.

6-2. Some Definitions and Fundamental Concepts. The groups bound to the central metal ion are called *ligands*, and the number of points at which they are attached to the metal ion is its *coordination number*. The coordination number can be two as in $Ag(NH_3)_2^+$, three as in $Cu(CN)_3^{--}$, four as in $Zn(OH)_4^{--}$, and six as in $Co(NO_2)_6^{---}$. There are rare and unimportant compounds in which the coordination number is five, seven, or eight. The most common values are four and six.

A particular metal ion will usually have the same coordination number in a wide variety of compounds. Cobalt(III) ion, for example, forms complexes in which its coordination number is always six, e.g., $[Co(NH_3)_6]^{+++}$, $[Co(NH_3)_5Cl]^{++}$, $[Co(NH_3)_3(NO_2)_3]$, $[Co(NH_3)_5H_2O]^{+++}$, and $[Co(NO_2)_6]^{---}$. Cobalt(II) ion, on the other hand, forms complexes in which its coordination number is sometimes four, sometimes six. By partial dehydration or addition of organic solvents, pink cobalt(II) salts are frequently turned to blue ones, and this has been attributed to change in coordination number from six to four. Complex ions in solution for which the apparent coordination number is abnormally low may use water molecules to fill the quota. The ferric thio-cyanate complex, for example, is apparently $FeSCN^{++}$ but more probably $FeSCN(H_2O)_5^{++}$.

The metal ions and tightly bound ligands are said to be within a *co-ordination sphere*. The compound with empirical formula $CuSO_4·4NH_3·H_2O$ has a copper ion and four ammonia molecules inside the coordination sphere and the sulfate ion and water molecule outside. A more significant formula would thus be $[Cu(NH_3)_4]SO_4·H_2O$. The total charge on the coordination sphere is the sum of the charges on its components. The charges on the cobalt complexes in the preceding paragraph, for example, are determined by the summation of charges on cobalt $(+3)$, nitrite (-1), chloride (-1), ammonia (0), and water (0).

6-3. Classical Studies of Coordination Compounds.

The concepts summarized in the previous section were introduced in 1893 by Werner. It is interesting and instructive to examine the evidence used by Werner to support his theory. Lacking the powerful tool of x-ray diffraction and other modern techniques, he had to rely on such classical methods as those based on chemical evidence, conductivity, and colligative properties. As an example let us consider the orange-yellow compound that can be isolated from an ammoniacal solution of cobalt(II) chloride after it has been exposed to the oxygen of air.[1]

Evidence	Deductions
1. Chemical analysis establishes the composition: 22.0% Co, 39.8% Cl, 31.4% N, and 6.8% H.	1. The simplest formula is $CoCl_3N_6H_{13}$ or $CoCl_3·6NH_3$.
2. All of the chloride rapidly precipitates as AgCl upon addition of $AgNO_3$. The compound $Co(NO_3)_3·6NH_3$ can be isolated from the solution.	2. The chloride is ionic and not tightly bound to the rest of the compound. It is outside the coordination sphere.
3. No ammonium chloride is produced when boiling HCl is added to the compound. Free NH_3 and HCl react very rapidly.	3. Ammonia is inside the coordination sphere in a complex ion $Co(NH_3)_6^{+++}$.
4. Hot, concentrated H_2SO_4 displaces HCl gas from the solid and leaves the salt $Co_2(SO_4)_3·12NH_3$. Ammonia and concentrated H_2SO_4 react violently.	4. This shows again that chloride is loosely bound and ammonia is in the coordination sphere. The formula of the sulfate appears to be more complex because $2Co(NH_3)_6^{+++}$ ions are required to balance $3SO_4^{--}$ ions.

These chemical experiments indicate that the true formula of the compound is $[Co(NH_3)_6]Cl_3$.

[1]Tassaert in 1798 was the first to report on the combination of cobalt salts with ammonia.

The chemical evidence is supported by physical measurements. The mole number i obtained from freezing point measurements of very dilute solutions of the orange-yellow compound is about 3.9. There are thus four ions formed per formula: $Co(NH_3)_6{}^{+++}$ and $3Cl^-$. If the ammonia molecules were not strongly bound to the cobalt, there would be a maximum of ten solute particles per formula, not four. Conductance measurements also show that four ions are produced or that the electrolyte is of the 3-1 valence type. This can be judged by comparing the specific conductances of electrolytes of known valence type with that of the compound at the same low molarity. For a 1-1 electrolyte like NaCl, the specific conductance of a 0.001 M solution is about 1.25×10^{-4} units; that of 0.001 M solutions of 2-1 or 1-2 electrolytes like $BaCl_2$ or K_2SO_4 is about 2.50×10^{-4}; and that of 0.001 M solutions of a 3-1 electrolyte like $LaCl_3$ is about 4.25×10^{-4}. The specific conductance of a 0.001 M solution of the coordination compound under consideration is 4.32×10^{-4} or about the same as that of $LaCl_3$. This supports the previous conclusion that the compound is a 3-1 electrolyte which gives a complex $[Co(NH_3)_6]^{+++}$ ion and three Cl^- ions.

Another and a most striking illustration of the use of conductance measurements in the study of complexes is given in Table 6-1.

TABLE 6-1.

The Specific Conductances of 0.001 M Solutions of Some Platinum(IV) Ammines

Empirical formula	Specific conductance	Valence type	Complex
$PtCl_4 \cdot 6NH_3$	5.23×10^{-4}	4-1	$[Pt(NH_3)_6]^{++++}$
$PtCl_4 \cdot 5NH_3$	4.04×10^{-4}	3-1	$[Pt(NH_3)_5Cl]^{+++}$
$PtCl_4 \cdot 4NH_3$	2.28×10^{-4}	2-1	$[Pt(NH_3)_4Cl_2]^{++}$
$PtCl_4 \cdot 3NH_3$	0.97×10^{-4}	1-1	$[Pt(NH_3)_3Cl_3]^{+}$
$PtCl_4 \cdot 2NH_3$	~ 0	nonelectrolyte	$[Pt(NH_3)_2Cl_4]$
$KCl \cdot PtCl_4 \cdot NH_3$	1.09×10^{-4}	1-1	$[Pt(NH_3)Cl_5]^-$
$2KCl \cdot PtCl_4$	2.56×10^{-4}	1-2	$[PtCl_6]^{--}$

The methods that have been illustrated by the study of the coordination compound of cobalt(III) chloride and ammonia are satisfactory only for substances containing inert complexes. The complex between copper(II) ion and ammonia is readily decomposed by acid, for ammonia is more readily removed from Cu^{++} ion than from Co^{+++} ion. There are other methods that can be used to determine the structure of these complexes that dissociate rapidly.

6-4. Rules for Naming Coordination Compounds. The complexities of structure of these compounds have given rise to several elaborate systems of nomenclature. One of the earliest was based on their colors. The compound

$[Co(NH_3)_6]Cl_3$ was called luteo cobaltic chloride, luteo being derived from the Latin word *luteus* meaning yellow. Later, more emphasis came to be placed on structure than on color and the term "luteo" was even used in naming colorless $[Ru(NH_3)_6]^{+++}$ ion. Werner introduced a more rational system based on structure, and this, with some modifications, has been adopted by the International Union of Pure and Applied Chemistry and is now in general use. We shall not have to concern ourselves with all the ramifications of nomenclature, but some familiarity with the system is desirable. The principal rules, which are illustrated by the examples in Table 6-2, are:

1. The cation is named first, then the anion if the substance is an electrolyte.

2. The names of all negative ligands end in -*o*, e.g., chloro (Cl^-), carbonato (CO_3^{--}), cyano (CN^-), nitro (NO_2^-), and hydroxo (OH^-).

3. Coordinated water is called *aquo* and ammonia is called *ammine*. (The spelling of the latter with a double *m* should be noted, for in organic chemistry the word "amine" is used for derivatives of ammonia such as methyl amine, CH_3NH_2.)

4. In the name of a complex cation the negative ligands are listed first, neutral ones next, and the metal last. Within each class of ligands the order of listing is alphabetical. A complex anion is named the same way but the metal is given the suffix -*ate* regardless of its oxidation state.

5. The number of ligands of each kind is indicated by the Greek prefixes *mono-*, *di-*, *tri-*, *tetra-*, *penta-*, *hexa-*, *hepta-*, and *octa-*.

6. The oxidation state of the central metal atom of a complex is shown by a Roman numeral in parentheses.

TABLE 6-2.

Some Examples of Nomenclature

Formula	Familiar or trivial name	Systematic name
$K_3Fe(CN)_6$	potassium ferricyanide	potassium hexacyanoferrate(III)
$Cu(NH_3)_4SO_4 \cdot H_2O$	copper ammonia sulfate	tetramminecopper(II) sulfate monohydrate
$Na_3Co(NO_2)_6$	sodium cobaltinitrite	sodium hexanitrocobaltate(III)
$Pb(C_2H_3O_2)_3^-$	lead triacetate ion	triacetatolead(II) ion
$[Co(NH_3)_5Br]^{++}$	bromopurpureo ion	bromopentamminecobalt(III) ion
$[Co(NH_3)_5H_2O]^{+++}$	roseo ion	aquopentamminecobalt(III) ion
$[Pd(NH_3)_4][PdCl_4]$	Vaquelin's salt	tetramminepalladium(II) tetra-chloropalladiate(II)

6-5. The Arrangement of Ligands in Space. The spatial arrangement of ligands about a central metal ion is always of theoretical interest and sometimes has an effect on the properties of the complex. The most common arrangements are shown in Fig. 6-1. For clarity the complexes are shown pulled apart so that the metal and ligand ions do not touch. Convenient simplified versions of the tetrahedron, square, and octahedron are also given. It should be noted that all corners of these figures are alike. This is shown by drawing the same octahedron in two different ways (Fig. 6-1e).[2]

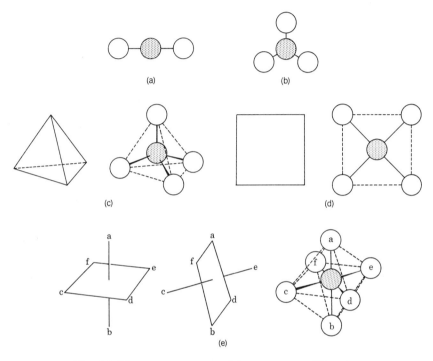

FIG. 6-1. The most common spatial arrangements of ligands.

The best evidence for these arrangements in crystals is given by x-ray diffraction measurements. An octahedral complex, $PtCl_6^{--}$, was pictured in Fig. 2-8c. The interpretation of such x-ray measurements is difficult because of the large number of atoms involved. X-ray measurements on solutions are even more difficult to interpret because of the scattering of x-rays by the solvent molecules. Nevertheless, it has been possible to establish that the arrangement of ligands in the $PtCl_6^{--}$ and $PtBr_6^{--}$ ions in aqueous solution is octahedral as it is in crystals.

Werner was able to establish the octahedral arrangement of ligands by classical methods. One type of evidence was based on the number of isomers

[2]Octahedral arrangements are often slightly distorted. In $(NH_4)_2Cu(SO_4)_2 \cdot 6H_2O$ the complex $Cu(H_2O)_6^{++}$ has two of its six water molecules, e.g., those at a and b in Fig. 6-1e, slightly farther away from the copper(II) ion than are the other four. In $Cu(H_2O)_4SO_4$ these two have been lost altogether and a planar complex is left.

of a compound that could be prepared. *Isomers* are compounds with the same
empirical formula but different arrangements of the atoms. Ethyl alcohol,
CH_3CH_2OH, and dimethyl ether, CH_3OCH_3, are two isomeric organic compounds. There are many examples of isomers among the cobaltammines, e.g.,
$[Co(NH_3)_4Cl_2]^+$ which exists in a dark purple form and a green form or
$[Co(NH_3)_4(NO_2)_2]^+$ which also occurs in two forms, one yellow-brown, the
other orange-yellow. The fact that only two such forms of each have been
prepared supports the hypothesis that the arrangement of ligands is octahedral. Four groups of one kind and two of another can be arranged on the
corners of an octahedron in only two ways: one in which the two chloro or
two nitro groups are on opposite corners and one in which they are on adjacent
corners (Fig. 6-2a, b). The first is called the *trans* isomer and the second the

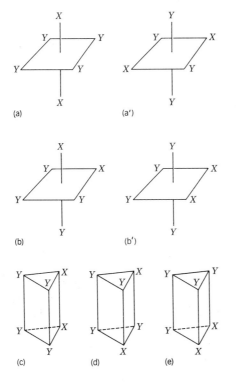

FIG. 6-2. Isomers of complexes of
the type CoX_2Y_4. (a) and (b) are
the two possible octahedral isomers; (a') and (b') are the same
two in different orientation. (c),
(d), and (e) are the three possible
prismatic isomers.

cis after Latin words meaning, respectively, "across" and "on this side" (compare cisalpine and transalpine Gaul). Were the ligands arranged on the
corners of a trigonal prism, three isomers should be possible (Fig. 6-2c, d, e).
That only two have ever been prepared we take to support the concept of the
octahedral arrangement. It may be objected that a third isomer might some
day be prepared. While we must be prepared to change our concept if this

should happen, we are confident that it never will, both because of the large number of attempts that have already failed and because many other experiments of an entirely different nature also point to an octahedral arrangement for these cobalt(III) complexes.

The dipole moment can be cited as an example of another property that can be used to establish the arrangement of ligands. Molecular platinum(IV) compounds of the type PtX_2Y_2 fall into two classes, those having a dipole moment and those having none. The latter must have a symmetrical arrangement of X and Y groups (Sec. 1-5). This is possible only in a planar complex with the two ligands of each kind on opposite corners of a square. The compounds that have a dipole moment are probably also planar but have the ligands on adjacent corners (Fig. 6-3).

FIG. 6-3. The two isomers of PtX_2Y_2. The arrows show the displacements of charge or bond moments. It has been assumed that X is more electronegative than Y.

6-6. Inert and Labile Complexes. Most of the complexes encountered in qualitative analysis are rapidly formed and easily dissociated. The addition of ammonia to a solution of a silver salt, for example, will convert the hydrated silver ion into an ammonia complex in no more time than it takes to mix the solutions together. If acid is added, the ammonia complex decomposes to give back silver ions. The equilibrium

$$Ag(NH_3)_2{}^+ \rightleftharpoons Ag^+ + 2NH_3$$

is established rapidly enough so that the effect of changed conditions on the extent of dissociation of the complex is readily predicted; e.g., an excess of ammonia will reduce the concentration of free silver ion and increase that of the complex. Practically all the complexes of aluminum, manganese(II), cobalt(II), nickel, zinc, silver, and many other metals come to equilibrium rapidly with their dissociation products. Taube has suggested that they be called *labile* complexes.

Other complexes, particularly those of cobalt(III) and chromium(III), decompose very slowly and never come to equilibrium with their components. These are called *inert* complexes.[3] It was their inertness that made possible Werner's classical study of coordination compounds. A solution of $[Co(NH_3)_6]^{+++}$ ion in 1 M hydrochloric acid can be kept almost indefinitely without decomposition. Yet at equilibrium in this acid medium only 0.01 %

[3]Labile complexes have also been called "normal" or "ionic"; inert complexes have been called "penetration" or "covalent" complexes.

of the cobalt should remain in the form of the complex. The complex is potentially unstable but persists indefinitely because the rate of decomposition is so slow.

The experimental study of inertness and lability provides some interesting illustrations of the use of isotopes as tracers. In Sec. 2-19 there was a description of exchange experiments with O^{18} which demonstrated that $Cr(H_2O)_6^{+++}$ ions were inert and other hydrated ions were labile. Exchange experiments can also be done with radioactive isotopes as tracers. The exchange reactions of cyanide complexes can be followed with cyanide labeled with radioactive C^{14}. A typical experiment might be an attempt to determine the rate of exchange represented by

$$Fe(CN)_6^{----} + C^*N^- \rightarrow [Fe(CN)_5(C^*N)]^{----} + CN^-$$

A solution of $K_4Fe(CN)_6$ was treated with a known amount of KC^*N. The mixture was shaken for some predetermined length of time, and then a cadmium salt was added to remove the complex ion as insoluble $Cd_2Fe(CN)_6$. After this was removed by centrifugation, the free cyanide ions were precipitated as zinc cyanide, and the radioactivity of this solid was determined. The lower its activity, the greater the rate of exchange. The inert complexes of iron(II), cobalt(III), iron(III), and chromium(III) exchanged less than 2% of their cyanide in 100 hours. Exchange with the labile complex of nickel was complete in five minutes.

Many of the inert complexes are also hard to prepare, and this is important in qualitative analysis. Although the $Cr(NH_3)_6^{+++}$ ion is inert and hard to decompose, the addition of ammonia to a solution of a chromium(III) salt causes precipitation of $Cr(OH)_3$, or hydrated Cr_2O_3. The ammonia complex is best formed by reaction of ammonia gas with solid chromium(III) chloride, an entirely different set of conditions from that used in qualitative analysis. As another example, the fact that hexacyanoferrate(III), or ferricyanide, ion is always formed by oxidation of the iron(II) complex may be noted. Direct reaction between Fe^{+++} and CN^- ions is too slow.

6-7. Complex Formation in Qualitative Analysis. Coordination compounds are occasionally added as reagents, e.g., $Na_3Co(NO_2)_6$ in testing for potassium and K_2HgI_4 for ammonia. More frequently, complexes are formed in the solution under test and these reactions are used to separate ions or to identify them. Separations are usually based on the low dissociation of complex ions. Copper(II) and bismuth, for example, can be separated by addition of excess ammonia. The concentration of Cu^{++} ion allowed by the equilibrium

$$Cu(NH_3)_4^{++} \rightleftharpoons Cu^{++} + 4NH_3$$

in the presence of excess ammonia is too low to permit the precipitation of copper(II) hydroxide along with the bismuth hydroxide. This control of the concentration of cupric ion is particularly effective because a small change in concentration of ammonia causes a large change in concentration of cupric ion.

If complex formation stabilizes an unusual oxidation state, the separation can be a very effective one. The separation of copper from cadmium by cyanide and sulfide is an example. The cyanide complex of copper(I), unlike most compounds of copper in this oxidation state, is much more stable than that of copper(II) or cadmium. Addition of sulfide to a solution that contains copper, cadmium, and excess cyanide gives a precipitate of cadmium sulfide alone.

Not all separations by complex formation are desirable. For example, if tartrate is present in a solution that is to be analyzed for Cation Group 3, aluminum may fail to precipitate because it forms a stable complex with tartrate. It is best to remove such complex-forming anions before testing for cations.

Separations can be based on properties of the complex other than its low dissociation. Certain complexes are soluble in organic solvents, and separations can be accomplished by extraction of the complex from the aqueous solution. Large amounts of iron(III) can be removed as a chloride complex by extraction with ether of a strong hydrochloric acid solution of the iron salt. Also, the solubility of the tetrathiocyanatocobalt(II) complex ion in ether-amyl alcohol mixture is used to separate and identify that metal.

The formation of colored complexes is a favorite method of identifying ions, the $Cu(NH_3)_4^{++}$, $Co(SCN)_4^{--}$, and $FeSCN^{++}$ complexes being noteworthy examples. Complex formation can also be used to mask the color of an interfering ion; e.g., the strong red color of ferric thiocyanate can be discharged in the test for cobalt by converting ferric ion to the stable, colorless FeF_6^{---} complex.

6-8. Chelates. All the complexes that have been considered up to this point contain ligands that each occupy only one coordination position, so that the number of ligands and the coordination number have been the same. There are other complexes, e.g., copper(II) glycinate, $Cu(NH_2CH_2CO_2)_2$; triethylenediaminecobalt(III) ion, $Co(NH_2CH_2CH_2NH_2)_3^{+++}$; and trioxalatoferrate(III) ion, $Fe(C_2O_4)_3^{---}$; in which the number of ligands is half the usual coordination number. It is supposed that more than one atom of the ligand molecule can be attached to the central metal ion. These points of attachment are shown by arrows in Fig. 6-4a. The copper glycinate complex is square; the other two are octahedral (Fig. 6-4b, c).

These compounds are called *chelates* (pronounced key′-lates) from a Greek word meaning "crab's claw," a reference to the pincer-like action of the ligand on the metal ion. The chelates described above included a neutral molecule, a cation, and an anion. The neutral molecule, copper diglycinate, is often called an *inner complex salt*, "inner" because of the formation of a ring structure, "complex" because of the coordination of the ligands with metal ions, and "salt" because of the cancellation of charges. Inner complexes are frequently characterized by (1) extreme stability or inertness [the cobalt(III) triglycinate chelate is not decomposed by being dissolved in concentrated sulfuric acid, and the aqueous solution gives practically no electrical conductivity]; (2) solubility in organic solvents and insolubility in water [nickel dimethylglyoxime is soluble in chloroform but not in water]; and (3) colors that bear little resemblance to that of the unchelated ion [the scarlet color of nickel dimethylglyoxime is a striking example].

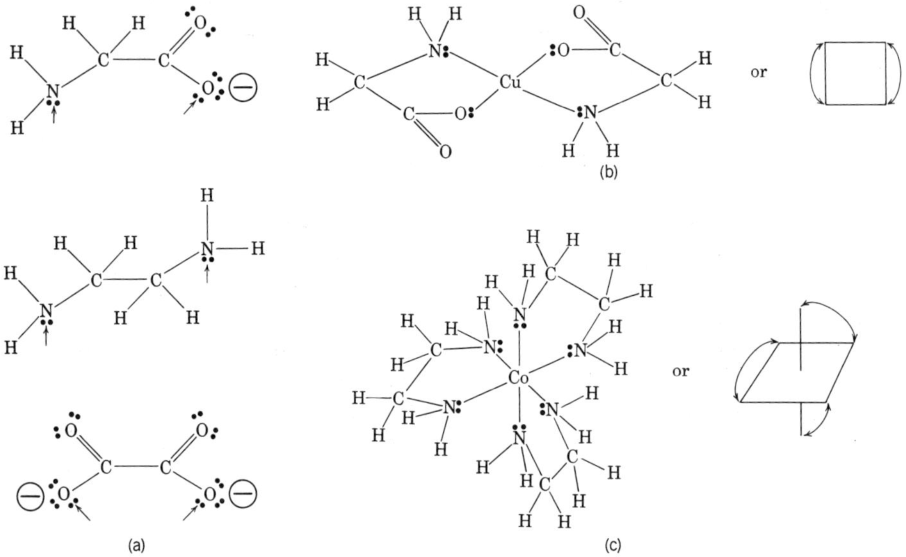

Fig. 6-4. Square and octahedral chelates.

The chelating ligand most frequently attaches itself to a metal ion through nitrogen, oxygen, or sulfur atoms. Usually the chelate ring contains five or six atoms; e.g., that in the copper glycinate complex contains one copper, one oxygen, one nitrogen, and two carbon atoms or five in all.

Chelates play a very important role in life processes. Both hemoglobin and the chlorophylls are chelates. The chelating agent in both is a ring structure containing nitrogen atoms that coordinate to an iron ion in the first and to a magnesium ion in the second. The appendages attached to outer parts of the ring structure are also different. The binding of metal ions by proteins uses the nitrogen, oxygen, and sulfur atoms in these complex molecules. Such chelates are apparently involved in enzyme action.

The anion of ethylenediaminetetraacetic acid (mercifully abbreviated to

EDTA) and related compounds form particularly stable chelates with calcium and iron. These are useful in water softening and in sequestration of undesirable ions in water. The EDTA anion has six coordinating atoms (marked by arrows):

and can so twist itself about a calcium ion as to cage it in completely.

Chelation is also involved in the formation of colored *lakes*,[4] which are combinations of metal oxides or hydroxides and a dye. They are used to fix the dye to cloth or, in analytical work, to distinguish between a gelatinous metal hydroxide such as $Al(OH)_3$ or $Mg(OH)_2$ and hydrous silica, $SiO_2 \cdot xH_2O$, which does not form chelates.

In analytical chemistry chelates are used for separations and identification reactions. The colored chelates of dithizone (short for "diphenylthiocarbazone") with zinc and other metals and of dimethylglyoxime with nickel are used in the cation analysis. The structure of the latter is well established; that given for the dithizone complex is less certain:

Dimethylglyoxime is a very specific reagent, for only the nickel salt preci-

[4]This term has no connection with bodies of water but is a variant of the word "lac" which is applied to a resin that is the source of a crimson dye.

pitates from ammoniacal solution. Its insolubility may be due to nickel-nickel bonds between molecules. Dithizone is not specific but combines with any of a large group of ions. Its chelates can be extracted into organic solvents to effect separations. By control of pH and by separation or masking of interfering ions it is possible to increase the selectivity of dithizone.

SOME THEORETICAL ASPECTS OF COMPLEX FORMATION

6-9. The Nature of the Bond Between Ligand and Metal Ion.   Ligands are either anions or polar, neutral molecules containing one or more lone pairs of electrons. Some typical examples are

$$\left(:\ddot{C}l:\right)^{-} \quad \left(:C \equiv N:\right)^{-} \quad \left(:\ddot{S}=C=N:\right)^{-} \quad \left(\begin{array}{c} \ddot{N} \\ \diagup \diagdown \\ \ddot{O} \quad \ddot{O}: \end{array}\right)^{-}$$

$$\begin{array}{c} \ddot{N} \\ \diagup | \diagdown \\ H \quad H \quad H \end{array} \qquad \begin{array}{c} \dot{\ddot{O}} \\ \diagup \diagdown \\ H \quad H \end{array}$$

The formulas of the chelating ligands given in Sec. 6-8 show that they too attach themselves to a metal ion either through a charged group or through a lone pair of electrons.

We can take two extreme views of the bonds formed between ligands and the metal ion. According to the first, such a bond is electrostatic (or ionic), the result of attraction between the positive metal ion and a negative ion or the negative end of a polar molecule. According to the other view, the bonds can be covalent, the result of sharing electrons between ligands and the metal ion. It is now clear that the bonds are intermediate in character, not completely ionic or completely covalent. Nevertheless it is instructive to adopt the electrostatic point of view and see how far it can lead us toward an understanding of complex formation.

The strength of the electrostatic bond between metal and ligand will depend on the nature of each. If the ligand is an anion, the strength of the bond will vary with its charge, oxide ions being more tightly held than chloride, for example. If it is a neutral molecule, the attraction varies with its dipole moment. Water molecules (dipole moment 1.84 debyes) are held more tightly than ammonia molecules (1.3 debyes) by sodium ions. Ammonia molecules can be polarized by some cations (Sec. 5-5) and their attraction for metal ions will depend on the sum of the permanent and induced dipole moments. The attraction between metal ion and ammonia is exceptionally strong with cobalt(III) and very weak with sodium, while cobalt(II) and calcium stand in between. Cations such as Ag^+, Cd^{++}, Hg^{++}, and Pb^{++}, which are themselves readily polarizable, form halide complexes which are most stable for iodide and least stable for fluoride, and their cyanide complexes are still more stable. Metal ions such as Co^{++} in the first transition series are small and less polarizable. Their bonds with halide ions are predominantly ionic and the most stable halide complexes are those with the small fluoride ion. It is well to recognize that the stability of complexes depends on many effects of which polarization is only one, and we cannot expect this concept to provide us with pat answers to all the problems concerning stability of complexes. To some of these problems there are no satisfactory answers as yet.[5]

6-10. The Effect of Size and Charge of the Metal Ion. In the preceding section the effect of the ligands on complex formation was examined. We now examine the effect of the metal ion itself. Small, highly charged cations should exert the strongest electrostatic force on ligands. This is conveniently expressed by the *ionic potential*, the ratio of ionic charge to radius. Values of this property are given in Table 6-3. They are calculated by dividing the number of positive charges on the cation by its radius (in angstrom units) in crystals; e.g., the ionic potential of the barium ion is 2/1.35, or 1.5. The data in Table 6-3 show that there is a general correspondence between ionic potential and ability to form complexes. Metal ions, such as those of the alkali metals, that have low ionic potentials form few complexes. Those that form exceptionally stable complexes, such as Co^{+++} and Cr^{+++} ions, have large ionic potentials. Yet there are some ions whose positions are clearly anomalous, e.g., Ag^+ and Pb^{++} ions which form more complexes than would be expected from their small ionic potentials, and Mg^{++} and Al^{+++} which are much poorer complex formers than their position indicates. Charge and radius alone are not sufficient guides. The electronic structure of the metal ion must also be considered. Ions that do not have inert gas structure are more effective than their ionic potentials indicate. Thus Ag^+ and Pb^{++} are better complex formers than Ba^{++}, Sr^{++}, or even Mg^{++}; and Fe^{+++}, Co^{+++}, and Cr^{+++} are far more effective than Al^{+++} ion. From the electrostatic point of view, this is attributed to the greater polarizing power (and sometimes

[5]It has been emphasized that the word "stability" must be used with some clearly formulated reaction in mind. In this discussion it will generally refer to dissociation of the complex into a hydrated metal ion and free ligands, e.g.,

$$Pb(NH_3)_2^{++} + 4H_2O \rightarrow Pb(H_2O)_4^{++} + 2NH_3$$

This ammine complex is not stable in aqueous solution and the reaction goes to completion. The solid ammine $Pb(NH_3)_2Cl_2$ is fairly stable with respect to the decomposition represented by

$$Pb(NH_3)_2Cl_2(solid) \rightleftharpoons PbCl_2(solid) + 2NH_3(gas)$$

since the pressure of ammonia gas above the solids is only 100 mm at 30°. A theoretical treatment of this decomposition would have to include the lattice energies of the two solids. The stability of complexes may also be influenced by restraints on their motions. This is particularly true of chelation.

greater polarizability) of ions that do not have inert gas structure, or it can be ascribed to the ability of these ions to form bonds with considerable covalent character. These ions are found in Cation Groups 1 to 3, and the analysis of these groups makes extensive use of complex formation.

TABLE 6-3.

The Ionic Potential

Ion	Crystal radius in Angstrom	Ionic potential, in ionic charges/Angstrom	Electrons in outer shell	Cation group
K^+	1.33	0.75	8	5
Ag^+	1.13	0.9	18	1
Na^+	0.98	1.0	8	5
Ba^{++}	1.35	1.5	8	4
Pb^{++}	1.21	1.65	18+2	1 and 2
Sr^{++}	1.14	1.75	8	4
Hg^{++}	1.10	1.8	18	2
Ca^{++}	0.99	2.0	8	4
Cd^{++}	0.97	2.1	18	2
Sn^{++}	0.90	2.2	18+2	2
Fe^{++}	0.75	2.7	14	3
Zn^{++}	0.74	2.7	18	3
Cu^{++}	0.70	2.9	17	2
Bi^{+++}	1.0	3.0	18+2	2
Mg^{++}	0.65	3.1	8	5
Fe^{+++}	0.75	4.5	13	3
Co^{+++}	0.64	4.7	14	3
Cr^{+++}	0.55	5.5	11	3
Al^{+++}	0.50	6.0	8	3

6-11. The Coordination Number. This is one of the most puzzling features of complexes. Why does cobalt(III) have a coordination number of six in its complexes? Why is the coordination number of silver only two and that of zinc four? There are no easy answers to such questions, but we can gain some insight by treating a complex as a cluster of anions or dipoles about a central metal ion.

A metal ion will tend to attract as many ligands as possible, because the attraction results in a release of energy. If r_{cl} is the distance between the nuclei of the cation and the ligand, q_c is the charge on the cation, and $-q_l$ is the charge on the ligand, the energy E_a released in attaching n anions to the cation is given by Coulomb's law:

$$E_a = -nq_cq_l/r_{cl} \qquad\qquad 1$$

The coordination number n seldom exceeds six because the attraction is partially counteracted by repulsion between the ligands and because the number of ligands that can crowd about a metal ion is limited by the space available. Suppose that r_{ll} is the distance between nuclei of two ligands. The repulsion between two anions is then q_l^2/r_{ll} and the total repulsive energy E_r is found by summing such expressions for all pairs of ligands. The net electrostatic energy is then

$$E = -n\frac{q_c q_l}{r_{cl}} + E_r \qquad\qquad 2$$

A number of simple deductions can be made from these electrostatic concepts. Repulsions will be stronger between doubly charged ligands; thus the coordination number in oxyanions will be lower than that in fluoroanions; compare SiO_4^{----} with SiF_6^{--}. A coordination number of eight is so rare because of the large repulsion between so many anions. A square arrangement of four ligands is less stable than a tetrahedral one because the ligands are closer together in the former. The angle between two metal-ligand bonds is $109°$ in the tetrahedron and $90°$ in the square. The only well-established examples of cations that form square planar complexes all have outer shells of 16 or 17 electrons, e.g., Ni^{++}, Pd^{++}, Pt^{++}, Cu^{++}, Ag^{++}, and Au^{+++}.

The relative size of cation and ligand is also of importance in fixing the coordination number. If the cation is too small, it rattles around ineffectually between the ligands. The repulsion between ligands is then greater than the attraction between metal ion and ligands and a ligand is pushed out (Fig. 6-5). If the cation is too large, there will be enough space about it to accommodate another ligand or two with a release of energy. The rarity of complexes with a coordination number of five or seven is explained, at least in part, by noting that if a cation is large enough to accommodate five ligands, it will always have room for a sixth, and, if it is large enough to accommodate seven, it can always take on one more to make eight.

The ratio of the radii of cation and ligand, r_c/r_l, is a convenient expression of the spatial requirement. By simple geometry it can be proved that a particular coordination number will be stable over a range of values of the radius ratio. Some of these ranges are given in Table 6-4. These data

TABLE 6-4.

The Radius Ratio and Coordination Number

Complex	Coordination number	Spatial arrangement	Range of $r_c\, r_l$
CL_2	2	Linear	Less than 0.155
CL_3	3	Triangular	0.155 to 0.225
CL_4	4	Tetrahedral	0.225 to 0.414
CL_4	4	Square	0.414 to 0.732
CL_6	6	Octahedral	0.414 to 0.732

can be used to estimate coordination numbers. Suppose that we have to predict the formula of a beryllium fluoride complex. The ratio of the crystal radii is 0.31/1.33, or 0.232, which falls in the tetrahedral range. The complex should have the formula BeF_4^{--}, and this agrees with the experimental value. It must be emphasized, however, that these ranges hold only for rigid, undistorted ligands about a central ion and will not necessarily apply if the bonds are polarized or partially covalent.

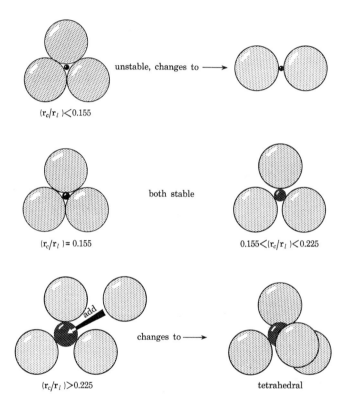

FIG. 6-5. The radius ratio effect for coordination number three.

The importance of covalent bonding is given some support by the success of Sidgwick's concept of *effective atomic number* (EAN). This resembles the familiar idea that stable ions and molecules form when the atoms they contain acquire the electronic structures of the inert gas atoms. Each ligand in a complex is pictured as donating a pair of electrons to the metal ion (or more than one pair if chelation occurs). The sum of these donated pairs and the electrons originally in the metal ion is frequently equal to the number of electrons in an atom of an inert gas or its atomic number. The concept can be illustrated by the HgI_4^{--} complex. The atomic number of mercury is 80 and the Hg^{++} ion contributes 78 electrons. Each iodide ion has a complete octet of electrons and donates two of these to the mercury. The EAN of mercury in the complex is then $78 + 4 \times 2$, or 86, which is the atomic number of the inert gas radon. If the complex were HgI_3^- or HgI_6^{--}, its EAN would not be equal to the atomic number of the inert gas. There are a number of complexes for which the EAN principle does not hold, e.g., $Fe(CN)_6^{---}$ (EAN = 35) and $Ni(NH_3)_6^{++}$ (EAN = 38) as compared with krypton (atomic number 36). Furthermore, it is unlikely for a metal ion to tolerate the large accumulation of negative charge that results from donation of the electron pairs. The mercury in the above complex would have a formal charge of -6 if the eight electrons donated by the iodides were assigned to it completely, and the charge would still be -2 if the mercury and iodide ions shared the electrons equally. It is more probable that the bonds are partially ionic and partially covalent in character.

6-12. The Orbital Structure and Magnetic Properties of Simple Ions. Substances may be classified on the basis of their magnetic behavior into two groups: those which are *diamagnetic* or repelled by a magnetic field and those which are *paramagnetic* or attracted into it. The attraction or repulsion can be measured by suspending a sample from one arm of a balance so that it hangs between the poles of an electromagnet. After the magnetic field is turned on, the attraction or repulsion is balanced by adding weights to or subtracting them from the other pan of the balance (Fig. 6-6). The repulsion experienced by diamagnetic substances is very weak in comparison with the attraction experienced by paramagnetic substances. Those substances which are exceptionally paramagnetic, such as metallic iron or Fe_3O_4, are called *ferromagnetic*.

We explain this behavior in terms of electronic configuration. An *orbital* has been defined (Sec. 1-4) as a region in an atom or molecule in which one or two electrons can be localized, i.e., where they will spend something like 90% of the time. According to the Pauli principle, each orbital can be occupied by at most two electrons and they will have the same energy but opposite spins. Orbitals can be grouped into classes designated by the letters s, p, d, f, etc.[6] The orbitals of each class have approximately the same energy and same average outreach from the nucleus but differ in their orientation. There is only one s orbital in any electron shell. It has the lowest energy of all the orbitals in that shell and the energies of the others increase from p to

---

[6]These letters were originally used in the study of spectra and referred to *s*harp, *p*rincipal, and *d*iffuse spectral lines. As applied to electronic orbitals, the letters have lost their original significance.

d to *f*. The two outer electrons in the sixth shell of a Pb^{++} ion are a pair of *s* electrons. A shorthand notation for the outer electronic structure of this ion is $6s^2$ in which the symbols represent, respectively, the shell, the orbital, and the number of electrons in it. The eight outer electrons of an ion such as Ca^{++} with inert gas structure are paired in one *s* and three *p* orbitals. Its outer electronic structure is represented by $3s^2 3p^6$. There are never more than three *p* orbitals so that in a shell of eighteen electrons the ten beyond the octet are in five *d* orbitals. The outer electronic structure of the zinc ion is represented by $3s^2 3p^6 3d^{10}$.

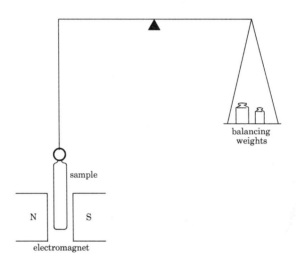

FIG. 6-6. The Gouy balance.

Diamagnetism is characteristic of substances containing paired electrons. All ions contain at least one pair of electrons in a closed shell and exhibit some diamagnetism, but in paramagnetic ions this is completely over-shadowed and can be neglected.

Most ions have all the electrons in their outer shells paired, and thus do not exhibit paramagnetism. These include ions with inert gas structure, e.g., Al^{+++} and Ca^{++} ions with outer shells containing four pairs, or eight electrons; ions with outer shells of nine pairs, or eighteen electrons, e.g., Ag^+ and Zn^{++} ions; and ions with two electrons more than the shell of eighteen, e.g., Pb^{++} and Bi^{+++} ions (Sec. 2-7). Another way of representing the typical diamagnetic structures discussed above (Pb^{++}, Ca^{++}, and Zn^{++}) is to show each orbital as a square and the pair of electrons as two arrows pointing in opposite directions, indicating their opposite spins, e.g.,

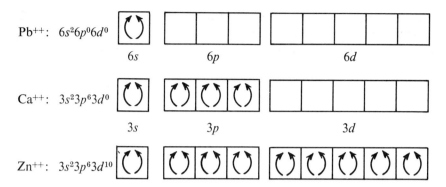

Paramagnetic substances contain unpaired electrons. The only metal ions that we encounter that have such structures are those of the transition series in the middle of the Periodic Table. Spinning electrons have a magnetic dipole moment and, like miniature bar magnets, tend to line up with an applied magnetic field. Just as the force of an electric field on a polar molecule depends on its electric dipole moment, so too does the force exerted by a magnetic field on an ion depend on its total magnetic moment. The paired electrons in an orbital have opposite spins, and their magnetic moments cancel just as those of two bar magnets would if laid north pole to south pole. Salts containing ions such as Cr^{+++}, Fe^{++}, or Cu^{++} are paramagnetic because of the presence of unpaired $3d$ electrons. The data in Fig. 6-7 show that the magnetic moments of these ions depend primarily on the number of unpaired electrons. According to Hund's rules, electrons, unless perturbed by external influences, spread over all available orbitals of the same energy, rather than pairing. The five $3d$ electrons in Mn^{++} and Fe^{+++} ions are just sufficient to spread over all five $3d$ orbitals; and these ions with five unpaired electrons have the largest magnetic moments.

6-13. The Magnetic Moments of Complex Ions. When ligands are brought up to a metal ion, a distortion of its electronic structure occurs. The degree of distortion varies with the ligand and the metal ion. Fluoride ions and water molecules cause little distortion, and the magnetic moments of iron(III) in Fe^{+++}, $Fe(H_2O)_6^{+++}$, and FeF_6^{---} ions are all virtually the same. Cyanide ions, at the other extreme, have a profound effect on the structure of the metal ion. The iron(III) ion in the complex $Fe(CN)_6^{---}$ has, according to its magnetic moment, only one unpaired electron, while the simple Fe^{+++} ion has five.

The effect of the ligands on the central metal ion of an octahedral complex can be pictured in the following way. There are five $3d$ orbitals in the metal ion, arranged in space as shown in Fig. 6-8. Each orbital consists of four lobe-shaped regions. The one or two electrons that can occupy it will wander around inside each and back and forth between them so that they effectively occupy all four lobes. For two of the orbitals, the lobes point

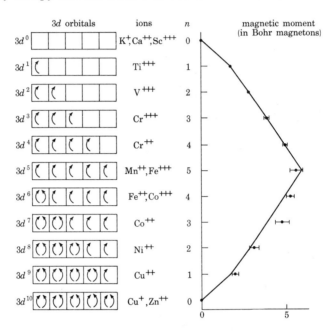

FIG. 6-7. The structure of the $3d$ subshell and the magnetic moments of some ions in the first Long Period.

toward the corners of the octahedron. If they contain electrons, they will be *antibonding* orbitals, because the electrons will repel the electron pairs of the ligands that point toward these corners. The other three orbitals have lobes that fall in between the corners of the octahedron. They are called *nonbonding* orbitals, since they have no effect on the ligands. In an ion containing a single $3d$ electron, e.g., Ti^{+++}, that electron may occupy any one of these five orbitals, for all have the same energy. If six water molecules are brought up with their lone pair electrons pointing toward the corners of the octahedron, the $3d$ electron will be repelled by the lone pairs and will seek a nonbonding orbital out of the range of their influence. The nonbonding orbitals in $Ti(H_2O)_6^{+++}$ ions will thus have lower energies than the antibonding ones. If the ion has more than one $3d$ electron, the electronic structure of its complexes will be determined by the opposing action of two repulsions: that between the $3d$ electrons and the electron pairs of the ligands and that between the $3d$ electrons themselves. The first type of repulsions tends to make the $3d$ electrons concentrate in the nonbonding orbitals and will be strongest for ligands such as CN⁻. The second type of repulsions tends to make the $3d$ electrons spread over all five orbitals in accord with Hund's rule (Sec. 6-12) and will be most effective with ligands such as H_2O or F^- which produce

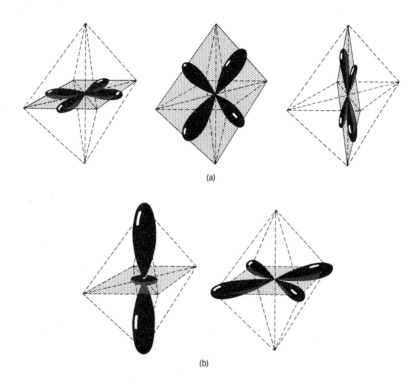

(a)

(b)

FIG. 6-8. The five $3d$ orbitals. (a) Nonbonding orbitals. (b) Antibonding orbitals. Lightly shaded planes are used only to make orientation of darkly shaded orbitals clear.

weak fields. In the $Fe(CN)_6^{---}$ ion, the strong field of the six cyanide ions forces the five $3d$ electrons into the nonbonding orbitals, and this leaves only one unpaired, as expected from its magnetic moment.

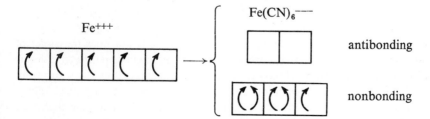

In $Fe(H_2O)_6^{+++}$ and FeF_6^{---} ions, the field of the ligands is weak, and the repulsion between the $3d$ electrons keeps them spread over all five orbitals.

Ligands that produce fields of intermediate strength will give complexes with magnetic moments in between those of FeF_6^{---} and $Fe(CN)_6^{---}$. It was once thought that the bonding in the first of these complexes was ionic and that in the second covalent. We now recognize that there is no sharp division between these types of bonds. The magnetic properties of complexes can be accounted for by the perturbing action of ligands on the electrons of the metal ion, as we have seen. It must be recognized that our discussion of this has necessarily been oversimplified, and that to interpret the finer details, we must allow for a certain amount of covalent bonding between cation and ligands.

6-14. The Colors of Complex Ions.   The visible colors of ions result largely from the absorption of light energy by the electrons of the ions (Sec. 5-5). The energy carried by light varies directly with its frequency (v, Greek nu) or inversely with its wavelength (λ, Greek lambda):

$$E = hv = hc/\lambda \tag{3}$$

where h is Planck's constant and c is the velocity of light. It is a fundamental tenet of the quantum theory that electrons in an atom or molecule are limited to certain values of energy, and cannot have values in between these. Therefore, an electron can change its energy in only a limited number of ways. It can jump to a higher energy level by absorbing light energy if the light has the correct frequency (or wavelength) as given by Eq. 3. If a vending machine is stocked with ten-cent candy bars, we can get one by putting in the correct amount of money but not by putting in seven cents or nine cents.

Ions with stable electronic structures, e.g., Ca^{++}, Zn^{++}, or Pb^{++}, are colorless. They can absorb only ultraviolet light, which carries more energy than visible light because it has a higher frequency. Complexes of these cations are also generally colorless, but the solid oxides, iodides, and sulfides of the more polarizable cations may be colored (Sec. 5-5).

The only ions with which we deal that are colored in solution are those of the transition series. The colors of the hydrated ions are given in Table 6-5. The colors of some of these are not readily observed in solution because of the instability of the ion. That of $Fe(H_2O)_6^{+++}$, for example, is best observed in crystals of ferric alum, $NH_4Fe(SO_4)_2 \cdot 12H_2O$, or of $Fe(NO_3)_3 \cdot 9H_2O$.

The colors given in Table 6-5 have not been precisely defined. The green of iron(II) salts is not the same as that of nickel salts nor does the violet of ferric nitrate match that of chromic nitrate. Our own response to color is often subjective. The psychological response is determined by the saturation, brightness, and hue of the color. *Saturation* expresses the purity or vividness of a color. *Brightness* expresses its lightness or darkness on a scale that goes

TABLE 6-5.

The Colors of the Hydrated Ions of the First Transition Series

Color transmitted	Ions and number of $3d$ electrons
White	$Ca^{++}(0)$, $Cu^+(10)$, $Zn^{++}(10)$
Red	$Co^{++}(7)$, $Mn^{++}(5)$
Green	$V^{+++}(2)$, $Fe^{++}(6)$, $Ni^{++}(8)$
Purple	$Ti^{+++}(1)$
Violet	$V^{++}(3)$, $Cr^{+++}(3)$, $Mn^{+++}(4)$, $Fe^{+++}(5)$
Blue	$Cr^{++}(4)$, $Co^{+++}(6)$, $Cu^{++}(9)$

from black to white. *Hue* is the characteristic that enables us to class colors as yellow, purple, green, etc. It is associated with the wavelength of the light and is that aspect of color best suited for consideration here.

The color of solutions is studied by passing light of various wavelengths through the solution and determining the percentage absorption at each wavelength (Fig. 2-1). An absorption spectrum obtained for a solution containing Cr^{+++} ions is given in Fig. 6-9. The minima in the curve occur at the wave-

FIG. 6-9. The absorption spectrum of aqueous chromium(III) perchlorate. The data are for a 0.06 M $Cr(ClO_4)_3$ solution that was made 0.1 M in $HClO_4$ to suppress hydrolysis. The molar absorptivity, a_m, is independent of concentration (C) and thickness of solution (b) through which the light passes. It is defined by $a_m bC = \log (100/\%T)$ where $\%T$ is the percentage transmission. The $\%$ absorption is $100 - \%T$. Below the spectrum the ranges of colors in white light are given. Adapted by permission from C. K. Jørgensen, "Studies in Absorption Spectra III," *Acta Chemica Scandinavica*, **8**, 1497 (1954).

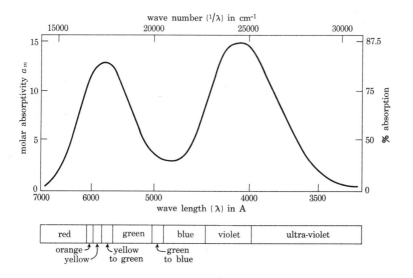

lengths that are largely transmitted, i.e., red, and blue to greenish-blue light, the combination of which is the violet color we see. The theoretical interpretation of this spectrum is too complex to give here.

Color changes are often associated with complex formation because of shifts in the electronic structure of the cation. Some of the more striking of these, e.g., the pink to blue color change of cobalt(II) chloride, are believed to accompany a change in coordination number. Still more striking color changes are attributed to a *charge-transfer* process. The violet color of the hydrated Fe^{+++} ion is pale in comparison with the intense blood-red color of the Iron(III) thiocyanate complex. Light provides the energy required to remove an electron from the thiocyanate ion and transfer it to a ferric ion:

$$h\nu + SCN^- \rightarrow (SCN)^0 + e^-$$

$$e^- + Fe^{+++} \rightarrow Fe^{++}$$

Eventually the electron will find its way back to a thiocyanate radical. The charge-transfer mechanism is believed to be responsible for the colors of many solid iodides and bromides and possibly for some oxides and sulfides.

Some of the most intensely colored substances are those that contain an element in two different oxidation states, e.g., $KFe^{III}Fe^{II}(CN)_6$ (Prussian blue), Pb_3O_4 (red lead), and Cu_2Cl_3. The color of these may also be caused by a charge-transfer, e.g., a shift of electrons from Fe(II) to Fe(III) in Prussian blue.

SUPPLEMENTARY READING

J. NORDMANN, *Qualitative Testing and Inorganic Chemistry*, Wiley, New York, 1957, Chapter 4.

T. R. HOGNESS and W. C. JOHNSON, *Qualitative Analysis and Chemical Equilibrium*, 4th ed., Holt, New York, 1954, Chapter 11.

G. I. BROWN, *A Simple Guide to Modern Valency Theory*, Longmans, Green, London, 1953, Chapter 7.

A. E. MARTELL, "The Behavior of Metal Complexes in Aqueous Solution," *J. Chem. Educ.*, **29**, 270 (1952).

S. Z. LEWIN and R. S. WAGNER, "The Nature of Iron(III) Thiocyanate in Solution," *J. Chem. Educ.*, **30**, 445 (1953). This is an excellent survey which brings out the difficulty of establishing the formula of a complex in solution.

D. H. BUSCH, "The Coordinate Bond and the Nature of Complex Inorganic Compounds," *J. Chem. Educ.*, **33**, 376, 498 (1956).

J. A. A. KETELAAR, *Chemical Constitution*, Elsevier, Houston, Texas, 1953, pp. 49–61, 72–75.

E. S. GOULD, *Inorganic Reactions and Structure*, Holt, New York, 1955, pp. 15–21 (electronic structure of atoms and ions), 62–66 (hybrid orbitals), Chapter 22 (chelates and isomerism), pp. 373–79 (magnetic studies).

H. J. EMELEUS and J. S. ANDERSON, *Modern Aspects of Inorganic Chemistry*, 2nd ed., Van Nostrand, New York, 1952, Chapter 6.

T. MOELLER, *Inorganic Chemistry*, Wiley, New York, 1952, Chapter 7.

A. MARTELL and M. CALVIN, *The Chemistry of Metal Chelate Compounds*, Prentice-Hall, Englewood Cliffs, N.J., 1952.

J. C. BAILAR, Jr., ed., *The Chemistry of the Coordination Compounds*, Reinhold, New York, 1956.

EXERCISES

6-1. A rose-colored compound is found to have the empirical formula, $CoCl_3 \cdot 5NH_3 \cdot H_2O$. One mole of it when treated with silver nitrate gives 3 moles of silver chloride. Two moles of it react with concentrated sulfuric acid to give hydrogen chloride gas and 1 mole of $Co_2(SO_4)_3 \cdot 10NH_3 \cdot 5H_2O$. This sulfate loses 3 moles of water when it is dried at room temperature; the remaining 2 moles are lost only after strong heating. What is the formula of the complex ion in both compounds?

6-2. There is a compound of empirical formula $CoCl_3 \cdot 5NH_3$. One mole of it when treated with silver nitrate gives 2 moles of silver chloride. Its specific conductance in 0.001 M solution is about 2.45×10^{-4}. Ammonia is not removed by treatment with concentrated sulfuric acid. Suggest a reasonable formula for the complex ion.

6-3. There are two compounds of chromium having the same empirical formula $CrCl_3 \cdot 6H_2O$. Salt A is green; salt B is violet. With silver nitrate A gives 1 mole of silver chloride per mole of salt, whereas B gives 3 moles of silver chloride. When both salts are dried by keeping them in a desiccator containing concentrated sulfuric acid, A loses 2 moles of water per mole of salt, but B does not lose water at all. From these data, deduce formulas of the two salts that show the groups inside and outside the coordination sphere.

6-4. The specific conductance of compound B in Ex. 6-3 at a certain concentration is 8.75×10^{-4}. That of an equimolar solution of A is 2.65×10^{-4} when the solution is freshly prepared, 5.8×10^{-4} after it has stood for 24 hours, and 8.2×10^{-4} after 88 hours. What conclusion do you draw from these data?

6-5. A compound with the simplest formula $PtCl_2 \cdot 2NH_3$ has the following properties. Concentrated sulfuric acid does not liberate either hydrogen chloride or ammonium sulfate from it. Its specific conductance is about the same as that of an equimolar solution of magnesium sulfate. Freezing point measurements indicate that its molecular weight is twice that expected from the simplest formula. What two complex ions does this salt contain?

6-6. (a) Predict the value of i for $K_2[Fe(CN)_5NO]$. (b) The freezing point depression of a 0.04 molal solution is $0.206°$. Calculate i and compare with your prediction.

6-7. Predict the specific conductance and i value of 0.001 M solutions of $[Co(NH_3)_5Cl]Cl_2$, $Na_3Co(NO_2)_6$, and $Co(NH_3)_3(NO_2)_3$.

6-8. Potassium can be identified by precipitation as a compound that was once believed to be a pyroantimonate $K_2H_2Sb_2O_7 \cdot 5H_2O$. Show that this can be rewritten to indicate the presence of a $Sb(OH)_6^-$ complex.

6-9. Give a systematic name for each of the following: (a) $K_4Fe(CN)_6$ (b) $[Co(NH_3)_4Cl_2]Cl$ (c) $NaAl(OH)_4$ (d) $K_2PtCl_4Br_2$.

6-10. Verify that three isomers of CoX_2Y_4 are possible if the six ligands were arranged on the corners of a hexagon with cobalt in the middle.

6-11. Verify that a tetrahedral arrangement of ligands in PtX_2Y_2 is inconsistent with the fact that two and only two isomers of such compounds can be prepared.

6-12. Read Chapter 7 of *The Chemistry of the Coordination Compounds* (BAILAR),and report examples of solvate, coordination, polymerization, ionization, structural, geometrical (cis-trans), and optical isomerism.

6-13. The complex $Mn(CN)_6^{---}$ ion is inert and $MnF_5(H_2O)^{--}$ is labile. What difference in behavior is implied by these terms?

6-14. Why is inertness or lability of complexes important in qualitative analysis?

6-15. Why does NH_3 form complexes with metals while CH_4 and NH_4^+ do not?

6-16. The compound $AgI \cdot PH_3$ is much less stable than the corresponding ammine. Suggest an explanation.

6-17. Calculate the ionic potentials of Li^+ ion and Be^{++} ion if their crystal radii are, respectively, 0.68 and 0.31 A. Suggest an explanation for the observation that more heat is released in forming solid $Li(H_2O)_2Br$ from water vapor and LiBr than in forming the analogous ammine. Also explain why more heat is released in forming $Be(NH_3)_4Cl_2$ than in forming the analogous hydrate.

6-18. Which complex in each pair would you expect to be more stable? (a) $Ca(NH_3)_6^{++}$, $Co(NH_3)_6^{++}$; (b) $K(H_2O)_6^+$, $Al(H_2O)_6^{+++}$; (c) AlF_6^{---}, FeF_6^{---}; (d) $Co(NH_3)_6^{++}$, $Co(NH_3)_6^{+++}$.

6-19. Prove by geometry that the minimum radius ratio for a square complex is 0.414.

6-20. Prove that if a cation bearing a charge of $+2$ and ligands of the same radius as the cation but bearing a charge of -1 combine, the complex CL_3^- has a lower energy than that of CL_2. (With somewhat more effort you can show that the tetrahedral complex CL_4^{--} has the lowest energy of all.)

6-21. The ionic radius of Sb(V) is estimated to be 0.62A and that of O^{--} or OH^- is 1.40. Calculate the radius ratio, and decide which of the following is the most probable formula for the antimonate ion: SbO_3^-, SbO_4^{---}, or $Sb(OH)_6^-$.

6-22. Repeat the calculations of 6-21 for the arsenate ion if the radius of As(V) is 0.45 A.

6-23. The radius of the fluoride ion is 1.33 A, that of Cr^{+++} ion is given in Table 6-3. Which is the more likely complex, CrF_4^- or CrF_6^{---}?

6-24. The ionic radius of zinc is given in Table 6-3. That of hydroxide or oxide ion is 1.40 A. Calculate the radius ratio, and use this to predict which of the following is the correct formula of the zincate ion if spatial considerations alone determine the coordination number: ZnO_2^{--}, $Zn(OH)_4^{--}$, or $Zn(OH)_6^{-4}$. Calculate the effective atomic number of zinc in these three complexes. Which formula does this calculation support?

6-25. Repeat the calculations of Ex. 6-24 for the chromite ion, i.e., CrO_2^-, $Cr(OH)_4^-$, and $Cr(OH)_6^{---}$.

6-26. Phosphorus(V) chloride and phosphorus(V) bromide vapors contain PX_5 molecules, but it has been established by x-ray diffraction that the solids contain, respectively, $PCl_4^+PCl_6^-$ and $PBr_4^+Br^-$ units. Suggest an explanation.

6-27. Calculate the effective atomic number of the metals in the following complexes and compare it with that of the nearest inert gas: $CdCl_4^{--}$, $Cu(NH_3)_4^{++}$, $Ag(CN)_2^-$, $Ni(CO)_4$, $Zn(NH_3)_4^{++}$, $Co(NH_3)_6^{+++}$, $Hg(SCN)_4^{--}$, $Co(NH_3)_6^{++}$.

6-28. Classify the following ions as diamagnetic or paramagnetic: Na^+, Cu^{++}, Sc^{+++}, Tl^+, Ni^{++}, Ti^{++++}, Co^{++}, La^{+++}, Zn^{++}, Mn^{++}.

6-29. Draw diagrams similar to those in Fig. 6-7 to show the distribution of electrons among the $3d$ orbitals of V^{++} and Mn^{+++} ions. Predict the magnetic moment of these ions. How are the Pauli principle and Hund's rule used in drawing the diagrams?

6-30. There are seven $4f$ orbitals. Show the distribution of electrons among these in Gd^{+++} and Dy^{+++} ions.

6-31. If an atom or ion contains n unpaired electrons, the quantum theory predicts a magnetic moment of $[n(n + 2)]^{1/2}$. The measured magnetic moment of $Mn(H_2O)_6^{+++}$ is 4.9 units and that of $Mn(CN)_6^{---}$ is 3.0 units. How many unpaired electrons does each complex contain? How are they distributed between non-bonding and antibonding orbitals?

6-32. Goldschmidt's values of the ionic radii of divalent ions in the first transition series are: Ti^{++}, 0.80; V^{++}, 0.72; Cr^{++}, 0.83; Mn^{++}, 0.91; Fe^{++}, 0.82; Co^{++}, 0.82; Ni^{++}, 0.78. It might be expected that the radius would decrease uniformly across the series. Explain. Santen and Wieringen (*Rec. trav. chim.*, **71**, 420 (1952); in English) have pointed out that the radius of an ion that has electrons in an antibonding orbital will be abnormally large because of the repulsion between these electrons and those of ligands. Show that this accounts for the anomalous values in the series.

6-33. Which of the following would you expect to be colored? Give a reason for each answer. Ti^{++++}, $Ni(ClO_4)_2$, Ga^{+++}, Ti^{++}, Pd^{++}, $Cs_2Au[AuCl_6]$, $Zn(OH)_4^{--}$, MoS_3, Mn_3O_4, La^{+++}.

6-34. Tell what is meant by each of the following and give an example of each: (a) orbital, (b) paramagnetism, (c) labile complex, (d) nonbonding orbital, (e) hue, (f) charge-transfer spectrum.

CHAPTER SEVEN

Reaction Rates and Chemical Equilibria in Solution

7-1. Introduction. Qualitative analysis is based on chemical reactions between electrolytes. There are two fundamental questions which can be asked about any reaction: how fast does it go and how far does it go? One concerns the rate of reaction and the other the final equilibrium state. It is convenient to consider first those reactions that take place in a single solution phase (homogeneous reactions) and then to take up the complications that arise when other phases, e.g., a gas or another liquid, are introduced (heterogeneous reactions). Rates and equilibria involving precipitates are considered in the next chapter.

REACTION RATES

7-2. The First Principle of Reaction Rates. Let us start by considering a reaction between two oppositely charged ions such as H_3O^+ and $C_2H_3O_2^-$. As these two kinds of ions wander about through the solvent, collisions between them will occur. After collision they may fly apart unchanged, or transfer of a proton may have occurred as expressed by the equation

$$H_3O^+ + C_2H_3O_2^- \rightarrow HC_2H_3O_2 + H_2O$$

The rate of reaction can be expressed as the rate of decrease of concentration of either ion or the rate of formation of the molecular acid.

Let us consider variations in the rate of combination caused by changes in the concentrations of the ions. These affect the frequency of the collisions. We can vary the number of hydronium ions per milliliter of solution by adding a strong acid, and we can vary the number of acetate ions per milliliter by adding a completely ionized acetate salt such as sodium acetate. Suppose that the concentration of hydronium ions is tripled by addition of hydrochloric acid. Then the chance of collision between acetate and hydronium ions is tripled. If both ion concentrations are tripled simultaneously, the frequency of collision and rate of reaction are 3×3, or 9 times as large as at first. If instead the concentrations of both ions are quadrupled, the rate is increased sixteen-fold. If one concentration is tripled and the other quadrupled, the rate is increased twelve-fold. These concepts are shown schematically in Fig. 7-1. Each line connecting the opposite charges represents a chance

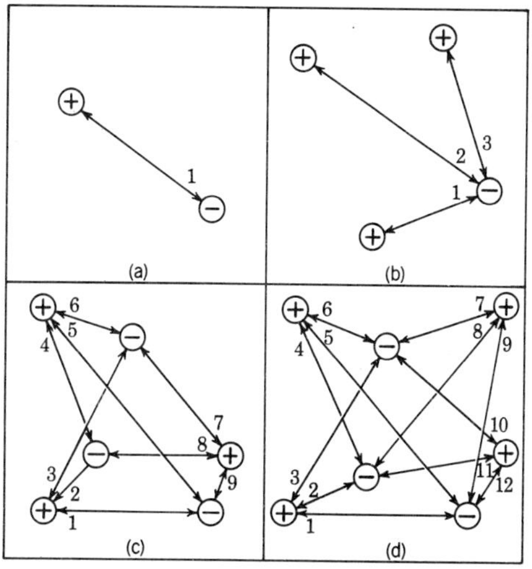

FIG. 7-1. Collisions between oppositely charged ions. The number of lines connecting the charges indicates the number of chances of collision.

of collision. The frequency of collision and hence the rate of combination of the ions is thus proportional to the product of their concentrations[1]:

$$\text{Rate} \;\propto\; [H_3O^+][C_2H_3O_2^-]$$
$$\text{Rate} \;=\; k[H_3O^+][C_2H_3O_2^-] \qquad\qquad 1$$

The proportionality constant k has the obvious property of being equal to the rate when the concentrations are both unity and is called the specific reaction rate or the *rate constant*.

The rate of recombination of the ions will depend not only on their concentrations but also on the temperature (Sec. 7-5) and on specific properties of the ions and the solvent. In Eq. 1 the effect of concentration is shown explicitly but the other effects are lumped together in the factor k. While k remains fixed as the concentrations vary, it is increased by a rise in temperature. The frequency of encounter of the ions, the speed of transfer of the proton, and the rapidity with which readjustments in the ionic atmospheres and solvation shells occur all depend, at least in part, on the specific nature of the ions and solvent. The fact that the ions bear opposite charges and attract each other, favors encounters between them. This being so, a solvent with a low dielectric constant would also have a favorable effect on their combination. To transfer the proton one of the three O—H bonds in

[1] It is convenient in writing rate and equilibrium expressions to use the symbol [X] to represent the molar concentration of X (Sec. 4-12).

the H_3O^+ ion must be broken. Some energy must be invested for this but it is more than repaid when the proton is added to the acetate ion. The transfer of this proton, like that between H_3O^+ ions and water molecules (Sec. 1-12), is exceedingly rapid and can occur even though the two ions are separated by a molecule or two of water:

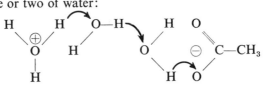

It is therefore necessary only for the two primary hydration shells of the ions to touch for proton transfer to occur; the ions themselves need not come in contact. Combination between other ions can be slow if proton transfer is not involved, for then the ions have to penetrate the hydration layers to reach each other. The act of combination of hydronium and acetate ions has been discussed in this detail to emphasize how the rate constant k and rate of reaction depend on specific properties of the ions and solvent molecules.

The actual rate of combination of hydronium and acetate ions is exceedingly rapid. At 20°, k is about 4.5×10^{10} when concentrations are expressed in moles per liter and time in seconds. This value indicates that if we mix 0.01 M solutions of the two ions, equilibrium would be virtually established in about 0.000005 second. Until recently the rates of such reactions were thought to be too fast to measure. Yet within the last few years not one but several ingenious methods have been developed that can be used to study very fast reactions. In several of these an equilibrium is suddenly disturbed by a change in conditions, such as the application of a very high voltage, and the return to equilibrium proceeds with a certain time lag that can be observed and related to the rate constants.

Though it has an unusually high rate, the reaction we have just discussed is otherwise typical of those that occur by simple combination of two particles. When a molecule or ion of substance A reacts with one of substance B, the rate of reaction is expressed by

$$\text{Rate} = k[A][B] \qquad 2$$

This is the *first principle of reaction rates*. The factor k includes the effects of temperature and specific properties of A, B, and the solvent molecules on the rate. Sometimes a reaction will occur between two molecules of the same substance. The frequency of collision then varies with $[A][A]$:

$$\text{Rate} = k[A]^2 \qquad 3$$

7-3. Rates of Reactions in Which Water is a Reactant. The rate of ionization of acetic acid

$$HC_2H_3O_2 + H_2O \rightarrow H_3O^+ + C_2H_3O_2^-$$

would be represented according to Eq. 2 by

$$\text{Rate} = k[\text{HC}_2\text{H}_3\text{O}_2][\text{H}_2\text{O}] \qquad\qquad 4$$

Now as long as our attention is confined to dilute solutions of acetic acid there will always be a large excess of water. One liter of 0.1 M acetic acid at $20°$ contains 55.2 moles of water. Less than 2% of the acid ionizes at this concentration, so that less than 0.002 mole of water is consumed. The concentration of water is virtually unchanged by the ionization reaction and can be considered constant. Then we can write for the rate,

$$\text{Rate} = k'[\text{HC}_2\text{H}_3\text{O}_2] \qquad\qquad 5$$

where the new rate constant k' is the product of two constants, k and $[\text{H}_2\text{O}]$. Eq. 5 is obtained directly if we ignore the hydration of the proton and write the equation for the ionization reaction in simplified form as

$$\text{HC}_2\text{H}_3\text{O}_2 \rightarrow \text{H}^+ + \text{C}_2\text{H}_3\text{O}_2^-$$

We shall usually use such simplified equations and rate expressions hereafter.

A kinetic interpretation of Eq. 5 is given in Fig. 7-2. In dilute solutions each molecule of acetic acid is completely surrounded by water molecules. This situation is not altered if the concentration of acid is doubled, and the chance of proton transfer remains unchanged, although the rate is doubled because there are twice as many molecules of acid per milliliter that can ionize.

We must consider the concentration of water to be constant only in dilute solutions. We cannot expect this to be true in a mixture that is 99% acetic acid and only 1% water; in fact, here the concentration of molecular acid is virtually constant, and the rate of ionization should vary with the concentration of water. Nor will the concentration of water be constant in a solvent mixture such as one that is 82% dioxane and only 18% water (Fig. 7-2d).

The rate constant k' for the ionization of acetic acid is 8×10^5, this is large but much less than that for recombination of the ions (4.5×10^{10}). The slower rate of ionization is doubtless due to the difficulty of breaking the O—H bond in the acetic acid molecule and the slowness with which ionic atmospheres and solvation layers form about the ions as they are created.

The self-ionization of water (Sec. 1-12),

$$\text{H}_2\text{O} + \text{H}_2\text{O} \rightarrow \text{H}_3\text{O}^+ + \text{OH}^-$$

should have a rate expressed by

$$\text{Rate} = k[\text{H}_2\text{O}][\text{H}_2\text{O}] = k[\text{H}_2\text{O}]^2 \qquad\qquad 6$$

but if solutes are at low concentration, this reduces to a constant:

$$\text{Rate} = k' \quad \text{where } k' = k[\text{H}_2\text{O}]^2 \qquad\qquad 7$$

7-4. Slow Reactions Between Ions.   Most proton transfer reactions are very rapid; i.e., in virtually every encounter between oppositely charged ions transfer of the proton occurs. In slow reactions only a small fraction of the total number of collisions is effective in leading to reaction. Such effective collisions occur when the particles have more than a certain minimum energy, the *activation energy*. This energy can be used in various ways. It may be required to break apart the solvation shells so that the ions can come in contact with each other. It may be required to overcome repulsion between the ions if they bear like charges. Or it may be required to loosen bonds in the reactants so that an atom can be transferred, as in the reaction between chlorate and sulfite (Sec. 3-10).

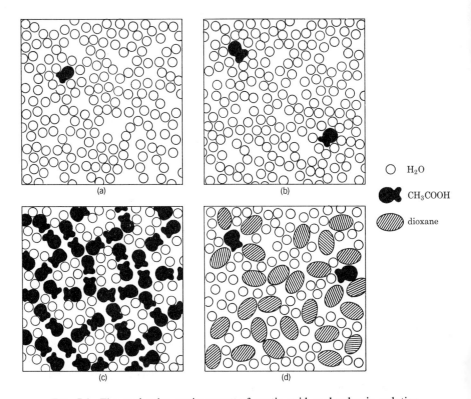

○ H_2O

🐾 CH_3COOH

▨   dioxane

FIG. 7-2. The molecular environment of acetic acid molecules in solution. Solutions (a) and (b) are dilute solutions of acetic acid in water; the concentration of acid in (b) is twice that in (a) but the concentration of water is almost unchanged. Solution (c) is a concentrated one. Solution (d) contains acetic acid in a mixture of water and dioxane. The chance of reaction between acetic acid and water is materially lower in (c) and (d) than in (a) or (b).

Many electron transfer reactions are not at all rapid. The reduction of Fe^{+++} ion by Sn^{++} ion in perchloric acid solution is very slow. This has been attributed in part to the repulsion between the two positive ions. Actually this reaction is a complex one. It is probable that the Sn^{++} ion transfers one electron at a time to an Fe^{+++} ion:

$$Sn^{++} \quad + Fe^{+++} \rightarrow Sn(III) + Fe^{++}$$
$$Sn(III) + Fe^{+++} \rightarrow Sn(IV) + Fe^{++}$$

where the symbols Sn(III) and Sn(IV) are used to represent tin in these two oxidation states, irrespective of the complex forms in which they undoubtedly occur. Electron exchange reactions such as

$$Fe^{++} + {}^*Fe^{+++} \rightarrow Fe^{+++} + {}^*Fe^{++}$$

can be followed by using radioactive iron. This one is slow in perchloric acid but more rapid in the presence of chloride. This is partly a result of the formation of complexes such as $FeCl_2{}^+$ or anion bridges such as $Fe^{++}\cdots Cl^-\cdots Fe^{+++}$ that reduce repulsion and bring the cations close enough together for electron transfer to occur.

Most reactions in solution are exceedingly complex. The over-all equation for the oxidation of iodide by ferric ion is

$$2Fe^{+++} + 2I^- \rightarrow 2Fe^{++} + I_2$$

The reaction is believed to occur in steps:

Step I	$Fe^{+++} + I^- \rightleftharpoons FeI^{++}$	(very fast)
Step II	$FeI^{++} + I^- \rightleftharpoons Fe^{++} + I_2{}^-$	(slow)
Step III	$I_2{}^- + Fe^{+++} \rightarrow Fe^{++} + I_2$	(slow)

These add to give the over-all equation. Each step is governed by a simple rate expression like Eq. 2, but the over-all rate is given by the relation

$$\text{Rate} = \frac{k[Fe^{+++}][I^-]^2}{1 + k' \dfrac{[Fe^{++}]}{[Fe^{+++}]}} \qquad\qquad 8$$

where k and k' are constants. Such expressions cannot be written down with only the over-all equation as a guide but must be derived by experimental study.

It will be observed that the reactions II and III above involve an unusual form of iodine, $I_2{}^-$. Such unstable intermediates are not uncommon, for they make possible the transfer of a single electron at a time. Other examples include oxalate complexes of Mn(III) in the oxidation of oxalate by permanganate in acid solution, chloride complexes of Sn(III) in the reduction of iron(III) ion by tin(II) chloride, and $(OH)^0$ radicals in the reactions of hydrogen peroxide.

7-5. The Effect of Temperature on Reaction Rates. An increase in temperature almost always causes a very large increase in the rate of reactions. Although the frequency of collision of the reacting particles increases with rise in temperature, this change is not large enough to account for a doubling or a tripling of the rate with a rise in temperature of ten degrees. The large change in rate is a result of an increase in the fraction of the particles which are activated, i.e., have energies as large as, or larger than, the activation energy.

It is common practice in the laboratory to accelerate slow reactions by heating the reaction mixture. The generation of sulfate ion by hydrolysis of sulfamate ion is one example:

$$NH_2SO_3^- + H_2O \rightarrow NH_4^+ + SO_4^{--}$$

The formation of sulfate can be detected by precipitation of the insoluble barium sulfate. At room temperature this precipitate forms very slowly from a sulfamic acid solution containing barium chloride. The precipitate appears quickly when the mixture is heated to boiling. Another example, the hydrolysis of thioacetamide, is discussed in Sec. 7-7.

7-6. The Effect of Catalysts on Reaction Rates.

Catalysts are substances that alter the speed of a reaction without themselves being permanently consumed. Some are solids; e.g., finely divided platinum, "platinum black," can adsorb hydrogen gas on its surface and reduce the activation energy required for its reactions. Iron(III) sulfate is not appreciably reduced by hydrogen gas until the catalyst is added. The platinum can be recovered at the end of the reaction.

Other catalysts can be solutes that participate in a reaction but are regenerated before its completion. Nitric acid, though a potentially active oxidizing agent, does not work very rapidly, but the presence of dissolved NO_2 acts as a catalyst and greatly accelerates its action. The rapid oxidizing action of aqua regia (a mixture of concentrated nitric and hydrochloric acids) owes much to the catalytic action of NOCl. Ions are frequently important catalysts, for they can form complexes that participate more readily in reaction than the original reactant. The role of halide ions in the reduction of iron(III) ion by tin(II) chloride has already been mentioned. The course of the uncatalyzed reaction is like that of a road that runs from a valley over the top of a mountain and down to another valley. The catalyst makes possible an alternate path that runs from one valley to the other over a low mountain pass.

Hydrogen and hydroxide ions are important catalysts. For example, sulfamate ion in basic solution is stable and does not hydrolyze; the hydrolysis is catalyzed by hydrogen ion. This is supported by the observation that the rate is proportional to the concentration of the catalyst even though H^+ ions do not appear in the over-all equation for the reaction (Sec. 7-5):

$$\text{Rate} = k[H^+][NH_2SO_3^-] \qquad\qquad 9$$

The rate of hydrolysis is a million times as fast in 0.1 M HCl ($[H^+] = 10^{-1}$) as in pure water ($[H^+] = 10^{-7}$). It is possible that the hydrogen ion is taken up by the anion to give the acid form $^+HNH_2SO_3^-$ which is more readily attacked by water than is the original anion. The hydrolysis of this acid releases hydrogen ions, and so, although they participate in the reaction, they are not permanently consumed.

7-7. The Hydrolysis of Thioacetamide. This reagent can be used to generate hydrogen sulfide for the precipitation of Cation Groups 2 and 3. A discussion of its rate of hydrolysis provides an understanding of how it works and an opportunity to summarize some of the foregoing remarks on reaction rates.

Complete hydrolysis of thioacetamide would produce hydrogen sulfide and ammonium acetate. Under the conditions used in the laboratory, the reaction seldom goes this far but rather gives acetamide and hydrogen sulfide:[2]

$$\underset{\underset{\displaystyle CH_3C}{\parallel}}{S} - NH_2 + H_2O \rightarrow \underset{\underset{\displaystyle CH_3C}{\parallel}}{O} - NH_2 + H_2S$$

Thioacetic acid HC_2H_3OS has also been identified as a product of the hydrolysis. At high temperatures the rate of hydrolysis in dilute acid solutions, such as are used in the precipitation of Cation Group 2, is found experimentally to be given by the expression

$$\text{Rate} = k[H^+][CH_3CSNH_2] \qquad\qquad \textbf{10}$$

The rate constant k depends on the nature of the reactants and solvent and on the temperature. It is 0.019 at 60° and 0.21 at 90° when concentrations are expressed in moles per liter and time in minutes. Hence

$$\frac{\text{Rate at } 90°}{\text{Rate at } 60°} = \frac{0.21}{0.019} = 11 \qquad\qquad \textbf{11}$$

if the concentrations of hydrogen ion and thioacetamide are the same at the two temperatures. This means that if it takes an hour to produce a certain concentration of hydrogen sulfide at 60°, it takes only a little over five minutes to achieve the same result at 90°. Clearly, when thioacetamide is used as a source of hydrogen sulfide, it is best to bring the reaction mixture as close to the boiling point as possible.[3]

The rate expression (Eq. 10) shows that a rapid reaction is favored by a high concentration of thioacetamide. The reagent is added in the form of a concentrated solution (8 to 13%). It has been recommended that the thioacetamide be added to a small volume of solution at first in the precipitation

---

[2]It will be observed that thioacetamide differs from acetamide in having sulfur in place of oxygen; hence its name (*thio*- is derived from the Greek word for sulfur). Acetamide is

the amide of acetic acid. The hydroxide group in the acid $\underset{\underset{\displaystyle CH_3C}{\parallel}}{O} - OH$ is replaced by the amide group $-NH_2$.

[3]The advantage of fast reaction at high temperatures is to some extent counterbalanced by loss of hydrogen sulfide gas owing to its lower solubility.

of Cation Group 2. Being initially at high concentration it would hydrolyze rapidly. Then the solution would be diluted to establish the proper hydrogen ion concentration for complete precipitation of the group.

The presence of the concentration of hydrogen ion in the rate expression (Eq. 10) indicates that the reaction is catalyzed by this ion. This catalysis is readily demonstrated. When thioacetamide is added to a solution of a cadmium, lead, or zinc salt, the sulfide forms very slowly, but its precipitation is visibly accelerated by the addition of a minute amount of acid. According to the rate expression, the hydrolysis of thioacetamide should be ten times as fast in $0.1 M$ HCl as it is in $0.01 \ M$ HCl. A solution of thioacetamide in water ($[H^+] = 10^{-7}$) can be kept at room temperature for several months with only slight decomposition.

Our knowledge of the course of the hydrolysis reaction is still far from complete, but from what we know at present, it is apparent that the reaction occurs in a series of steps. At an early stage a proton joins the thioacetamide molecule to give an unstable intermediate that is more readily attacked by water than is thioacetamide itself. At a later stage the proton is split off again, so no hydrogen ions are consumed in the over-all reaction.

The hydrolysis of thioacetamide is still more rapid in basic solutions. This and other features of the reaction connected with precipitation of sulfides will be discussed in Chapter 8.

EQUILIBRIUM

7-8. Equilibrium of an Ionization Reaction. The concept of equilibrium was introduced in Sec. 2-16. A system at equilibrium shows no measurable change in properties with passage of time unless its condition is disturbed by some change imposed from outside. The equilibrium state is nevertheless not a static condition, such as that exhibited by a brick laid lengthwise on the ground, but a dynamic one, a balance between two opposing reactions; e.g.,[4]

$$HC_2H_3O_2 \rightleftharpoons H^+ + C_2H_3O_2^-$$

The properties of this system, such as its hydrogen ion concentration, its vapor pressure, its absorption spectrum, and its specific conductance, will remain the same as long as this balance is undisturbed. An increase in temperature of the solution from 25 to 35° would tip the balance in favor of more molecular acid and less ions. The addition of hydrochloric acid from outside would have a similar effect. As a result of either disturbance, a shift in the equilibrium would occur until a new balance consistent with the changed conditions is obtained.

[4]Hereafter H^+ will be used for the hydronium ion. The role of water in ionization will be understood but not represented explicitly.

The balance of opposing reactions can be formulated with the rate expressions developed in Secs. 7-2 and 7-3 and used to establish a relation between the equilibrium concentrations. Eqs. 1 and 5 express the rates of recombination and ionization:

Rate of recombination $= k[H^+][C_2H_3O_2^-] = 4.5 \times 10^{10}[H^+][C_2H_3O_2^-]$ **11**

Rate of ionization $\quad= k'[HC_2H_3O_2] = 8 \times 10^5[HC_2H_3O_2]$ **12**

At equilibrium both reactions still occur, but balance is achieved by equal rates:

$$\text{Rate of recombination} = \text{rate of ionization}$$
$$k[H^+][C_2H_3O_2^-] = k'[HC_2H_3O_2]$$ **13**

If both sides are divided by $k[HC_2H_3O_2]$, we obtain the constants on one side and the concentrations on the other:

$$\frac{[H^+][C_2H_3O_2^-]}{[HC_2H_3O_2]} = \frac{k'}{k} = \frac{8 \times 10^5}{4.5 \times 10^{10}} = 1.8 \times 10^{-5} = K_a$$ **14**

The ratio of rate constants K_a is called the *acidity constant* or *ionization constant* of acetic acid. Like the rate constants, its value is fixed with regard to changes in the concentrations but varies with temperature.

Although the ionization constant has been obtained as the ratio of two rate constants, it is not a rate constant itself but is a property of the equilibrium state. It can be found without resort to rate measurements by determining the concentrations of hydrogen and acetate ions and molecular acetic acid in an equilibrium mixture. The value so obtained agrees with that given in Eq. 14 from the rate measurements.[5] This agreement substantiates our assumption that the equilibrium is a dynamic one with two reactions going on at equal rates.

Ionization constants can be written for other weak acids; e.g.,

$$HCN \rightleftharpoons H^+ + CN^- \qquad K_a = \frac{[H^+][CN^-]}{[HCN]} = 4 \times 10^{-10}$$ **15**

$$HSO_4^- \rightleftharpoons H^+ + SO_4^{--} \qquad K_a = \frac{[H^+][SO_4^{--}]}{[HSO_4^-]} = 1 \times 10^{-2}$$ **16**

Because the rate constants depend on the nature of the ions and molecules involved (Sec. 7-2), the numerical value of the ionization constant is different for different acids. The general form of these constants is the same: the numerator contains the product of the concentrations of the hydrogen ion and

---

[5]The agreement between the constants derived from rate and equilibrium measurements is not always as close as it is for acetic acid. It is much more difficult to measure rates than to measure equilibrium concentrations, and the constants obtained from rate measurements are not as accurate as those calculated from equilibrium data. They agree within the limited accuracy of the rate measurements.

the ionized form of the acid, and the denominator contains the concentration of the un-ionized form of the acid.

Equilibrium constants can also be written for the ionization of bases, e.g.,

$$NH_3 + H_2O \rightleftharpoons NH_4^+ + OH^- \qquad K_b = \frac{[NH_4^+][OH^-]}{[NH_3]} = 1.8 \times 10^{-5} \qquad 17$$

This is called the *ionization constant* of ammonia as a base. As we saw in Sec. 7-3, the concentration of water is virtually constant; it has been included in the value of K_b.

7-9. The Ion Product of Water. The ionization of water is represented most simply by the chemical equation

$$H_2O \rightleftharpoons H^+ + OH^-$$

An ionization constant for this equilibrium can be derived from rate expressions by the same method we used for acetic acid:

$$\text{Rate of ionization} = \text{rate of recombination}$$

$$k'[H_2O] = k[H^+][OH^-]$$

whence using numerical values from rate measurements at 25°

$$K = \frac{k'}{k} = \frac{[H^+][OH^-]}{[H_2O]} = \frac{2.6 \times 10^{-5}}{1.3 \times 10^{11}} = 2.0 \times 10^{-16} \qquad 18$$

But in dilute solutions the concentration of water is constant and equal to about 55 moles per liter (Sec. 7-3). Hence, we can combine this with K to get a new constant, the *ion product of water:*

$$K_w = [H^+][OH^-] = K[H_2O] = 2.0 \times 10^{-16} \times 55 = 1.1 \times 10^{-14} \qquad 19$$

A more accurate value of the ion product from equilibrium measurements is 1.0×10^{-14} at 25°. The value varies with temperature, being 0.11×10^{-14} at 0° and 9.6×10^{-14} at 60°. At a given temperature its value is fixed, regardless of variations in the concentrations of the ions. This constancy of the product means that the ion concentrations cannot vary independently; if one is increased, the other must decrease if the product is to remain fixed. The following diagrams use symbols of different size to represent this graphically:

Neutral solution: $[H^+] = [OH^-]$ $K_w = [H^+][OH^-]$

Acid solution: $[H^+] > [OH^-]$ $K_w = [H^+][OH^-]$

Basic solution: $[H^+] < [OH^-]$ $K_w = [H^+][OH^-]$

The constant K_w is the same in all three solutions.

7-10. The Law of Chemical Equilibrium. The treatment of ionization reactions can be generalized. There is for any homogeneous equilibrium a ratio of concentrations that has a fixed value at a given temperature. This ratio is by custom written as the product of the concentrations of the substances on the right-hand side of the chemical equation divided by the product for those on the left-hand side. The numerical value of this constant will depend on the temperature and the particular substances involved but will be at least approximately[6] independent of the concentrations.

The equilibrium constants for many reactions will have a more complex form than those considered so far. In the equilibrium $2A \rightleftharpoons B + C$ the rate of formation of B and C from A will depend on the frequency of collision of two particles of A or on $[A][A] = [A]^2$. The equilibrium constant will have the form

$$K = \frac{[B][C]}{[A]^2} \qquad \qquad 20$$

In general, if the chemical equation shows x moles of substance X, the equilibrium constant will contain the factor $[X]^x$. For the equilibrium

$$3HNO_2 \rightleftharpoons H^+ + NO_3^- + 2NO + H_2O \qquad \qquad A$$

the equilibrium constant has the form

$$K = \frac{[H^+][NO_3^-][NO]^2}{[HNO_2]^3} \qquad \qquad 21$$

The law of chemical equilibrium was derived in Sec. 7-8 for a system of two simple opposing reactions. We found in Sec. 7-4 that most reactions go in a series of steps that cannot be predicted from the chemical equation for the over-all reaction. Each step follows a simple rate law (Eq. 2) but the over-all rate expression is not determinable from the equation alone and may be very complex (Eq. 8 for example). The expression for the equilibrium constant, on the other hand, can always be written down if the over-all equation is known just as Eq. 21 was written to correspond to A. The same result is obtained by combination of the experimentally determined rate expressions:

$$\text{Net forward rate} = k_1 \frac{[HNO_2]^4}{[NO]^2} \qquad \qquad 22$$

$$\text{Net reverse rate} = k_2[HNO_2][H^+][NO_3^-] \qquad \qquad 23$$

When these rates are set equal we obtain

$$\frac{k_1}{k_2} = \frac{[H^+][NO_3^-][NO]^2}{[HNO_2]^3}$$

which is identical with Eq. 21. Few reactions have been worked out in such detail; for many the exact sequence of steps required to convert the reactants

---

[6]This reservation is entered here because, as we shall see in Sec. 7-16, the value of K is influenced by interionic forces. These vary with the concentration of the ions, and hence K is indirectly altered by changes in concentration.

into the products is still unknown. Yet we can always write out the expression for the equilibrium constant if we know the over-all equation. The equilibrium constant is a property of the equilibrium state as expressed by this equation and does not depend on the path, however devious, that was taken to reach equilibrium.

The value of the equilibrium constant for a given reaction depends on how the over-all equation is written. The equilibrium in an acetic acid solution could be represented by any one of these chemical equations and equilibrium constants:

$$HC_2H_3O_2 \rightleftharpoons H^+ + C_2H_3O_2^- \qquad K_a = \frac{[H^+][C_2H_3O_2^-]}{[HC_2H_3O_2]}$$

$$2HC_2H_3O_2 \rightleftharpoons 2H^+ + 2C_2H_3O_2^- \qquad K' = \frac{[H^+]^2[C_2H_3O_2^-]^2}{[HC_2H_3O_2]^2} = K_a^2$$

$$H^+ + C_2H_3O_2^- \rightleftharpoons HC_2H_3O_2 \qquad K'' = \frac{[HC_2H_3O_2]}{[H^+][C_2H_3O_2^-]} = \frac{1}{K_a}$$

Custom has favored the first of these, the un-ionized form being on the left-hand side of the chemical equation and in the denominator of the equilibrium constant; for this reaction and most other common ones there is no question about what is meant by the "equilibrium constant." For less typical reactions such as the decomposition of nitrous acid A either the chemical equation or the expression for K must be written out explicitly.

7-11. The Relation Between Ionization Constant and Extent of Ionization. The next seven sections deal with properties and uses of equilibrium constants. Ionization constants are given particular attention because of the importance of ionization equilibria in qualitative analysis and the study of electrolytes. The behavior of weak electrolytes has until now been described by their extents of ionization (Secs. 2-16, 4-11). Let us see how this is related to their acidity constants.

The extent of ionization is the fraction of the weak electrolyte that ionizes (Sec. 4-11). Let it be represented by the Greek letter alpha α. Then

$$\alpha = \frac{\text{concentration of ionized electrolyte}}{\text{total concentration of electrolyte}} \qquad\qquad 24$$

Consider for the purposes of illustration a weak acid like HCN. Its ionization equilibrium is represented by

$$HCN \rightleftharpoons H^+ + CN^- \qquad K_a = \frac{[H^+][CN^-]}{[HCN]} \qquad\qquad 25$$

In a C molar solution of this acid

$$\alpha = \frac{[CN^-]}{C} = \frac{[H^+]}{C} \qquad\qquad 26$$

where we have assumed on the basis of the chemical equation that equal numbers of hydrogen and cyanide ions are present.[7] Then

$$\alpha C = [CN^-] = [H^+]$$ 27

and

$$C - \alpha C = C(1 - \alpha) = [HCN]$$ 28

When these are substituted for the concentrations in the acidity constant (Eq. 25) we obtain

$$K_a = \frac{\alpha C \cdot \alpha C}{C(1 - \alpha)} = \frac{C\alpha^2}{(1 - \alpha)}$$ 29

A useful approximate version of this relation is obtained when α is less than 0.1, or K_a/C is less than 0.01. Then

$$\alpha^2 C \simeq K_a \qquad \text{or} \qquad \alpha \simeq \sqrt{\frac{K_a}{C}}$$ 30

If two acids are compared at the same concentration C, the one with the smaller acidity constant will be more weakly ionized. The extent of ionization varies also with the concentration as Eq. 30 shows; when a solution of the acid is diluted, C decreases and α increases. The extent of ionization can always be calculated when the acidity constant and concentration are known. The ionization constant of acetic acid is the same in all the following solutions: 0.00001 M $HC_2H_3O_2$, 0.01 M $HC_2H_3O_2$, 0.05 M $HC_2H_3O_2$, a mixture that contains 0.01 mole of $HC_2H_3O_2$ and 0.01 mole of $NaC_2H_3O_2$ per liter, and a mixture that contains 0.1 mole of HCl and 0.01 mole of $HC_2H_3O_2$ per liter; the percentage of ionization varies from almost zero to almost 100. It is more practicable to tabulate a small number of ionization constants from which extents of ionization can always be derived than it is to construct a mammoth table of extents of ionization to cover all conceivable situations. A table of ionization constants contains far more information than the small number of entries would indicate.

Before leaving this section we must return to Eq. 30 and sound a warning. This formula and many that we encounter later on are valid only within certain limits. We have noted that K_a/C must be less than 0.01. We note further that Eq. 27, on which this relation is based, requires that no common ions be present. If we apply Eq. 30 automatically to any solution, we court disaster. Consider, for example, 0.01 M sulfamic acid for which K_a/C is 10; from Eq. 30 we would predict an extent of ionization of 3.2 or 320%. Or consider 0.00001 M acetic acid for which K_a/C is 1.8; from Eq. 30 we would predict the acid to be 130% ionized. In both examples $1 - \alpha$ is not virtually one, and Eq. 29 should be used. For a buffer that contains 0.1 mole each of acetic acid and sodium acetate per liter, the extent of ionization is not 1.3%, as predicted by Eq. 30, but 0.018%, because the excess of acetate represses

[7]The validity of this assumption is examined in Chapter 11.

the ionization of the acid. Eq. 30 is a useful guide but its limitations must be remembered.

7-12. Ionization Constants and the Structure of Acids. The foregoing discussion has shown that the ionization constant is a property of the weak electrolyte in a given solvent. There is as yet no comprehensive theory that connects the structure of acids and their ionization constants. The ionization process is complicated by the effects of temperature and hydration of the molecules and ions of the acid. Our understanding is also limited by the dearth of accurate data.

The ionization constants of organic acids are, in some respects, easiest to interpret. Many of these acids have the same ionizing group and differ only in the rest of the molecule. Acetic acid, monochloroacetic acid, and the glycinium ion, whose ionizations are represented by

$$CH_3COOH \rightleftharpoons CH_3COO^- + H^+ \qquad K_a = 1.8 \times 10^{-5}$$

$$ClCH_2COOH \rightleftharpoons ClCH_2COO^- + H^+ \qquad K_a = 1.4 \times 10^{-3}$$

$$H_3\overset{+}{N}CH_2COOH \rightleftharpoons H_3\overset{+}{N}CH_2COO^- + H^+ \qquad K_a = 4.5 \times 10^{-3}$$

all contain the acidic carboxyl group —COOH. The glycinium ion is the strongest acid of the three because it contains a positively charged group that repels the proton. A similar, but weaker, repulsion occurs between the polar C—Cl bond and the proton in monochloroacetic acid; hence this acid is stronger than acetic acid. In a more detailed treatment, which we shall not attempt, the hydration of the ions and increase in restraints on water that results therefrom must be considered.

Inorganic acids include hydroacids, such as H_2S and HCl, and oxyacids, such as H_3PO_4 or HNO_3. The hydroacids of the nonmetals in a family increase in strength as the size of the nonmetal atom increases. Hydrofluoric acid is weak ($K_a = 6.7 \times 10^{-4}$) while hydrochloric acid is strong ($K_a > 10$); water is more weakly ionized ($K_a = 2 \times 10^{-16}$) than hydrogen sulfide ($K_a = 1 \times 10^{-7}$). The hydroacids in a period increase in strength as the atomic number of the nonmetal increases; e.g., K_a of NH_3 is about 10^{-23}, K_a of water is 2×10^{-16}, and K_a of HF is 6.7×10^{-4}.

A basis for understanding these generalizations is laid if we imagine the ionization of an acid HX to be the sum of the following steps:

1. HX in solution $\rightarrow HX$ in gaseous form
2. HX gas $\rightarrow$ separate gaseous H and X atoms
3. $H \rightarrow H^+ + e^-$ in the gas
4. $e^- + X \rightarrow X^-$ in the gas
5. $H^+(gas) + X^-(gas) \rightarrow$ hydrated H^+ and X^- ions

---

Total: HX in solution $\rightarrow H^+ + X^-$ in solution

Hydrogen fluoride is a weaker acid than hydrogen chloride largely because more (free) energy is required to bring about steps 1 and 2 for HF. Hydrogen fluoride molecules are stabilized, in other words, by being strongly hydrogen bonded to water and having a F—H bond that is hard to dissociate. Less energy is required in steps 1 and 2 for hydrogen chloride and more is released in step 4. The balance of these effects makes hydrogen chloride a strong acid. It is more difficult to interpret the change in acidity of the hydroacids in a period, for the energy data for use with steps 1 to 5 are not always known. It is probable that water is a weaker acid than hydrogen fluoride because less energy is released in steps 4 and 5.

The behavior of many oxyacids can be correlated with some simple rules. In these acids the acidic hydrogen is always attached to oxygen, as shown by the structural formulas for the halogen acids:

$$\text{H:}\overset{..}{\underset{..}{\text{O}}}\text{:}\overset{..}{\underset{..}{\text{Cl}}}\text{:} \qquad \text{H:}\overset{..}{\underset{..}{\text{O}}}\text{:}\overset{}{\underset{\overset{..}{\underset{..}{\text{O}}}\text{:}}{\text{Cl}}}\text{:} \qquad \text{H:}\overset{..}{\underset{..}{\text{O}}}\text{:}\overset{\overset{..}{\underset{..}{\text{O}}}\text{:}}{\underset{\overset{..}{\underset{..}{\text{O}}}\text{:}}{\text{Cl}}}\text{:} \qquad \text{H:}\overset{..}{\underset{..}{\text{O}}}\text{:}\overset{\overset{..}{\underset{..}{\text{O}}}\text{:}}{\underset{\overset{..}{\underset{..}{\text{O}}}\text{:}}{\text{Cl}}}\text{:}\overset{..}{\underset{..}{\text{O}}}\text{:}$$

In passing from left to right in this series, the oxidation number of chlorine increases from $+1$ to $+7$, and the size of the chlorine atom decreases. The actual positive charge on the chlorine atom is less than the oxidation number but should follow the same trend. This being so, the small, highly charged chlorine atom in $HClO_4$ attracts the oxygen atoms strongly and repels the hydrogen, so H^+ is readily lost. This acid is very strong; the others to the left are progressively weaker.

If oxyacids are represented by the type formula $XO_m(OH)_n$, a simple rule, proposed by Pauling and by Ricci, relates acid strength to m, the number of oxygen atoms in the molecule that are not in hydroxide groups. If m is 2 or 3, the acid is strong with K_a greater than 10; if m is 1, the acid is moderately strong with K_a about 10^{-2}; and if m is zero, the acid is very weak with K_a about 10^{-8}. The effect can be understood if it is supposed that the negative charge of the anion of the acid is spread over these nonhydroxide oxygen atoms. The more such atoms there are, the more diffuse the charge on the anion and the lower its affinity for protons.

According to this rule acids such as ClOH, BrOH, and $As(OH)_3$ should all have an ionization constant of 10^{-8}; the observed values are, respectively, 6.3×10^{-8}, 2.5×10^{-9}, and 6.3×10^{-10}. Arsenic acid, H_3AsO_4 or $AsO(OH)_3$, should have an ionization constant of 10^{-2}; it is 6.3×10^{-3}. Sulfuric acid, $SO_2(OH)_2$, should be, and is, a strong acid with respect to the loss of the first proton ($K_a > 10$). The predictions will usually agree with the observed values to about a power of ten.

If an acid has more than one ionizable proton, the second is always lost with greater difficulty than the first. The second ionization constant of an oxyacid is roughly 10^{-5} as large as the first. For arsenic acid K_1 is $10^{-2.2}$ and K_2 is $10^{-7.0}$; for H_3PO_3 K_1 is $10^{-1.8}$ and K_2 is $10^{-6.2}$. This decrease in strength is not surprising since the second proton has to be pulled away from a larger negative charge than that acting on the first proton.

7-13. Equilibrium Constants and the Direction of Chemical Reactions.

Equilibrium constants are often useful guides when the direction of a chemical reaction must be predicted. Consider, for example, the neutralization of acetic acid (Sec. 3-7, Example 4):

$$HC_2H_3O_2 + OH^- \rightleftharpoons H_2O + C_2H_3O_2^-$$
$$K_a = 1.8 \times 10^{-5} \qquad K_w = 10^{-14}$$

Water is more weakly ionized than acetic acid, as the constants show; so hydrogen ions are removed when the reaction goes from left to right. By contrast, the reaction

$$HCN + C_2H_3O_2^- \rightleftharpoons HC_2H_3O_2 + CN^-$$
$$K_a = 4 \times 10^{-10} \qquad K_a = 1.8 \times 10^{-5}$$

would actually go from right to left because acetic acid has a larger constant than hydrocyanic acid and its tendency to ionize is greater. If the two constants are close together, as for the reaction

$$HCN + CO_3^{--} \rightleftharpoons HCO_3^- + CN^-$$
$$K_a = 4 \times 10^{-10} \qquad K_a = 4.7 \times 10^{-11}$$

it is often possible by changing the concentrations to send the reaction in either direction. A high concentration of carbonate ion would push the reaction to the right; a high concentration of cyanide ion would make it go to the left. A more detailed discussion is given in Chapter 9.

7-14. The Use of Equilibrium Constants to Establish Formulas.

Because equilibrium constants have fixed values regardless of changes in concentrations, it is possible to use them to establish formulas. Let us take as an example the determination of the formula of the mercury(I) ion. The two possibilities are Hg^+ and Hg_2^{++}. Several solutions of mercury(II) nitrate containing a little nitric acid to suppress hydrolysis were shaken with metallic mercury until the solution was saturated with the metal. The concentration of dissolved metal is very low but can be determined by using radioactive mercury. The concentrations of mercury(I) and mercury(II) ions in the solutions were determined by analysis. The equilibrium can be expressed either by

$$Hg^{++} + Hg^0 \rightleftharpoons 2Hg^+ \qquad K = \frac{[Hg^+]^2}{[Hg^{++}][Hg^0]}$$

or by

$$Hg^{++} + Hg^0 \rightleftharpoons Hg_2^{++} \qquad K' = \frac{[Hg_2^{++}]}{[Hg^{++}][Hg^0]}$$

In the first equilibrium constant expression the concentration of mercury(I) is squared, but in the second it is not. The data of Table 7-1 show that the ratio K' remains fixed even when the concentrations of the ions are more than doubled, whereas K increases by more than 100%. The formula Hg_2^{++} is thus substantiated.

TABLE 7-1.

The Formula of the Mercury(I) Ion

Solution	$[Hg^{++}]$	$[Hg^0]$	$[Hg(I)]$ as Hg^+	$[Hg(I)]$ as Hg_2^{++}	K	K'
A	0.00216	0.00000030	0.0516	0.0258	4.1×10^7	4.0×10^8
B	.00419	.00000030	.1004	.0502	8.0×10^7	4.0×10^8
C	.00461	.00000030	.1106	.0553	8.8×10^7	4.0×10^8

Equilibrium measurements alone are often not sufficiently reliable to establish a formula with certainty. The experimental accuracy may be low or the measurements may be made in concentrated solutions in which the law of chemical equilibrium as we have used it is not strictly valid (Sec. 7-16). The formula Hg_2^{++} is backed up by other evidence besides the equilibrium measurements. Many formulas of complex ions have been reported only on the basis of apparent constancy of equilibrium constants; they must be accepted with reservation until they are supported by other evidence.

7-15. The Effects of Catalysts, Solvents, and Temperature on the Equilibrium Constant. We have been concerned up to this point with equilibria that are rapidly established in aqueous solution at room temperature, and they will continue to be our principal concern hereafter. Brief consideration is given here to deviations from these conditions.

A fundamental assumption is implicit in all of our discussion, namely, that equilibrium has been established. This may not be true if the reactions are very slow ones. The rate of approach to equilibrium can be accelerated by catalysts (Sec. 7-6). It is important to note that they have no effect on the final equilibrium: catalysts accelerate both reactions to an equal extent and do not alter the final balance between them.

The equilibrium *is* altered by changes in the solvent. If dioxane is added to water, the dielectric constant of the solvent is decreased. This causes a decrease in extent of ionization of weak electrolytes in solution because the attraction between the ions is stronger (Sec. 1-3). The ionization constant of acetic acid in a mixture that is 82% dioxane-18% water (dielectric constant 9.5) is 7.24×10^{-11} as compared with 1.75×10^{-5} in pure water. Solvation of the ions is also altered by changing the solvent, and this will have an effect on the constant.

All ionization constants are also altered by a change in temperature, but it is difficult to lay down a general rule. With many acids the ionization reaction is endothermic at low temperatures. By van't Hoff's rule the extent of ionization and the ionization constant then increase with a rise in temperature. Generally a maximum value is reached, and thereafter the constant begins to decrease again. Thus above the temperature of the maximum, the ionization reaction becomes exothermic. For many organic acids the maximum is reached at room temperature or below, e.g., at 22° for acetic acid. Remarkably few data are available for the inorganic acids. The first ionization constant of phosphoric acid attains its maximum value below 0°, and the maximum for boric acid is reached at about 90°. The ion product of water increases very rapidly with rising temperature. Its maximum value is reached at about 275°, a temperature that can be attained only by keeping the water under high pressure.

It is worth noting that changes in solvent and temperature will not only alter the absolute values of the ionization constants, but will often change the ratio of constants of two acids. In other words, the relative strength of two acids is not fixed but depends upon the solvent and the temperature.

7-16. The Effect of Interionic Forces on Equilibrium Constants. We have assumed that equilibrium constants are unaffected by changes in concentration. This is not strictly correct. Table 7-2 shows the variation in the ionization

TABLE 7-2.

The Ionization Constant of Acetic Acid

C in moles/l	$K_a = \dfrac{[H^+][C_2H_3O_2^-]}{[HC_2H_3O_2]}$
0.00002801	1.756×10^{-5}
.00011135	1.779×10^{-5}
.0002184	1.782×10^{-5}
.0010283	1.797×10^{-5}
.002414	1.810×10^{-5}
.009912	1.823×10^{-5}

constant of acetic acid as the concentration of the acid is varied. The change in K is not large, being only 4% over the entire range of concentration. All the values of K in the table would be rounded off to 1.8×10^{-5}. The trend to higher values of K at higher concentrations is nevertheless unmistakable.

Considerably larger variations in the ionization constants are obtained by addition of other electrolytes to the solution of the weak electrolyte. The effects of sodium chloride, potassium chloride, lithium chloride, and barium chloride on the ionization constant of acetic acid are shown in Fig. 7-3. These are "neutral" salts: they do not hydrolyze and affect the hydrogen ion concentration. Yet the ionization constant of acetic acid can be doubled by the addition of a suitable amount of one of these salts. At low concentrations the three alkali metal halides have the same effect but that of barium chloride is larger. This is what we would expect if the change in the constant is caused by interionic forces, for the alkali metal halides all contain ions of the same charge, while barium chloride gives doubly charged cations and more anions mole for mole.

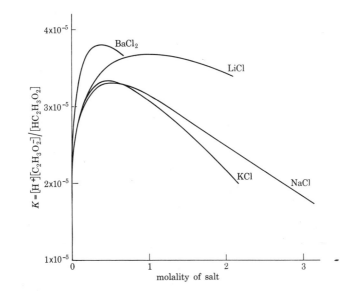

FIG. 7-3. The effect of neutral salts on the ionization constant of acetic acid at 25°.

The effect of interionic forces is to cause a decrease in the rate of recombination of ions (Eq. 11). Ions are pictured as being surrounded by atmospheres of opposite charge (Sec. 5-14). The ionic atmospheres about hydrogen and acetate ions act as screens and prevent the two ions from exerting their full attraction for each other. When sodium chloride, for example, is added to an acetic acid solution, the density of the atmospheres and their screening effects increase. The rate of recombination of the hydrogen and acetate ions slows down, and, when a new equilibrium is established, more of the acid is in the ionic form.

Because equilibrium constants are often strongly affected by interionic forces, we shall usually use them only as a rough guide. It is possible to make corrections for interionic forces if the solutions are dilute, and we shall discuss these in Chapters 10 and 11.

DISTRIBUTION EQUILIBRIA

7-17. Distribution of a Solute Between Immiscible Liquids. Carbon disulfide and water do not dissolve in each other to an appreciable extent; they are immiscible. Iodine is more soluble in carbon disulfide than in water. When some water containing dissolved iodine is shaken with carbon disulfide, the iodine distributes itself between the two liquids. At first some iodine molecules escape across the interface into the carbon disulfide layer. The rate of escape is proportional to the concentration of iodine in the water layer and the area A of the interface; i.e.,

$$\text{Rate from } H_2O \text{ layer} = k[I_2]_{H_2O}A \qquad 31$$

As iodine accumulates in the carbon disulfide layer, some of the molecules in their wanderings will return to the interface and go back into the water layer. The frequency of collision with the interface and the rate of return will depend on the concentration of iodine in the carbon disulfide layer and the area of the interface; i.e.,

$$\text{Rate of return to } H_2O \text{ layer} = k'[I_2]_{CS_2}A \qquad 32$$

At equilibrium the rates expressed by Eqs. 31 and 32 will be equal:

$$k[I_2]_{H_2O}A = k'[I_2]_{CS_2}A$$

and from this we obtain the distribution ratio

$$K_D = \frac{[I_2]_{CS_2}}{[I_2]_{H_2O}} \qquad 33$$

The area of the interface cancels in taking this ratio and K_D depends only on the nature of the two liquids and iodine and on the temperature. At 25° K_D is 600, so most of the iodine goes into the carbon disulfide layer. Although the individual concentrations may be varied, their ratio must maintain this fixed value. If we add a small amount of solid iodine to the system, a little of it will go into the water layer and the rest into the carbon disulfide layer. If sodium thiosulfate is added to the water layer, iodine is reduced and $[I_2]_{H_2O}$ decreases. Iodine will pass from the carbon disulfide layer into the water layer to restore equilibrium and maintain a constant ratio.

Distribution between immiscible solvents is used in two ways in qualitative analysis. Identification reactions can be based on the extraction of a colored form of a substance from a water solution into another solvent. The violet color of iodine, the orange color of bromine in carbon disulfide or carbon tetrachloride, and the blue color of the $Co(SCN)_4^{--}$ complex ion in amyl alcohol-ether mixtures are examples. Extraction can also be used to remove large quantities of a troublesome ion. Iron in a ferrous alloy is present in such overwhelming quantity that it makes tests for other metals difficult. If the iron is converted to ferric chloride, it can be extracted by ether, leaving the other metals behind in the water layer.

7-18. Some Numerical Problems with Distribution Ratios. Typical problems are illustrated by the following examples.

EXAMPLE 1. Suppose 2 ml of water containing 4 mg of bromine is shaken with 1 ml of carbon tetrachloride. How much bromine is extracted? The distribution ratio is

$$K_D = \frac{[Br_2]_{CCl_4}}{[Br_2]_{H_2O}} = 22.7 \text{ at } 25°$$

Step 1. Let $x =$ mg of bromine extracted and $y =$ mg of bromine left in the water layer. Material balance or the law of conservation of mass (Sec. 4-13) requires that $4 = x + y$, or $y = 4 - x$.

Step 2. These values are converted to concentrations by dividing by the volumes. Then

$$\frac{x \text{ mg}/1 \text{ ml}}{(4 - x) \text{ mg}/2 \text{ ml}} = 22.7 = \frac{2x}{4 - x}$$

and after multiplication by $(4 - x)$

$$90.8 - 22.7x = 2x$$

$$x = \frac{90.8}{24.7} = \boxed{3.7 \text{ mg extracted}}$$

$$y = 4 - x = 0.3 \text{ mg left in the water layer}$$

Although the distribution ratio was expressed as the ratio of molar concentrations we have used the ratio of concentrations in mg/ml. The conversion from mg/ml to molarity is the same in numerator and denominator and cancels.

EXAMPLE 2. What volume of carbon disulfide is required to extract all but 1×10^{-5} mmoles of iodine from 10 ml of a 0.0005 M solution of iodine in water? The distribution ratio is 600 at 25° (Eq. 33).

Step 1. We start with 0.0005 $M \times$ 10 ml $= 0.005$ mmoles of iodine. Material balance requires

$$0.005 \text{ mmoles put in} = 1 \times 10^{-5} \text{ mmoles in water layer}$$
$$+ x \text{ mmoles in the carbon disulfide layer}$$

or $x = 0.005 - 0.00001 = 0.00499 = 4.99 \times 10^{-3}$.

Step 2. Put $V =$ ml of carbon disulfide required. Then

$$\frac{(4.99 \times 10^{-3})/V}{(1 \times 10^{-5})/10} = 600$$

whence

$$V = \frac{4.99 \times 10^{-3}}{6 \times 10^{-4}} = \boxed{8.3 \text{ ml}} \text{ of } CS_2$$

7-19. Equilibria Between Gases and Their Aqueous Solutions. When a solution is saturated with a gas an equilibrium exists between the rate of entry of gas into solution and the rate of escape from solution. The distribution of hydrogen sulfide, for example, between the gaseous phase and a water solution can be expressed by

$$K = \frac{[H_2S]_{H_2O}}{P_{H_2S}} \qquad 34$$

The pressure of the gas has been used as a measure of its concentration; the two quantities are related by the ideal gas law: $P_{H_2S} = RT[H_2S]_g$, where RT is the molar volume, e.g., 22.4 liter at $0°$ and 1 atm. Eq. 34 can be rearranged to read

$$[H_2S]_{H_2O} = KP_{H_2S} \qquad 35$$

or, in words, the solubility of a gas at constant temperature is proportional to its pressure above the solution. This is often called *Henry's law*. The constant K can be interpreted as the solubility when the pressure of the gas is 1 atm. For hydrogen sulfide it is 0.175 M at $5°$, 0.102 M at $25°$, and 0.054 M at $60°$.

All distribution expressions will hold only if the same form of the substance is used in both numerator and denominator. In water hydrogen sulfide ionizes to a slight extent, but only the molecular form goes into the gaseous phase. We must then use the concentration of molecular hydrogen sulfide in the numerator of Eq. 34. In referring to this as the solubility of hydrogen sulfide we have neglected the amount that ionizes. This is possible because hydrogen sulfide is a very weak acid. In hydrochloric acid solutions the ionization of hydrogen sulfide is repressed by the strong acid, and the solubility of hydrogen sulfide is virtually the same as $[H_2S]_{H_2O}$. The assumption that $[H_2S]_{H_2O}$ can be equated with its solubility in pure water is substantiated by the fact that the solubility changes from 0.1023 M in water to 0.1015 M in 0.3 M HCl, a negligibly small change.

Under the conditions used for the precipitation of Cation Group 2, the solution is saturated with hydrogen sulfide and the concentration of molecular hydrogen sulfide in solution is fixed. We can use this fact to derive an important relation. The ionization equilibria in such solutions and their constants are

$$H_2S \rightleftharpoons H^+ + HS^- \qquad K_{H_2S} = \frac{[H^+][HS^-]}{[H_2S]} \qquad 36$$

$$HS^- \rightleftharpoons H^+ + S^{--} \qquad K_{HS^-} = \frac{[H^+][S^{--}]}{[HS^-]} \qquad 37$$

In these expressions the concentration of hydrogen ion is the same, and the concentration of hydrogen sulfide ion is the same, since Eqs. 36 and 37 apply to one and the same solution. There is no distinction between hydrogen sulfide ions that take part in the first equilibrium and those that take part in the second. Consequently, when we take the product of the two constants, the concentration of hydrogen sulfide ion will cancel

$$K_{H_2S}K_{HS^-} = \frac{[H^+]^2[S^{--}]}{[H_2S]} \qquad 38$$

If the solution is saturated with hydrogen sulfide, the denominator of this expression is fixed by Eq. 35 when the pressure of gaseous hydrogen sulfide is constant. We can therefore combine it with the product of the ionization constants to obtain a new constant, the *ion product of hydrogen sulfide*:

$$[H_2S]K_{H_2S}K_{HS^-} = [H^+]^2[S^{--}] = K_{ip}(H_2S) \qquad 39$$

This expression shows that the sulfide ion concentration in an aqueous solution which is saturated with hydrogen sulfide varies inversely as the square of the hydrogen ion concentration. The separation of Cation Group 2 depends on the regulation of the sulfide ion concentration at a low level, and this can be done by adjusting the hydrogen ion concentration to between 0.1 and 0.3 M. The precipitation of Cation Group 3 requires a much higher sulfide ion concentration, and this is obtained by making the solution alkaline with ammonia. In a basic solution the hydrogen ion concentration is low (Sec. 7-9), and the sulfide ion concentration must be high to satisfy Eq. 39.

The numerical value of the ion product of hydrogen sulfide can be estimated from the solubility and the known values of the ionization constants. At 25° and 1 atm pressure these are

$$[H_2S]_{H_2O} = 0.10 \ M \qquad K_{H_2S} = 1 \times 10^{-7} \qquad K_{HS^-} = 1.3 \times 10^{-13}$$

whence

$$K_{ip}(H_2S) = 0.10 \times 1 \times 10^{-7} \times 1.3 \times 10^{-13} = 1.3 \times 10^{-21} \qquad 40$$

The solubility and the ionization constants are affected by interionic forces, so we cannot expect this value to hold in all solutions. It will nevertheless be useful for approximate calculations.

Ion products can be derived for other gases provided their solubilities and extents of ionization are low. This will be true, for example, for carbon dioxide but not for hydrogen chloride.

7-20. Equilibrium Between a Solid Weak Electrolyte and its Aqueous Solution. The solubility of a solid nonelectrolyte or of the molecular part of a weak electrolyte can also be expressed by a distribution law. Benzoic acid ($HC_7H_5O_2$) is a slightly soluble acid that is weakly ionized in aqueous solutions. The distribution law takes the form for $HC_7H_5O_2$ (solid) $\rightleftharpoons HC_7H_5O_2$ (in solution) of

$$K = [HC_7H_5O_2]_{ss} \qquad 41$$

or, in words, the concentration of molecular benzoic acid in a saturated solution (*ss*) is fixed at a given temperature. The concentration of solid benzoic acid does not appear as a denominator in this expression because it is not materially altered by ordinary changes in pressure. The rate of escape of benzoic acid molecules from the solid into solution depends only on the surface area exposed to the solution, on the forces holding the molecules in the crystal lattice, and on the attraction between water and benzoic acid molecules. The packing of the molecules in the crystal and the forces between them are changed only by large changes in pressure or by changes in temperature. At a given temperature the escaping tendency of benzoic acid from the solid phase is fixed.

The ionization equilibrium of benzoic acid is expressed by

$$HC_7H_5O_2 \rightleftharpoons H^+ + C_7H_5O_2^- \qquad K_a = \frac{[H^+][C_7H_5O_2^-]}{[HC_7H_5O_2]} \qquad \qquad 42$$

If the solution is saturated with benzoic acid, we can replace the denominator of the ionization constant by K from Eq. 41 and write an ion product for benzoic acid

$$K_{sp} = KK_a = [H^+]_{ss}[C_7H_5O_2^-]_{ss} \qquad \qquad 43$$

This is generally called the *solubility product* of benzoic acid. Unlike Eq. 42, which holds in any solution of the acid, this is valid only for a saturated solution, and the subscripts *ss* have been used to emphasize this. The addition of salts can cause changes in all these expressions including the concentration of the molecular acid, and they are therefore to be used only as rough guides.

7-21. The Omission of Certain Concentrations from Equilibrium Constant Expressions. We have considered several equilibrium constants in this chapter in which the concentration of one substance in the equilibrium did not appear. Sometimes a substance is present at such high concentration that its concentration does not vary appreciably. This was true of water in dilute solutions. The ion product of water K_w (Eq. 19) and equilibrium constants for other reactions in which water is involved do not contain the factor $[H_2O]$; it is included in the value of the constant.

The concentration of molecular hydrogen sulfide does not appear explicitly in the ion product (Eq. 40) but is combined with the other constants. This will be valid only if the solution is saturated with the gas at a fixed pressure. In general, the concentrations or pressures of gases will be factors in the equilibrium constant expression.

The concentration of solid benzoic acid does not appear explicitly in its solubility product (Eq. 43) nor does the concentration of the molecular acid in solution appear here. The latter is fixed by the presence of the solid phase (Eq. 41) and the former is altered only by large changes in pressure if the temperature is fixed.

In Sec. 7-14 we considered the equilibrium between mercury metal and its ions. The data of Table 7-1 show that the concentration of metallic mercury in solution is fixed when an excess of liquid mercury is present. Instead of writing

$$K' = \frac{[\text{Hg}_2{}^{++}]}{[\text{Hg}^0][\text{Hg}^{++}]}$$

for the equilibrium constant we might perfectly well write

$$K = K'[\text{Hg}^0] \rightleftharpoons \frac{[\text{Hg}_2{}^{++}]}{[\text{Hg}^{++}]} \qquad \textbf{44}$$

as long as the solution is saturated with metallic mercury. To generalize, if the equilibrium involves a pure solid or pure liquid, its concentration is not shown explicitly in the equilibrium expression.

A last example will serve to illustrate some of these points. When metallic mercury is shaken with silver nitrate solution, the following equilibrium is set up:

$$2\text{Ag}^+ + 2\text{Hg}^0 \rightleftharpoons \text{Hg}_2{}^{++} + 2\text{Ag}^0$$

The silver metal dissolves in the mercury to give an amalgam, a solution of silver in mercury. The concentration of silver in the amalgam is always low, so the concentration of mercury is virtually constant. The equilibrium constant has the form

$$K = \frac{[\text{Hg}_2{}^{++}][\text{Ag}^0]^2}{[\text{Ag}^+]^2} \qquad \textbf{45}$$

If the concentration of silver nitrate is sufficiently high, the amount of silver produced is enough to saturate the amalgam. At a fixed temperature the factor $[\text{Ag}^0]$ is constant for a saturated solution and the equilibrium constant then becomes

$$K' = \frac{[\text{Hg}_2{}^{++}]}{[\text{Ag}^+]^2} \qquad \textbf{46}$$

Neither this expression or Eq. 45 contains $[\text{Hg}^0]$ for the same reason that equilibrium constants for equilibria in dilute aqueous solutions do not contain explicitly the factor $[\text{H}_2\text{O}]$.

SUPPLEMENTARY READING

M. SIENKO and R. PLANE, *Chemistry*, McGraw-Hill, New York, 1957, Chapter 12 (chemical kinetics), Chapter 13 (chemical equilibrium), pp. 330–35 (ionization constants), and pp. 338–39 (K_w).

T. R. HOGNESS and W. C. JOHNSON, *Qualitative Analysis and Chemical Equilibrium*, 4th ed., Holt, New York, 1954, Chapters 6 and 7.

T. MOELLER, *Qualitative Analysis*, McGraw-Hill, New York, 1958, Chapter 4 (reaction rates and chemical equilibria), and pp. 76–82 (ionization equilibria).

J. E. RICCI, "The Aqueous Ionization Constants of Inorganic Oxygen Acids," *J. Am. Chem. Soc.*, **70**, 109 (1948).

R. P. BELL, *Acids and Bases*, Wiley, New York, 1952, Chapter 5 (acid-base strength and molecular structure).

E. H. SWIFT and E. A. BUTLER, "Precipitation of Sulfides from Homogeneous Solutions by Thioacetamide," *Anal. Chem.*, **28**, 146 (1956).

D. F. EVANS, "Blue Perchromic Acid," *J. Chem. Soc.* (London), **1957**, 4013. The formula of the compound is established by equilibrium measurements.

EXERCISES

7-1. Write expressions for the rates of the following reactions in dilute aqueous solution. Assume that the number of particles participating in the collisions is correctly indicated by the equations.

(a) $H_2S + H_2O \rightleftharpoons H_3O^+ + HS^-$

(b) $CO_2 + OH^- \rightarrow HCO_3^-$

(c) $CH_3CO_2CH_3 + OH^- \rightarrow C_2H_3O_2^- + CH_3OH$

7-2. Show that for n particles of substance A the number of possible bimolecular collisions is $n(n-1)/2$ if no collision is counted twice. How can Eq. 3 hold if this is true? (See second reference, pp. 112–3).

7-3. What features of the ionization of acetic acid influence the value of k' in Eq. 5? Why is this rate constant much smaller than k in Eq. 1?

7-4. Account for the observation that the rate of the reaction $CH_3CO_2CH_3 + H_2O \rightarrow CH_3CO_2H + CH_3OH$ in dilute solutions is given by $k[CH_3CO_2CH_3]$ even though water is a reactant. When would you expect this simple rate expression to fail?

7-5. Explain how the exchange of electrons between manganate ions MnO_4^{--} and permanganate ions MnO_4^- might be studied using radioactive manganese-54. [J. Sheppard and A. Wahl, *J. Am. Chem. Soc.*, **79**, 1020 (1957).]

7-6. A rise in temperature of ten degrees increases the number of collisions between iodine and hydrogen molecules in the gaseous state by only about 2%, yet the rate of their reaction to give hydrogen iodide more than doubles. Explain.

7-7. The rate constant for the hydrolysis of sulfamic acid (Eq. 9) is 1.3 at 80.35°, 4.2 at 90°, and 10.5 at 98°.

(a) What would be the approximate relative rate of hydrolysis of equimolar solutions of sulfamic acid at 80.35° and 98°?

(b) Which would hydrolyze faster: a mixture at 90° that is 0.1 M in hydrogen and sulfamate ions or a mixture at 98° that is 0.05 M in each ion?

7-8. What are some ways of speeding up a slow reaction? Give some examples.

7-9. In which of the following solutions, all at the same temperature, would the hydrolysis of thioacetamide be most rapid? (a) 1 M thioacetamide in pure water, (b) 0.3 M thioacetamide which is also 0.5 M in acetic acid, (c) 0.2 M thioacetamide which is also 0.5 M in hydrochloric acid, (d) 0.5 M thioacetamide which is also 0.1 M in hydrochloric acid.

7-10. How much faster will hydrogen sulfide form in a 0.5 M thioacetamide solution that is 0.2 M in hydrochloric acid than it does in a 0.1 M thioacetamide solution that is 0.1 M in the acid if (a) both solutions are at 90°, (b) the first is at 60° and the second is at 90°?

7-11. Explain why the rate expression for the hydrolysis of thioacetamide (Eq. 10) contains the factor $[H^+]$ but not $[H_2O]$.

7-12. The rate constant for the ionization of ammonia in dilute solutions is 5×10^5 at 20° and the rate constant for the recombination of ammonium and hydroxide ions is 3×10^{10} at the same temperature. Write out expressions for the two rates and derive the equilibrium constant.

7-13. The rate constant for the ionization of HSO_4^- ions in dilute aqueous solution is about 10^9 and that for the recombination of the hydrogen and sulfate ions is about 10^{11}. Write out expressions for the two rates and derive the equilibrium constant.

7-14. If the effects of interionic forces (Sec. 7-16) are neglected, which of the following operations would cause a significant change in the value of the ionization constant of acetic acid? (a) addition of more water to the solution of acetic acid, (b) addition of sodium hydroxide, (c) addition of alcohol, (d) addition of sodium acetate, (e) increase in temperature from 25 to 35°.

7-15. What effect would the operations in Ex. 7-14 have on the extent of ionization of acetic acid?

7-16. In which of the following solutions will the expression $[H^+][OH^-] = 10^{-14}$ be valid if the effect of interionic forces (Sec. 7-16) is ignored? (a) 0.01 M HCl in water at 25°, (b) 0.01 M HCl in a dioxane-water mixture containing 70% dioxane at 25°, (c) 0.01 M acetic acid in water at 25°, (d) 0.01 M KOH in water at 25°, (e) 0.01 M NH_3 in water at 25°.

7-17. Prove that for an X molar solution of ammonia the extent of ionization of the base is given by $(K_b/X)^{1/2}$.

7-18. For which of the following solutions is the extent of ionization given by Eq. 30? (a) 0.1 M nitric acid, (b) 0.1 M $HC_3H_3O_2$, (c) 0.0001 M $HC_2H_3O_2$, (d) 0.1 M HCN, (e) 0.0001 M HCN.

7-19. The first ionization constant of H_2S is 10^{-7} and that of H_2Se is 10^{-4}. Account for the difference.

7-20. The ionization constant of HSe^- ion is about 10^{-15}. Why is this smaller than the value for H_2Se given in Ex. 7-19?

7-21. The first ionization constant of germanic acid is $10^{-8.5}$. Using Ricci's rule estimate what the constant would be if the formula were H_2GeO_3 and what it would be if it were H_4GeO_4 or $Ge(OH)_4$. Which formula is apparently correct?

7-22. The first ionization constant of telluric acid is $10^{-7.5}$. Using Ricci's rule show that the correct formula of the acid is H_6TeO_6 and not H_2TeO_4. The first ionization constant of selenic acid is $10^{-2.6}$. What is its correct formula?

7-23. The first ionization constants of H_3PO_4, H_3PO_3, and H_3PO_2 are all about 10^{-2}. The usual relation between oxidation number and acid strength would lead us to expect H_3PO_4 to be the strongest of the three. Show that Ricci's rule correctly predicts the same ionization constant for all three if their structures are $PO(OH)_3$, $HPO(OH)_2$, and $H_2PO(OH)$ in which there are always four atoms attached to the phosphorus.

7-24. Potassium hydrogen sulfate is added to an ammonium acetate solution. Will any reaction occur? (A table of ionization constants is given in the Appendix.)

7-25. When metallic copper is shaken with copper(II) sulfate solution, the equilibrium mixture is found to contain some Cu(I) ions. The concentration of

Cu(I) can be found by titration with a standard solution of an oxidizing agent such as cerium(IV) sulfate. The equilibrium can be formulated either as $Cu^{++} + Cu \rightleftharpoons 2Cu^{+}$ or as $Cu^{++} + Cu \rightleftharpoons Cu_2^{++}$. Calculate the equilibrium constants for these two formulations from the following data at 60°. [E. Heinerth, *Z. Elektrochem.*, **37**, 61 (1931)] and decide which formula of the Cu(I) ion is correct. Assume that [Cu°] is constant. Why?

$$[Cu^{++}]: 1.037 \quad ; \quad 0.7530 \quad ; \quad 0.5052 \quad ; \quad 0.2526 \quad ; \quad 0.1010$$
$$[Cu(I)] \text{ as } Cu^{+}: 0.00492; \quad 0.00416; \quad 0.00358; \quad 0.00246; \quad 0.00155$$
$$[Cu(I)] \text{ as } Cu_2^{++}: \text{half the above values.}$$

7-26. When metallic mercury is shaken with silver nitrate solution the following equilibrium is set up (Sec. 7-21):

$$2Ag^{+} + 2Hg^{0} \rightleftharpoons Hg_2^{++} + 2Ag^{0}$$

or

$$Ag^{+} + Hg^{0} \rightleftharpoons Hg^{+} + Ag^{0}$$

depending on the formula of the mercury(I) ion. Show that the following data support the first formulation by calculating the two equilibrium constants [A. Ogg, *Z. physik. Chem.*, **27**, 285 (1898)].

$$[Ag^{+}] \text{ in moles/l: } 0.00391; 0.00315; 0.00191; 0.00155$$
$$[Hg^{+}] \text{ in moles/l: } .1969 \; ; \; .0995 \; ; \; .0504 \; ; \; .0261$$
$$[Hg_2^{++}] \text{ in moles/l: } .0984 \; ; \; .0498 \; ; \; .0252 \; ; \; .01305$$
$$[Ag^{0}] \text{ in g/cc of Hg: } .0062 \; ; \; .0062 \; ; \; .0067 \; ; \; .0063$$

7-27. Account for the fact that the ionization constant of a molecular weak electrolyte is increased by addition of a neutral salt.

7-28. Which of the following operations on a mixture of carbon disulfide, water, and iodine would cause a significant change in the distribution ratio? (a) Setting the mixture in a refrigerator, (b) transferring it from a 3 ml test tube to a 250 ml beaker, (c) adding potassium sulfite, a reducing agent, to it, (d) adding more iodine to it, (e) adding ethyl alcohol to it.

7-29. A solution of iodine containing 0.335 g of iodine in 25 ml of CCl_4 is shaken with 250 ml of water. The aqueous layer is found to contain 0.035 g of iodine. Calculate $K_D = [I_2]_{CCl_4}/[I_2]_{H_2O}$.

7-30. The distribution ratio $[Br_2]_{CCl_4}/[Br_2]_{H_2O}$ is 28 if the water layer is acidified to suppress hydrolysis of the bromine.

(a) If 5 ml of water containing 2 mg of bromine is shaken with 2 ml of CCl_4, how much bromine is extracted?

(b) How much would be removed if a similar 5-ml portion of this aqueous solution was extracted with two successive 1-ml portions of CCl_4? What conclusion can be drawn regarding the efficiency of a single extraction as against multiple extraction with the same total volume of liquid?

7-31. The distribution ratio of bromine between water and bromoform $(CHBr_3)$, $[Br_2]_{CHBr_3}/[Br_2]_{H_2O}$ is 69.

(a) What volume of bromoform would be required to extract 99% of the bromine from 5 ml of a certain aqueous solution in a single extraction?

(b) What volume would be required in all to extract 99% if two equal portions are to be used successively?

7-32. It is proposed to separate Fe^{+++} ion from a solution that also contains Mn^{++}, Ni^{++}, and Mg^{++} ions by making the solution 7 *M* in HCl and extracting it with isopropyl ether. Iron(III) chloride distributes between the two layers in the ratio

$$[\text{Iron(III) chloride}]_{\text{ether}}/[\text{iron(III) chloride}]_{\text{water}} = 246$$

Suppose the concentration of iron(III) chloride is 0.05 M in the aqueous layer to begin with, and the volume of this layer is 2 ml. What volume of ether must be used if no more than 0.06 mg of Fe^{+++} ion is to be left per milliliter of the water layer?

7-33. Suppose a solution is saturated with carbon dioxide at a fixed, low pressure of the gas. Show that the expression $[H^+]^2[CO_3^{--}] = K_{ip}$ holds for this system.

7-34. What is the value of the ion product of hydrogen sulfide at 25° if the partial pressure of the gas above the solution is 0.2 atm?

7-35. The solubility of hydrogen sulfide in water is 0.1 mole per liter at 25° when the pressure of hydrogen sulfide is 1 atm.

(a) What is the solubility when the gas is compressed until its pressure is 3 atm, the temperature being held constant?

(b) What is the solubility of the gas if the barometric pressure is 740 mm and the vapor pressure of water is 23 mm?

7-36. To which of the following solutions is Eq. 40 applicable? (a) 0.01 M H_2S in water at 25°, (b) 0.05 M HCl saturated with H_2S at 1 atm pressure and 25°, (c) water at 100° saturated with H_2S at 1 atm pressure, (d) 0.1 M $NaHCO_3$ in water containing 0.1 mole of H_2S per liter.

7-37. When do the following expressions hold?

(a) $K = [H^+]^2[S^{--}]$ (b) $K = [H^+][HS^-]/[H_2S]$
(c) $K = [H_2S]$ (d) $a = (K_{H_2S}/C)^{\frac{1}{2}}$

7-38. Explain why each of the following expressions has no denominator: K_w, $K_{ip}(H_2S)$, K_{sp}(benzoic acid).

CHAPTER EIGHT

Precipitates and Colloidal Suspensions

8-1. Introduction. Precipitates occupy a pre-eminent position in qualitative analysis. The identification of most ions must be preceded by their separation from interfering ions, and precipitation is the method of separation most commonly used. The systematic division of cations into analytical groups is based on four successive precipitation reactions. In addition, many ions are identified by precipitation in some compound that is colored or has some other easily recognized characteristic. Separations can be made by dissolving selectively some of the precipitates in a mixture; e.g., the sulfides of the arsenic section of Cation Group 2 are dissolved by potassium hydroxide and separated from the sulfides of the copper section.

To gain an understanding of precipitates and their behavior, we start by considering the equilibrium between precipitates and their saturated solutions. With the solubility product principle as a guide, we can predict in a general way the conditions used in forming and dissolving precipitates. But equilibrium principles alone do not enable us to solve all analytical problems. This is not surprising, for systems containing more than one phase are usually slow in coming to equilibrium. It takes time to transfer material across a phase boundary, and equilibrium between a precipitate and solution is often not established for hours or even days. Yet in qualitative analysis we can seldom allow more than five or ten minutes for a reaction, so true equilibrium may not be established. The behavior of precipitates is also complex because of their tendency to adsorb ions from the solution. By this and other means precipitates may be contaminated with foreign material. Since analytical chemistry is concerned to a large extent with the preparation of pure compounds, it is necessary to establish conditions of precipitation that keep contamination to a minimum, and equilibrium principles are of little help in doing this. The adsorption of ions on the surface of finely dispersed solids also leads to the formation of colloidal suspensions which resist centrifugation. We shall consider conditions under which they form and methods of coagulating them. This chapter is thus concerned with the behavior of precipitates caused by (1) their equilibrium with the solution,

(2) their slow rate of formation and dissolution, and (3) the adsorptive properties of their surfaces.

8-2. The Solubility Product Principle.   We found in Sec. 7-20 that, for a saturated solution of a slightly soluble weak electrolyte such as benzoic acid, the product of the ion concentrations was fixed at a given temperature. The solubility product (Eq. 43, Chapter 7) was a combination of the ionization constant of the weak electrolyte with the constant concentration of molecular form.

For slightly soluble strong electrolytes such as silver chloride, there is no molecular form in the saturated solution. We have seen that both solid silver chloride (Sec. 2-6) and the salt in solution (Sec. 2-20) are completely ionized.[1] Nevertheless, the product of the ion concentrations in the saturated solution has a fixed value at a given temperature:

$$Ag^+Cl^- \downarrow \; \rightleftharpoons Ag^+ + Cl^- \qquad K_{sp} = [Ag^+]_{ss}[Cl^-]_{ss} \qquad\qquad 1$$

The subscripts *ss* call attention to the fact that these are the concentrations in the saturated solution. The constancy of this product is supported by the data in Table 8-1.[2]

TABLE 8-1.

The Solubility Product of Silver Chloride at 25°

$[Ag^+]_{ss}$	$[Cl^-]_{ss}$	$K_{sp} = [Ag^+]_{ss}[Cl^-]_{ss}$
1.353×10^{-5}	1.323×10^{-5}	1.790×10^{-10}
1.332×10^{-5}	1.349×10^{-5}	1.797×10^{-10}
1.326×10^{-5}	1.336×10^{-5}	1.775×10^{-10}
1.969×10^{-5}	0.905×10^{-5}	1.781×10^{-10}
2.868×10^{-5}	0.620×10^{-5}	1.778×10^{-10}
		Average
		1.784×10^{-10}

[1]Certain strong electrolytes such as $BaSO_4$ can form ion-pairs in solution.

[2]These data were obtained by mixing very dilute solutions of silver nitrate and potassium chloride. The formation of the precipitate removes ions (Sec. 3-2):

$$Ag^+ + NO_3^- + K^+ + Cl^- \rightarrow Ag^+Cl^- \downarrow + K^+ + NO_3^-$$

The reaction can be followed by observing the decrease in conductance. It is interesting to note that the results as first reported were too high [C. W. Davies and A. L. Jones, *Discussions Faraday Soc.*, **5**, 105 (1949)]. Despite the fact that the reactions were followed for between 5 and 18 hours, as much as 7% of the silver chloride had not yet precipitated at the conclusion of the experiment [*Trans. Faraday Soc.*, **51**, 812 (1955)]. The data in Table 8-1 have been corrected for this. These investigators also obtained virtually the same value of the solubility product as that in the table from measurements on the saturated solution prepared by shaking an excess of silver chloride with water. The equilibrium expressed in Eq. 1 has thus been approached from both directions with the same results.

The opposing reactions in the equilibrium between silver chloride and its saturated solution are the direct escape of ions from the surface of the crystal into solution and the deposition of the ions on the crystal surfaces. These are very complex processes, so any kinetic derivation of Eq. 1 that could be given here would be highly oversimplified. Let us regard the solubility product principle as one that is established by experiments such as those recorded in Table 8-1. Later, at a more sophisticated level, these and other equilibrium constants will be shown by the methods of thermodynamics to be properties of the equilibrium state alone. Their validity does not rest on kinetic arguments, which are often based on a crude picture of the reactions.

Like several equilibrium constants discussed in Chapter 7, the solubility product has no denominator. The surface concentration of silver and chloride ions in crystals of silver chloride is constant and included in the solubility product. This surface concentration, which determines the rate of escape of the ions into solution, is determined by the spacing of the ions in the crystal, and this can be altered only slightly even by large changes in pressure or temperature. It can, however, be varied readily in one way: when silver chloride is precipitated in the presence of bromide ions, some of the latter are found distributed at random throughout the crystal. This is said to be a *solid solution* of silver bromide in silver chloride. The rate of escape of chloride ions from the surface of the crystal is now dependent on the fraction of the surface that is occupied by silver chloride. For this special situation we must write

$$K = \frac{[\text{Ag}^+]_{ss}[\text{Cl}^-]_{ss}}{[\text{Ag}^+\text{Cl}^-]_{\text{solid soln}}} \qquad \text{1a}$$

Otherwise, the concentration of the solid phase is not shown explicitly in the solubility product.

Solubility products can be written for other slightly soluble strong electrolytes:

$$\text{Ba}^{++}\text{SO}_4^{--}\downarrow \; \rightleftharpoons \; \text{Ba}^{++} + \text{SO}_4^{--} \qquad K_{sp} = [\text{Ba}^{++}]_{ss}[\text{SO}_4^{--}]_{ss} \qquad 2$$

$$(\text{Ag}^+)_2\text{CrO}_4^{--}\downarrow \; \rightleftharpoons \; 2\text{Ag}^+ + \text{CrO}_4^{--} \qquad K_{sp} = [\text{Ag}^+]^2{}_{ss}[\text{CrO}_4^{--}]_{ss} \qquad 3$$

$$(\text{Hg}_2^{++})(\text{Cl}^-)_2\downarrow \; \rightleftharpoons \; \text{Hg}_2^{++} + 2\text{Cl}^- \qquad K_{sp} = [\text{Hg}_2^{++}]_{ss}[\text{Cl}^-]^2{}_{ss} \qquad 4$$

$$\tfrac{1}{2}(\text{Ag}^+)_2\text{O}^{--}\downarrow \; + \tfrac{1}{2}\text{H}_2\text{O} \rightleftharpoons \text{Ag}^+ + \text{OH}^- \qquad K_{sp} = [\text{Ag}^+]_{ss}[\text{OH}^-]_{ss} \qquad 5$$

$$\text{Mg}^{++}\text{NH}_4^+\text{PO}_4^{---}\downarrow \; \rightleftharpoons \; \text{Mg}^{++} + \text{NH}_4^+ + \text{PO}_4^{---}$$
$$K_{sp} = [\text{Mg}^{++}]_{ss}[\text{NH}_4^+]_{ss}[\text{PO}_4^{---}]_{ss} \qquad 6$$

To emphasize that we are dealing with ionic crystals the charges have been shown in the formulas, and to emphasize that the concentrations are those in the saturated solution the subscripts *ss* have been used. Hereafter these will usually be omitted for convenience. It will be noted that the concentrations are raised to powers determined by the coefficients of the symbols in the chemical equation (Sec. 7-10).

8-3. The Relation Between Solubility in Water and Solubility Product. Solubility and solubility product are not to be confused, but there is frequently a simple relation between them. Let us consider a slightly soluble salt that is dissolved in pure water. Suppose that the ions of the salt undergo no reaction with the water. Let S be the number of moles of salt that dissolve per liter of solution.[3] Then if a kome of the salt contains equal numbers of positive and negative ions, $[Me^+] = [X^-] = S$ and

$$K_{sp} = S^2$$
$$S = \sqrt{K_{sp}} \qquad \qquad 7$$

This will hold for a salt such as AgCl or $BaSO_4$ in pure water. For solutions of a unibivalent salt such as Ag_2CrO_4 or $Ca(IO_3)_2$, the concentration of bivalent ion is S, but that of the univalent ion is $2S$, because each kome contains two of these ions. Hence

$$K_{sp} = S(2S)^2 = 4S^3$$
$$S = \sqrt[3]{K_{sp}/4} \qquad \qquad 8$$

That S must be doubled to get the concentration of silver or iodate ions is a result of having to find the molarity of the ion from that of the salt. That $2S$ must then be squared is a requirement of the solubility product expression. This will perhaps be clearer if we derive K_{sp} for Ag_2CrO_4 in another way. If we put $Y = [Ag^+]$, then $[CrO_4^{--}] = \frac{1}{2}Y$ and $K_{sp} = Y^2(\frac{1}{2}Y) = \frac{1}{2}Y^3$ (see Example 2, Sec. 4-10). Here Y is *not* doubled before it is squared, for Y was defined as the molarity of the Ag^+ ion, and the solubility product requires only that it be squared.

These expressions show that for electrolytes of the same valence type we can judge relative solubilities in water by comparing solubility products. The solubility product of silver chloride, for example, is 1.77×10^{-10} and that of silver bromide is 5.08×10^{-13}. These values immediately indicate that silver bromide is less soluble than silver chloride in water. More quantitatively, the relative *molar* solubility is given by

$$\frac{S_{AgCl}}{S_{AgBr}} = \sqrt{\frac{K_{sp}(AgCl)}{K_{sp}(AgBr)}} = \sqrt{\frac{1.77 \times 10^{-10}}{5.08 \times 10^{-13}}} = 19$$

We cannot, however, compare directly the solubility products of electrolytes of different valence types. The solubility product of silver chromate, for example, is less than that of silver chloride, but the latter is less soluble in water. By Eqs. 7 and 8 we see that the solubility S of silver chloride varies

[3] If solubility is expressed in other units, e.g., g/100 ml, it can be readily converted to moles/l. See Sec. 4-10.

with the square root of the solubility product and that of silver chromate with the cube root of it:

$$\frac{S_{AgCl}}{S_{Ag_2CrO_4}} = \frac{\sqrt{K_{sp}(AgCl)}}{\sqrt[3]{K_{sp}(Ag_2CrO_4)/4}} = \frac{(1.77 \times 10^{-10})^{1/2}}{(2.44 \times 10^{-12}/4)^{1/2}} = 0.16$$

Once again a note of warning must be sounded against the indiscriminate use of formulas such as Eqs. 7 and 8. These relations are not valid if a common ion is present, for this depresses the solubility. In pure water the solubility of silver chloride is $1.3 \times 10^{-5}\ M$ (Eq. 7), but in 0.01 M silver nitrate solution it is only 4.9×10^{-7}. These relations also do not apply if one or both ions of the salt are involved in ion-pair formation or hydrolysis. The solubility of sulfides, in particular, is far larger than that predicted by the equations because of the reaction

$$S^{--} + H_2O \rightleftharpoons HS^- + OH^-$$

which removes sulfide from the field of action to a large extent.

8-4. Determination of Solubility and Solubility Product.   There are a host of methods for determining solubility. Usually an excess of the solid is shaken with solvent for a protracted period. A sample of the saturated solution is withdrawn and analyzed. The sampling is repeated after further shaking; and if equilibrium has been established, the two results will agree. The solution can be analyzed by titration, by colorimetry, and by many other methods. A particularly convenient method for relatively insoluble compounds is based on conductance measurements.

Let us use silver chloride as an example, for this is a well-behaved electrolyte that does not hydrolyze appreciably. In a typical experiment the specific conductance L_{ss} of the saturated solution and the specific conductance L_w of water used to make the solution were measured. The net specific conductance of the silver and chloride ions in the solution is the difference between these:[4]

$$\begin{aligned} L_{AgCl} &= L_{ss} - L_w \\ &= 1.926 \times 10^{-6} - 0.086 \times 10^{-6} \\ &= 1.840 \times 10^{-6} \end{aligned} \qquad 9$$

By Eq. 6 of Chapter 5, the specific conductance is related to the normality C of silver chloride and the equivalent conductance Λ:

$$C = L_{AgCl}\frac{1000}{\Lambda} \qquad 10$$

The equivalent conductance of the saturated solution is not known, but it can be estimated. The saturated solution is very dilute because of the low solubility

[4]Data from J. Gledhill and G. Malan, *Trans. Faraday Soc.*, **48**, 258 (1952).

of silver chloride. The ions will be far apart and move almost independently, so we may expect the equivalent conductance to be not far from the limiting value

$$\Lambda \simeq \Lambda_0 = \lambda_{0\,Ag^+} + \lambda_{0\,Cl^-} \qquad\qquad 11$$

The limiting ionic conductances are usually available in tables, and from one such we obtain 61.92 and 76.34 for the silver and chloride ions. Combining these data with Eqs. 9-11, we find

$$C = 1.840 \times 10^{-6} \frac{1000}{138.26} = 1.331 \times 10^{-5}$$

For silver chloride this normality is numerically equal to the molarity. The solubility product[5] is the square of this value, or 1.772×10^{-10}.

There are several indirect methods of obtaining a solubility product which often give more accurate values than methods based on Eqs. 7 and 8. Some of these will be considered in the next chapter.

8-5. The Common Ion Effect on Solubility.   The data in Table 8-1 show that as the concentration of silver ion is increased that of chloride ion decreases. This is necessary if the solubility product is to remain constant, for by Eq. 1, the chloride ion concentration is inversely proportional to that of the silver ion:

$$[Cl^-] = \frac{K_{sp}}{[Ag^+]} \qquad\qquad 12$$

The amount of silver chloride that dissolves per liter of a silver nitrate solution is measured by the chloride ion concentration. Eq. 12 thus shows that the solubility of silver chloride in the silver nitrate solution varies inversely with the total concentration of the common ion. The same effect is observed with other salts. With silver chromate, for example, the solubility in silver nitrate solution is equal to the concentration of chromate ion, and this varies inversely as the square of the silver ion concentration:

$$[CrO_4^{--}] = \frac{K_{sp}}{[Ag^+]^2} \qquad\qquad 13$$

In forming a precipitate it is important to decrease its solubility so as to leave as little as possible in solution. This is commonly done by adding a slight excess of the precipitating agent, e.g., hydrochloric acid in the precipitation of Cation Group 1. The reduction in concentration of silver ion left in solution can be pictured as

$$K_{sp} = [Ag^+][Cl^-]$$

The popular theory that, if one drop in excess is desirable, a liter will be still more so is a dangerous one. A large excess of precipitating agent may form

---

[5]A minor correction for the effect of interionic forces must be applied in more accurate work.

a complex with the ion to be removed and keep it in solution. This is true of hydrochloric acid in the precipitation of silver chloride, as Fig. 8-1 shows. If too much chloride is added in the precipitation of Cation Group 1, complexes such as $AgCl_2^-$ and $PbCl_4^{--}$ may form.

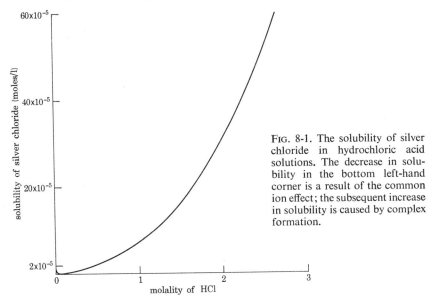

FIG. 8-1. The solubility of silver chloride in hydrochloric acid solutions. The decrease in solubility in the bottom left-hand corner is a result of the common ion effect; the subsequent increase in solubility is caused by complex formation.

8-6. Conditions That Affect Both Solubility and Solubility Product. Though it is roughly independent of changes in concentration that affect the solubility, the solubility product can be made to vary in several ways. A rise in temperature causes an increase in the solubility and solubility product of most substances, for they dissolve with absorption of heat to break down the crystal lattice. Soluble and moderately insoluble substances such as lead chloride or silver sulfate are readily brought into solution in this way. A few substances such as calcium sulfate dissolve with evolution of heat and their solubility products decrease with increase in temperature.

The addition of an organic solvent to an aqueous solution usually lowers the solubility of the solutes, for the dielectric constant of the medium is decreased and this strengthens the forces between the ions. The addition of alcohol or other organic solvent is sometimes used in analysis to make the separation of a moderately insoluble substance, e.g., potassium perchlorate, strontium chromate, or calcium sulfate, more nearly quantitative.

With very small crystals, the solubility and solubility product increase with decreasing particle size. Kolthoff has calculated that barium sulfate crystals with a diameter of 4×10^{-6} cm are almost 1000 times as soluble as the usual coarsely crystalline material. As a precipitate containing a mixture of small and large particles stands in contact with solution, the small, more soluble crystals gradually dissolve, and the large crystals grow still larger. This process is called *digestion* and is used to make precipitates easier to separate by filtration or centrifugation.

8-7. The Effect of Interionic Forces on Solubility and Solubility Product. Slightly soluble electrolytes are somewhat more soluble in solutions of foreign salts than in pure water. This is analogous with the increase in extent of ionization and acidity constant of weak acids caused by the addition of moderate amounts of neutral salts (Sec. 7-16). The ionic atmospheres about the ions lower their energies and screen them from interacting with each other or with the surface of the precipitate. At the same molarity foreign salts of high valence type have a larger effect than those of low. This is what we would expect if interionic forces are responsible for the increase in solubility. The effect of various salts on the solubility of thallium(I) iodate is shown in Fig. 8-2.

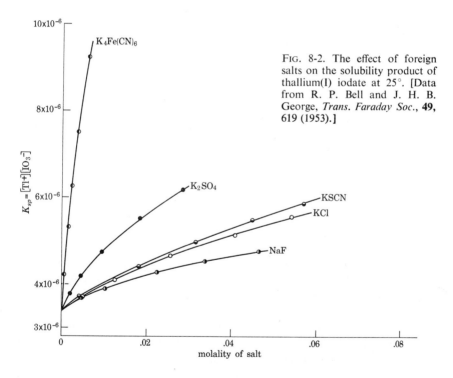

FIG. 8-2. The effect of foreign salts on the solubility product of thallium(I) iodate at 25°. [Data from R. P. Bell and J. H. B. George, *Trans. Faraday Soc.*, **49,** 619 (1953).]

The combined effect of valence and concentration of the ions is expressed by the *ionic strength*. To find the ionic strength we multiply the concentration of each kind of ion by the square of its valence, add all these products, and divide the sum by two. We shall usually use the symbol I for ionic strength and express it in molarity units.[6] The calculation of ionic strength is illustrated by the following examples (we assume that all the salts are completely ionized and neglect the contribution of hydrogen and hydroxide ions from water):

EXAMPLE 1. Find the ionic strength of 0.03 M potassium nitrate.

$$I = \tfrac{1}{2} ([K^+] \times 1^2 + [Cl^-] \times 1^2) = \tfrac{1}{2} (0.03 + 0.03) = \boxed{0.03}$$

EXAMPLE 2. Find the ionic strength of 0.01 M barium chloride.

$$I = \tfrac{1}{2} ([Ba^{++}] \times 2^2 + [Cl^-] \times 1^2) = \tfrac{1}{2} (0.04 + 0.02) = \boxed{0.03}$$

EXAMPLE 3. Find the ionic strength of a mixture that contains 0.01 mole of sodium nitrate and 0.0067 mole of calcium nitrate per liter.

$$I = \tfrac{1}{2} ([Na^+] \times 1^2 + [NO_3^-] \times 1^2 + [Ca^{++}] \times 2^2)$$
$$= \tfrac{1}{2} (0.01 \times 1 + 0.0234 \times 1 + 0.0067 \times 4) = \boxed{0.03}$$

According to the *principle of ionic strength* the equilibrium constant of any slightly soluble or weakly ionized electrolyte will be the same in all *dilute* solutions of the same ionic strength. If each of the solutions of Examples 1-3 were saturated with silver chloride, the solubility product of the precipitate would be the same in all three. Or if each solution were made 0.001 M in acetic acid, the ionization constant of the acid would be the same in all three.

The principle of ionic strength simplifies the discussion of the salt effect, because it rationalizes the behavior of salts of different valence types. This is illustrated in Figs. 8-3 and 8-4. Potassium sulfate has a larger effect than potassium chloride on the solubility product of thallium(I) iodate when equimolar solutions are compared (Fig. 8-2), but an equal effect when the comparison is made at the same ionic strength (Fig. 8-3). Barium chloride has a larger effect on the ionization constant of acetic acid than equimolal solutions of the alkali halides (Fig. 7-3), but an equal effect when the comparison is made at the same *low* ionic strength (Fig. 8-4). It is apparent from Fig. 8-4 that the principle of ionic strength fails at high concentrations. This is to be expected, for we have seen (Sec. 5-13) that in concentrated solutions the interactions between ions no longer depend only on their charge and concentration but now depend on specific details of their structure. The differing interactions of ions with water molecules are also important in concentrated solutions.

Although their values are sensitive to the presence of foreign salts, solubility products and ionization constants are still useful as rough guides to the equilibrium behavior of precipitates and weak electrolytes. The solutions used in qualitative analysis are not very dilute, but they are also seldom

[6]As originally introduced by Lewis and Randall in 1921, the ionic strength was expressed in molality units, for which we shall use the symbol μ (Greek mu). The use of molarities corresponds to the usage of qualitative analysis and is supported by the Debye-Hückel theory of interionic attraction. It will be noted that the concept of ionic strength was introduced two years before publication of the theory which justified it.

very concentrated. This intermediate range of concentrations corresponds roughly to the region in Fig. 8-4 in which the curves go through a maximum. It is in just this region that a change in ionic strength causes the smallest change in equilibrium constant; in very dilute solutions where the curves rise steeply, a small change in ionic strength causes a large change in the constant.

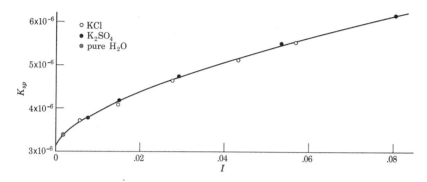

FIG. 8-3. The solubility product of thallium(I) iodate and the principle of ionic strength. Small corrections for ion-pair formation have been made.

FIG. 8-4. The ionization constant of acetic acid and the principle of ionic strength. The data are for acetic acid at exceedingly low concentration in the salt solutions at 25°. The ionic strength is in molality units. [Data from H. S. Harned and F. C. Hickey, *J. Am. Chem. Soc.*, **59**, 1284, 2303 (1937).]

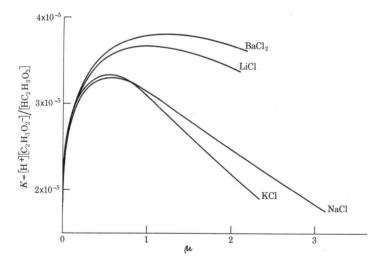

This is our justification for assuming in qualitative analysis that the equilibrium constants we use have fixed values roughly independent of concentration changes. We shall learn in a later chapter how to make numerical corrections for the salt effect in dilute solutions.

FORMATION OF PRECIPITATES

8-8. Supersaturation and Precipitation. In order that a precipitate can form, a solution must be supersaturated, i.e., contain a higher concentration of solute than can remain at equilibrium with the precipitate. This is expressed by the inequality

$$Q = \left[\; + \;\right]_{sss} \left[\; - \;\right]_{sss} > K_{sp} = [\; + \;]_{ss} [\; - \;]_{ss} \qquad 14$$

where the subscript *sss* stands for a supersaturated solution. It is found in practice that the product of the concentrations Q must exceed the solubility product by a considerable extent before a visible precipitate forms. For silver chloride Q must be at least twice K_{sp}, and for barium sulfate it must be at least 160 times K_{sp}. The large difference in the critical value of Q for these two precipitates shows that precipitation is a highly specific process. Silver chloride and barium sulfate are the principal examples in the following discussion, because they have been extensively investigated. They do not behave alike and, although in some respects they represent opposite extremes, their modes of precipitation are not necessarily representative of those of other substances.

The precipitation of barium sulfate occurs by formation of ion clusters, then nuclei, and finally macroscopic crystals. First ions come together to give clusters of gradually increasing size:

$$Ba^{++} + SO_4^{--} \rightleftharpoons Ba^{++}SO_4^{--}$$
$$2Ba^{++}SO_4^{--} \rightleftharpoons (Ba^{++}SO_4^{--})_2$$
$$(Ba^{++}SO_4^{--})_2 + Ba^{++}SO_4^{--} \rightleftharpoons (Ba^{++}SO_4^{--})_3$$
$$\vdots$$

In the vapor state such clusters are more stable than the separate ions (Sec. 5-2). This is not true in solution, for the ions are stabilized by hydration and by their ionic atmospheres. Clusters are therefore more prone to break apart than they are to stay together. Only a few survive long enough to combine into a crystal nucleus. Nuclei are larger than clusters and may contain hundreds or thousands of ions. Though still too small to see and comparatively unstable, they have a good chance of growing into macroscopic crystals if the solution is highly supersaturated. The rate of formation of nuclei increases with the supersaturation because of the greater chance of picking up more ions. Nucleation in supersaturated solutions of silver chloride is rapid. With barium sulfate a considerable time may elapse after mixing the reagents before a visible precipitate appears. During this "induction period" nuclei are gradually forming.

What has been described so far is spontaneous nucleation. Nucleation can be induced (1) by seeding with crystallites of the substance, (2) by vigorous stirring, and (3) by the presence of impurities which provide a surface on which the ions can deposit and form nuclei with less effort than in the solution. The last effect is perhaps responsible for the recent observation that nucleation of barium sulfate is most rapid when freshly prepared reagent solutions are mixed. Nucleation is retarded by using aged reagents and by thorough cleaning of the glassware.

Nucleation is ultimately superseded by growth of the existing nuclei to macroscopic size. The rate of growth varies with the supersaturation. Growth is a complex process; ion-pairs do not deposit at random on the surface of the crystal. In slow growth each face of the crystal grows a layer at a time. The most energy is released when an ion-pair deposits on the edge of a growing layer (Fig. 8-5). It may get there directly from the solution, by diffusion along the surface of the crystal, or from an adsorbed layer of hydrated ions. As the edge grows the layer spreads like cake batter in a pan until it covers the whole face. Starting a new layer is harder than finishing an old one and begins only with the formation of a nucleus on top of the old layer. A two-dimensional nucleus of barium sulfate contains about two ion-pairs, that of silver chloride one. By building layer on layer the crystal gradually grows to macroscopic size.

The growth process has been described for a perfect crystal. All crystals contain imperfections, as indicated by the fact that their mechanical strengths are less than one-hundredth of the theoretical values for perfect crystals. Such imperfections make crystal faces irregular and assist growth by providing sites more energetically favorable for deposition of ion-pairs. Dislocations in the center of a face can produce a structure like that pictured in Fig. 8-5*d*. The crystal face then grows continuously "up a spiral staircase" rather than a layer at a time, a process that is rapid because it avoids the difficult step of starting a new layer.

When supersaturation is very high, growth occurs in a confused, less systematic way. The precipitate is made up of less regular crystals and may often be amorphous when first obtained. Von Weimarn showed that barium sulfate prepared by mixing $7N$ solutions of manganese(II) sulfate and barium thiocyanate was a gel with none of the crystalline character of barium sulfate prepared from less highly supersaturated solutions. In rapid growth foreign ions momentarily adsorbed on the surface may be covered over by the next crystal layer much as paint is slapped over dirt by a careless painter. Droplets of the solution may even be trapped in the crystal. Some of these faults are remedied as the crystals age. Amorphous precipitates become more crystalline on standing. This is often associated with a decrease in solubility; e.g., freshly precipitated aluminum hydroxide is much more soluble in acids than the aged precipitate is. Moreover, impurities near the surface can be squeezed out as the change to a more stable crystal structure occurs. Even so, precipitates formed rapidly are generally less pure than those that grow slowly.

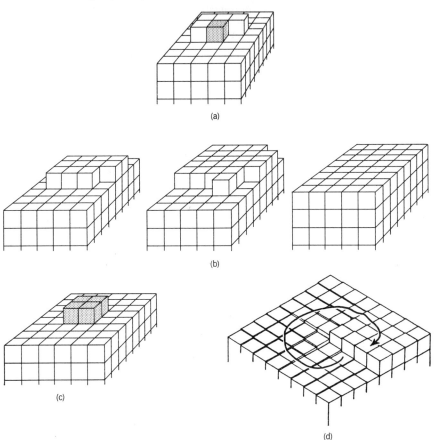

FIG. 8-5. Schematic representation of crystal growth. The cubes represent ion-pairs. (a) Most favorable site for deposition of ion-pair. (b) Stages in the growth of a layer. (c) Two-dimensional nucleus on top of old layer. (d) Crystal face with screw dislocation. Arrow shows direction of growth "up the spiral staircase." [Adapted by permission from F. C. Frank, *Discussions Faraday Soc.*, **5**, 49 (1949).]

8-9. Completeness of Precipitation. The extent to which precipitation occurs is governed by the equilibrium effects discussed in Secs. 8-2 through 8-7: presence of common ions, presence of foreign ions or the ionic strength effect; and conditions that affect the solubility product itself. In addition to these effects, when only five or ten minutes are allowed for precipitation, as in qualitative analysis, completeness will depend on the time required for nucleation and crystal growth. For some moderately insoluble substances nucleation may be so slow that a supersaturated solution can persist for some time. Lead chloride (Cation Group 1), magnesium ammonium arsenate (Cation Group 2), magnesium ammonium phosphate (Cation Group 5), strontium sulfate (Cation Group 4), and sodium magnesium uranyl acetate (Cation Group 5) are typical compounds that tend to supersaturate badly. This effect can be minimized by stirring vigorously and by rubbing the inner walls of the vessel with a glass rod, for these operations induce nucleation. In preparative work crystallization is often started by seeding; this is, of course, not suitable for analytical work.

8-10. Coprecipitation.   As a precipitate forms it carries down with it impurities from the solution. There are various ways in which a normally soluble substance can be incorporated in a precipitate, but regardless of how it takes place such a process is called *coprecipitation*. If we exclude compound formation, which is rare, there are three important types of coprecipitation: (1) occlusion (and inclusion), (2) adsorption, and (3) formation of solid solutions.

Occlusion occurs when an impurity that is adsorbed on a crystal face is covered over by a rapidly growing layer, as described in Sec. 8-8. If a small portion of solution is similarly incorporated in the crystal, this is called inclusion.

Adsorption occurs when ions or molecules adhere to the surface of the precipitate. In chemisorption the adsorbed particle is bound to the surface by covalent bonds as water is bound to crystals of some metal oxides. In physical adsorption the bonding is of the weak van der Waals type. It is not always easy to distinguish between these two types experimentally. There is an equilibrium established between the adsorbed material and what remains of this material in solution. If C is the concentration of adsorbed material in solution at equilibrium, the weight adsorbed per unit quantity of precipitate (X) is given by Freundlich's empirical equation

$$X = kC^{1/n} \qquad\qquad \textbf{15}$$

where k and n are constants. This relation shows that the amount adsorbed varies with the concentration of the substance in the solution. Contamination of a precipitate by adsorption can be reduced by forming the precipitate in dilute solution.

Precipitates have the greatest tendency to adsorb the same kinds of ions of which they are composed. Thus silver chloride precipitated from a solution that contains excess chloride ions will contain adsorbed chloride ions. Metal sulfides will adsorb sulfide or hydrogen sulfide ions. These are the ions that fit most readily into the crystal pattern. Adsorption can occur on all kinds of precipitates, from crystalline barium sulfate to amorphous, highly hydrated sulfides and hydroxides. In qualitative analysis a certain amount of contamination by adsorption is tolerable, but sometimes the adsorption on sulfides or hydroxides is so great as to make a good separation impossible. In some analytical procedures, for example, the hydroxides of aluminum, iron(III), and chromium(III) are precipitated before the sulfides of the bivalent metals such as zinc and cobalt. This does not work well in practice because of extensive coprecipitation of the bivalent ions by the gelatinous hydroxides. Zinc, which forms the least soluble hydroxide of the bivalent metals in Cation Group 3, is most strongly adsorbed.

Solid solutions of silver bromide in silver chloride were mentioned in Sec. 8-2. When barium sulfate is precipitated in the presence of radium ions, the latter are always incorporated in the precipitate by formation of a solid solution. This will happen even though the concentration of radium is far too low to permit the precipitation of radium sulfate by itself. Solid solutions can be formed to a limited extent even when two substances, e.g., $PbCl_2$ and $BaCl_2$, do not have similar crystal structures.

8-11. Methods of Minimizing Coprecipitation. The use of low concentrations or a large volume in precipitation as a method of reducing adsorption has already been mentioned. The precipitations of Cation Groups 2 and 3 are carried out in large volumes for this reason.

Sometimes the interfering ion can be eliminated before the precipitation. Manganese(II) and chromium(III) ions cause trouble in the analysis of Cation Group 3, for they coprecipitate with zinc on metal hydroxides. Both are removed early in the analysis of the group: manganese by oxidation to MnO_2 and chromium by oxidation to chromate.

If the precipitate is heated with its solution, the amount of foreign material adsorbed will generally decrease since adsorption is an exothermic process. Heating may, however, accelerate other reactions that increase the contamination of the precipitate.

The tedious process of dissolving the first precipitate and then reprecipitating it can be used to reduce contamination. Only a small fraction of the impurities are coprecipitated the first time. The concentration of these in the solution from which the second precipitate forms is much lower than in the first solution, and coprecipitation is correspondingly greatly reduced.

Since the late 1930's an elegant method of reducing contamination has been increasingly exploited: *precipitation from homogeneous medium*. The precipitating reagent is not added to the solution but is generated slowly within it by chemical action. Sulfate, for example, can be generated for the precipitation of barium sulfate by the slow hydrolysis of sulfamic acid (Secs. 7-5, -6). The hydrolysis of thioacetamide can be used as a source of sulfide ion (Secs. 7-7, 8-13). The hydrolysis of urea in boiling solutions gradually forms ammonia:

$$CO(NH_2)_2 + H_2O \rightarrow 2NH_3 + CO_2 \uparrow$$

and neutralizes acid. Aluminum can be precipitated as a basic succinate, $AlOH(C_4H_4O_4)$, by adding urea to a hot solution that contains succinic acid and an aluminum salt. The basic succinate is denser and less adsorptive than $Al(OH)_3$. A basic formate of iron(III) has similar properties. The foregoing examples have illustrated the generation of anions. In the method of cation release a complex of the metal ion is gradually decomposed. Silver chloride can be precipitated slowly from a solution containing $Ag(NH_3)_2^+$ and Cl^- ions by carrying out a reaction that generates hydrogen ions.

Precipitation from homogeneous medium is based on the principle that slowly formed precipitates are purer than those that are formed rapidly (Sec. 8-8). Such precipitates also contain larger crystals, and are thus easier to filter or to settle by centrifugation. Ordinarily two solutions are mixed to obtain a precipitate; the degree of supersaturation is then very high, and precipitation occurs rapidly. During the few seconds of mixing, the medium is not homogeneous, and local regions of it may momentarily contain very high concentrations of a reagent. This source of contamination could be reduced by mixing very dilute solutions of the reagents, but such a technique is tedious and awkward. If instead one reagent is generated slowly within the solution, the degree of supersaturation is always low and the precipitate forms slowly. Contamination is not entirely eliminated in this way; it may still occur toward the beginning of precipitation, when the crystallites are small and highly adsorptive, and at the end, after generation of the reagent has ceased. But contamination is reduced by precipitation from homogeneous medium; e.g., coprecipitation of zinc by mercury(II) sulfide is thirty times as great when hydrogen sulfide is used as when the sulfide is generated slowly by hydrolysis of thioacetamide.

8-12. Precipitation of Sulfides by Hydrogen Sulfide. Sulfides are so important in qualitative analysis that a detailed discussion of their precipitation is required. The extent of precipitation under various conditions is shown in Table 8-2. In using this table it must be borne in mind that the precipitation of one sulfide is often assisted by the presence of others and that certain anions at high concentration can retard or prevent precipitation. A large excess of chloride ion, for example, whether from hydrochloric acid or ammonium chloride, inhibits the precipitation of PbS, CdS, and SnS_2 by forming chlorocomplexes with these metal ions.

The order of precipitation of the sulfides agrees in general with what we would expect from equilibrium principles. For a saturated solution of hydrogen sulfide (Sec. 7-19, Eq. 39)

$$K_{ip}(H_2S) = [H^+]^2[S^{--}] \qquad\qquad\qquad \textbf{16}$$

We see from this that in strongly acid solutions the sulfide ion concentration is low, and in basic solutions for which $[H^+]$ is very small $[S^{--}]$ is high. The sulfide ion concentration is thus controlled by regulating the hydrogen ion concentration. The solubility products of some of the sulfides are given in Table 8-2. Although the accuracy of some of these values is not very high, they do show that the sulfides of Cation Group 2 have lower solubility products than those of Cation Group 3. The dividing line comes between cadmium sulfide, the most soluble member of Group 2, and zinc sulfide, the least soluble one of Group 3. It is found experimentally that if the sulfide ion is controlled by adjustment of the concentration of hydrochloric acid to between 0.1 and 0.3 M, zinc sulfide can be kept in solution while cadmium sulfide (and the other sulfides of Group 2) is precipitated:

$$K_{sp}(CdS) < [Cd^{++}][S^=] \qquad K_{sp}(ZnS) > [Zn^{++}][S^=]$$

Some zinc is always coprecipitated with the sulfides of Group 2 even though zinc sulfide cannot be precipitated from a solution of a pure zinc salt in this acidic solution.

Little is known of the actual mechanism of precipitation of sulfides. Direct reaction between sulfide and metal ions is improbable, for 0.1 M hydrochloric acid saturated with hydrogen sulfide at room temperature contains only about 80 sulfide ions per milliliter. There are some 6,000,000,000,000 HS⁻ ions per milliliter and combination of these with the metal ions is more probable. Perhaps complexes such as MeSH⁺ first form, then a number of these unite and expel hydrogen ions to give the sulfide precipitate.

8-13. Precipitation of Sulfides by Thioacetamide.

This reagent has been in use only since 1949 and much less is known about the conditions of precipitation with it than with gaseous hydrogen sulfide. Thioacetamide was introduced partly because of the unpleasant and dangerous character of hydrogen sulfide and partly because of the advantages of precipitation in homogeneous medium. Though slow to form, the sulfides obtained by hydrolysis of thioacetamide are coarser, more crystalline precipitates than those obtained with hydrogen sulfide. They are easier to settle by centrifugation and are less contaminated by coprecipitated ions.

Experience has shown that most of the sulfides are precipitated at about the same acidities by hydrogen sulfide and thioacetamide. The principal exceptions are cadmium and arsenic(V) sulfides. Precipitation of cadmium sulfide

TABLE 8-2.

The Extent of Precipitation of Sulfides in Various Media

KEY: P = complete or almost complete precipitation, I = incomplete precipitation, S = slow but eventually complete precipitation, CP = not precipitated alone but coprecipitated with other sulfides to an extent dependent on the other sulfides present, — = no precipitate.

	K_{sp}	In 6 M HCl	In 3 M HCl	In 1 M HCl	In 0.5 M HCl	In 0.2 M HCl	In buffer [H⁺]= 10^{-2}*	In buffer [H⁺]= 10^{-6}†	In NH₃ + NH₄Cl + (NH₄)₂S
Cation group 2									
As_2S_5		P	S	S	S	S	S	S	‡
As_2S_3		P	P	P	P	P	P	P	‡
HgS	3×10^{-52}	P	P	P	P	P	P	P	P
CuS	8×10^{-36}	P	P	P	P	P	P	P	P
Sb_2S_5		I	P	P	P	P	P	P	‡
Sb_2S_3		—	P	P	P	P	P	P	‡
SnS_2		—	I	P	P	P	P	P	‡
SnS		—	—	P	P	P	P	P	I‡
Bi_2S_3	1×10^{-96}	—	—	P	P	P	P	P	P
PbS	8×10^{-28}	—	I	I	I	P	P	P	P
CdS	7×10^{-27}	—	—	I	P	P	P	P	P
Cation group 3									
ZnS	8×10^{-25}	—	—	—	—	CP	S	P	P
CoS	8×10^{-23}	—	—	—	—	CP	CP	P	P
NiS	2×10^{-21}	—	—	—	—	CP	CP	P	P
FeS	5×10^{-18}	—	—	—	—	—	—	CP	P
MnS	1×10^{-11}	—	—	—	—	—	—	—	P

*Buffers that maintain [H⁺] = 10^{-2} can be prepared from mixtures of sulfate and hydrogen sulfate ions or of formic acid and a formate.

†Buffers that maintain [H⁺] = 10^{-6} can be prepared from mixtures of acetic acid and an acetate.

‡These sulfides do not precipitate in strongly basic solutions because of the formation of thiocomplex ions such as AsS_4^{---}, SbS_3^{---}, and SnS_3^{--}.

References:

Reprinted with permission from G. E. F. Lundell and J. I. Hoffman, *Outlines of Methods of Chemical Analysis*, 1938, John Wiley & Sons, Inc., New York, pp. 49–54.

From *Introductory Quantitative Analysis*, by Ernest H. Swift, pp. 422–423. Copyright, 1950, by Prentice-Hall, Inc., Englewood Cliffs, N.J. Reproduced by permission of the publisher.

by thioacetamide is frequently incomplete unless the acid concentration is reduced to 0.1 M. A qualitative separation of cadmium from zinc is still possible, for the precipitation of zinc sulfide does not occur until the hydrogen ion concentration is reduced to about 0.01 M. Arsenic(V) is reduced by thioacetamide, and precipitation of As_2S_3 follows. In a solution that contains 5 mg of As(V) per milliliter and is 0.3 M in HCl and 0.5 M in thioacetamide 99.9 % of the arsenic is reduced in one minute at 90°.[7] Precipitation of arsenic(V), as well as of molybdenum(VI), is slow and troublesome with hydrogen sulfide gas but straightforward with thioacetamide.

The hydrolysis of thioacetamide in acid solutions is proportional to the concentrations of hydrogen ion and thioacetamide (Sec. 7-7). Swift has found that, if thioacetamide is added to solutions of lead, cadmium, arsenic, or zinc salts that are at least 0.001 M in H^+, precipitation of the metal sulfide occurs as fast as hydrogen sulfide is produced:

$$\text{Rate of precipitation} = k[CH_3CSNH_2][H^+] \qquad \textbf{17}$$

It follows that if the acidity of the solution is increased, the precipitation will occur more rapidly. This will not continue indefinitely, however, for the increase in hydrogen ion concentration also lowers the sulfide ion concentration according to the relation[8]

$$K_{ip} = [H^+]^2[S^{--}] \qquad (16)$$

and precipitation stops when the product $[Zn^{++}][S^{--}]$, for example, falls below K_{sp}, the equilibrium value.

A thorough study of the use of thioacetamide in precipitating sulfides has barely started. Some preliminary work on the hydrolysis in basic solutions has shown that it follows a more complex course. The rate of decomposition and of precipitation in basic solution, particularly in ammonia-ammonium chloride mixtures, is much faster than in acid solution. In acid solutions less than 0.001 M in H^+ direct reaction between thioacetamide and cations occurs without the formation of hydrogen sulfide. A better understanding of the action of thioacetamide will doubtless develop as more physico-chemical studies of its action are made.

8-14. Precipitation of Hydroxides.

When a base is gradually added to a solution of a salt, the initial precipitate almost always contains some of the anions of the salt. These may be incorporated by adsorption, occlusion, or formation of a definite compound such as BiOCl, Ni(OH)Cl, or

---

[7] The original reference should be consulted for much valuable information on the use of thioacetamide: E. Butler and E. Swift, *Anal. Chem.*, **29**, 419 (1957).

[8] This expression was derived for a saturated solution of hydrogen sulfide gas. If, in the hydrolysis of thioacetamide, hydrogen sulfide is being consumed by precipitation as fast as it is produced, the balance between production and consumption will keep [H_2S] very small but roughly constant during precipitation. The ion product relation will still hold, but its numerical value will be smaller than that for a saturated solution of the gas.

$Co(OH)Cl \cdot 4Co(OH)_2 \cdot 4H_2O$. As more base is added, the precipitate gradually changes to a crystalline form of the hydroxide or hydrated oxide. Most hydroxides of trivalent metals [also HgO and $Sn(OH)_2$] have very low solubility products and are first precipitated while the solution is still acid. Iron(III) hydroxide, for example, will sometimes precipitate when the hydrogen ion concentration is as high as 0.01 M. The hydroxides of most bivalent metals have higher solubility products and will not begin to precipitate until the solution has been made neutral or strongly basic. A separation between the two classes of hydroxides is possible with a reagent, such as a mixture of ammonium chloride and ammonia, that maintains a low concentration of hydroxide ion. This will be discussed in Chapter 12. Such separations are seldom very successful, because of extensive coprecipitation. An attractive alternative is the precipitation of basic salts from homogeneous medium (Sec. 8-11).

DISSOLUTION OF PRECIPITATES

8-15. General Requirements. A precipitate will begin to dissolve if it is brought into contact with an unsaturated solution of the substance. This corresponds to the requirement

$$Q = [+]_{uss} [-]_{uss} < K_{sp} = [+]_{ss} [-]_{ss} \qquad 18$$

This condition can be established for the more soluble precipitates such as lead(II) chloride by heating, for the solubility product is increased by raising the temperature. More commonly condition 18 is established by a chemical reaction that decreases the concentration of one or both ions. Cations can be removed by complex formation; anions are usually removed by a proton transfer reaction. Either kind of ion can be removed by a redox reaction. All these reactions are used to dissolve sulfides, as we shall see in the next section.

The process of dissolving a precipitate is often a slow one. Surface films often form on the solid which prevent contact between the precipitate and fresh reagent. Many metals, e.g., iron, aluminum, and chromium, are protected by films of oxide. Nitric acid, which tends to maintain these films, is a poorer solvent for these metals than hydrochloric acid. Lead dissolves very slowly in sulfuric acid as a result of the formation of a surface coating of lead sulfate. Conversion of one precipitate to another may be incomplete if the second precipitate forms a coating around particles of the first. It is generally better to dissolve the first precipitate completely with some other reagent and then precipitate the second from this solution.

8-16. Dissolution of Sulfides. Acidic reagents are generally used to dissolve sulfides. The three most common ones are hydrochloric acid, nitric acid, and aqua regia (3 parts of HCl to 1 part HNO_3). Hydrochloric acid can act in two ways. In the first mode of action a proton transfer reaction occurs, e.g.,

$$ZnS\downarrow + 2H^+ \rightarrow Zn^{++} + H_2S\uparrow$$

If enough hydrogen sulfide forms to saturate the solution, we can represent the situation by the two relations

$$K_{ip}(H_2S) = [H^+]^2[S^{--}] \qquad K_{sp}(ZnS) > [Zn^{++}][S^{--}]$$

The sulfide ion concentration is repressed by the high concentration of hydrogen ion, and the product of the concentrations falls below that required by the solubility product for a saturated solution and the precipitate dissolves. The more soluble sulfides are dissolved in this way.

The second mode of action of hydrochloric acid on sulfides involves formation of chlorocomplexes, e.g.,

$$CdS\downarrow + 2H^+ + 4Cl^- \rightarrow H_2S\uparrow + CdCl_4^{--}$$

$$SnS_2\downarrow + 4H^+ + 6Cl^- \rightarrow 2H_2S\uparrow + SnCl_6^{--}$$

Not only is sulfide ion removed but also the concentration of metal ion is decreased by formation of the complex. Even mercury(II) sulfide, which has an exceptionally low solubility product, will dissolve in concentrated hydrochloric acid, although the rate of reaction is slow.

Nitric acid is a better solvent than hydrochloric acid for many sulfides because it can oxidize sulfide ion to free sulfur. This removes sulfide more effectively than its reversible conversion to H_2S. The less soluble sulfides, except HgS, can be dissolved in this way:

$$8H^+ + 2NO_3^- + Bi_2S_3\downarrow \rightarrow 2Bi^{+++} + 3S^0\downarrow + 2NO + 4H_2O$$

Even this is not effective on mercury(II) sulfide, perhaps because the sulfide ion concentration allowed by its very small solubility product is enough to satisfy the equilibrium between S^{--} and S^0.

The complexing action of hydrochloric acid and the oxidizing action of nitric acid are combined in aqua regia. This reagent will dissolve mercury(II) sulfide, for it oxidizes sulfide to sulfur and forms chlorocomplexes such as $HgCl_4^{--}$ with mercury. The action of aqua regia is also possibly more rapid than that of nitric acid alone. The latter, though potentially a powerful oxidizing agent, is slow in its action unless NO_2 is present to act as a catalyst (Sec. 7-6). Nitric and hydrochloric acids combine to give NOCl (nitrosyl chloride), NO_2, Cl_2, and H_2O. The first three of these products are very rapid oxidizing agents; they may be no more powerful than nitric acid itself but they act more rapidly.

A number of sulfides dissolve in solutions of bases. This is not surprising when we remember that many oxides dissolve in an excess of strong base.

Sulfur and oxygen belong to the same group of the Periodic Table, so their compounds should resemble each other. Compare

$$As_2O_3 \downarrow + 6OH^- \rightarrow 2AsO_3^{---} + 3H_2O$$

$$As_2S_3 \downarrow + 6OH^- \rightarrow AsS_3^{---} + AsO_3^{---} + 3H_2O$$

$$As_2S_3 \downarrow + 6SH^- \rightarrow 2AsS_3^{---} + 3H_2S$$

$$As_2S_3 \downarrow + 3S^{--} \rightarrow 2AsS_3^{---}$$

In view of these reactions we may call As_2S_3 an "acidic sulfide" just as we call As_2O_3 an acidic oxide. The formation of the thioarsenite ion[9] brings about the dissolution of the sulfide; acidification of the solution reverses the changes and reprecipitates the sulfide.

The principal acidic sulfides are those of arsenic, antimony, and tin. They are separated from the rest of the sulfides of Cation Group 2 by the action of a basic reagent such as KOH, K_2S, $(NH_4)_2S$, or $(NH_4)_2S_x$.[10] The relative advantages and disadvantages of these are summarized in Table 8-3.

TABLE 8-3.

Basic Reagents for Separation of Arsenic, Antimony, and Tin Sulfides

Reagent	Advantages	Disadvantages
KOH, KHS, K_2S	Clean separations of most ions	Some HgS is dissolved; Bi_2S_3 may dissolve in concentrated reagent SnS is not dissolved
$(NH_4)_2S$	HgS is not dissolved	Some CuS is dissolved SnS is not dissolved
$(NH_4)_2S_x$	HgS is not dissolved SnS is oxidized and dissolved as SnS_3^{--}	Some CuS dissolves Considerable S^0 is precipitated when the solution is acidified to recover the sulfides

Those elements of Cation Group 2 that form strongly acidic oxides also form acidic sulfides. The higher the oxidation state of the element, the more acidic the sulfide or oxide. Thus SnS_2 is acidic and dissolves readily in bases; SnS is much less acidic and not very soluble in bases.

[9]The Greek prefix *thio-* is used to indicate substitution of sulfur for oxygen. Hence AsO_3^{---} being arsenite, AsS_3^{---} is thioarsenite. Mixed thiooxyanions such as AsO_2S^{---} are known.

[10]The symbol S_x^{--} stands for a polysulfide ion formed by adding a sulfide ion to a chain of sulfur atoms: $:\ddot{S}:^{--} + \ddot{S}:\ddot{S}: \rightarrow :\ddot{S}:\ddot{S}:\ddot{S}:^{--}$

8-17. Dissolution of Hydroxides.   The neutralization of a basic hydroxide or oxide by an acid is a familiar proton transfer reaction. Thus nickel hydroxide dissolves in hydrochloric acid:

$$Ni(OH)_2 \downarrow \; + 2H^+ \rightarrow Ni^{++} + 2H_2O$$

because the removal of hydroxide ions to give weakly ionized water establishes the condition for dissolution of a precipitate:

$$K_{sp} > [Ni^{++}] [OH^-]^2$$

Many hydroxides are most soluble in acids when freshly precipitated. Other hydroxides or oxides are acidic and react readily with bases, e.g.,

$$As(OH)_3 + 3OH^- \rightarrow AsO_3^{---} + 3H_2O$$

There are a number of *amphoteric hydroxides* (or oxides) that are recognized by their ability to dissolve in an excess of either a strong acid or a strong base. There is still no universally accepted interpretation of these observations. Some believe that the action of the base is to break the precipitate apart into pieces of colloidal size much as large chunks of rock are broken off a cliff by spring thaws. Most authorities believe that the action of the acid or base usually gives simple ionic particles, but they differ as to the degree of hydration of these ions. This is a difficult problem to solve by experiment.

The behavior of aluminum hydroxide is typical of many amphoteric substances. In one experiment 0.090 M sodium hydroxide was added slowly to some 0.0067 M aluminum sulfate (Fig. 8-6) and the concentration of hydrogen ion was measured at intervals during the titration. Precipitation began as the hydrogen ion concentration fell below 10^{-4} and continued until it had reached 10^{-9}:

$$Al^{+++} + 3OH^- \rightarrow Al(OH)_3 \downarrow$$

At this point a little under 3 moles of hydroxide had been added per g-atom of aluminum. As more base was added the hydrogen ion concentration fell until it reached $10^{-10.8}$ at which point the precipitate had completely redissolved. Here a total of 4.13 moles of hydroxide had been added per g-atom of aluminum. This could be represented by

$$Al(OH)_3 \downarrow \; + OH^- \rightarrow \begin{cases} Al(OH)_4^- \\ \text{or} \\ H_2AlO_3^- + H_2O \\ \text{or} \\ AlO_2^- + 2H_2O \end{cases}$$

The presence of a hydroxide complex is inferred from the existence of crystalline compounds such as $NaAl(OH)_4 \cdot 2H_2O$ and $Ca_3[Al(OH)_6]_2$. It was once thought that the compound "spinel," $MgAl_2O_4$, contained AlO_2^- ions, and this would have supported the last formulation. But the structure of spinel as revealed by x-ray measurements is complex; each aluminum is surrounded not by two but by six oxygen atoms. Some authors still prefer the formula AlO_2^- on the principle that all ions are understood to be hydrated anyway. The hydroxide complex is used in this text.

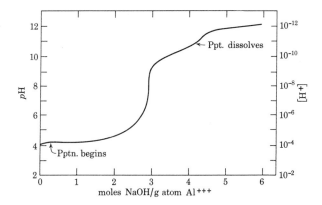

Fig. 8-6. The titration of Al^{+++} ion with OH^- ion. [Adapted by permission from H. T. S. Britton, *J. Chem. Soc.*, **127**, 2121 (1925).]

The formation of the hydroxide complex decreases the concentration of aluminum ions to such an extent that the condition for dissolution of the precipitate is established:

$$K_{sp} > [Al^{+++}][OH^-]^3$$

Some oxides and hydroxides are predominantly acidic but dissolve in certain acids, e.g., HCl, by formation of complexes or molecules:

$$SnO_2 + 4H^+ + 6Cl^- \rightarrow SnCl_6^{--} + 2H_2O$$
$$As(OH)_3 + 3H^+ + 3Cl^- \rightarrow AsCl_3 + 3H_2O$$

These reactions occur most probably because of the formation of the weakly dissociated chloride compounds rather than because of the reaction of the oxide or hydroxide as a base.

COLLOIDAL SUSPENSIONS

8-18. Some Properties of Colloidal Suspensions. In the laboratory we sometimes obtain a cloudy mixture that cannot be clarified by filtration or centrifugation. It may form in a precipitation reaction or in washing a precipitate. The colloidal suspension,[11] for this is what it is, may be flocculated

[11]The word "colloid" from the Greek word for glue was introduced by Thomas Graham in 1860.

slowly by heating or more rapidly by addition of an electrolyte such as an ammonium salt.

Further light on the nature of colloids is cast by some of their other properties. Many such systems are virtually transparent, although others, such as colloidal sulfur, have a peculiar opalescence. But if a strong beam of light is passed through the mixture and observed transversely, the beam is visible; and under the microscope a large number of luminous points are seen moving around at random. This Tyndall effect is caused by a scattering of the light by the particles of the colloid. The particles must be very small, for they pass through filters and cannot be seen under a microscope (only the light they scatter can be seen). Yet they cannot be of molecular size, for molecules or ions are too small to scatter light; the Tyndall effect is not obtained with a true solution. There are no definite limits that can be set on the size of colloidal particles but roughly their diameters lie between 10 A (10^{-7} cm) and 5000 A (5×10^{-5} cm). Mixtures with larger particles are coarse suspensions that settle in a few hours at most. The rate of settling of colloidal particles is so low that convection currents caused by small inequalities of temperature in the mixture keep the suspension from settling for long periods of time.

When two electrodes are put into a colloidal suspension, the particles move during the electrolysis. Colloidal arsenic sulfide migrates toward the positive electrode; its particles must be negatively charged. Colloidal iron(III) oxide migrates toward the negative electrode; its particles bear positive charges. The migration is called *electrophoresis*.

The colloidal suspensions that we have considered are called *lyophobic sols*. The word sol is used to distinguish them from true solutions. The term lyophobic comes from Greek words meaning to "fear the solvent" and applies to sols such as those of gold, arsenic sulfide, sulfur, or iron(III) oxide, in which the particles are only weakly solvated. Lyophilic ("solvent loving") sols, which include glue, gelatin, starch, and hydrous SnO_2, are highly solvated and have somewhat different properties. Besides sols, colloidal systems include other mixtures in which a finely dispersed phase is distributed through a medium, e.g., emulsions in which one liquid is dispersed in another. We shall confine our attention to lyophobic sols.

8-19. Stabilization of Sols. The charge on colloidal particles is caused by ions adsorbed on their surfaces. Adsorption occurs to a large extent on these particles because of their high surface area relative to their volume. Consider a cube 1 cm on each edge: its surface area is 6 cm^2, its volume 1 cm^3, and the ratio of area to volume 6. If it is subdivided into cubes of colloidal size, 10^{-5} cm on each edge, for example, the total surface area of all the cubes is 60 m^2, while the volume remains 1 cm^3, and the ratio of area to volume is 600,000.

A surface will generally attract from solution ions that are the same as or similar to ions in the surface. The surface of a particle of silver iodide is most likely to attract silver or iodide ions. A slight excess of electrolyte is essential for the formation of a sol. When silver iodide sols are prepared with a slight excess of silver nitrate, silver ions are plentiful in the solution and are adsorbed preferentially over nitrate ions which are foreign to silver iodide. When the sol is prepared with a slight excess of potassium iodide, iodide ions are adsorbed. The first sol is positively charged; the second is negatively charged. An excess of hydrogen sulfide is generally used in preparing an arsenic sulfide sol and this sol is negative because of the adsorption of HS^- ions on the surfaces. Such a sol particle is pictured schematically in Fig. 8-7.

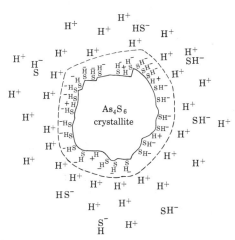

FIG. 8-7. Schematic representation of a particle of an arsenic trisulfide sol. The dotted line separates the adsorbed (negative) layer from the counter ion region (positive).

Because the surfaces of colloidal particles bear charges, they will attract around them in solution ions of opposite charge. These are called *counter ions*. Unlike the ions in the adsorbed layer which are more or less fixed, the counter ions are free to move and the counter ion region is diffuse. The oppositely charged adsorbed layer and counter ion region are said to be an electrical *double layer*. The extension of the counter ion region into the solution shrinks as the concentration of ions in the solution is increased and also shrinks if univalent ions are replaced by ions of higher charge. Both of these changes increase the attraction between the counter ion region and the adsorbed layer and pull the two layers together.

All particles of a sol bear charges of the same sign; e.g., all arsenic sulfide particles are negatively charged and have positive counter ions. When two such particles approach each other until the double layers begin to overlap, they begin to repel each other. It is this repulsion that stabilizes the sol and prevents it from flocculating.

8-20. Flocculation of Sols. There is, in addition to the repulsion, an attraction between sol particles which is of the van der Waals type. Attraction of this type is weak between single molecules (Sec. 1-6) but becomes increasingly strong as molecules (or ions) aggregate into larger particles. If the repulsion can be overcome so that two sol particles can approach each other closely, they will stay together and attract other particles. A loose agglomerate will eventually form that is large enough to settle, and the sol is then flocculated.

The repulsion can be decreased by an increase in temperature, for the particles acquire more thermal motion. By traveling faster they can overcome the mutual repulsion.

The repulsion can also be decreased by shrinking the double layer. This happens when electrolytes are added to the sol. Ions of the electrolyte that have a charge opposite to that of the adsorbed layer are drawn into the counter-ion region and the increased attraction draws the counter-ion region closer to the particle. The effectiveness of the electrolyte depends on its concentration and on the charge on the ion that is opposite in sign to the charge on the colloidal particle. In flocculating a positive iron(III) oxide sol, for example, doubly charged sulfate ions are more effective than singly charged chloride ions. Further data illustrating this effect, the Schulze-Hardy rule, are given in Table 8-4. According to theory the effectiveness of ions of charge 1, 2, and 3 increases by $1^6 : 2^6 : 3^6$; or $1 : 64 : 729$; this is in rough agreement with experiment. It will be observed in examining Table 8-4 that not all ions of the same charge are equally effective; there are specific effects that would not be predicted from the oversimplified picture that we have drawn.

TABLE 8-4.

Flocculation of Negatively Charged Silver Iodide Sol

KEY: C = minimum concentration in mmoles/l required to cause flocculation

Electrolyte	C	Electrolyte	C
$LiNO_3$	165	$Ba(NO_3)_2$	2.20
$NaNO_3$	140	$Zn(NO_3)_2$	2.50
KNO_3	136	$UO_2(NO_3)_2$	3.15
$RbNO_3$	126	$Al(NO_3)_3$	0.067
$Mg(NO_3)_2$	2.53	$La(NO_3)_3$	0.069
$Ca(NO_3)_2$	2.38	$Ce(NO_3)_3$	0.069
$Sr(NO_3)_2$	2.33	$Th(NO_3)_4$	0.013

Reference:
H. R. Kruyt and M. A. M. Klompé, *Kolloid-Beih.*, **54,** 484 (Darmstadt, Dr. Dietrich Steinkopf Verlag, 1943).

8-21. Peptization. A flocculated sol is a loose agglomerate of small particles that is contaminated not only by the adsorbed ions but also by many of the counter ions. Some of these will gradually be lost as the precipitate ages. If we try to remove the impurities by washing the precipitate, it is frequently found that the sol is re-formed. This is called *peptization*. Washing removes the electrolyte that caused flocculation, and the particles again repel each other so that the precipitate is redispersed. Peptization can be avoided by washing with a very dilute solution of an innocuous electrolyte, such as an ammonium salt, which replaces the impurities and prevents repulsion. This technique is generally used in qualitative analysis both for flocculating sols and for washing precipitated sulfides that are easily peptized.

SUPPLEMENTARY READING

L. HAMMETT, *Solutions of Electrolytes*, 2nd ed., McGraw-Hill, New York, 1936, Chapter 2.

J. NORDMANN, *Qualitative Testing and Inorganic Chemistry*, Wiley, New York, 1957, Chapter 8.

T. MOELLER, *Qualitative Analysis*, McGraw-Hill, New York, 1958, Chapter 7.

T. HOGNESS and W. JOHNSON, *Qualitative Analysis and Chemical Equilibrium*, 4th ed., Holt, New York, 1954, Chapter 8.

E. SWIFT, *Introductory Quantitative Analysis*, Prentice-Hall, Englewod Cliffs, N.J., 1950, pp. 295–315, 418–25.

I. KOLTHOFF and E. SANDELL, *Textbook of Quantitative Inorganic Analysis*, 3rd ed., Macmillan, New York, 1952, Chapters 7 and 8.

L. GORDON, "Slow Precipitation Processes," *Record Chem. Progr. (Kresge-Hooker Sci. Lib.)*, **17**, 125–43 (1956).

J. GLEDHILL and G. MALAN, "The Solubility of Silver Chloride at 25° C," *Trans. Faraday Soc.*, **48**, 258 (1952).

C. W. DAVIES and A. JONES, "The Precipitation of Silver Chloride from Aqueous Solutions," *Discussions Faraday Soc.*, **5**, 103 (1949).

EXERCISES

8-1. Write solubility product expressions for (a) Ag_3PO_4, (b) CaC_2O_4, (c) $MgNH_4AsO_4$, (d) Bi_2S_3, (e) HgO (in equilibrium with Hg^{++} and OH^- ions).

8-2. The operations listed below are carried out on separate portions of a saturated solution of silver chromate in contact with the precipitated salt. If ionic strength effects are ignored, which of these operations will affect (1) the molar solubility; (2) the solubility product? (a) addition of alcohol, (b) addition of silver nitrate, (c) addition of water, (d) addition of potassium chromate, (e) increase in temperature.

8-3. Which of the statements below applies to all four of the following solutions: (1) saturated solution of AgCl in water; (2) saturated solution of AgCl in 0.01 M $AgNO_3$; (3) saturated solution of AgCl in 0.01 M NaCl; (4) saturated solution of AgCl in 0.01 M K_2CrO_4? (a) The solubility of silver chloride is the same. (b) The solubility product is the square of the molar solubility. (c) The solubility product is the same. (d) The concentration of silver ion is the same.

8-4. Distinguish between solubility and solubility product.

8-5. Explain why the solubility product of barium sulfate does not show explicitly the concentration of solid barium sulfate.

8-6. Show that for a slightly soluble salt MeX_3 the solubility product is related to the molar solubility by the equation $K_{sp} = 27S^4$. What assumptions are made in this derivation?

8-7. Show that for a slightly soluble salt Me_2X_3 the molar solubility of the salt in water is given by the equation $S = (K_{sp}/108)^{1/5}$. Why would this expression fail for Bi_2S_3?

8-8. With the solubility product values (see table in the Appendix) as a guide, arrange the members of each set in order of increasing solubility in water.

(a) CaC_2O_4, BaC_2O_4, MgC_2O_4, SrC_2O_4 (b) $SrCrO_4$, $PbCrO_4$, $BaCrO_4$, $CaCrO_4$
(c) CuS, HgS, NiS, MnS   (d) $CaCO_3$, $SrCO_3$, $BaCO_3$, $MnCO_3$
(e) $Mg(OH)_2$, $Co(OH)_2$, $Mn(OH)_2$, $Cu(OH)_2$

8-9. Arrange the members of each set in order of increasing concentration of the specified ion when the precipitates are in equilibrium with solutions containing the other ions at 0.1 M concentration. Consult the Appendix for values of solubility products.

(a) $[Ag^+]$ for AgSCN, AgI, AgCN, AgBr
(b) $[S^{--}]$ for CdS, CoS, PbS, MnS, ZnS
(c) $[OH^-]$ for $Sn(OH)_2$, $Fe(OH)_2$, $Cu(OH)_2$, $Mg(OH)_2$
(d) $[Pb^{++}]$ for $Pb(OH)_2$, PbF_2, PbI_2, $PbCl_2$

8-10. Which member of each pair is more soluble in water?

(a) $Fe(OH)_2$; $Fe(OH)_3$ (b) CaF_2; CaC_2O_4 (c) Ag_2S; AgI

8-11. The specific conductance of a saturated solution of silver chloride at 55° is 1.0350×10^{-5} units, and the average specific conductance of the water used in preparing the solution is 0.0233×10^{-5}. The limiting equivalent conductance of silver chloride at this temperature is 226.2. Calculate the molar solubility and solubility product from these data. [J. Gledhill and G. Malan, *Trans. Faraday Soc.*, **50**, 126 (1954).]

8-12. The specific conductance of a saturated solution of silver bromide is 1.92×10^{-7} units at 25°. That of the water used in preparing the solution is 0.92×10^{-7}. The limiting ionic conductances of the silver and bromide ions are, respectively, 61.92 and 78.30. Calculate the molar solubility and solubility product of silver bromide from these data. [J. Gledhill and G. Malan, *Trans. Faraday Soc.*, **49**, 166 (1953).]

8-13. The specific conductance of a saturated solution of barium sulfate is 2.943×10^{-6} at 25° after correction for the conductance of the water used in preparing the solution. The limiting equivalent conductances of the barium and sulfate ions are, respectively, 63.64 and 80.00. Calculate the molar solubility and solubility product from these data. (Hint: what is the relation between normality and molarity for barium sulfate?) [D. Rosseinsky, *Trans. Faraday Soc.*, **54**, 116 (1958).]

8-14. Explain why addition of a foreign electrolyte causes an increase in the solubility of a precipitate.

8-15. Calculate the ionic strengths of each of the following solutions: (a) 0.06 M NaCl, (b) 0.01 M $K_3Fe(CN)_6$ (neglect ion-pair formation), (c) 0.01 M KNO_3, (d) 0.01 M sucrose, (e) 0.01 M $Co(NH_3)_6Cl_3$, (f) a mixture 0.01 M in $CaCl_2$, 0.02 M in KNO_3.

8-16. Calculate the ionic strength of a Ringer's solution prepared by mixing 960 ml of 0.154 M NaCl, 20 ml of 0.154 M KCl, and 20 ml of 0.11 M $CaCl_2$.

8-17. Calculate the ionic strength of a sea water in which the major constituents and their concentrations are: Cl^-, 0.550 M; Na^+, 0.471 M; Mg^{++}, 0.054 M; SO_4^{--}, 0.028 M; Ca^{++}, 0.011 M; K^+, 0.001 M.

8-18. Calculate the ionic strength of the solution in Exercise 4-8.

8-19. In which of the following solutions would the solubility and solubility product of silver chloride be largest? (a) 0.02 M KNO_3, (b) 0.01 M $Ca(NO_3)_2$, (c) 0.01 M $MgSO_4$.

8-20. In which of the following solutions would the ionization constant of formic acid be largest? (a) 0.01 M NaCl, (b) 0.01 M $CaCl_2$, (c) a mixture 0.005 M in NaCl, 0.005 M in $LaCl_3$.

8-21. To what kinds of solution do the following relations apply? (a) $K_{sp} = [Cu^{++}][S^{--}]$, (b) $K_{sp} > [Cu^{++}][S^{--}]$, (c) $K_{sp} < [Cu^{++}][S^{--}]$.

8-22. Why must a solution of barium sulfate be highly supersaturated before precipitation will occur?

8-23. If a precipitate of barium sulfate is formed by mixing 0.1 M solutions of barium nitrate and sodium sulfate, which of these statements will be true? (a) The individual crystals will be very large. (b) Crystallization will be very rapid. (c) The crystals will be impure.

8-24. What is meant by "coprecipitation"? Describe several ways in which it can occur and several ways in which it can be minimized.

8-25. Why is precipitation of sulfides with thioacetamide called "precipitation from homogeneous medium"? What are the advantages of this method?

8-26. Explain in words and by reference to appropriate equilibrium constants how it is possible to separate slightly soluble sulfides into two groups by use of hydrogen sulfide in the presence of a controlled concentration of hydrogen ion.

8-27. Write the chemical equation for the hydrolysis of thioacetamide in acid solutions. What is the function of the acid? In what respects does the use of thioacetamide differ from that of hydrogen sulfide?

8-28. Three solutions were prepared containing equal concentrations of Pb^{++} ion and of thioacetamide but three different concentrations of nitric acid. All three tubes were placed in a boiling water bath and heated for two minutes. In the tube containing 2 M HNO_3 no precipitate formed, a large precipitate appeared in the tube containing 0.2 M acid, and a small precipitate formed in the tube containing 0.02 M acid. Account for these results.

8-29. Iron(II) sulfide is soluble in 1 M HCl, antimony(III) sulfide is soluble in 6 M HCl, and bismuth sulfide is insoluble in HCl but dissolves in nitric acid. Write chemical equations for these reactions and account for the difference in behavior.

8-30. Why is aqua regia used to dissolve mercury(II) sulfide?

8-31. Mercury(II) sulfide is insoluble in 3 M HNO_3 and yet bismuth sulfide, which has a lower solubility product, is dissolved. Account for this.

8-32. What is meant by an "acidic sulfide"? Illustrate by writing appropriate chemical equations for the behavior of SnS_2.

8-33. Ammonium sulfide solution is virtually an equimolar mixture of ammonia and ammonium hydrogen sulfide. Suggest an explanation for its slight solvent action on copper(II) sulfide.

8-34. By what experiments would you verify that a certain hydroxide was amphoteric?

8-35. One mole of tin(II) hydroxide reacts with one mole of sodium hydroxide to give a clear solution. Suggest several possible formulas for the complex anion that are consistent with the observation. A solid compound with empirical formula $BaSn_2O_3 \cdot 3H_2O$ has been isolated. Rewrite this so that it contains the water combined in complex ions. What does this suggest?

8-36. The solid salt with empirical formula $Na_2CuO_2 \cdot 2H_2O$ loses 1 H_2O above 180° and turns black because of decomposition to CuO and $NaOH$. The second water molecule is not driven off below 500° but is evolved if the mixture is fused with sodium dichromate (sodium chromate is the other product). Show that these observations are consistent with the formula $Na_2Cu(OH)_4$ but not with $Na_2CuO_2 \cdot 2H_2O$.

8-37. Cite evidence in support of the formula $Al(OH)_4^-$ for the aluminate ion.

8-38. Define and give an example of each term: sol, counter ions, lyophobic, digestion, electrophoresis, peptization, double layer.

8-39. Colloidal iron(III) oxide is prepared by hydrolyzing iron(III) chloride:

$$2Fe^{+++} + 6Cl^- + 3H_2O \rightarrow Fe_2O_3 + 6H^+ + 6Cl^-$$

What ions will be in the adsorbed layer and what ions will predominate in the counter ion region?

8-40. What are some consequences of (a) the small size of colloidal particles and (b) the fact that they bear a charge?

8-41. Equimolar solutions of the following substances are added to portions of an arsenic(III) sulfide sol; arrange them in order of increasing volume required to produce flocculation: $CaCl_2$, K_2SO_4, $LaCl_3$, KCl.

8-42. Why is a flocculated sol contaminated with ionic impurities?

8-43. Colloidal arsenic(III) sulfide is readily prepared by passing hydrogen sulfide gas through a saturated solution of the acid:

$$2H_3AsO_3 + 3H_2S \rightarrow As_2S_3 + 6H_2O$$

The same treatment of a solution of arsenic(III) chloride gives a precipitate, not a sol:

$$2AsCl_3 + 3H_2S \rightarrow As_2S_3 + 6H^+ + 6Cl^-$$

Suggest an explanation.

8-44. The following are common techniques or operations in the laboratory work. Explain why each is used.

(a) In forming a precipitate a slight excess of reagent is added but a large excess is avoided.

(b) In precipitating certain substances the solution is stirred vigorously, the stirring rod is rubbed against the inner walls of the tube, and then the mixture is set aside for several minutes.

(c) Precipitates are often heated for several minutes in the solution from which they formed before being separated by centrifugation.

(d) Certain precipitates (sulfides and hydroxides) are precipitated from a large volume of solution and others $[K_2NaCo(NO_2)_6]$ from a very small volume.

(e) Precipitates are often washed with water containing a little ammonium chloride.

CHAPTER NINE

The Direction of Reversible Ionic Reactions

9-1. Introduction. Most of the reactions we use in qualitative analysis are reversible. If, after mixing the reagents, we leave a reaction to its own devices, it will proceed spontaneously until an equilibrium state is reached. The direction of spontaneous reaction will not depend on how we may have chosen to write the chemical equation for the reaction. If we know the direction of spontaneous change, our equation will generally show this as the reaction from left to right. But sometimes, if the direction of reaction is unknown beforehand or for other reasons, the spontaneous change may correspond to the equation read in the opposite direction. The problem of predicting the direction of spontaneous reaction is a fundamental one, and the extent to which we can do this from equilibrium principles is explored in this chapter. Criteria for establishing the direction will be formulated first with equilibrium constants. In later sections of the chapter these criteria will be recast in other forms appropriate for the use of electrical and thermochemical data. Finally, some of the limitations of equilibrium principles will be summarized.

9-2. The Study of Ionic Reactions. Typical ionic reactions occur when we mix solutions of barium nitrate and ammonium sulfate or solutions of hydrochloric acid and sodium hydroxide. We know that both reactions eventually come to equilibrium. If we wish to establish the equilibrium point exactly, we must stopper the test tubes in which the reactions take place so that no extraneous matter can get in, and none of the contents can spill out. In addition, we must set the tubes in a thermostated bath so that their temperatures come to some fixed value. Then if portions of each mixture are withdrawn from time to time and tested, it will be found that the properties of the mixture, e.g., the hydrogen ion concentration or the specific conductance, change from one sample to the next. The change is pronounced at first and then gradually becomes smaller until eventually no further change in properties

195

occurs. We then assume that the system is at equilibrium. The rate of establishment of equilibrium is exceedingly rapid for the reaction between hydrochloric acid and sodium hydroxide but is slower for the precipitation of barium sulfate. We have seen in Chapters 7 and 8 that the equilibrium states are characterized by equilibrium constants that are relations between the concentrations of substances in solution.

The properties of these systems will remain the same as long as no disturbance of equilibrium takes place. Displacement away from equilibrium requires a change in conditions. If the tube containing barium sulfate and its saturated solution is removed from the thermostat and heated over a gas burner, the solution is no longer saturated, and some barium sulfate dissolves to restore equilibrium. The displacement is accomplished at the expense of the combustion of gas, an oxidation reaction which brings the mixture of gas and air to an equilibrium of its own.

Some generalizations suggested by these experiments are expressions of general experience. All chemical systems when left to themselves tend toward an equilibrium state. A displacement of a system away from equilibrium occurs only at the expense of progression of another system toward its own equilibrium state. These statements are restricted versions of a more general summary of experience, entitled impressively the *second law of thermodynamics*.

The reactions that we carry out in qualitative analysis are not so carefully controlled as those described in the first paragraph. The temperature may change during the reaction, and a careful check is not usually made to see that equilibrium is attained. A study of carefully controlled reactions and reproducible equilibrium states will nevertheless be a useful guide in understanding reactions as carried out in the laboratory.

9-3. The Equilibrium Constant and Direction of Reaction.   We found in Chapter 3 that ionic reactions are associated with removal of ions from the field of action. In a reaction such as that between lead chloride and sodium sulfate, reaction occurs because the lead sulfate is less soluble than lead chloride and wins the competition for lead ions. We seek now a more quantitative method of predicting the direction of an ionic reaction. The use of equilibrium constants for this purpose was suggested in Sec. 7-13, and we shall review the method briefly.

Consider the equilibrium that results when pure, anhydrous acetic acid is put in water. It is expressed by

$$HC_2H_3O_2 \rightleftharpoons H^+ + C_2H_3O_2^- \qquad K_a = \frac{[H^+][C_2H_3O_2^-]}{[HC_2H_3O_2]} = 1.8 \times 10^{-5}$$

The ionization reaction occurs to only a slight extent, and this is indicated by the small numerical value of the ionization constant. Conversely, if sodium acetate and hydrochloric acid are mixed, the reverse of the ionization reaction occurs:

$$H^+ + C_2H_3O_2^- \rightarrow HC_2H_3O_2 \qquad K = \frac{1}{K_a} = \frac{[HC_2H_3O_2]}{[H^+][C_2H_3O_2^-]} = 5.6 \times 10^4$$

As we would expect from the large value of its constant, this reaction occurs to a large extent. The displacement of copper by zinc

$$Cu^{++} + Zn^0 \rightarrow Zn^{++} + Cu^0 \qquad K = \frac{[Zn^{++}]}{[Cu^{++}]} = 10^{37}$$

goes virtually to completion.

Let us summarize these ideas. Suppose that we are given a chemical equation and the equilibrium constant that corresponds to it.[1] Then, if the value of the constant is very large, the reaction will normally proceed in the direction that is indicated by reading the chemical equation from left to right. If the constant is very small, the reaction will normally go in the reverse direction. The word "normally" is inserted to allow for the possibility of changing the direction of reaction by varying the concentrations.

A reaction can often be driven further by increasing the concentrations of the reactants or reversed by increasing those of the products. Copper can even be made to displace zinc if the concentration of cupric ion is reduced to a sufficient extent. As we have seen, when pure acetic acid is added to water some ionization does occur because no acetate ions are originally present. Yet the small value of the ionization constant indicates that if approximately equal amounts of acetic acid, hydrogen ions, and acetate ions are mixed, the spontaneous reaction will be the reverse of ionization. Equilibrium constants are most useful for deciding the direction of a reaction when all substances, reactants and products, are at comparable concentrations, and no concentration is very high or very low. This restriction is very important if the value of the equilibrium constant is close to one, for then the reaction is easily sent in one direction or the other by small changes in concentrations. The effect of concentrations is considered further in Sec. 9-5.

9-4. Combination of Equilibrium Constants. For many reactions the equilibrium constant is not found directly in a table. It is frequently possible, however, to combine tabular values of ionization constants and solubility products to give the required constant. Two ways of doing this will be described.

Method A. If a given equation can be represented as the sum (or

---

[1]By this we mean (Sec. 7-10) that the numerator of the equilibrium constant contains the product of the concentrations of the substances on the right-hand side of the chemical equation and the denominator contains the product of those on the left-hand side.

difference) of two equations, the equilibrium constant is the product (or quotient) of the equilibrium constants of the separate steps.[2]

Method B. Start with the expression for the equilibrium constant and look for some combination of known constants that gives this. This is a simpler but somewhat more intuitive method than the first.

The use of these methods is best learned from specific examples.

EXAMPLE 1.

$$Ag_2CrO_4 \downarrow + 2Cl^- \rightleftharpoons 2AgCl \downarrow + CrO_4^{--} \qquad K = \frac{[CrO_4]^{--}}{[Cl^-]^2}$$

According to Method A, this is split into two reactions with known equilibrium constants:

I. $Ag_2CrO_4 \downarrow \rightleftharpoons 2Ag^+ + CrO_4^{--} \qquad K_{sp} = [Ag^+]^2[CrO_4^{--}]$

II. $2AgCl \downarrow \rightleftharpoons 2Ag^+ + 2Cl^- \qquad K_{sp}^2 = [Ag^+]^2[Cl^-]^2$

The required equation is the difference between these. The required constant is the quotient of the two: $K_{sp}(Ag_2CrO_4)/K_{sp}^2(AgCl)$.

According to Method B, we recognize that there are two precipitates in the reaction and look for some combination of their solubility products. If this is not seen at a glance, it can be inferred after a little juggling. The numerator is transformed into the solubility product of silver chromate if we multiply it by $[Ag^+]^2$, but then we must do the same to the denominator:

$$K \frac{[Ag^+]^2}{[Ag^+]^2} = \frac{[Ag^+]^2[CrO_4^{--}]}{[Ag^+]^2[Cl^-]^2} = \frac{K_{sp}(Ag_2CrO_4)}{K_{sp}^2(AgCl)} = \frac{2.44 \times 10^{-12}}{(1.77 \times 10^{-10})^2}$$

$$= 7.8 \times 10^7$$

[2]Chemical equations for reversible reactions are not strictly algebraic. Consider the ionization of hydrogen sulfide:

I. $H_2S \rightleftharpoons H^+ + HS^- \qquad K_1 = 1 \times 10^{-7}$
II. $HS^- \rightleftharpoons H^+ + S^{--} \qquad K_2 = 1.3 \times 10^{-13}$

III. $H_2S \rightleftharpoons 2H^+ + S^{--} \qquad K = K_1K_2 = 1.3 \times 10^{-20}$

The first equation is correctly read as "each mole of H_2S that ionizes gives one mole of H^+ and one mole of HS^- ion." The second equation can be read correctly as "each mole of HS^- ion that ionizes further gives one mole each of H^+ and S^{--} ions." But the sum (III) *cannot* be read as "each mole of H_2S that ionizes gives 2 moles of H^+ ion and 1 mole of S^{--} ion" because only a small fraction f of the HS^- ions produced in I ionizes in II. A correct statement would be "each mole of H_2S that ionizes produces ultimately $(1 + f)$ moles of H^+ ion, $(1 - f)$ moles of HS^- ion, and f moles of S^{--} ion"—but this is too cumbersome to express by a chemical equation.

Equilibrium constants are strictly algebraic expressions. The combination $K = K_1K_2$ is equivalent to

$$\left(\frac{ab}{c}\right)\left(\frac{ad}{b}\right) = \frac{a^2d}{c}$$

The constant K is a perfectly reputable expression, although it apparently corresponds to the disreputable Equation III. In using it, however, we must be careful not to introduce factitious relations such as $[H^+] = 2[S^{--}]$ that follow by misinterpretation of III.

The large value of this constant shows that the conversion of silver chromate to silver chloride should occur.

EXAMPLE 2.

$$CO_3^{--} + H_2O \rightleftharpoons HCO_3^- + OH^- \qquad K = \frac{[HCO_3^-][OH^-]}{[CO_3^{--}]}$$

In this example there is a competition between two weak electrolytes, H_2O and HCO_3^- ion, for a proton. Constants for the ionization reactions are given in tables:

I. $\quad H_2O \quad \rightleftharpoons H^+ + OH^- \qquad K_w \quad = [H^+][OH^-] = 1.0 \times 10^{-14}$

II. $\quad HCO_3^- \rightleftharpoons H^+ + CO_3^{--} \qquad K_{HCO_3^-} = \dfrac{[H^+][CO_3^{--}]}{[HCO_3^-]} = 4.7 \times 10^{-11}$

The given chemical equation is the algebraic difference between Equations I and II, and K is the ratio $K_w/K_{HCO_3^-} = 2.1 \times 10^{-4}$.

The alternative way of finding this relation is

$$K\frac{[H^+]}{[H^+]} = [H^+][OH^-] \times \frac{[HCO_3^-]}{[H^+][CO_3^{--}]} = \frac{K_w}{K_{HCO_3^-}} = \frac{1.0 \times 10^{-14}}{4.7 \times 10^{-11}} = 2.1 \times 10^{-4}$$

The small value of K shows that this reaction occurs to only a limited extent.

EXAMPLE 3.

$$Cd^{++} + H_2S \rightleftharpoons CdS \downarrow + 2H^+ \qquad K = \frac{[H^+]^2}{[Cd^{++}][H_2S]}$$

Constants for the following equilibria are given in tables:

I. $\quad CdS \downarrow \rightleftharpoons Cd^{++} + S^{--} \qquad K_{sp} = [Cd^{++}][S^{--}] = 7 \times 10^{-27}$

II. $\quad H_2S \quad \rightleftharpoons H^+ + HS^- \qquad K_{H_2S} = \dfrac{[H^+][HS^-]}{[H_2S]} = 1 \times 10^{-7}$

III. $\quad HS^- \quad \rightleftharpoons H^+ + S^{--} \qquad K_{HS^-} = \dfrac{[H^+][S^{--}]}{[HS^-]} = 1.3 \times 10^{-13}$

The given equation is the sum of II and III minus I. Hence

$$K = \frac{K_{H_2S}\,K_{HS^-}}{K_{sp}} = \frac{1 \times 10^{-7} \times 1.3 \times 10^{-13}}{7 \times 10^{-27}} = 1.9 \times 10^6$$

We can arrive at the same combination by operating on K directly:

$$K\frac{[HS^-]\,[S^{--}]}{[HS^-]\,[S^{--}]} = \frac{[H^+][HS^-]}{[H_2S]}\frac{[H^+][S^{--}]}{[HS^-]}\frac{1}{[Cd^{++}][S^{--}]} = \frac{K_{H_2S}\,K_{HS^-}}{K_{sp}}$$

The large value of K shows that conversion of Cd^{++} to CdS should occur to a large extent.

9-5. The Effect of Concentrations on Direction of Reactions. We know that the precipitation of cadmium sulfide is reversible, for it is dissolved by strong acid, and it cannot be precipitated if the solution is too acid. Even though the equilibrium constant is large, the extent of precipitation will depend critically on the hydrogen ion concentration. The reaction of carbonate ion with water can also be reversed by addition of sodium hydroxide. Silver chloride can be converted to silver chromate if the chromate ion concentration is made very high and the chloride ion concentration very low. These are all examples of the common ion effect.

The effect of changes in concentration can also be shown schematically by using large symbols for high concentrations and small symbols for low ones.

EXAMPLE 1. $Ag_2CrO_4 \downarrow + 2Cl^- \rightleftharpoons 2AgCl \downarrow + CrO_4^{--}$

original equilibrium

$$K = 7.8 \times 10^7 = \frac{[CrO_4^{--}]}{[Cl^-]^2}$$

at instant of addition of K_2CrO_4

$$7.8 \times 10^7 < \frac{[CrO_4^{--}]}{[Cl^-]^2}$$

new equilibrium

$$7.8 \times 10^7 = \frac{[CrO_4^{--}]}{[Cl^-]^2}$$

EXAMPLE 2. $CO_3^{--} + H_2O \rightleftharpoons HCO_3^- + OH^-$

original equilibrium

$$K = 2.1 \times 10^{-4} = \frac{[HCO_3^-][OH^-]}{[CO_3^{--}]}$$

at instant of addition of NaOH

$$2.1 \times 10^{-4} < \frac{[HCO_3^-][OH^-]}{[CO_3^{--}]}$$

new equilibrium

$$2.1 \times 10^{-4} = \frac{[HCO_3^-][OH^-]}{[CO_3^{--}]}$$

EXAMPLE 3. $Cd^{++} + H_2S \rightleftharpoons CdS \downarrow + 2H^+$

original equilibrium

$$K = 1.9 \times 10^6 = \frac{[H^+]^2}{[Cd^{++}][H_2S]}$$

at instant of addition of HCl

$$1.9 \times 10^6 < \frac{[H^+]^2}{[Cd^{++}][H_2S]}$$

new equilibrium

$$1.9 \times 10^6 = \frac{[H^+]^2}{[Cd^{++}][H_2S]}$$

The second concentration ratio in each example is of the same form as the equilibrium expression but has a larger numerical value. Let Q stand for the concentration ratio regardless of whether or not the system is at equilibrium.[3] The form of Q is such that at equilibrium it becomes identical with the equilibrium constant: $Q_{eq} = K$. In the examples above the systems are not at equilibrium at the instant of mixing, $K < Q$, and the reactions go from right to left or the reverse of the way the chemical equations are written. The system is also not at equilibrium if $K > Q$, but reaction will now occur from left to right. The following examples show the application of these ideas.

EXAMPLE A. Some solid silver chromate is shaken with a solution that contains 0.2 mole of K_2CrO_4 and 0.1 mole of NaCl per liter. Will any silver chloride form?

The chemical equation has been written in the preceding paragraph and K is 7.8×10^7; $Q = 0.2/(0.1)^2 = 20$, which is less than K. Hence the reaction will go from left to right and some silver chloride will form.

EXAMPLE B. Suppose equal volumes of 0.04 M calcium nitrate and 0.02 M sodium fluoride are mixed. Will any calcium fluoride precipitate?

From the table of solubility products we find

$$CaF_2 \rightarrow \rightleftharpoons Ca^{++} + 2F^- \qquad K_{sp} = [Ca^{++}][F^-]^2 = 1.7 \times 10^{-10}$$

As a result of mixing equal volumes, each reagent is diluted to one-half its initial concentration. Therefore, at the instant of mixing $[Ca^{++}] = 0.02$ M and $[F^-] = 0.01$ M. Then $Q = 0.02 \times (0.01)^2 = 2 \times 10^{-6}$. Since this is much larger than K, the reaction goes from right to left, and calcium fluoride should precipitate. We have found (Sec. 8-8) that Q must exceed K to a considerable extent, as it does in this example, if supersaturation is to be overcome.

[3] See Secs. 8-8 and 8-15 for the use of Q to express the conditions for formation and dissolution of precipitates.

The conclusions of this section can be summarized in two ways:[4]

$$\left.\begin{array}{l} \text{at equilibrium: } K = Q \\ \text{reaction from left to right: } K > Q \\ \text{reaction from right to left: } K < Q \end{array}\right\} \qquad \textbf{1}$$

If each relation is divided by Q, we obtain another version of these criteria of the direction of reaction:

$$\left.\begin{array}{l} \text{at equilibrium: } K/Q = 1 \\ \text{reaction from left to right: } K/Q > 1 \\ \text{reaction from right to left: } K/Q < 1 \end{array}\right\} \qquad \textbf{2}$$

These are two versions of the same principle, and still others will be developed in subsequent sections. All are expressions of the second law of thermodynamics; i.e., for every reaction there is a "downhill" direction that leads to equilibrium, and in this direction the reaction proceeds spontaneously. The criteria for establishing the direction that have been developed in this section are for systems held at a fixed temperature and pressure (Sec. 9-2).

9-6. A Logarithmic Version of the Criteria for Direction of Reaction. Logarithms are familiar tools for computations, but this humble role is not their only one. They have many convenient properties, several of which make them useful in expressing equilibrium relations. The logarithm of y to the base a is defined by

$$\log_a y = x, \qquad \text{if} \qquad y = a^x \qquad \textbf{3}$$

A large variation in the quantity y corresponds to a small variation in its logarithm x; e.g., if y changes from 10^{-5} to 10^{+4}, x varies only from -5 to $+4$. Logarithms can thus be used to condense a wide range of values of equilibrium constants into a narrower, more convenient scale.

Logarithms have another property that makes them convenient to use. The logarithm of a product is the sum of the logarithms of the factors, or

$$\text{if } p = qr, \qquad \text{then} \qquad \log p = \log q + \log r \qquad \textbf{4}$$

Likewise, the logarithm of a quotient is obtained by subtracting the logarithm of the denominator from that of the numerator, or

$$\text{if } p = q/r, \qquad \text{then} \qquad \log p = \log q - \log r \qquad \textbf{5}$$

We have seen that if chemical equations are added or subtracted, their equilibrium constants are combined by multiplication or division. But the *logarithms* of these equilibrium constants will be added or subtracted in the

---

[4]In learning these relations you may find it convenient to visualize the inequality sign as part of an arrowhead pointing in the direction of the reaction.

same way as the chemical equations. Consider, for example, the conversion of barium sulfate to barium carbonate:

$$BaSO_4 + CO_3^{--} \rightarrow BaCO_3 + SO_4^{--} \qquad K = [SO_4^{--}]/[CO_3^{--}]$$

This is equivalent to the difference between equations I and II:

I. $\quad BaSO_4 \rightleftharpoons Ba^{++} + SO_4^{--} \qquad K_I = 1.0 \times 10^{-10} \qquad \log K_I = -10.0$

II. $\quad BaCO_3 \rightleftharpoons Ba^{++} + CO_3^{--} \qquad K_{II} = 1.6 \times 10^{-9} \qquad \log K_{II} = -8.8$

Since $K = K_I/K_{II}$, $\log K = \log K_I - \log K_{II} = -10.0 - (-8.8) = -1.2$.

The criteria for direction of a reaction given in relation 2 of the preceding section have a particularly simple logarithmic version because the logarithm of 1 is zero:

$$\left. \begin{array}{l} \text{at equilibrium: } \log K/Q = 0 \\ \text{reaction from left to right: } \log K/Q > 0 \text{ (or positive)} \\ \text{reaction from right to left: } \log K/Q < 0 \text{ (or negative)} \end{array} \right\} \qquad 6$$

9-7. The Direction of Redox Reactions. It is customary to describe the equilibrium state of a redox reaction not by an equilibrium constant but by a *standard electromotive force* $\mathcal{E}^0$. For our purposes at this point, it will be sufficient to note that for a redox reaction $\mathcal{E}^0$ is proportional to the logarithm of its equilibrium constant:

$$\mathcal{E}^0 \propto \log_{10} K \qquad 7$$

We have learned that a large equilibrium constant corresponds to a reaction that normally goes from left to right spontaneously, and that, for a small equilibrium constant, the reaction normally goes in the reverse direction. Since the logarithm of a large number is positive and that of a number less than 1 is negative,[5] these criteria can be adapted for use with $\mathcal{E}^0$:

$$\left. \begin{array}{l} \text{reaction from left to right: } \mathcal{E}^0 > 0 \\ \text{reaction from right to left: } \mathcal{E}^0 < 0 \\ \text{indecisive: } \mathcal{E}^0 \simeq 0 \end{array} \right\} \qquad 8$$

No direction can be specified for the last, borderline situation, for the reaction can be driven in either direction by comparatively small changes in concentrations. This is also true of reactions for which K is close to 1. The first two conditions in 8 are satisfactory criteria as long as all substances are at comparable concentrations (Sec. 9-3).

When redox reactions are carried out in electric cells, a transfer of electrons occurs from one electrode to the other through a connecting wire. Thus it is possible (and relatively simple) to study redox reactions by making electrical measurements. This is the reason that the direction of a redox reaction is usually decided by reference to the standard electromotive force

---

[5]Note, for example, that $\log 0.1 = -1$, $\log 0.001 = -3$, or $\log 10^{-x} = -x$. The logarithm of $\frac{1}{2}$ is equal to $-\log 2 = -0.30$, though this is often obscured as $9.70 - 10$ or as $\bar{1}.70$.

rather than to the equilibrium constant. The measurement of electromotive force is discussed in Chapter 15.

9-8. Standard Oxidation Potentials.   It is convenient to consider any redox reaction as the difference between two oxidation half reactions (Sec. 3-13). The oxidation of iron(II) ion by chlorine, for example, can be written

I. $2Fe^{++} \rightarrow 2Fe^{+++} + 2e^-$ $\mathcal{E}^0(Fe^{++} \rightarrow Fe^{+++}) = -0.77$ v

II. $2Cl^- \rightarrow Cl_2 + 2e^-$ $\mathcal{E}^0(Cl^- \rightarrow Cl_2) = -1.36$ v

The over-all reaction is the difference I − II:

$$2Fe^{++} + Cl_2 \rightarrow 2Fe^{+++} + 2Cl^- \qquad \mathcal{E}^0_t = -0.77 - (-1.36) = +0.59 \text{ v}$$

The standard electromotive force of the redox reaction is the difference between the two *standard oxidation potentials* for the half reactions. The oxidation potential for the oxidizing agent (chlorine in this example) is always subtracted from that for the reducing agent. According to relation 8, the positive value of the standard electromotive force means that the oxidation of iron(II) ions by chlorine will go spontaneously from left to right when all solutes are at about unit concentration, and the pressure of chlorine gas is 1 atm. The value of $\mathcal{E}^0$ is large enough so that the reaction will still occur in this direction even when the concentrations are not held close to unity.

A selection of standard oxidation potentials at 25° is given in the Appendix. For qualitative information about the extent of the reaction the actual calculation of $\mathcal{E}^0$ is usually unnecessary. Any reducing agent (to the left of the arrows in the table) will reduce any oxidizing agent (to the right of the arrows) below it in the table. This combination gives a positive $\mathcal{E}^0$ or a large K. The following example will illustrate the use of the table.

EXAMPLE. What reaction occurs between hydrogen peroxide and iron(II) sulfate in acid solution?

Possibility A. Hydrogen peroxide reduces iron(II) to metallic iron and is oxidized to oxygen. In the table we find

$$H_2O_2 \rightarrow O_2 + 2H^+ + 2e^- \qquad \mathcal{E}^0 = -0.68 \text{ v}$$
$$Fe \rightarrow Fe^{++} + 2e^- \qquad \mathcal{E}^0 = +0.44 \text{ v}$$

Clearly this reaction will not occur to an appreciable extent. Hydrogen peroxide, the reducing agent, is below Fe^{++} ion, the oxidizing agent, in the table. Or $\mathcal{E}^0_t = -0.68 - 0.44 = -1.12$ v, which is large and negative.

Possibility B. Hydrogen peroxide oxidizes iron(II) to iron(III) and is reduced to water. In the table we find

$$2H_2O \rightarrow H_2O_2 + 2H^+ + 2e^- \qquad \mathcal{E}^0 = -1.77 \text{ v}$$
$$2Fe^{++} \rightarrow 2Fe^{+++} + 2e^- \qquad \mathcal{E}^0 = -0.77 \text{ v}$$

This reaction will go, because Fe^{++} ion, the reducing agent, is above hydrogen peroxide, the oxidizing agent. Or $\mathcal{E}_t^0 = -0.77 - (-1.77) = +1.00$ v, which is large and positive.

9-9. The Free Energy Change and the Direction of Reaction. We have used K and $\mathcal{E}^0$ to express the criteria for the direction of a chemical reaction when all concentrations are about the same, and we have used K/Q or $\log(K/Q)$ when changes in concentration can affect the direction. The same basic principle is restated in this section in terms of the change in free energy ΔF. The introduction of ΔF may seem like pouring wine from clear glass bottles into dark brown ones. But there are advantages to expressing the same principle in various ways, particularly when the data are derived from several different types of experiments. Free energy changes are frequently obtained from thermochemical measurements.[6]

To begin with, let us regard ΔF as a quantity that is proportional to $-\log(K/Q)$. Then the criteria expressed in relation 6 of Sec. 9-6 can be rewritten as

$$\left.\begin{array}{l}\text{at equilibrium } \Delta F = 0 \\ \text{reaction from left to right: } \Delta F < 0 \text{ (decrease in free energy)} \\ \text{reaction from right to left: } \Delta F > 0 \text{ (increase in free energy)}\end{array}\right\} \quad 9$$

These relations constitute a general test of what a system will do if left to itself at constant temperature and pressure and are thus another expression of the second law of thermodynamics. They merely rephrase the same ideas previously expressed in relations 2 and 6.

The sign of ΔF necessarily depends on the way the chemical equation is written. Suppose the free energy change ΔF_1 for the equation $A + B \rightarrow C$ is negative (spontaneous reaction from left to right). If the equation is reversed to read $C \rightarrow A + B$, K and Q are inverted, the sign of $\log(K/Q)$ is changed, and the free energy change for this equation, though numerically the same as ΔF_1, is positive (reaction from right to left). These changes in sign with the direction of the equation are necessary, for A and B spontaneously react to give C, whether we write the equation from left to right, right to left, north to south, or east to west. If this were not so, we would have to write the equation and hold it up for the system to read before any reaction could occur.

For making calculations it is useful to know the exact relation between ΔF and $\log(K/Q)$. It is

$$\Delta F = -2.3RT \log(K/Q) \qquad 10$$

where R is a constant and T is the absolute temperature. No derivation of the factor $2.3RT$ will be attempted here. It may be noted that the number 2.3 converts common logarithms (to the base 10) to natural logarithms (to the

---

[6]Free energy was introduced in Sec. 5-6 in connection with hydration of ions. The name is not a felicitous one—"chemical affinity" would be better—but it is well established.

base $e = 2.7183...$). The factor RT confers on ΔF the dimensions of energy.[7] We shall generally express ΔF in calories or kilogram calories, and the factor $2.3RT$ has the value 1364 cal or 1.364 kcal at 25°C (298°A).

9-10. Standard Free Energies of Formation. It is not convenient or necessary to tabulate free energy changes for a multitude of different conditions. Suppose that we arbitrarily choose a standard way of carrying out the reaction: let all reactants and products in solution be at unit concentration and all gaseous reactants and products be at one atmosphere pressure. Then $Q = 1$ since all its factors are unity. Eq. 10 then becomes

$$\Delta F^0 = -2.3RT \log K \qquad\qquad 11$$

The superscript zero is used to indicate that the reaction is carried out in this standard way. The quantity ΔF^0 is called the *standard free energy change* of the reaction. It may be surmised correctly that for redox reactions this quantity is proportional to $\mathcal{E}^0$.

We have seen that the logarithms of equilibrium constants can be added or subtracted in the same way as the chemical equations to which they correspond. This is likewise true of ΔF^0 values. Consider as an example the reaction $CuS \downarrow \rightleftharpoons Cu^{++} + S^{--}$. This can be split into three steps:

I.	$2e^- + S \rightarrow S^{--}$	$\Delta F^0_I = +20.6$ kcal
II.	$Cu \rightarrow Cu^{++} + 2e^-$	$\Delta F^0_{II} = 15.5$ kcal
III.	$Cu + S \rightarrow CuS \downarrow$	$\Delta F^0_{III} = -11.7$ kcal

The given reaction is obtained from I + II − III. The standard free energy change is given by

$$\Delta F^0_I + \Delta F^0_{II} - \Delta F^0_{III} = 20.6 + 15.5 - (-11.7) = 47.8 \text{ kcal}$$

This large positive value means that if copper(II) and sulfide ions are mixed so that each is at 1 M concentration, reaction from right to left, i.e., precipitation of CuS, occurs to a large extent.

Equations I, II, and III represent the formation of S^{--}, Cu^{++}, and CuS from the elements. The free energy changes are called the *standard free energies of formation*, ΔF^0_f. Selected values of this property are given in a table in the Appendix. These are standard free energies per mole, and they must be multiplied by the number of moles specified in the chemical equation. Let any chemical reaction be represented by the equation

$$aA + bB + ... \rightleftharpoons xX + yY + ...$$

[7]The product RT also occurs in the ideal gas equation $PV = RT$ for a mole of gas. For that reason R is called the "gas constant." At 0° when the pressure of the gas is in atmospheres and its volume is in liters per mole, RT has the value 22.4 1-atm per mole. If the pressure is 1 atmosphere, this is the volume of a mole at 0°C.

Then the standard free energy change for this reaction is obtained from the standard free energies of formation by

$$\Delta F^0 = x\Delta F_f^0(X) + y\Delta F_f^0(Y) + \ldots -a\Delta F_f^0(A) -b\Delta F_f^0(B) - \ldots \qquad 12$$

For the example above,

$$\Delta F^0 = \Delta F_f^0(Cu^{++}) + \Delta F_f^0(S^{--}) - \Delta F_f^0(CuS)$$

and for $Bi_2S_3 \downarrow \rightleftharpoons 2Bi^{+++} + 3S^{--}$,

$$\Delta F^0 = 2\Delta F_f^0(Bi^{+++}) + 3\Delta F_f^0(S^{--}) - \Delta F_f^0(Bi_2S_3)$$

As an example of the usefulness of the standard free energy data, consider the problem of determining the solubility product of copper(II) sulfide. The direct determination of the solubility and K_{sp} of this substance is an exceedingly difficult experimental problem, for the total amount of the compound that dissolves is exceedingly minute and is influenced by unavoidable side reactions such as the hydrolysis of the sulfide ion. It is more practicable to determine the solubility product by using standard free energies of formation obtained from thermal data. We have found that $\Delta F^0 = 47.8$ kcal at $25°$, and $2.3RT = 1.364$ kcal. Substituting these in Eq. 11, we obtain

$$47.8 = -1.364 \log K_{sp}$$

$$\log K_{sp} = \frac{-47.8}{1.364} = -35.0$$

$$K_{sp} = \text{antilog}\,(-35.0) = \boxed{1 \times 10^{-35}}$$

A table of standard free energies thus makes it possible to calculate equilibrium constants that are difficult, if not impossible, to determine directly.

The manipulation of logarithms in these calculations requires some comment. The logarithm of an equilibrium constant is a number that can be handled like any other number. Suppose, for example, that we know that the ionization constant of acetic acid is 1.75×10^{-5} at $25°$ and we wish to find the standard free energy change for the ionization reaction. Then

$$\log K_a = \log\,(1.75 \times 10^{-5}) = \log 1.75 + \log 10^{-5}$$

$$= 0.24 - 5 = -4.76$$

and by Eq. 11

$$\Delta F^0 = -1.364 \times (-4.76) = \boxed{6.49 \text{ kcal}}$$

Here the logarithm has been treated as an ordinary number in multiplication. It is a negative number because K is less than one.

The operation of finding K when $\log K$ is known sometimes gives students trouble. If log K is positive, the antilog of the mantissa is found directly from the table of logarithms and the characteristic gives the power of ten, for example,

$$\log K = 15.7$$
$$K = \text{antilog } 15.7 = (\text{antilog } 0.7)\,(\text{antilog } 15) = 5 \times 10^{15}$$

If log K is a negative number, it must be transformed so that the mantissa is positive. This is most easily done by adding and subtracting the next whole number larger than the characteristic. For example, if log $K = -29.7$, add and subtract 30 to get $0.3 - 30$. This is numerically still -29.7, but the mantissa is positive and its antilog can be found in a table of logarithms; the -30 gives the power of ten:

$$K = (\text{antilog } 0.3)\,(\text{antilog } -30) = 2 \times 10^{-30}$$

9-11. Logarithmic Relations in Theoretical Chemistry.   Logarithms are most familiar as useful tools for performing multiplications, divisions, and extraction of roots. They were first introduced in this chapter as convenient devices for expressing a wide range of values of equilibrium constants on a narrow, less awkward scale. Then it was shown that logarithms of equilibrium constants had the further convenient property of combining by addition and subtraction in the same way as chemical equations. But the subsequent introduction of $\mathcal{E}^0$ and $\varDelta F^0$, properties proportional to log K, indicates that the significance of logarithms goes beyond mere convenience.

There are many logarithmic relations in theoretical chemistry. These are really transformations of more fundamental exponential relations. The exponential function is e^x, where e is the irrational number $2.7183\ldots$; it is related to natural (Naperian) logarithms by the equation $\log_e e^x = x$. Graphs of e^x for positive and negative values of x are given in Fig. 9-1. Exponential functions frequently occur in growth and decay laws, such as the growth in rate of hydrolysis of thioacetamide with rising temperature, the decay or disintegration of a radioactive isotope, or—to cite an example from another science—the unrestricted growth of a colony of amoebas. All the growth curves have a common feature: the rate of growth is slow at first but accelerates rapidly. This is exactly the form of the exponential curve $y = e^x$ in Fig. 9-1a.[8]

We learned in Chapter 7 that an equilibrium constant could be expressed as the ratio of two rate constants. The latter change with temperature according to an exponential law, and therefore K too can be expressed by an

---

[8]These ideas are expressed more neatly in the language of the differential calculus. If $y = e^x$, $dy/dx = y$, or the rate of change of y is proportional to y itself. Thus the rate of decay of a radioactive isotope is proportional to N, the number of atoms of that isotope present at a given time t, for N is given by $N = N_0 e^{-kt}$ where N_0 is the initial number of atoms and k is the rate constant for the decay.

exponential relation. This follows also from Eq. 11, for the equation

$$\Delta F^0 = -2.3RT \log_{10} K = -RT \log_e K$$

is equivalent to

$$K = e^{-\Delta F^0/RT}$$

The purpose of these passing remarks is to call attention to the prevalence of exponential or logarithmic relations in any description of natural processes and to emphasize that logarithms are more than convenient tools. A detailed treatment of such processes must be deferred to later courses.

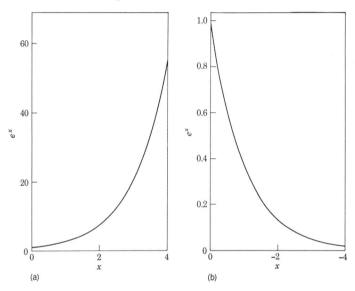

FIG. 9-1. The exponential function. (a) The growth curve. (b) The decay curve.

9-12. A Summary. The general problem considered in this chapter has been the prediction of the direction of a reversible reaction for some prescribed temperature, pressure, and concentrations. If the reaction is carried out in a standard way, i.e., with solutes at unit concentrations and gases at unit pressure, the problem can be solved by examination of K, ΔF^0, or $\mathcal{E}^0$. If K is large, if ΔF^0 is negative, or if $\mathcal{E}^0$ is positive, the reaction will proceed from left to right as indicated by the chemical equation. The quantities K, ΔF^0, and $\mathcal{E}^0$ are given in tables for many reactions. Equilibrium constants for reactions that are not in tables can be obtained by multiplication or division of known constants. Values of ΔF^0 that are not given in tables can be obtained by addition or subtraction of known values of ΔF_f^0. Values of $\mathcal{E}^0$ for redox reactions are obtained as the difference between two oxidation potentials from a table.

If the prescribed conditions are not standard, i.e., if the concentrations differ from unity, the direction will often still be indicated by examination of K, ΔF^0, or $\mathcal{E}^0$ as long as K is not close to 1 and the other two are not close to zero. If this is not true or in any case of doubt, the direction of reaction must be determined by examination of K/Q or of ΔF. If the former is greater than 1 or the latter is negative, reaction occurs from left to right.

9-13. The Limitations of Predictions Based on Equilibrium Principles. While the methods of prediction developed in the preceding sections have a sound theoretical basis, there are certain practical difficulties in their application that limit their usefulness. This need not prevent us from making predictions any more than the knowledge that accidents happen prevents us from crossing streets. But in either situation we must learn to keep our eyes open. We shall now consider some of the limitations.

1. Limitations Inherent in the Available Data. In making predictions we are dependent on tables of ionization constants, solubility products, standard free energies, and oxidation potentials. Certain problems arise in the use of these values.

a. Missing data. Since there are thousands of chemical compounds, it is not surprising that in many cases the value of the property of a compound that we are interested in may not have been measured.

b. Different conditions. The data in tables are usually for a temperature of 25°, a pressure of 1 atmosphere, and aqueous solutions. We frequently carry out reactions at higher temperatures. The range of temperatures for reactions in solutions lies between the freezing and boiling points. Over this fairly narrow range equilibrium constants do not usually change by more than one hundred-fold. This will generally not materially affect predictions about the direction of reaction, although it will change quantitative estimates of the extent. The pressure seldom varies much from 1 atmosphere unless we elect to study ionic equilibria below the surface of the ocean. A change in solvent can make a big difference in the direction of a reaction, but our interest is almost altogether centered on water solutions.

c. Accuracy of the data. The data in tables can vary considerably in reliability. The ionization constant of acetic acid at 25° is found by con- ductance measurements to be 1.753×10^{-5} and by measurements on electric cells to be 1.749×10^{-5}. These results agree within 0.2%, far more closely than our rough calculations require, and our confidence in them is increased by the fact that they were obtained by two entirely different methods. The ionization constants of moderately strong acids ($K_a > 0.01$) or very weak acids ($K_a < 10^{-11}$) are much more difficult to determine, and frequently only approximate values are known. The ionization constant of the HS^- ion, for example, was considered to be 1×10^{-15} until recent, more accurate measure- ments proved that it was more than one hundred times as large as this. The solubility products of well-behaved precipitates such as silver chloride are also accurately known. Others, particularly those of sulfides and hydroxides, are difficult to determine and widely differing values will be found in different works of reference. Values of the solubility product of bismuth sulfide, for example, given by various sources range from 10^{-70} to 10^{-96}. Variations of 10^5 in the reported solubility products of other sulfides are not unusual.

2. The Neglect of Interionic Forces.   The effect of ionic strength on equilibrium constants (Sec. 8-7) has been ignored in the preceding sections. In dilute solutions an increase in ionic strength generally makes a weak electrolyte somewhat stronger and a precipitate somewhat more soluble than we would expect. These effects will have an important influence on the direction of a reaction only if its equilibrium constant is close to one. For example, interionic forces make it more difficult to form HSO_4^- ions or to precipitate silver acetate than we might suppose, but their equilibrium constants are comparatively close to 1.

3. Limitations Associated with Rate of Reaction.   We have assumed that reaction occurs spontaneously in a downhill direction toward an equilibrium state. The approach to equilibrium may actually be very slow for reactions with a high activation energy (Sec. 7-4); these reactions must climb uphill before they can coast down to the equilibrium state on the other side. Proton transfer reactions are generally fast although some hydrolysis reactions are slow to come to equilibrium. Many redox reactions are slow. According to the standard oxidation potentials, permanganate ion should oxidize water to oxygen. The rate of this reaction is fortunately very slow if MnO_2, a catalyst for the reaction, is excluded; and permanganate solutions can be kept almost indefinitely at room temperature. Transfer of a substance between phases is also generally a slow process. In the distribution of iodine between water and carbon disulfide, prolonged and vigorous shaking is required to establish equilibrium. Precipitation reactions start with nucleation in supersaturated solutions (Sec. 8-8), frequently a slow process. The dissolution of precipitates can be very slow when surface films prevent contact between the precipitate and fresh reagent (Sec. 8-15).

4. Limitations Caused by Inaccurate Description of the Change.   It is seldom possible in a single chemical equation to show all the changes that occur in a reaction. Frequently several reactions occur in parallel. The reduction of concentrated nitric acid, for example, produces a mixture of oxides of nitrogen. We customarily represent in the equation only the formation of NO_2, the principal product. Other reactions give first an unstable product that gradually changes to the stable form. Freshly precipitated sulfides and hydroxides are usually more soluble than the stable forms to which they change on standing. It is often observed in qualitative analysis that the behavior of a substance by itself is not the same as when it is associated with other substances. For example, the solubility of mercury(II) sulfide in potassium hydroxide in the subdivision of Cation Group 2 depends markedly on the presence or absence of other sulfides of the arsenic section. An equation also gives no indication of the extent to which a precipitate can be contaminated by coprecipitation. These effects may not alter the direction of the chemical reaction, but they can reduce its usefulness for analytical purposes. The reaction must not only go in the right direction; it must also be as free as possible of complicating effects.

The discrepancies between theory and experiment that have just been summarized constitute a challenge to zealous researchers for years to come. On the one side, to make our tables more useful we need more accurate determinations of ionization constants, solubility products, standard oxidation potentials, and standard free energies of formation. The applicability of the constants can be extended if more systematic studies are made of the effects of temperature, solvent, and ionic strength. Our information about these is still surprisingly sketchy. We also need more experimental work and more theoretical insights into the problems of interionic forces, crystal growth, reaction mechanisms, and the like. In the meantime, we use our theoretical predictions as useful, if only approximate, guides and take care always to test them by actual experiment.

SUPPLEMENTARY READING

E. GILREATH, *Qualitative Analysis*, McGraw-Hill, New York, 1954, Chapter 9 (free energy and oxidation-reduction).

T. MOELLER, *Inorganic Chemistry*, Wiley, New York, 1952, Chapter 8 (oxidation potentials).

D. DeFORD, "The Reliability of Calculations Based Upon the Law of Chemical Equilibrium," *J. Chem. Educ.*, **31**, 460 (1954).

J. GOATES, M. GORDON, and N. FAUX, "Calculated Values of the Solubility Product Constants of the Metal Sulfides," *J. Am. Chem. Soc.*, **74**, 835 (1952).

W. KIEFFER, "The Activity Series of the Metals," *J. Chem. Educ.*, **27**, 659 (1950).

D. LEUSSING and I. KOLTHOFF, "The Solubility Product of Ferrous Hydroxide and the Ionization of the Aquo-Ferrous Ion," *J. Am. Chem. Soc.*, **75**, 2476 (1953). This is an interesting account of measurements on a difficult system. The discordant results of earlier workers are summarized.

Sources of Data

W. LATIMER, *The Oxidation States of the Elements and Their Potentials in Aqueous Solutions*, 2nd ed., Prentice-Hall, Englewood Cliffs, N. J., 1952. This is an outstanding source of values of K, $\mathcal{E}^0$, and ΔF^0.

F. ROSSINI, D. WAGMAN, W. EVANS, S. LEVINE, and I. JAFFE, "Selected Values of Chemical Thermodynamic Properties," *Natl. Bur. Standards Circ.*, **500** (1950). This is the best source of values of ΔF_f^0.

H. S. HARNED and B. B. OWEN, *The Physical Chemistry of Electrolytic Solutions*, 3rd ed., Reinhold, New York, 1958. This is the best source of ionization constants.

EXERCISES

Consult the Appendix for equilibrium constants, oxidation potentials, and standard free energies of formation.

9-1. For each of the following pairs (1) write an ionic equation for the most probable reaction; (2) derive the value of the equilibrium constant by combination of constants from tables; and (3) decide whether the reaction will go to an appreciable extent in the direction indicated if all substances in solution are at unit concentration. (a) lead sulfate and sodium sulfide, (b) acetic acid and sodium cyanide, (c) barium sulfate and hydrochloric acid, (d) ammonium nitrate and potassium hydroxide, (e) copper(II) sulfide and hydrochloric acid, (f) strontium sulfate and sodium carbonate, (g) sulfamic acid and sodium acetate, (h) manganese(II) sulfide and hydrochloric acid, (i) calcium oxalate and hydrochloric acid, (j) barium chromate and sodium sulfate.

9-2. The hydroxide ion concentration of a mixture of equimolar quantities of ammonium chloride and ammonia is about 1.8×10^{-5}. Suppose that 0.01 mole each of magnesium chloride and aluminum chloride are added to a liter of the mixture. Will one or both of the hydroxides precipitate? What is K/Q for each hydroxide?

9-3. A mixture that is 0.01 M in HCl and 0.2 M in $Mn(NO_3)_2$ is saturated with hydrogen sulfide at a pressure of 1 atmosphere so that the concentration of H_2S in the solution is 0.1 M. Find K/Q for $Mn^{++} + H_2S \rightarrow MnS \downarrow + 2H^+$. Will any manganese(II) sulfide precipitate?

9-4. If lead chloride is shaken with a solution that is 0.001 M in Cl^- and 0.2 M in SO_4^{--}, will any lead sulfate form? What is K/Q for $PbCl_2 \downarrow + SO_4^{--} \rightarrow PbSO_4 \downarrow + 2Cl^-$?

9-5. Will any iron(III) hydroxide precipitate from a solution that is 0.05 M in iron(III) perchlorate and in which the hydroxide ion concentration is regulated to 1×10^{-8} by a suitable buffer? What is K/Q for $Fe(OH)_3 \downarrow \rightleftharpoons Fe^{+++} + 3OH^-$?

9-6. If silver chloride is shaken with a solution that is 0.001 M in Cl^- ion and 0.2 M in CO_3^{--} ion, will any silver chloride be changed to silver carbonate? What is K/Q for $2AgCl \downarrow + CO_3^{--} \rightarrow Ag_2CO_3 \downarrow + 2Cl^-$?

9-7. What is the best oxidizing agent in the table of standard oxidation potentials? The best reducing agent? Which is a better reducing agent: Ag^0 or Br^-?

9-8. The oxidation potentials for the oxidation of aluminum in acid solution and in basic solution are given in the table. In which solution is aluminum a better reducing agent? Why?

9-9. To judge by $\mathscr{E}^0$ values, which is a better oxidizing agent: potassium permanganate or nitric acid? Under what conditions is this comparison to be made?

9-10. Why does metallic copper dissolve in nitric acid but not in hydrochloric acid? Explain by reference to the $\mathscr{E}^0$ values. [Hint: What is the oxidizing agent in hydrochloric acid?]

9-11. Which of the halide ions, F^-, Cl^-, Br^-, or I^-, will be oxidized by iron(III) ion? Prove by reference to $\mathscr{E}^0$ values.

9-12. When metallic iron is dissolved in hydrochloric acid, is iron(II) chloride or iron(III) chloride formed? When iron is dissolved in nitric acid, what is the product?

9-13. Cobalt(II) is to be separated from zinc and aluminum by oxidation to cobalt(III) and precipitation of $Co(OH)_3$, insoluble in excess sodium hydroxide. By reference to the $\mathcal{E}^0$ values decide whether it is better to carry out the oxidation in acid solution and then add the base to precipitate the hydroxide or to do the oxidation in basic solution.

9-14. Separation of iron from other metal ions is best accomplished when the iron is in the $+3$ state. Suppose that we have a solution containing Fe^{++}, Al^{+++}, Co^{++}, Pb^{++}, and Ni^{++} ions. Which of the following oxidizing agents, according to their $\mathcal{E}^0$ values, would be powerful enough to oxidize iron(II) to iron(III)?

$$MnO_2, Zn^{++}, H_2O_2, HClO, Br_2, Sn^{++}$$

Which would be the most practicable choice for use in the laboratory? [Hint: This may be determined by other considerations than the magnitude of the standard oxidation potentials.]

9-15. A test for iodide can be obtained by oxidizing it to free iodine and extracting the element into carbon tetrachloride to give a violet solution. If bromide is present and is oxidized to bromine, it may escape detection in a subsequent step. Select an oxidizing agent that would oxidize selectively the iodide but not the bromide.

9-16. Calculate the standard free energy change for the reaction between silver chloride and sodium sulfide. What is the significance of the result?

9-17. Calculate the standard free energy changes for the two following reactions.

$$Cu^{++} + Cu \rightarrow 2Cu^+$$
$$Cu^{++} + 4Cl^- + Cu \rightarrow 2CuCl_2^-$$

Which reaction goes to the larger extent?

9-18. Calculate the standard free energy changes for the two following reactions.

$$O_2 + 4Co^{++} + 4H^+ \rightarrow 4Co^{+++} + 2H_2O$$
$$O_2 + 2H_2O + 4Co(NH_3)_6^{++} \rightarrow 4Co(NH_3)_6^{+++} + 4OH^-$$

Is it easier to oxidize cobalt(II) in acid solution or in ammoniacal solution?

9-19. Calculate the standard free energy change for

$$Ag_2S(c) + 4CN^- \rightarrow 2Ag(CN)_2^- + S^{--}$$

Is potassium cyanide a satisfactory solvent for silver sulfide?

9-20. Calculate the solubility product of zinc sulfide from the standard free energies of formation.

9-21. Calculate the equilibrium constant for $Cu^{++} + Cu \rightleftharpoons 2Cu^+$ from standard free energies of formation at $25°$.

9-22. Calculate the equilibrium constant for $CaCO_3(c) + 2F^- \rightleftharpoons CaF_2(c) + CO_3^{--}$ from standard free energies of formation at $25°$.

9-23. Calculate the equilibrium constants for the following from standard free energies of formation at $25°$. What is the significance of the results for qualitative analysis?

$$PbS(c) + 2H^+ \rightarrow Pb^{++} + H_2S(g)$$
$$FeS(c) + 2H^+ \rightarrow Fe^{++} + H_2S(g)$$

9-24. Calculate the equilibrium constants for the following from standard free energies of formation at $25°$. What is the significance of the results for qualitative analysis?

$$3HgS(black) + 8H^+ + 2NO_3^- \rightleftharpoons 2NO(g) + 4H_2O(l) + 3Hg^{++} + 3S^0$$
$$3PbS(c) + 8H^+ + 2NO_3^- \rightleftharpoons 2NO(g) + 4H_2O(l) + 3Pb^{++} + 3S^0$$

CHAPTER TEN

An Introduction to Calculations with Equilibrium Constants

10-1. Introduction. We shall consider in this chapter calculations that make use of ion products and solubility products. In such expressions the concentration of one ion is inversely proportional to some power of the concentration of the other ion, and the numerical solution of these problems is relatively easy. The calculation of pH values is introduced in connection with the ion product of water. It is common practice in making calculations with equilibrium constants to introduce simplifying assumptions. The validity of these assumptions is most readily examined with the aid of the principles of electroneutrality (Sec. 4-12) and material balance (Sec. 4-13). In the final sections of the chapter a method of introducing corrections for interionic forces into the numerical calculations is developed.

10-2. The Ion Product of Water. In Sec. 7-9 the ion product of water

$$K_w = [H^+][OH^-] \qquad\qquad \mathbf{1}$$

was introduced as an expression valid for all dilute aqueous solutions. According to this relation, when the hydrogen ion concentration is large, as it is in acid solution, the hydroxide ion concentration must be small. If one concentration and K_w are known, the other concentration can be found.

EXAMPLE 1. Find the concentrations of hydrogen and hydroxide ions in 0.020 M HCl. At this concentration the acid is completely ionized (Sec. 2-21), so the concentration of hydrogen ion is virtually 0.020 M or 2.0×10^{-2}. Then since $K_w = 1.0 \times 10^{-14}$ at $25°$

$$[OH^-] = \frac{10 \times 10^{-15}}{2.0 \times 10^{-2}} = \boxed{5 \times 10^{-13}\ M}$$

Note the convenient device of writing 1.0×10^{-14} as 10×10^{-15} to eliminate the necessity of juggling the exponent and the decimal point after division.

EXAMPLE 2. Find the hydrogen and hydroxide ion concentrations in a mixture of 1 drop of 6 M NaOH and 14 drops of water at $25°$. Here again we assume complete ionization and take the concentration of hydroxide ion as equal to that of the base. It follows that

$$[OH^-] = 6\ M\ \frac{1\ \text{drop}}{15\ \text{drops}} = \boxed{0.4\ M}$$

$$[H^+] = \frac{10 \times 10^{-15}}{4 \times 10^{-1}} = \boxed{2.5 \times 10^{-14}\ M}$$

For one special situation, i.e., in a neutral solution, both concentrations can be found simultaneously, because they are equal:

$$K_w = [H^+]^2 = [OH^-]^2 \quad \text{(neutral solution)} \qquad\qquad 2$$

EXAMPLE 3. Find the concentrations of hydrogen and hydroxide ions in a neutral solution at 20° if $K_w = 6.9 \times 10^{-15}$ at this temperature.

$$[H^+] = [OH^-] = (6.9 \times 10^{-15})^{\frac{1}{2}} = (69 \times 10^{-16})^{\frac{1}{2}}$$

$$= \boxed{8.3 \times 10^{-8}\ M}$$

The decimal point and exponent of K_w were adjusted before taking the square root so that the exponent in the answer would be a whole number.[1] It will be noted that the hydrogen ion concentration of a neutral solution is not 1×10^{-7} at 20°.

10-3. The pH Scale. For our purposes it is sufficient to define pH by the relation[2]

$$pH = -\log_{10}[H^+] \qquad \text{or} \qquad [H^+] = 10^{-pH} \qquad\qquad 3$$

Hydrogen ion concentrations usually lie between 10 M and 10^{-15} M. This tremendous range of values is condensed on the pH scale to the range -1 to $+15$. Although this is a convenience, there are some pitfalls for the unwary. The pH *decreases* as the hydrogen ion concentration *increases*. A small decrease in pH corresponds to a large increase in hydrogen ion concentration, e.g., a change in pH from 3 to 4 corresponds to a change of $[H^+]$ from 10^{-3} to 10^{-4}, a ten-fold change. The pH corresponding to a hydrogen ion concentration of 5.5×10^{-4} is not half-way between 3 and 4 but is 3.26. All these peculiarities of pH values are necessary consequences of the use of a logarithmic scale (Fig. 10-1).

The following examples will illustrate the calculation of a pH value and the conversion of pH to $[H^+]$. These cause no difficulty if a few simple rules are observed.

---

[1]The square root can be obtained by logarithms or, more easily, with a slide rule. The square root of 69 is obviously a little larger than 8. Set the hairline of the sliding indicator over 69 on the righthand scale of the *A* scale and read the square root under it on the *D* scale.

[2]This term was originally introduced by the Danish chemist Sørensen in 1909. He wrote the symbol as p_H and called p the "hydrogen ion exponent" (*Wasserstoffionenexponent*); it is the initial letter of *Potenz* (German), *puissance* (French), and *power* (English). It is customary now to write the symbol as pH; the version Ph, though sometimes encountered, is incorrect.

EXAMPLE 1. Find the *pH* corresponding to a hydrogen ion concentration of 0.00047 *M*.

Step 1. Rewrite the number so that there is a single digit to the left of the decimal point, i.e., 4.7×10^{-4}.

Step 2. Take the negative logarithm of this:

$$pH = -\log (4.7 \times 10^{-4}) = -\log 4.7 - \log 10^{-4} = -0.67 - (-4) = \boxed{3.33}$$

EXAMPLE 2. Find the $[H^+]$ corresponding to a *pH* of 5.72.

Step 1. Change the sign of the *pH* value: -5.72.

Step 2. Add and subtract the next whole number larger than the characteristic:

$$-5.72 + 6.00 - 6 = 0.28 - 6$$

Step 3. The antilog of this result is $[H^+]$:

$$[H^+] = \text{antilog } (0.28 - 6) = (\text{antilog } 0.28)(\text{antilog} - 6) = \boxed{1.9 \times 10^{-6} \; M}$$

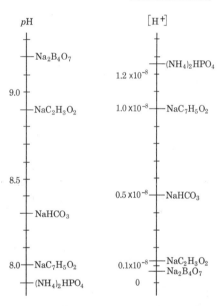

FIG. 10-1. Logarithmic and linear scales. The *pH* values and hydrogen ion concentrations of 0.1 *M* solutions of some salts.

The addition and subtraction of six in this example gives a positive mantissa that can be found in a table of logarithms. We could add and subtract any number greater than the characteristic, e.g., 10, but by taking the next whole number we get directly the exponent of ten in the answer.

The following definitions are analogous to that of *pH* and are often useful:

$$pOH = -\log_{10}[OH^-] \qquad\qquad 4$$
$$pX = -\log_{10}[X] \qquad\qquad 5$$
$$pK = -\log_{10}K \qquad\qquad 6$$

where X is any ion and K is any equilibrium constant. For water at 25°, $K_w = 1.00 \times 10^{-14}$ and $pK_w = 14.00$. It is easily shown that at 25°

$$pH + pOH = 14.00 \qquad\qquad 7$$

EXAMPLE 3. Find the pH of 0.04 M NaOH at 25°.

Method A. From $[OH^-] = 0.04$ and K_w find $[H^+]$. Convert this to pH as in Example 1.

Method B. Find pOH and subtract from 14.00 to obtain the pH.

$$pOH = -\log (4 \times 10^{-2}) = 1.40$$

$$pH = 14.00 - 1.40 = \boxed{12.60}$$

In more advanced work the definition of pH given by Eq. 3 is unsatisfactory. For dilute solutions of a strong acid the relation has a definite physical meaning, because the concentration of hydrogen ion in these solutions is accurately known. This is not true of other solutions. If we attempt to measure the pH of these, our measuring device, whether it be an indicator paper or an electric "pH meter," responds not only to the hydrogen ion concentration but also to interionic forces. Thus the measured value of the pH of 0.1 M HCl is 1.10, not 1.00, and other strong acids give slightly different values because of specific interactions of their anions. In spite of these ambiguities, the pH remains a useful, empirical measure of acidity.

10-4. The Accuracy of Our Calculations.   In the examples of the preceding section the pH values have been rounded off to two decimal places. Some comments on the accuracy of calculations should be added to the earlier ones in Sec. 4-5. It was pointed out in Sec. 9-13 that uncertainties in the constants, failure to correct for interionic forces, and lack of true equilibrium conditions limit the reliability of predictions or calculations based on equilibrium principles. Consider, for example, a 1 molal solution of potassium chloride. If we use 1.00×10^{-14} for K_w, we would expect the pH of this neutral solution to be 7.00. Actually, interionic forces cause the ion product to be larger in the potassium chloride solution than in pure water. The experimental value of $[H^+][OH^-]$ is 1.69×10^{-14}, and the pH of the solution is thus 6.89 or 0.11 units lower than the first prediction. The error caused by neglect of interionic forces is not always as large as this. We shall carry two decimal places in pH values with the understanding that the second is highly uncertain.

10-5. The Ion Product of Hydrogen Sulfide.   It was proved in Sec. 7-19 that in any solution saturated with hydrogen sulfide gas

$$K_{ip} = [H^+]^2[S^{--}] \qquad\qquad 8$$

where K_{ip} is the product $K_{H_2S}K_{HS}-[H_2S]$. At 25° and a pressure of hydrogen sulfide equal to one atmosphere, the ion product of hydrogen sulfide has the value 1.3×10^{-21}. If the pressure is some other value P (in atm), the ion product at 25° is $1.3 \times 10^{-21}P$. The validity of this expression when thio-acetamide is used was discussed in Sec. 8-13.

The ion product expression is most useful for calculations of the sulfide ion concentration in a solution that not only is saturated with hydrogen sulfide but also contains another acid. Hydrogen sulfide itself is a very weak acid ($K_{H_2S} = 1 \times 10^{-7}$; $K_{HS^-} = 1.3 \times 10^{-13}$) and its ionization will be repressed because of the high concentration of hydrogen ion provided by the other acid.

EXAMPLE. Find the sulfide ion concentration in 0.5 M HCl that is saturated with H_2S at 25°. We assume that the hydrogen ion concentration is virtually fixed by the hydrochloric acid alone. Thus $[H^+] = 0.5$ and

$$(0.5)^2[S^{--}] = 1.3 \times 10^{-21}$$

$$[S^{--}] = \frac{1.3 \times 10^{-21}}{0.25} = \boxed{5.2 \times 10^{-21}\ M}$$

10-6. The Ion Product of Carbon Dioxide. Solutions of carbon dioxide are important in life processes. The equilibria in a saturated solution of carbon dioxide are expressed by

$$CO_2(g) \rightleftharpoons CO_2 \text{ (in soln)} \qquad K = \frac{[CO_2]}{P_{CO_2}} = 0.0337$$

$$CO_2 + H_2O \rightleftharpoons H^+ + HCO_3^- \qquad K_1 = \frac{[H^+][HCO_3^-]}{[CO_2]} = 4.4 \times 10^{-7}$$

$$HCO_3^- \rightleftharpoons H^+ + CO_3^{--} \qquad K_2 = \frac{[H^+][CO_3^{--}]}{[HCO_3^-]} = 4.7 \times 10^{-11}$$

Only about 0.25% of the dissolved carbon dioxide is in the form of H_2CO_3 and this has been ignored. The values of the constants are those at 25°. The ion product of carbon dioxide is obtained by multiplying these constants together with the pressure of carbon dioxide:

$$KK_1K_2P_{CO_2} = K_{ip} = [H^+]^2[CO_3^{--}] \qquad \qquad 9$$

At 25° and a pressure of one atmosphere the value of this constant is 7.0×10^{-19}. Calculations with this expression are handled in the same way as those with the ion product of hydrogen sulfide.

EXAMPLE. A solution saturated with carbon dioxide at 25° and one atmosphere pressure is to be prepared with a carbonate ion concentration of $1 \times 10^{-9}\ M$. To what pH must the solution be adjusted if this is to hold?

$$[H^+]^2 \times 1 \times 10^{-9} = 7.0 \times 10^{-19}$$

$$[H^+] = (7.0 \times 10^{-10})^{1/2}$$

$$pH = -\log(7.0 \times 10^{-10})^{1/2} = -\tfrac{1}{2}\log(7.0 \times 10^{-10}) = -0.42 + 5 = \boxed{4.58}$$

10-7. A Check on the Validity of These Calculations. We have assumed in a number of these calculations that the hydrogen ion (or hydroxide ion) concentration of a solution can be ascribed to a strong acid (or base), the contribution of water or a weak acid (or base) being ignored. We can test this assumption by using the electroneutrality condition (Sec. 4-12).

EXAMPLE 1. Consider again 0.020 M HCl (Example 1, Sec. 10-2). This solution contains H^+, Cl^-, and OH^- ions. The condition of electroneutrality requires that the total concentrations of positive and negative charge be equal:

$$EN: [H^+] = [Cl^-] + [OH^-]$$

In effect this is equivalent to dividing the total hydrogen ion concentration of the solution into contributions from HCl and H_2O. Now $[Cl^-] = 0.02$ and $[OH^-] = 5 \times 10^{-13}$; hence

$$[H^+] = 0.02 + 0.0000000000005$$

or virtually 0.02.[3] It is thus satisfactory to assume that all the hydrogen ions come from the strong acid.

If the simplifying assumptions had not been valid, we would have discovered this upon examination of the electroneutrality condition. Suppose that we had a 10^{-7} M solution of hydrochloric acid. Then $[H^+] = [OH^-] = 10^{-7}$ if the usual assumption is made. Clearly this cannot be right, for $[H^+] = [Cl^-] + [OH^-]$ and $[Cl^-] = 10^{-7}$. An accurate calculation gives $[H^+] = 1.62 \times 10^{-7}$ or 62% greater than that from HCl alone.[4]

EXAMPLE 2. Consider again 0.5 M HCl saturated with H_2S (Example, Sec. 10-5). The ions present are H^+, OH^-, HS^-, S^{--}, and Cl^-. The balance of charge takes the form

$$EN: [H^+] = [Cl^-] + [OH^-] + [HS^-] + 2[S^{--}]$$

in which the concentration of sulfide is doubled to allow for its double charge. In Sec. 10-5 we assumed that $[H^+] = 0.5 = [Cl^-]$. In this solution the other concentrations are : $[OH^-] = (1 \times 10^{-14}/0.5) = 2 \times 10^{-14}$; $[S^{--}] = 5.2 \times 10^{-21}$; and $[HS^-] = 2 \times 10^{-8}$ (by calculations described in Chapter 11). Hence

$$[H^+] = 0.5 + 2 \times 10^{-14} + 2 \times 10^{-8} + 2 \times 5.2 \times 10^{-21}$$

$$= 0.5 + 0.00000000000002 + 0.00000002 + 0.000000000000000000000104$$

or $[H^+]$ is virtually 0.5 as we had assumed.

10-8. The Solubility Product and Solubility in Water. When a slightly soluble compound MeX is dissolved in pure water, the Me^+ and X^- ions come only from the compound. If these ions remain free in solution and the concentration of one is known, the solubility product can be calculated. Conversely, if

[3]Skeptical readers may believe that it is unfair to use the result for the hydroxide ion concentration from the earlier approximate calculation to verify the approximation. They may find it without making any simplifying assumptions by solving the equation

$$K_w = 1.00 \times 10^{-14} = ([OH^-] + 0.02)[OH^-]$$

This is not easy to solve, but the answer is still $[OH^-] = 5 \times 10^{-13}$.

[4]This answer can be verified by solving the accurate relation

$$1.00 \times 10^{-14} = [OH^-](10^{-7} + [OH^-])$$

For methods of solving a quadratic equation of this type see Chapter 11.

the solubility product is known, it is possible to calculate the concentrations of both ions. Relations between molar solubility and solubility product were given in Sec. 8-3. Their application will now be illustrated by some examples. The next section will deal with the effect of common ions and the section after that with a critical examination of these calculations.

EXAMPLE 1. Find the solubility of thallium(I) iodate in water if its solubility product is 3.06×10^{-6}.

Step 1. Write the chemical equation and expression for the constant:

$$TlIO_3 \downarrow \rightleftharpoons Tl^+ + IO_3^- \qquad K_{sp} = [Tl^+][IO_3^-].$$

Step 2. Give an explicit definition of the unknown: Let $S =$ the solubility of the salt in moles per liter.

Step 3. Use the unknown to formulate expressions for the ionic concentrations: $S = [Tl^+] = [IO_3^-]$ because one kome of this salt contains one ion of each kind.

Step 4. Combine these expressions with the solubility product and solve for the unknown: $S^2 = 3.06 \times 10^{-6}$, or $S = (3.06 \times 10^{-6})^{1/2} =$

$$\boxed{1.75 \times 10^{-3} \, M}$$

EXAMPLE 2. Solid lead chloride was shaken with water at 15°. The chloride ion concentration of the solution was determined by converting the chloride to silver chloride which was then weighed. The same weight of silver chloride, namely 0.895 g/100 ml of solution, was obtained from a sample taken after four days of shaking as from one taken after seven hours, so that a saturated solution was actually obtained. Find the solubility product of lead chloride.

$$PbCl_2 \downarrow \rightleftharpoons Pb^{++} + 2Cl^- \qquad K_{sp} = [Pb^{++}][Cl^-]^2$$

The number of moles of silver chloride is

$$\frac{0.895 \text{ g per } 100 \text{ ml}}{143.5 \text{ g per mole}} = 0.00624 \text{ moles}/100 \text{ ml}$$

| Ag: 108 |
| Cl : 35.5 |
| ——— |
| 143.5 |

Because 0.00624 mole of AgCl corresponds to an equal number of moles of chloride, the concentration of chloride ion in the saturated solution is 0.0624 M. Each kome of $PbCl_2$ contains one Pb^{++} ion and two Cl^- ions. Hence the concentration of lead ion must be one-half of 0.0624, or 0.0312 M. The solubility product at 15° is

$$K_{sp} = 3.12 \times 10^{-2} \times (6.24 \times 10^{-2})^2 = \boxed{1.2 \times 10^{-4}}$$

For various reasons this is only a rough approximation (Sec. 10-10).

EXAMPLE 3. The solubility of thallium(I) chromate is 0.00427 g of salt per 100 ml at 20°. Find the solubility product.

$$Tl_2CrO_4 \downarrow \rightleftharpoons 2Tl^+ + CrO_4^{--} \qquad K_{sp} = [Tl^+]^2[CrO_4^{--}]$$

The molar solubility is (Sec. 4-10)

$$\frac{0.0427 \text{ g per liter}}{525 \text{ g per mole}} = 8.1 \times 10^{-5} \, M$$

| 2 Tl: 409 |
| Cr: 52 |
| 4 O: 64 |
| ——— |
| 525 |

Each mole of salt is assumed to give one mole of CrO_4^{--} ion and two moles of Tl^+ ion. Therefore

$$[Tl^+] = 2 \times 8.1 \times 10^{-5} \quad \text{and} \quad [CrO_4^{--}] = 8.1 \times 10^{-5}$$

and hence

$$K_{sp} = (1.6 \times 10^{-4})^2 (8.1 \times 10^{-5}) = \boxed{2.1 \times 10^{-12}}$$

Students are sometimes puzzled by the fact that the solubility is first doubled to obtain $[Tl^+]$ and then squared. As we have noted before (Sec. 8-3), the squaring is required by the form of the solubility product, but the initial doubling is required only because the solubility is expressed in moles of salt per liter. Had it been expressed in terms of the Tl^+ ion or had $[Tl^+]$ been directly determined, no doubling would have been required (compare with Example 2).

10-9. Solubility in the Presence of a Common Ion. We now have to deal with an added complication: one kind of ion comes from two sources, the slightly soluble electrolyte and another electrolyte. The concentration of any substance in an equilibrium constant is always the total number of moles of it per liter. No distinction can be made between ions from different sources; all are alike.

EXAMPLE 1. Calculate the solubility of calcium fluoride in 0.06 M sodium fluoride. The solubility product is 1.6×10^{-10} at 25°.

Step 1 Write the chemical equation and expression for the solubility product:

$$CaF_2 \downarrow \rightleftharpoons Ca^{++} + 2F^- \qquad K_{sp} = [Ca^{++}][F^-]^2$$

Step 2. Define the unknown explicitly: Let S = the solubility of calcium fluoride in moles per liter.

Step 3. Use the unknown and the other data to formulate expressions for the ionic concentrations. Each kome contains one calcium and two fluoride ions. If S moles of calcium fluoride dissolve per liter, S moles of Ca^{++} ion and $2S$ moles of fluoride ion are put into solution. Hence $[Ca^{++}] = S$ and $[F^-] = 2S + 0.06$. The last expression is the total concentration of fluoride ion from calcium fluoride and sodium fluoride. The subsequent calculations are simplified if we assume that $2S$ is much smaller than 0.06 and write $[F^-] \simeq 0.06$. This is a reasonable assumption, for the solubility of calcium fluoride is repressed by the presence of the common ion.

Step 4. Combine these expressions with the solubility product and solve for the unknown:

$$1.6 \times 10^{-10} = S(0.06)^2$$

$$S = \boxed{4.4 \times 10^{-8} \ M}$$

We can use this to verify the approximation in step 3:

$$0.06 + 2S = 0.06 + 0.000000088, \text{ or virtually } 0.06$$

EXAMPLE 2. Some solid silver oxalate is shaken with 0.05 M sodium oxalate until equilibrium is attained. The concentration of silver ion in the solution, measured by an electrical method, is 1.4×10^{-5} M. Calculate the solubility product of silver oxalate.

$$Ag_2C_2O_4 \downarrow \rightleftharpoons 2Ag^+ + C_2O_4^{--} \qquad K_{sp} = [Ag^+]^2[C_2O_4^{--}]$$

We assume that silver and oxalate occur only as the simple ions. Then $[Ag^+] = 1.4 \times 10^{-5}$ and $[C_2O_4^{--}] = 0.05 + \frac{1}{2}(1.4 \times 10^{-5}) = 0.05 + 0.000007$, or virtually 0.05. Hence

$$K_{sp} = (1.4 \times 10^{-5})^2(0.05) = \boxed{1.0 \times 10^{-11} \ M}$$

It will be noted that 1.4×10^{-5} has been squared but not doubled in this calculation.

10-10. A Critical Examination of the Calculations With Solubility and Solubility Product.

There are two fundamental assumptions in all the problems of the preceding two sections that require examination: (1) the ions of the slightly soluble electrolyte remain free and uncombined and (2) interionic forces are negligible.

In Example 1, Sec. 10-8, there are at least two possible side reactions that could remove thallium(I) and iodate ions:

$$Tl^+ + IO_3^- \rightleftharpoons TlIO_3^- \qquad K = 2$$
$$H^+ + IO_3^- \rightleftharpoons HIO_3 \qquad K = 6$$

If S is the molar solubility, the principle of mole balance (Sec. 4-13) requires

$$MB\ (Tl):\ S = [Tl^+] + [TlIO_3^-]$$
$$MB\ (I):\ \ S = [IO_3^-] + [TlIO_3^-] + [HIO_3]$$

If either reaction proceeded to an appreciable extent, S would be greater than $[Tl^+]$ or $[IO_3^-]$ or $K_{sp}^{1/2}$. Since both equilibrium constants are not very large, this source of error will be small.

The neglect of interionic forces is a more serious mistake, but even this error is not large because the ionic strength is very low (about 0.0018). The solubility determined experimentally is 1.84×10^{-3}; this is only 5% larger than the value calculated in Sec. 10-8.

Similar criticisms of the calculation of the solubility of CaF_2 in 0.06 M NaF (Example 1, Sec. 10-9) can be made. The formation of ion-pairs such as CaF^+ or $CaOH^+$ or of molecular HF is probably not a serious source of error in approximate calculations. The ionic strength is about 0.06, which is larger than that in the thallium(I) iodate problem, and the correction for interionic forces will be more important.

Both kinds of errors will be serious for the lead chloride solution of Example 2, Sec. 10-8. An appreciable amount of Pb^{++} ions is removed to give $PbCl^+$ ion-pairs:

$$Pb^{++} + Cl^- \rightarrow PbCl^+ \qquad K = 37$$

According to the mole balance requirement,

$$MB\ (Pb):\ 3.13 \times 10^{-2} = [Pb^{++}] + [PbCl^+]$$

the concentration of lead ion is smaller than 3.13×10^{-2}. Because lead chloride is fairly soluble and Pb^{++} ions bear a double charge, the ionic strength will be close to 0.1 and interionic forces will have an important effect. The true solubility product is lower than the value that was calculated.

When one or both ions of the salt react extensively with water, the solubility is larger than we would predict by the methods of the preceding sections. This is particularly true of sulfides, phosphates, carbonates, and similar salts that contain anions of very weak acids. The hydrolysis reactions

$$S^{--} \quad + H_2O \rightleftharpoons HS^- \quad + OH^- \quad K = 0.08$$

$$PO_4^{---} + H_2O \rightleftharpoons HPO_4^{--} + OH^- \quad K = 0.01$$

$$CO_3^{--} \quad + H_2O \rightleftharpoons HCO_3^- \quad + OH^- \quad K = 0.0002$$

have smaller constants than those quoted earlier for ion-pair formation, but at the low concentrations existing in saturated solutions of salts such as ZnS, Ag_3PO_4, or $CaCO_3$ these reactions are forced to the right by the slowness of recombination of the products that are so far apart. In a saturated solution of zinc sulfide there are about a million HS^- ions to every S^{--} ion, and the solubility of this salt is about a thousand times as large as we would expect from the square root of the solubility product.

A different source of error must be considered in calculations of solubility in the presence of a common ion. We have assumed that because the common ion represses the solubility, the contribution of the slightly soluble compound to the total concentration of this ion can be neglected. The numerical calculation is greatly simplified by this assumption, but it will lead to erroneous results if the precipitate is fairly soluble or if the concentration of the common ion is low. A practical question then is, how can we tell when to make the simplifying assumption and when not to? The best procedure is to try it and see if a reasonable answer is obtained. Suppose, for example, that we have to calculate the solubility of calcium fluoride in 0.0001 M sodium fluoride. If we follow the same procedure as in Example 1, Sec. 10-9, $[Ca^{++}]$ is S and $[F^-]$, which is accurately given by $10^{-4} + 2S$, is approximated by 10^{-4}. Hence

$$S(10^{-4})^2 = 1.6 \times 10^{-10}$$

$$S = 1.6 \times 10^{-2} \ M$$

This answer is absurd, because $2S$ is then larger than 10^{-4}. We see that our assumption was wrong, and we must solve the accurate relation

$$S(10^{-4} + 2S)^2 = 1.6 \times 10^{-10}$$

$$S = 3.1 \times 10^{-4} \ M$$

As a general rule, factors of the form $(C + x)$ will be approximated by C

if x is less than 10% of C. The answer is then good to 10 or 20%, and this is sufficiently accurate for our purposes.

10-11. Competing Equilibria. Fractional Precipitation. Frequently there are in a solution several equilibria competing for the same ion or molecule. Consider, for example, a solution containing two cations, A^+ and B^+, that form slightly soluble precipitates with the same anion X^-. Then if the solubility product of AX is much less than that of BX, it is often possible to precipitate only AX by careful addition of X^- ions to the solution. Similarly, two anions can be separated if they form precipitates of widely differing solubility products with the same cation.

EXAMPLE. Powdered sodium sulfate is added a little at a time to a solution in which the concentrations of Ba^{++} and Ca^{++} ions are, respectively, 0.10 and 5.0 mg/ml. The mixture is stirred thoroughly during and after each addition of the solid. We shall neglect the change in volume of the solution in this process. The solubility products are

$$K_{sp} = [Ba^{++}][SO_4^{--}] = 1.0 \times 10^{-10}$$

$$K_{sp} = [Ca^{++}][SO_4^{--}] = 2.4 \times 10^{-5}$$

For use with these constants the concentrations of the cations must be expressed in mmoles/ml; they are

$$[Ba^{++}] = \frac{0.10 \text{ mg/ml}}{137 \text{ mg/mmole}} = 7.3 \times 10^{-4} \ M$$

$$[Ca^{++}] = \frac{5.0 \text{ mg/ml}}{40 \text{ mg/mmole}} = 1.2 \times 10^{-1} \ M$$

The conditions for precipitation of these sulfates are

Ba: $7.3 \times 10^{-4} [SO_4^{--}] > 1.0 \times 10^{-10}$ or $[SO_4^{--}] > 1.4 \times 10^{-7}$

Ca: $1.2 \times 10^{-1} [SO_4^{--}] > 2.4 \times 10^{-5}$ or $[SO_4^{--}] > 2.0 \times 10^{-4}$

Because barium sulfate requires a much lower concentration of sulfate it should precipitate first.

Suppose that addition of sodium sulfate is continued until calcium sulfate also begins to precipitate. When the solution is simultaneously saturated with respect to both salts, the two solubility product expressions must be satisfied by the same concentration of sulfate ion, for there can be no distinction between sulfate ions that are in equilibrium with barium sulfate and those that are in equilibrium with calcium sulfate. Hence the ratio of the solubility products gives the ratio of the metal ion concentrations in the solution that is saturated with respect to both precipitates; viz.,

$$\frac{[Ca^{++}]_{ss}}{[Ba^{++}]_{ss}} = \frac{K_{sp}(CaSO_4)}{K_{sp}(BaSO_4)} = \frac{2.4 \times 10^{-5}}{1.0 \times 10^{-10}} = 2.4 \times 10^5$$

This is much larger than the initial molar ratio of 160 to 1 because most of the barium has been precipitated. When precipitation of the calcium sulfate is about to begin, all the calcium ions originally present are still in solution and $[Ca^{++}]$ is 1.2×10^{-1}, the initial concentration. The concentration of barium left in solution at this point is given by

$$2.4 \times 10^5 = \frac{1.2 \times 10^{-1}}{[Ba^{++}]}$$

$$[Ba^{++}] = 5 \times 10^{-7} \ M$$

This is $100 \ (5 \times 10^{-7})/(7.3 \times 10^{-4}) = 0.07\%$ of the barium originally present, so $100.00 - 0.07 = 99.93\%$ has precipitated before calcium sulfate starts to form.

These calculations show how, in principle, it is possible to separate two ions by fractional precipitation, but they are necessarily idealized. A high degree of supersaturation is required for the formation of both precipitates (Sec. 8-8) so that more sodium sulfate would have to be added to precipitate them than we calculated. The barium sulfate formed in the first step will be far from pure, for as the experiment is carried out coprecipitation will inevitably occur. Sulfate ion was added in the form of a solid salt. As this solid dissolves, a high concentration of sulfate ion will build up around the solid particles. Since the original solution contained a large excess of calcium over barium, it is probable that, in the presence of a local excess of sulfate, some calcium sulfate will precipitate along with the barium compound. A better procedure would have been to add a solution of sulfate ion. (This would increase the volume of the solution and make the calculations more complicated.) Even so, efficient stirring during the addition of the reagent solution is required, and some coprecipitation of calcium is inevitable. A still better procedure would be to generate sulfate slowly within the solution by hydrolysis of sulfamic acid (Sec. 8-11). Even this technique fails when two sulfates form solid solutions, e.g., barium and radium sulfates.

For qualitative analysis, it is true, we do not always require that precipitates be free of contamination, and fractional precipitation is a useful method of separating ions. For a successful separation the concentration ratio of the ions should be very large when precipitation of the more soluble compound starts. As in the separation of barium and calcium, it should be greater than 10^5. Thus barium and strontium cannot be satisfactorily separated by fractional precipitation of the sulfates because

$$\frac{[Sr^{++}]_{ss}}{[Ba^{++}]_{ss}} = \frac{K_{sp}(SrSO_4)}{K_{sp}(BaSO_4)} = \frac{7.6 \times 10^{-7}}{1.0 \times 10^{-10}} = 7.6 \times 10^3$$

The concentration ratio for precipitation of the chromates of these two metals is more satisfactory:

$$\frac{[Sr^{++}]_{ss}}{[Ba^{++}]_{ss}} = \frac{K_{sp}(SrCrO_4)}{K_{sp}(BaCrO_4)} = \frac{5 \times 10^{-6}}{1.2 \times 10^{-10}} = 4 \times 10^4$$

and the effectiveness of the separation is increased by control of the chromate ion concentration by using the equilibria

$$2H^+ + 2CrO_4^{--} \rightleftharpoons 2HCrO_4^- \rightleftharpoons Cr_2O_7^{--} + H_2O$$

Separation of calcium and strontium by fractional precipitation of the sulfates is difficult because the concentration ratio when precipitation of calcium sulfate begins is only about 32:1. A satisfactory qualitative test for strontium in the presence of small amounts of calcium can nevertheless be obtained if triethanolamine is added to remove calcium as a complex and keep the ratio below 32.

The separations of the alkaline earth metals that have been used to illustrate the principles of fractional precipitation are difficult ones. Many other ions can be separated very successfully by fractional precipitation, particularly when the concentration of the cation or anion can be controlled by complex formation or buffering. Such separations are discussed in the chapters that follow this one.

10-12. Competing Equilibria. Formation and Dissolution of Hydroxides, Sulfides, and Carbonates. The precipitation of these compounds involves a competition between metal ions and hydrogen ion for the anion, OH^-, S^{--}, or CO_3^{--}.

EXAMPLE 1. Calculate the concentration of aluminum ion that can remain in equilibrium with aluminum hydroxide if the pH of the solution is regulated to 6.0. The competing equilibria are represented by

$$Al(OH)_3 \downarrow \rightleftharpoons Al^{++} + 3OH^- \qquad K_{sp} = [Al^{+++}][OH^-]^3 = 1.4 \times 10^{-34}$$
$$H_2O \rightleftharpoons H^+ + OH^- \qquad K_w = [H^+][OH^-] = 1 \times 10^{-14}$$

The hydroxide ion is common to both reactions and $[OH^-]$ forms a link between the two constants. The problem can be solved by either of two methods which differ only slightly.

Method A. Step by step.

Step 1. Find the $[H^+]$ that corresponds to pH 6.0: it is 1.0×10^{-6} M.

Step 2. Find the $[OH^-]$ in equilibrium with this $[H^+]$:

$$[OH^-] = \frac{1.0 \times 10^{-14}}{1.0 \times 10^{-6}} = 1.0 \times 10^{-8} \ M$$

Step 3. Find the $[Al^{+++}]$ in equilibrium with this $[OH^-]$:

$$[Al^{+++}] = \frac{1.4 \times 10^{-34}}{(1.0 \times 10^{-8})^3} = \boxed{1.4 \times 10^{-10} \ M}$$

Method B. Combination of constants.

Step 1. Find $[H^+]$ as in Method A.

Step 2. Solve each equilibrium constant for the linking concentration and set the two expressions equal. Insert the numerical values and solve for $[Al^{+++}]$:

$$[OH^-]^3 = \left(\frac{K_w}{[H^+]}\right)^3 = \frac{K_{sp}}{[Al^{+++}]}$$

$$\left(\frac{1.0 \times 10^{-14}}{1.0 \times 10^{-6}}\right)^3 = \frac{1.4 \times 10^{-34}}{[Al^{+++}]}$$

$$[Al^{+++}] = \boxed{1.4 \times 10^{-10}\ M}$$

This method differs from the first only in eliminating the extra step of finding the linking concentration, $[OH^-]$.

EXAMPLE 2. Calculate the maximum concentration of hydrogen ion that can be present in a cadmium nitrate solution saturated with hydrogen sulfide at $25°$ and 1 atm pressure if no more than 2×10^{-5} mmole/ml of cadmium is to be left unprecipitated. The competing equilibria are

$$CdS \downarrow\, \rightleftharpoons Cd^{++} + S^{--} \qquad K_{sp} = [Cd^{++}][S^{--}] = 7 \times 10^{-27}$$

and that in a saturated solution of hydrogen sulfide expressed by (Secs. 7-19, 10-5)

$$K_{ip} = [H^+]^2[S^{--}] = 1.3 \times 10^{-21}$$

The linking concentration is that of sulfide ion.

Method A. Step by step.

Step 1. Find $[S^{--}]$ at equilibrium when $[Cd^{++}] = 2 \times 10^{-5}\ M$:

$$[S^{--}] = \frac{K_{sp}}{[Cd^{++}]} = \frac{7 \times 10^{-27}}{2 \times 10^{-5}} = 3.5 \times 10^{-22}\ M$$

Step 2. Find $[H^+]$ in equilibrium with this $[S^{--}]$:

$$[H^+]^2 = \frac{K_{ip}}{[S^{--}]} = \frac{13 \times 10^{-22}}{3.5 \times 10^{-22}} = 3.7$$

$$[H^+] = (3.7)^{1/2} = \boxed{1.9\ M}$$

Method B. Combination of constants. Solve both expressions for the linking concentration:

$$[S^{--}] = \frac{K_{ip}}{[H^+]^2} = \frac{K_{sp}}{[Cd^{++}]}$$

$$\frac{1.3 \times 10^{-21}}{[H^+]^2} = \frac{7 \times 10^{-27}}{2 \times 10^{-5}}$$

$$[H^+] = \left(\frac{1.3 \times 10^{-21} \times 2 \times 10^{-5}}{7 \times 10^{-27}}\right)^{1/2} = \boxed{1.9\ M}$$

The solubility product that was used is for crystalline cadmium sulfide. The freshly precipitated sulfide is more soluble and the concentration of hydrogen ion that can be tolerated is actually lower than $1.9\ M$ (Sec. 8-12).

EXAMPLE 3. The pH of a saturated solution of carbon dioxide is about **4**. Find the concentration of Sr^{++} ion left unprecipitated when a strontium nitrate solution is saturated with carbon dioxide at a pressure of 0.5 atm. The competing equilibria are

$$SrCO_3 \downarrow \rightleftharpoons Sr^{++} + CO_3^{--} \qquad K_{sp} = [Sr^{++}][CO_3^{--}] = 7 \times 10^{-10}$$

and that in a saturated solution of CO_2 expressed by (Sec. 10-6)

$$[H^+]^2[CO_3^{--}] = K_{ip} = 7 \times 10^{-19} \times 0.5$$

The link between these expressions is $[CO_3^{--}]$.

Method A. Step by step.

$$[H^+] = 1.0 \times 10^{-4} \ M$$

$$[CO_3^{--}] = \frac{7 \times 10^{-19} \times 0.5}{(1.0 \times 10^{-4})^2} = 3.5 \times 10^{-11} \ M$$

$$[Sr^{++}] = \frac{7 \times 10^{-10}}{3.5 \times 10^{-11}} = \boxed{20 \ M}$$

Method B. Combination of constants.

$$[H^+] = 1.0 \times 10^{-4} \ M$$

$$[CO_3^{--}] = \frac{K_{ip}}{[H^+]^2} = \frac{K_{sp}}{[Sr^{++}]}$$

$$[Sr^{++}] = \frac{7 \times 10^{-10} \times (1 \times 10^{-4})^2}{7.0 \times 10^{-19} \times 0.5} = \boxed{20 \ M}$$

The ion product of carbon dioxide is only slightly larger than that of hydrogen sulfide, and the concentrations of both carbonate and sulfide ions in acid solutions are very low. But the solubility products of metal carbonates are not so low as those of the sulfides, and the carbonates cannot be precipitated in acid solution. The concentration of strontium found in the example is too high to be attained experimentally; thus any solution of strontium carbonate at this pH will be unsaturated. Carbonates are precipitated from basic solutions by ammonium or sodium carbonate.

Separations are sometimes made by dissolving selectively some of the compounds from a mixture of precipitates. The following example illustrates the separation of sulfides (Sec. 8-16). The ion product of hydrogen sulfide can still be applied if a sufficient quantity of one sulfide dissolves to saturate the solution with hydrogen sulfide gas.

EXAMPLE 4. A mixture of aged precipitates of cobalt(II) and iron(II) sulfides is to be separated by the action of hydrochloric acid. What must the concentration of hydrochloric acid be if no more than 0.01 mg Co/ml is to dissolve? What concentration of Fe^{++} ion will be present in a solution of this acidity? Assume that sufficient acid is used so that $[H^+]$ remains constant. The competing equilibria are

$$CoS \downarrow \rightleftharpoons Co^{++} + S^{--} \qquad K_{sp} = [Co^{++}][S^{--}] = 8 \times 10^{-23}$$
$$FeS \downarrow \rightleftharpoons Fe^{++} + S^{--} \qquad K_{sp} = [Fe^{++}][S^{--}] = 5 \times 10^{-18}$$

and for a saturated solution of hydrogen sulfide

$$K_{ip} = [H^+]^2[S^{--}] = 1.3 \times 10^{-21}$$

The concentration of sulfide ion is the link between these constants. The final concentration of cobalt must be expressed in molarity units:

$$[Co^{++}] = \frac{0.01 \text{ mg Co/ml}}{59 \text{ mg Co/mmole}} = 1.7 \times 10^{-4} \ M$$

Then

$$[S^{--}] = \frac{8 \times 10^{-23}}{1.7 \times 10^{-4}} = 4.7 \times 10^{-19} \ M$$

$$[H^+]^2 = \frac{13 \times 10^{-22}}{4.7 \times 10^{-19}} = 2.8 \times 10^{-3} \ M^2$$

$$[H^+] = \boxed{0.053 \ M}$$

The concentration of iron(II) in equilibrium with sulfide is

$$[Fe^{++}] = \frac{K_{sp}}{[S^{--}]} = \frac{5 \times 10^{-18}}{4.7 \times 10^{-19}} = \boxed{10.6 \ M}$$

This calculation indicates that the two sulfides can be separated by treatment with 0.053 M HCl. Actually this separation is only moderately successful. We have used the solubility product of crystalline cobalt sulfide in our calculation; the freshly precipitated sulfide is much more soluble and ages only slowly to the other form. In qualitative analysis a cobalt sulfide precipitate that is aged for ten minutes is still sufficiently soluble in hydrochloric acid to contaminate the solution of iron sulfide with a troublesome amount of cobalt. Longer aging, though desirable, would delay the analysis.

10-13. Competing Equilibria. Transpositions. It is sometimes necessary to convert one precipitate directly into another. This is generally avoided, because it is difficult to obtain complete conversion, for the second precipitate frequently forms a coating on the particles of the first that protects the latter from the reagent. Such transpositions are nevertheless required to convert certain compounds such as $BaSO_4$ to a more soluble form, e.g., the carbonates, which are easily dissolved by acids.

EXAMPLE. Ten ml of 1 M Na_2CO_3 solution is shaken with 500 mg of $BaSO_4$. Calculate the concentrations of carbonate and sulfate ions in solution at equilibrium and the extent of conversion of barium sulfate to the carbonate. The equilibria are represented by

$$BaSO_4 \downarrow \rightleftharpoons Ba^{++} + SO_4^{--} \qquad K_{sp} = [Ba^{++}][SO_4^{--}] = 1.0 \times 10^{-10}$$

$$BaCO_3 \downarrow \rightleftharpoons Ba^{++} + CO_3^{--} \qquad K_{sp} = [Ba^{++}][CO_3^{--}] = 1.6 \times 10^{-9}$$

The linking concentration of barium ion is readily eliminated if we take the ratio of the solubility products:

$$\frac{[SO_4^{--}]}{[CO_3^{--}]} = \frac{K_{sp}(BaSO_4)}{K_{sp}(BaCO_3)} = \frac{1.0 \times 10^{-10}}{1.6 \times 10^{-9}} = 6.2 \times 10^{-2}$$

$$[SO_4^{--}] = 6.2 \times 10^{-2} \ [CO_3^{--}]$$

This is equivalent to the equilibrium constant for the transposition reaction

$$BaSO_4 \downarrow + CO_3^{--} \rightleftharpoons BaCO_3 \downarrow + SO_4^{--}$$

To find the concentrations of the two anions we need one more relation, and this is given by the principle of electroneutrality:

$$EN: [Na^+] + 2[Ba^{++}] = 2[CO_3^{--}] + 2[SO_4^{--}]$$

in which the concentrations of the bivalent ions have been doubled because we are counting charges, not ions.[5] Because of the high concentration of carbonate, the concentration of barium ion will be very low and can be neglected. The concentration of sodium ion is twice that of sodium carbonate. Hence

$$1 = [SO_4^{--}] + [CO_3^{--}]$$

and combining this with the ratio of the concentrations, we obtain

$$1 = 0.062[CO_3^{--}] + [CO_3^{--}]$$

Thus

$$[CO_3^{--}] = \frac{1}{1.062} = \boxed{0.94 \ M}$$

$$[SO_4^{--}] = 0.062 \times 0.94 = \boxed{0.059 \ M}$$

The assumption that $[Ba^{++}]$ is negligible is readily verified:

$$[Ba^{++}] = \frac{K_{sp}(BaCO_3)}{[CO_3^{--}]} = 1.7 \times 10^{-9} \ M$$

The extent of conversion of barium sulfate to barium carbonate is most easily measured by

$$\% \ conversion = \frac{mmoles \ SO_4^{--} \ in \ solution}{initial \ mmoles \ of \ BaSO_4} 100 = \frac{10 \ ml \times 0.059 \ mmoles/ml}{500 \ mg/ \ 233 \ mg/mmole} 100$$

$$= \frac{0.59}{2.14} 100 = \boxed{28\%}$$

To obtain a greater conversion we would have to use either a larger volume of $1 \ M \ Na_2CO_3$ or 10 ml of a more concentrated solution of this reagent.

10-14. A Method of Measuring the Effect of Interionic Forces. We have been using ion and solubility products as if they had fixed values at a given temperature and pressure, whereas they actually vary with changes in the ionic strength. Expressions such as $K_w = [H^+][OH^-]$, $K_{sp} = [Ag^+][Cl^-]$, and $K_{ip} = [H^+]^2[S^{--}]$ are *ideal* laws, for they are based on the implicit assumption that the solute particles are strictly well-behaved. In ideal solutions all particles, whether of solute or solvent, are alike in the volume they occupy and in the forces they exert on other particles. Mixtures of similar substances, e.g., CCl_4 and $SiCl_4$, are close to ideal in their behavior. Solutions of electrolytes, because they contain charged particles that exert strong forces on each other and on molecules, are far from ideal.

[5]We have neglected the concentrations of H^+, HCO_3^-, and OH^- ions in writing the electroneutrality relation. The first is entirely negligible because the solution is strongly basic. The error caused by the neglect of the other two is 10% or more only if the concentration of sodium carbonate is below about 0.02 M.

We need a measuring stick, so to speak, against which we can hold the ideal constant so that we can judge the effect of interionic forces. This standard of comparison is found by measuring the equilibrium constant at such low ionic strengths that interionic forces are negligible. Let us write K^0 for this constant and estimate the effect of interionic forces from the ratio

$$\frac{K^0}{K} = Y \qquad\qquad 10$$

with the understanding that, as the concentrations of the ions approach zero, Y approaches 1. The factor Y is usually less than one in dilute solutions; the lower it is the more the system deviates from ideal behavior.

To use Eq. 10 we must first find K^0. The method of doing this will be illustrated for K_w^0 of water and $K_{s_p}^0$ of thallium(I) iodate. Pure water itself has an ionic strength of about 10^{-7}, which is low enough so that Y should be practically 1. But measurements on pure water are too difficult to make and the ion product is determined in salt solutions of various ionic strengths. When these results are plotted as shown in Fig. 10-2, the curves can be

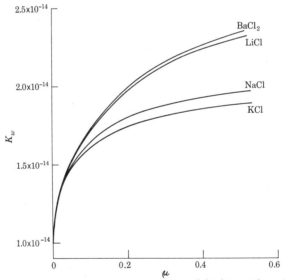

FIG. 10-2. Determination of K_w^0, the activity ion product of water, at 25° by extrapolation of measurements in salt solutions to zero ionic strength. Ionic strength on the molality scale.

extended until they intersect the axis for zero ionic strength. This intercept where interionic forces are negligible is K_w^0. The graphical method is a simple and elegant way of finding the limit which K_w approaches when a small amount of the salt solution is diluted with a lake full of water. Because the curves for all the salt solutions come into the same intercept, we have found a property of water and its ions, independent of the salt. A similar procedure can be used for thallous iodate. The solubility product of the salt in various potassium chloride and sulfate solutions was plotted in Fig. 8-3 and the curve can be extended to the axis to obtain K_{sp}^0.[6]

Once K^0 is known, Eq. 10 can be used to estimate the effect of interionic forces. Most of the equilibrium constants given in tables are K^0 values.

EXAMPLE 1. For thallium(I) iodate K_{sp}^0 is 3.060×10^{-6} at 25°. Bell and George measured the solubility of this compound in 0.045 M potassium thiocyanate and found it to be 2.346×10^{-3} M. Calculate Y for thallium(I) iodate in this solution. The ideal constant K is found from the square of the solubility (Sec. 10-8); then

$$Y = \frac{K_{sp}^0}{K_{sp}} = \frac{3.060 \times 10^{-6}}{(2.346 \times 10^{-3})^2} = \boxed{0.557}$$

Because the solubility of thallium(I) iodate is increased by the potassium thiocyanate, Y is less than 1.

EXAMPLE 2. Find the $pH = -\log$ [H+] of 0.725 molal sodium chloride solution if Y is 0.517 and K^0 is 1.008×10^{-14} at 25°.

$$K_w = [\text{H}^+][\text{OH}^-] = \frac{K_w^0}{Y} = \frac{1.008 \times 10^{-14}}{0.517} = 1.950 \times 10^{-14}$$

Because a sodium chloride solution is neutral, [H+] = [OH−] and

$$[\text{H}^+]^2 = 1.950 \times 10^{-14}$$

from which we find

$$pH = \boxed{6.86}$$

This result may be compared with 7.00 obtained from $(K_w^0)^{1/2}$ without making correction for interionic forces. The 0.725 molal sodium chloride solution is an interesting one because it has the same ionic strength as an average sample of sea water.

10-15. Activity Coefficients and Activities. It is convenient to separate the factor Y into contributions from each kind of ion (or molecule). The separation follows the same pattern as the product of the concentrations in the equilibrium constant as the following examples show:[7]

$$\text{water: } Y = y_{\text{H}+}y_{\text{OH}-}$$
$$\text{silver chloride: } Y = y_{\text{Ag}+}y_{\text{Cl}-}$$
$$\text{calcium fluoride: } Y = y_{\text{Ca}++}y^2_{\text{F}-}$$
$$\text{bismuth sulfide: } Y = y^2_{\text{Bi}+++}y^3_{\text{S}--}$$

[6]The logarithm of K is usually plotted against the square root of the ionic strength. This method of graphing gives the simplest curves and is supported by theory (Sec. 10-16). We have already found (Sec. 5-10) that the equivalent conductance varies most simply with the square root of the normality. The measurements on water are actually more complex than have been described, and what is plotted is close to, but not exactly, $\log K_w$.

[7]For all but very dilute solutions, Y for water and hydrogen sulfide must include the activity coefficients of the molecular species because even these molecules do not behave ideally when the solution is not dilute.

The y's are called *activity coefficients*. Let us define a quantity called the *activity* as the product of activity coefficient and the concentration:

$$a_X = [X]\, y_X \qquad\qquad 11$$

with the understanding that the activity and concentration become identical at very low concentrations or

$$y_X \to 1 \qquad \text{as} \qquad [X] \to 0 \qquad\qquad 12$$

Since $K^0 = KY$ we can write out expressions for K^0 that are of the same form as those for K, except that concentrations are replaced by activities:

$$K^0_w = [\text{H}^+][\text{OH}^-] y_{\text{H}^+} y_{\text{OH}^-} = a_{\text{H}^+} a_{\text{OH}^-} \qquad\qquad 13$$

$$K^0_{sp} = [\text{Ag}^+][\text{Cl}^-] y_{\text{Ag}^+} y_{\text{Cl}^-} = a_{\text{Ag}^+} a_{\text{Cl}^-} \qquad\qquad 14$$

$$K^0_{sp} = [\text{Ca}^{++}][\text{F}^-]^2 y_{\text{Ca}^{++}} y^2_{\text{F}^-} = a_{\text{Ca}^{++}} a^2_{\text{F}^-} \qquad\qquad 15$$

$$K^0_{sp} = [\text{Bi}^{+++}]^2 [\text{S}^{--}]^3 y^2_{\text{Bi}^{+++}} y^3_{\text{S}^{--}} = a^2_{\text{Bi}^{+++}} a^3_{\text{S}^{--}} \qquad\qquad 16$$

Thus we can regard K^0 as a true equilibrium constant applicable to solutions of all ionic strengths, because it includes the correction factors for interionic forces and other causes of deviation from ideal behavior. Seen from this point of view, Y and the activity coefficients are the corrections required to make the ideal law fit real systems.

The constants K^0 and K go by various names: the "true," "thermodynamic," or *activity* constant for K^0; and the "ideal," "classical," or *concentration* constant for K. The italicized adjectives will be used in this text.

There are many ideal expressions besides the ion and solubility products that we have considered. Equations relating freezing point depression, boiling point elevation, vapor pressure lowering, osmotic pressure, free energy, and electromotive force to the concentrations of solutes are all improved by substituting activities for concentrations. There is no reason to restrict the activity concept to weak or slightly soluble electrolytes; we can apply relations 11 and 12 to any solute species. For hydrochloric acid the activity product

$$a_{\text{H}^+} a_{\text{Cl}^-} = [\text{H}^+][\text{Cl}^-] y_{\text{H}^+} y_{\text{Cl}^-}$$

can be obtained from measurements of freezing point depression, electromotive force, or other properties. None of these measurements gives the activity or activity coefficient of either ion alone. This would be as impossible as preparing a solution that contained only one kind of ion. There are various ingenious, if artificial, ways of estimating the activity coefficients of individual ionic species, but we shall pass over these.

The variation with concentration of the activity coefficients of some typical electrolytes is shown in Fig. 10-3. At a given *low* concentration all 1-1 electrolytes, i.e., those with singly charged ions, have about the same activity coefficient. Other results show that as the charges on the ions increase, Y, the activity coefficient product, decreases. This is what we must expect if Y is less than 1 because of interionic forces. In more concentrated solutions the behavior of Y shows that more specific properties of the ions than their charges come into play (Sec. 5-13). At high concentrations Y may even be larger than 1.

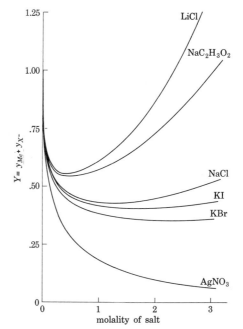

FIG. 10-3. The variation in the activity coefficient factor $Y = y_{Me^+} y_{X^-}$ for some 1-1 electrolytes at 25°.

10-16. The Theoretical Prediction of Activity Coefficients. Various aspects of the Debye-Hückel theory of interionic attraction have been presented already (Secs. 5-13 to 5-15). As long as ions are far apart the only significant interactions between them are those due to their charges. Even so, the orienting effect of the charges, which makes negative ions swarm about positive ones and vice versa, is supposed to be less than the thermal motion of the ions, which tends to mix them at random. The interionic forces will then cause only *small* deviations from ideal behavior. The energy of any ion is decreased as a result of the combined action on it of all of the other ions in the solution. This is neatly expressed as an interaction of the specified ion with a surrounding atmosphere of opposite charge.

Debye and Hückel applied these concepts to the calculation of activity coefficients. Consider an ion of valence z. For very dilute solutions (10^{-3} M or less)

$$\log_{10} y_{ion} = -z^2 \mathcal{S} \sqrt{I} \qquad 17$$

The constant $\mathcal{S}$ is the same for all electrolytes but varies with the dielectric constant and temperature. For water solutions at 25° it is 0.509. The negative sign indicates that log y is negative and y is less than 1. From Eq. 17 we can derive expressions for the activity coefficient product Y, e.g.,

$$\text{HCl:}\quad \log Y = \log y_{H^+} y_{Cl^-} = \log y_{H^+} + \log y_{Cl^-}$$
$$= -S\sqrt{I} - S\sqrt{I} = -2S\sqrt{I}$$

$$\text{CaCl}_2:\ \log Y = \log y_{Ca^{++}} y^2_{Cl^-} = \log y_{Ca^{++}} + 2\log y_{Cl^-}$$
$$= -4S\sqrt{I} - 2S\sqrt{I} = -6S\sqrt{I}$$

According to these equations a graph of log Y against $\sqrt{I}$ should be a straight line in very dilute solutions. The intercept must be zero and the slope will be $-2S$ for a 1-1 electrolyte like HCl or $-6S$ for a 2-1 electrolyte like $CaCl_2$. Equation 17 is sometimes called the *Debye-Hückel limiting law* for activity coefficients, and $-2S$ or $-6S$ is the limiting slope.

The theory can be tested against experiment by constructing graphs (Fig. 10-4) of the types discussed in the preceding paragraph; the experimental results do fall along the limiting slopes in dilute solutions. At a sufficiently low concentration all three 1-1 electrolytes in Fig. 10-4 behave alike; only the

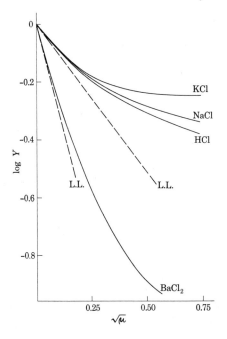

Fig. 10-4. Verification of the Debye-Hückel theory. The lines labeled L.L. are graphs of the limiting laws: log $Y = -2S\sqrt{I}$ for 1-1 electrolytes and log $Y = -6S\sqrt{I}$ for $BaCl_2$.

ionic charges matter. At higher concentrations the curves bow up away from the limiting slopes, and this can be accounted for by the effect of the different sizes of the ions. A number of equations have been proposed that hold at higher concentrations than Eq. 17. For rough calculations the following is convenient for 1-1 electrolytes:

$$\log Y = \frac{-2S \sqrt{I}}{1 + \sqrt{I}} \qquad\qquad 18$$

A more accurate version proposed by Guggenheim adds a term BI to the right-hand side where B is a constant for each electrolyte. A typical calculation with Eq. 18 follows.

EXAMPLE. Find the molar solubility S of silver chloride in 0.0286 M potassium nitrate. The ionic strength is almost entirely due to the potassium nitrate, so $I = 0.0286$. The activity constant $K_{sp}^0 = 1.765 \times 10^{-10}$. To solve this problem by the method of Sec. 10-8 we need the concentration constant K.

$$\log Y = \log y_{Ag^+} y_{Cl^-} = \frac{-2 \times 0.509 \sqrt{0.0286}}{1 + \sqrt{0.0286}} = -0.1475 = 0.8528 - 1$$

$$Y = 0.7121.$$

Then

$$K_{sp} = [Ag^+][Cl^-] = S^2 = \frac{K_{sp}^0}{Y} = \frac{1.765 \times 10^{-10}}{0.7121} = 2.484 \times 10^{-10}$$

$$S = \boxed{1.576 \times 10^{-5} \; M.}$$

This agrees very well with the value 1.569×10^{-5} determined experimentally by Brown and MacInnes but is considerably higher than the value 1.328×10^{-10} calculated from the square root of K_{sp}^0 without making any activity coefficent corrections.

SUPPLEMENTARY READING

T. HOGNESS and W. JOHNSON, *Qualitative Analysis and Chemical Equilibrium*, 4th ed., Holt, New York, 1954, Chapters 8 and 9.

T. MOELLER, *Qualitative Analysis*, McGraw-Hill, New York, 1958, pp. 94–97 and Chapter 7.

E. GILREATH, *Qualitative Analysis*, McGraw-Hill, New York, 1954, Chapter 5.

J. NORDMANN, *Qualitative Testing and Inorganic Chemistry*, Wiley, New York, 1957, Chapter 8.

G. CHARLOT, *Qualitative Inorganic Analysis*, Wiley, New York, 1954, Chapters 10 and 11.

J. EDSALL and J. WYMAN, *Biophysical Chemistry*, Academic Press, New York, 1958, Chapter 10 (carbon dioxide and carbonic acid).

EXERCISES

10-1. Find the hydrogen and hydroxide ion concentrations of the following solutions. Assume complete ionization of all solutes. (a) 0.5 M HCl, (b) 0.25 M LiOH, (c) a mixture of 5 drops of 3 M HNO_3 and 20 drops of H_2O, (d) a mixture of 3 drops of 0.1 M KOH and 17 drops of H_2O.

10-2. Calculate the pH of the following solutions. (a) 0.3 M HNO_3, (b) HCl with $[H^+] = 10^{-3.2}$, (c) 0.15 M KOH, (d) 2 M $HClO_4$, (e) 0.00002 M HCl, (f) 10^{-8} M HNO_3, (g) a mixture of 2 drops of 3 M HBr and 6 drops of H_2O.

10-3. Prove the following relations. Make your proofs general; do not restrict them to particular numerical values of the constants or concentrations. (a) $pH + pOH = pK_w$, (b) $pH = \frac{1}{2} pK_w$ for a neutral solution.

10-4. Calculate the concentrations of hydrogen and hydroxide ions in each solution at 25°. (a) lemon juice, pH 2.3, (b) milk, pH 6.6, (c) 0.1 M baking soda, pH 8.3, (d) 0.1 M washing soda, pH 11.5.

10-5. Calculate the pH of a neutral solution (a) at 0° if $K_w = 1.14 \times 10^{-15}$, (b) at 37° (normal body temperature) if $K_w = 2.40 \times 10^{-14}$, (c) at 25° in water at a pressure of almost 800 atm if $K_w = 2.0 \times 10^{-14}$.

10-6. Calculate the concentration of sulfide ion in solutions having the following pH values if they are saturated with hydrogen sulfide at 25° and 1 atm pressure. (a) pH 0.0, (b) pH 0.7, (c) pH 1.0, (d) pH 7.0.

10-7. Calculate the concentration of sulfide ion in a solution saturated with hydrogen sulfide at 25° and 0.01 atm that is 0.3 M in $HClO_4$.

10-8. Calculate the carbonate ion concentration of 0.02 M nitric acid saturated with carbon dioxide at 25° and 1 atm.

10-9. What is the concentration of Al^{+++} in a saturated solution of the hydroxide at pH 7.0?

10-10. What is the number of mg Sr^{++}/ml in a saturated solution of $SrCrO_4$ if the chromate ion concentration is found by a colorimetric method to be 3×10^{-3} M?

10-11. The sulfide ion concentration of a cadmium nitrate solution is controlled at 5.2×10^{-21} M. Calculate the number of mg Cd/ml left unprecipitated.

10-12. Some solid SrF_2 is shaken with 0.01 M $Sr(NO_3)_2$ solution until equilibrium is reached. The fluoride ion concentration of this solution was found to be 5.3×10^{-4} M. Calculate the solubility product of strontium fluoride.

10-13. A saturated solution of $Ba(IO_3)_2 \cdot H_2O$ is prepared by shaking excess solid salt with pure water. A 50-ml sample of the saturated solution was analyzed by titration and found to contain 0.0810 mmoles of iodate ions. Calculate (a) K_{sp}; (b) the solubility in grams of the monohydrate per 100 ml of solution.

10-14. The solubility of PbI_2 is 0.0701 g/100 ml at 25°. Calculate K_{sp}. What assumptions are made in this calculation?

10-15. Solid silver oxide is shaken with carbon dioxide–free water until the equilibrium

$$\tfrac{1}{2} Ag_2O + \tfrac{1}{2} H_2O \rightleftharpoons Ag^+ + OH^-$$

is established. The pH of this solution is 10.3 at 25°. Calculate the solubility product.

10-16. When solid calcium sulfate is shaken with 0.01 M Na_2SO_4 until equilibrium is attained, 33 mg of $CaSO_4$ dissolves per 100 ml of solution. Calculate K_{sp} of $CaSO_4$.

10-17. How many mg of silver and lead remain per ml of solution after precipitation of Group 1 if the final volume of the solution is 30 drops and if it contains an excess of 1 drop of 3 M HCl? (Hint: The chloride ion concentration is determined by this excess.)

10-18. A saturated solution of lead iodate in water contains 5.34×10^{-5} moles of $Pb(IO_3)_2$ per liter. Calculate (a) the solubility product, (b) the solubility in 0.1 M lead nitrate solution in grams of $Pb(IO_3)_2$ per 100 ml of solution, (c) the solubility in 0.1 M potassium iodate in grams of $Pb(IO_3)_2$ per 100 ml of solution.

10-19. What difficulties may be anticipated with the following calculations? (a) the solubility of silver carbonate in water from its solubility product, (b) the solubility of lead chloride in 0.001 M lead nitrate, (c) the solubility of silver sulfate in water from its solubility product, (d) the solubility of lead chloride in 6 M hydrochloric acid.

10-20. Solid silver nitrate is added gradually to a solution that contains 0.001 mole of chromate and 0.02 mole of chloride per liter. Assume that the volume remains constant during the addition.

(a) Which will precipitate first, AgCl or Ag_2CrO_4?

(b) Calculate the concentration of Ag^+ ion when each precipitate first begins to form.

(c) What will be the concentration of Cl^- ion when Ag_2CrO_4 first begins to precipitate?

(d) What percentage of the chloride has precipitated when silver chromate begins to form?

10-21. It is proposed to separate zinc and copper(II) by fractional precipitation of the sulfides in a solution of controlled acidity. Sulfide will be generated gradually by hydrolysis of thioacetamide. The metal ions are both at 0.01 M concentration.

(a) Which will precipitate first, ZnS or CuS?

(b) Calculate the concentrations of sulfide ion required to form these precipitates.

(c) What will be the concentration of Cu^{++} ion when ZnS starts to precipitate?

(d) What percentage of the copper has precipitated when ZnS begins to form?

10-22. Why would you expect the following separations by fractional precipitation to be unsuccessful? (a) separation of barium from strontium by precipitation of the carbonates, (b) separation of iodide from chloride by precipitation of the silver salts (Hint: See Sec. 8-2), (c) separation of aluminum from zinc by precipitation of the hydroxides, (d) separation of lead from calcium by precipitation of the fluorides.

10-23. From the solubility products calculate the pH at which each of the following hydroxides should just begin to precipitate from 0.01 M solutions of the metal ions. (a) $Fe(OH)_3$, (b) $Cd(OH)_2$, (c) $Mg(OH)_2$. The experimentally observed values are, respectively, 2 to 3, 6.7, and 10.5. How are the calculations oversimplified?

10-24. What is the minimum concentration of perchloric acid that must be present if no FeS is to precipitate from a solution that contains 0.5 mg Fe/ml when the solution is saturated with H_2S at 25° and 1 atm pressure?

10-25. The pH at which ZnS starts to precipitate from 0.01 M zinc nitrate solution saturated with H_2S at 25° and 1 atm pressure is 1.15. To what value of the solubility product of ZnS does this correspond? Why is it different from the one in the table?

10-26. Calcium chloride solutions are kept saturated with CO_2 at 0.9 atm pressure, and the pH is maintained at a predetermined value by addition of ammonia. Calculate the mg Ca/ml left unprecipitated at (a) pH 5, (b) pH 6, (c) pH 7.

10-27. Calculate the percentage conversion of 500 mg of $SrSO_4$ to $SrCO_3$ after treatment with 10 ml of 0.2 M Na_2CO_3.

10-28. Calculate the solubility of silver chloride in 0.04 M $NaNO_3$ if the activity coefficient factor Y is 0.68.

10-29. Calculate the solubility of silver chloride in 0.04 M NaCl if the activity coefficient factor Y is 0.68. Why is the same value of Y used in this and the preceding problem?

10-30. Calculate the pH of 1 M LiCl solution at 25° if the activity coefficient factor Y is 0.40.

10-31. Prove that the ratio of the Y factors for saturated solutions of $TlIO_3$ at two different concentrations of KCl is given by S_1^2/S_2^2 where S_1 and S_2 are the two molar solubilities.

10-32. Explain how K^0 values can be obtained.

10-33. Express K^0 for Ag_2CrO_4 in terms of activities and in terms of activity coefficients and concentrations.

10-34. Derive an expression for the relation between log Y for silver chromate and the ionic strength if Eq. 17 holds.

10-35. Prove that if Eq. 17 holds, then

$$pK_w^0 = pK_w + 2\mathcal{S}\sqrt{I}$$

10-36. Estimate the solubility of silver chloride in 0.01 M nitric acid if Eq. 18 holds.

10-37. Estimate the pH of a neutral 0.02 M NaCl solution if Eq. 18 holds.

10-38. Estimate the pH of neutral 0.01 M $BaCl_2$ and 0.03 M KCl solutions if Eq. 18 holds.

10-39. Explain how the Debye-Hückel theory of activity coefficients can be tested against experimental results.

10-40. The solubility product of calcium sulfate at the bottom of the ocean under a pressure of 1000 bars (987 atm) is about four times as large as the value at 1 atm. How much more soluble is calcium sulfate at the bottom of the ocean than it is at the surface at the same temperature? If the pressure increases by 1 atm for every 10 meters depth, how deep is the ocean when the pressure is 1000 bars?

10-41. The activity coefficient factor of water in 0.725 molal sodium chloride at 0° is 0.523, and K_w is doubled when the pressure is increased to 1000 bars. Calculate the pH of this simulated sea water at this pressure. (Real sea water is actually buffered by bicarbonates and borates.)

CHAPTER ELEVEN

Acids and Bases

11-1. Introduction.   Characteristic Behavior of Acids and Bases.   Centuries ago certain substances were recognized for their sour taste, their action in turning vegetable blues (litmus, for example) red, their solvent power, and their ability to neutralize alkalies to give salts. To these the name "acid" (from the Latin root *ac-*, meaning sharp, as in *acetum*, vinegar) was first applied in the seventeenth century. The name "alkali" (from Arabic words for the alkaline ashes of plants) was given to substances that are soapy to the touch, cut grease, and neutralize or reverse the effect of acids. Later the word "base" was used in the broader sense of any substance that gives a salt by reaction with an acid.

The most significant of these properties of acids and bases are (1) their effect on indicators (Chapter 12) and (2) their ability to react together to give salts. To these we can add two more: (3) their catalytic action (e.g., the hydrolysis of thioacetamide, Sec. 7-7) and (4) their ability to displace weaker acids or bases (e.g., displacement of acetic acid by hydrochloric acid added to an acetate).

In this chapter we are first concerned with various interpretations of acid-base behavior. Reactions in which proton transfer occurs are emphasized. Ionization constants are introduced as measures of relative acid or base strength, and calculations based on these constants are discussed in detail. The chapter concludes with a section on activity coefficient corrections for acid-base equilibria.

11-2. Changing Interpretations of the Terms Acid and Base.   The compulsion to find a structural basis for the properties of substances has led to many interpretations of acid-base behavior. According to one ancient hypothesis, acids are composed of pointed particles that are responsible for the sharp taste. The familiar definitions of acids and bases as sources of, respectively, hydrogen and hydroxide ions date only from the introduction of the theory of ionization in the late nineteenth century. More recent definitions have been introduced to broaden the scope of acid-base reactions just as oxidation-reduction has been extended to include reactions in which molecular oxygen and hydrogen do not participate. We have set down four experimental criteria of acids and bases in the preceding section. We can define "acid" and "base" as we please as long as the definitions lead to reasonable structural interpretations of the four characteristic properties. The choice of particular definitions is determined by the type of systems under study. We are concerned with aqueous solutions and want definitions that simplify the mathematical treatment of equilibria. The ones proposed independently in 1923 by J. N. Brønsted, a Danish chemist, and T. M. Lowry, an English chemist, are most useful for our purposes. They are:

> An acid is a proton donor.
> A base is a proton acceptor.

Proton donors and acceptors were introduced in Sec. 3-8.

11-3. Brønsted-Lowry Acids and Bases.   These definitions are summarized in the relation

$$\text{acid} \rightleftharpoons \text{base} + p \qquad\qquad 1$$

where the proton is represented by p because we use H^+ as an abbreviation for H_3O^+. The acid and base in this relation are said to be a *conjugate* pair. The scope of the definitions is shown by the examples in Table 11-1. Acids

TABLE 11-1.

Brønsted-Lowry Acids and Bases

Substance	Acid	Conjugate base
Hydrogen nitrate	HNO_3	NO_3^-
Acetic acid	$HC_2H_3O_2$	$C_2H_3O_2^-$
Water	H_2O	OH^-
Orthophosphoric acid	H_3PO_4	$H_2PO_4^-$
Potassium dihydrogen phosphate	$H_2PO_4^-$	HPO_4^{--}
Sodium hydrogen sulfate	HSO_4^-	SO_4^{--}
Ammonium chloride	NH_4^+	NH_3
Ethylene diammonium dinitrate	$^+NH_3CH_2CH_2NH_3^+$	$^+NH_3CH_2CH_2NH_2$
Hydrochloric acid	H_3O^+	H_2O

include such old friends as molecular $HC_2H_3O_2$ and the anion HSO_4^-. Certain cations, e.g., NH_4^+, are now regarded as acids. The term "base" is no longer restricted to sources of hydroxide ions but includes any anion, molecule, or cation that can take up a proton and form an acid, e.g., CN^- ion, NH_3, and

$Ag(NH_3)_2^+$. Some substances, e.g., H_2O and $H_2PO_4^-$, can act as either proton donors or acceptors. They are called *ampholytes*.

11-4. Protolytic Reactions.   The recasting of such familiar concepts as acid or base into new molds is worth while only if it leads to useful generalizations. The Brønsted-Lowry definitions extend the scope of acid-base reactions and bring out essential similarities between seemingly different reactions. Protolysis reactions were discussed in Sec. 3-8 and can now be reformulated as

$$\text{acid(1)} \rightleftharpoons \text{base(1)} + p$$
$$p + \text{base(2)} \rightleftharpoons \text{acid(2)}$$

$$\text{acid(1)} + \text{base(2)} \rightleftharpoons \text{acid(2)} + \text{base(1)} \qquad\qquad \mathbf{2}$$

The examples in Table 11-2 demonstrate that a considerable variety of reactions are protolytic. It should be noted in particular that there is no essential difference between ionization of hydrocyanic acid and that of the

TABLE 11-2.

Protolytic Reactions

General type	Acid(1)	+ Base(2)	$\rightleftharpoons$ Acid(2)	+ Base(1)
Ionization of H_2O	H_2O	+ H_2O	$\rightleftharpoons H_3O^+$	+ OH^-
Ionization of HCN	HCN	+ H_2O	$\rightleftharpoons H_3O^+$	+ CN^-
Hydrolysis of NH_4Cl	NH_4^+	+ H_2O	$\rightleftharpoons H_3O^+$	+ NH_3
Ionization of NH_3	H_2O	+ NH_3	$\rightleftharpoons NH_4^+$	+ OH^-
Hydrolysis of $NaC_2H_3O_2$	H_2O	+ $C_2H_3O_2^-$	$\rightleftharpoons HC_2H_3O_2$	+ OH^-
Neutralization of HCl by NaOH	H_3O^+	+ OH^-	$\rightleftharpoons H_2O$	+ H_2O
Neutralization of NH_3 by $HC_2H_3O_2$	$HC_2H_3O_2$	+ NH_3	$\rightleftharpoons NH_4^+$	+ $C_2H_3O_2^-$
Dissolution of BiOCl by HCl	$2H_3O^+$	+ BiOCl	$\rightleftharpoons Bi(H_2O)^{+++}$	+ $2H_2O + Cl^-$
Decomposition of $Ag(NH_3)_2^+$ by HNO_3	$2H_3O^+$	+ $Ag(NH_3)_2^+$	$\rightleftharpoons 2NH_4^+$	+ $3H_2O + Ag^+$
Displacement of HCN by $HC_2H_3O_2$	$HC_2H_3O_2$	+ CN^-	$\rightleftharpoons HCN$	+ $C_2H_3O_2^-$
Displacement of NH_3 by $Ca(OH)_2$	NH_4^+	+ OH^-	$\rightleftharpoons H_2O$	+ NH_3

ammonium ion, although the latter is customarily termed "hydrolysis." Nor does the ionization of ammonia as a base differ materially from that of the acetate ion as a base, although again the latter is usually called a hydrolysis reaction. In doing numerical calculations we shall not need to make any distinction between hydrolysis and ionization; the calculations take the same mathematical form. Both HCN and NH_4Cl give acid solutions, for both contain an acid that liberates from water an excess of hydronium ions. Both NH_3 and $NaC_2H_3O_2$ give basic solutions, for both contain a base that reacts with water to give an excess of hydroxide ions.

The hydronium ion has been written as H_3O^+ in the equations of Table 11-2 to make clear its role as a proton donor. The simpler symbol H^+ will again be used in later sections of this chapter.

11-5. Relative Strengths of Acids and Bases. Free protons are exceedingly small positive charges unshielded by any orbital electrons. They do not exist free in solution (Sec. 1-12), so it is impossible to determine the intrinsic tendency of an acid to lose a proton. The general protolytic reaction (Eq. 2) shows that we shall always have to compare the tendency of one acid, e.g., Acid(1), to lose a proton with that of some other acid, e.g., Acid(2). It is customary to take the ions of the solvent, H_3O^+ and OH^-, as the standard acid and base, respectively.

The acid strength of hydrofluoric acid relative to the hydronium ion is determined from the equilibrium

$$HF + H_2O \rightleftharpoons H_3O^+ + F^-$$

A quantitative measure of the relative strength is given by the *acidity constant* or *acid ionization constant*:

$$K_a = \frac{[H_3O^+][F^-]}{[HF]} = 6.7 \times 10^{-4}$$

The small value of this constant indicates that hydrofluoric acid is a much weaker acid than the hydronium ion. A still weaker acid is the ammonium ion. Its ionization as an acid

$$NH_4^+ + H_2O \rightleftharpoons NH_3 + H_3O^+$$

corresponds to an acidity constant

$$K_a = \frac{[H_3O^+][NH_3]}{[NH_4^+]} = 5.7 \times 10^{-10}$$

Of the three acids H_3O^+ is strongest, HF is next, and NH_4^+ is the weakest.

The bases F^- and NH_3 are compared with the standard base OH^- in the equilibria

$$F^- + H_2O \rightleftharpoons OH^- + HF$$
$$NH_3 + H_2O \rightleftharpoons OH^- + NH_4^+$$

The *basic ionization constants*

$$K_b = \frac{[OH^-][HF]}{[F^-]} = 1.5 \times 10^{-11}$$

$$K_b = \frac{[OH^-][NH_4^+]}{[NH_3]} = 1.8 \times 10^{-5}$$

show that OH^- is the strongest base, NH_3 is next, and F^- is the weakest. It is apparent that HF, a stronger acid than NH_4^+, has the weaker conjugate base. Anions of strong acids such as Cl^- or NO_3^- are exceptionally weak bases. Molecules of HCl readily give up protons; chloride ions do not readily take them up again.

For any conjugate pair of acid and base, the two constants are related by the ion product of water:

$$K_a K_b = K_w \qquad\qquad\qquad 3$$

This is readily verified for HF and F^-:

$$\frac{[H_3O^+][F^-]}{[HF]} \frac{[HF][OH^-]}{[F^-]} = [H_3O^+][OH^-] = K_w$$

For NH_4^+ and NH_3,

$$K_a(NH_4^+) K_b(NH_3) = K_w$$

$$K_a(NH_4^+) = \frac{K_w}{K_b(NH_3)}$$

$$K_b(NH_3) = \frac{K_w}{K_a(NH_4^+)}$$

These relations show that a single table of either acidity constants or basic ionization constants will suffice. Usually the constants for the molecular substances are given, i.e., K_a of HF and K_b of NH_3 rather than K_b of F^- and K_a of NH_4^+. In this text a table of acidity constants is given in the Appendix. A few of the more useful basic ionization constants are also given; others can be derived from the acidity constants by using Eq. 3.

In Sec. 11-4 we noted that reactions such as

$$NH_4^+ + H_2O \rightleftharpoons H_3O^+ + NH_3$$
$$F^- \ \ + H_2O \rightleftharpoons OH^- + HF$$

are often called "hydrolysis" reactions. The corresponding constants are called "hydrolysis constants," K_h. They are easily seen to be, respectively, the acidity constant of the ammonium ion and the basic ionization constant of fluoride ion:

$$K_h = K_a(NH_4^+) = \frac{K_w}{K_b(NH_3)}$$

$$K_h = K_b(F^-) \quad\ \ = \frac{K_w}{K_a(HF)}$$

Such specialized terminology is not actually necessary but it is firmly established.

As a simple illustration of the use of acidic and basic ionization constants, consider the problem of predicting whether a salt solution will be acid, basic, or neutral when it contains both an acidic and a basic ion.

EXAMPLE 1. Sodium hydrogen sulfite. The anion is an ampholyte and can undergo two reactions:

as an acid: $HSO_3^- + H_2O \rightleftharpoons H_3O^+ + SO_3^{--}$ $K_a(HSO_3^-) = 6.2 \times 10^{-8}$

as a base: $HSO_3^- + H_2O \rightleftharpoons H_2SO_3 + OH^-$ $K_b(HSO_3^-) = \dfrac{K_w}{K_a(H_2SO_3)}$

$$= 6 \times 10^{-13}$$

Because the basic ionization constant is less than the acidity constant, the first reaction will go to a larger extent than the second and the solution will be acid.

EXAMPLE 2. Ammonium oxalate. This is the salt of a weak acid and weak base; i.e., it gives an acid cation and a basic anion. The two ionization reactions are

acid: $NH_4^+ + H_2O \rightleftharpoons NH_3 + H_3O^+$ $K_a(NH_4^+) = 5.7 \times 10^{-10}$

base: $C_2O_4^{--} + H_2O \rightleftharpoons HC_2O_4^- + OH^-$ $K_b(C_2O_4^{--}) = K_w/K_a(HC_2O_4^-)$

$$= 1.9 \times 10^{-10}$$

Because the ammonium ion is a slightly stronger acid than the oxalate is a base, the solution is very slightly acidic.[1]

11-6. Hydrated Metal Ions as Acids. The binding of water molecules by ions is sometimes sufficiently strong so that a proton of a water molecule in the primary hydration shell is repelled by the metal ion and lost. The hydrated metal ion acts as a proton donor or acid. This is pictured schematically in Fig. 11-1. The acid ionization reaction of the aluminum ion is represented by[2]

$$Al(H_2O)_6^{+++} + H_2O \rightleftharpoons Al(H_2O)_5OH^{++} + H_3O^+$$

It is usually convenient to simplify this to

$$Al^{+++} + H_2O \rightleftharpoons AlOH^{++} + H^+$$

unless the behavior of the hydrated metal ion as a proton donor is to be demonstrated.

The acid strength of the hydrated Al^{+++} ion relative to the standard H_3O^+ ion is measured by the acidity constant

$$K_a = \frac{[H^+][AlOH^{++}]}{[Al^{+++}]} = 1.1 \times 10^{-5}$$

This hydrated metal ion is a little weaker than acetic acid ($K_a = 1.8 \times 10^{-5}$). The acidity constants of other hydrated cations are given in Table 11-3. Few of these constants are as accurately known as those of the molecular acids. We shall find shortly that there are other equilibria in solutions of salts, and it is difficult to unravel these. Furthermore, the acidity constants of highly

[1] Further reaction of $HC_2O_4^-$ to give $H_2C_2O_4$ can be ignored because the basic constant of $HC_2O_4^-$ is so small: $K_b = 2.6 \times 10^{-13}$.

[2] The number of water molecules in the primary hydration shells of these ions is unknown. Aluminum ions have a coordination number of six in crystals, and this same number has been assumed for solutions, for convenience.

charged ions are very sensitive to changes in temperature and ionic strength. Most of the data in the table refer to perchlorate solutions; the behavior of the metal ion in the presence of chloride or sulfate is often complicated by complex formation.

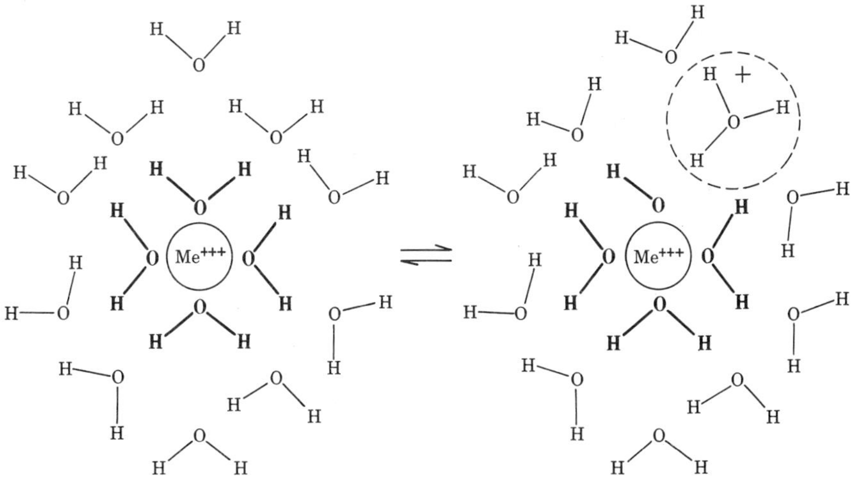

FIG. 11-1. The ionization of a hydrated metal ion as an acid.

Some rough correlations between structure and acid strength can be made. The ease with which a proton can be lost varies with the strength of the cation-oxygen bond. If the bond is strong (as in *a*, below), a proton is repelled readily. If the cation-oxygen bond is weak (as in *b*), the oxygen-hydrogen bond is more difficult to break and only water can be split off.

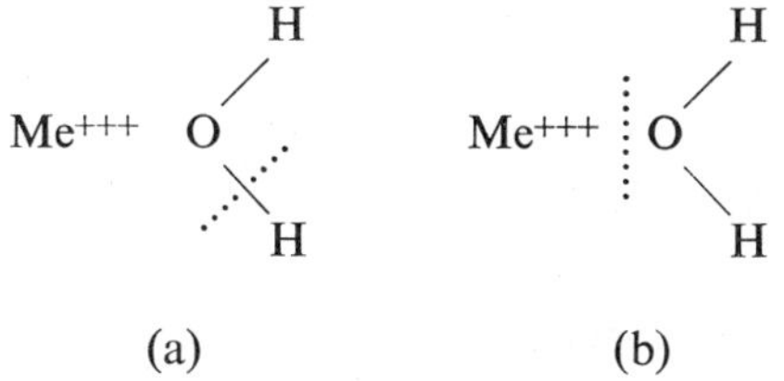

(a)   (b)

Assuming for the moment that the bond between cation and oxygen is purely electrostatic, we expect small, highly charged ions to give the most strongly acidic hydrated cations. In other words, the acidity constant should vary with the ionic potential, the ratio of charge to radius (Sec. 6-10). All the ions in Table 11-3 have comparatively large ionic potentials. The alkali metal ions and Ca^{++}, Sr^{++}, and Ba^{++} have low ionic potentials and are not normally acidic.[3] The smallest ions of Periodic Group IIA, Mg^{++} and Be^{++}, are acidic, although the hydrated Mg^{++} ion is a very weak acid ($K_a \cong 10^{-12}$). The data of Table 11-3 show that acid strength increases with charge on the cation. The trivalent ions are usually stronger than the bivalent, and singly charged ions such as Ag^+ have negligible acidic character. The structure of the cation is also important. Although the Al^{+++} ion has a high ionic potential, it is less acidic than Cr^{+++} and Fe^{+++} ions with noninert gas structures. The ions of the heavier elements in Groups IIB to VB are, with the exception of Pb^{++}, highly acidic. This is particularly notable for the bivalent ions Sn^{++} and Hg^{++}. All these ions have outer shells of 18 or $18 + 2$ electrons and form polarized bonds with oxygen (Sec. 5-5).

TABLE 11-3.

Acidity Constants for Hydrated Metal Ions at 25°

Ion	Ionization equilibrium				Ionic potential	I	K_a
Tl^{+++}	Tl^{+++}	$+ H_2O$	$\rightleftharpoons TlOH^{++}$	$+ H^+$	3	3	7×10^{-2}
Bi^{+++}	Bi^{+++}	$+ H_2O$	$\rightleftharpoons BiOH^{++}$	$+ H^+$	3	3	2.6×10^{-2}
Fe^{+++}	Fe^{+++}	$+ H_2O$	$\rightleftharpoons FeOH^{++}$	$+ H^+$	4.5	0	6.7×10^{-3}
						1	1.6×10^{-3}
						3	0.9×10^{-3}
Hg^{++}	Hg^{++}	$+ H_2O$	$\rightleftharpoons HgOH^+$	$+ H^+$	1.8	0.5	2×10^{-4}
	Hg^{++}	$+ 2H_2O$	$\rightleftharpoons Hg(OH)_2$	$+ 2H^+$		0.5	2.5×10^{-3}
Sn^{++}	Sn^{++}	$+ H_2O$	$\rightleftharpoons SnOH^+$	$+ H^+$	2.2	3	1×10^{-4}
Cr^{+++}	Cr^{+++}	$+ H_2O$	$\rightleftharpoons CrOH^{++}$	$+ H^+$	5.5	0.05	1.6×10^{-4}
Al^{+++}	Al^{+++}	$+ H_2O$	$\rightleftharpoons AlOH^{++}$	$+ H^+$	6.0	0	1.1×10^{-5}
Sc^{+++}	Sc^{+++}	$+ H_2O$	$\rightleftharpoons ScOH^{++}$	$+ H^+$	3.8	1	1.1×10^{-5}
Fe^{++}	Fe^{++}	$+ H_2O$	$\rightleftharpoons FeOH^+$	$+ H^+$	2.7	0	5×10^{-9}
Cu^{++}	Cu^{++}	$+ H_2O$	$\rightleftharpoons CuOH^+$	$+ H^+$	2.9	0.3	5×10^{-9}
Ni^{++}	Ni^{++}	$+ H_2O$	$\rightleftharpoons NiOH^!$	$+ H^+$	2.9	0	5×10^{-10}
Zn^{++}	Zn^{++}	$+ H_2O$	$\rightleftharpoons ZnOH^+$	$+ H^+$	2.7	0	2.5×10^{-10}
	Zn^{++}	$+ 2H_2O$	$\rightleftharpoons Zn(OH)_2$	$+ 2H^+$		0	1.4×10^{-11}

It should be possible for a hydrated cation to give off more than one proton just as a molecular acid such as H_3PO_4 can. Thus an $Al(H_2O)_6^{+++}$ ion would form, successively, $AlOH(H_2O)_5^{++}$, $Al(OH)_2(H_2O)_4^+$, $Al(OH)_3(H_2O)_3$, $Al(OH)_4(H_2O)_2^-$, $Al(OH)_5(H_2O)^{--}$, and $Al(OH)_6^{---}$. Removal of the protons

---

[3]Acidic behavior is sometimes noted at high temperatures. When the chlorides of these ions are fused in the presence of moisture, some HCl gas is lost, and the residue turns phenolphthalein pink. Under these extreme conditions such a reaction as

$$Na^+Cl^- + H_2O \rightarrow Na^+OH^- + HCl \uparrow$$

can occur.

becomes progressively more difficult as the charge decreases from a high positive value to a negative one. The anions $Al(OH)_4^-$ and $Al(OH)_6^{---}$ are known to occur in certain solids (Sec. 8-17) and probably occur in strongly basic solutions. They do not form to an appreciable extent in acidic or weakly ammoniacal solutions, for H_2O and NH_3, unlike OH^-, are not sufficiently strong bases to remove the last three protons from $Al(OH)_3(H_2O)_3$. The existence of the other species, e.g., $Al(OH)_2(H_2O)_4^+$, is difficult to establish because the $AlOH(H_2O)_5^{++}$ ions tend to polymerize rather than lose more protons. In dilute solutions of aluminum chloride the principal ions are Al^{+++} and $AlOH^{++}$, but the latter polymerize in more concentrated solutions to ions such as $Al_4(OH)_{10}^{++}$ or $Al_6(OH)_{15}^{+++}$.

In ferric perchlorate solutions the polymerization gives a dimer:

$$2FeOH^{++} \rightleftharpoons Fe_2(OH)_2^{+4} \qquad K = 30\ (I = 0) \quad \text{to} \quad 700\ (I = 1)$$

The hydroxide groups form bridges between the two iron ions:

$$\begin{bmatrix} & \text{H} & \\ & \text{O} & \\ \text{Fe} & & \text{Fe} \\ & \text{O} & \\ & \text{H} & \end{bmatrix}^{+4}$$

In solutions of bismuth salts the principal ions are Bi^{+++}, $BiOH^{++}$, and $Bi_6(OH)_{12}^{+6}$; there is no evidence for $Bi(OH)_2^+$.

The acidic ionization or hydrolysis of cations is complicated further by formation of precipitates. This normally occurs only with the more acidic cations:

$$Bi^{+++} + H_2O + Cl^- \rightleftharpoons BiOCl \downarrow + 2H^+$$
$$Hg^{++} + H_2O \rightleftharpoons HgO \downarrow + 2H^+$$
$$Sn^{++} + H_2O + Cl^- \rightleftharpoons Sn(OH)Cl \downarrow + H^+$$
$$2Fe^{+++} + 3H_2O \rightleftharpoons Fe_2O_3 \downarrow + 6H^+$$

The last reaction probably occurs by continued polymerization giving larger and larger units until particles of colloidal size are produced. All these reactions are reversed by addition of acid, and solutions of the salts are always prepared with an excess of acid to suppress the hydrolysis. The less acidic cations, e.g., Cu^{++}, Zn^{++}, or Pb^{++}, do not form precipitates with water unless a base such as HCO_3^-, or OH^- is added to drive the ionization to virtual completion.

11-7. Acids and Bases in Nonaqueous Solvents. Although qualitative analysis is usually concerned with aqueous solutions, much can be learned about acids and bases by studying their behavior in other solvents. The ionization reaction will be affected by the dielectric constant and solvating power of the solvent and its acidity or basicity. Alcohols resemble water in having O—H groups capable of forming hydrogen bonds, but they have much lower dielectric constants. The acidity constants of acids in alcoholic solutions are only one-ten thousandth or one-one hundred thousandth as large as they are for water solutions.

Some solvents are more basic than water and promote the ionization of acids. In liquid ammonia, for example, acetic and benzoic acids are as strong as nitric, hydrochloric, and perchloric acids. The reactions

$$HC_2H_3O_2 + NH_3 \rightleftharpoons NH_4^+ + C_2H_3O_2^-$$
$$HCl + NH_3 \rightleftharpoons NH_4^+ + Cl^-$$

go to an equal extent. Ammonia is said to have a *leveling effect* in making all five of these acids equally strong. Only nitric, hydrochloric, and perchloric acid of the five are leveled to equal strength by water, which is less basic than ammonia. Pure acetic acid is still less basic than water, and only the strongest acids react with it to an appreciable extent:

$$HClO_4 + HC_2H_3O_2 \rightleftharpoons H_2C_2H_3O_2^+ + ClO_4^-$$

Thus in this solvent it is possible to detect differences in acid strength among acids that are equally strong in water: $HClO_4$ strongest, HBr, H_2SO_4, HCl, and HNO_3 weakest. Pure HF and H_2SO_4 are highly acidic and very weakly basic solvents; almost all acids are weakly dissociated when dissolved in them. Because of their highly acidic nature they exert a leveling effect on bases and bring out basic properties in some substances that are normally acids:

$$H_2SO_4 + HC_2H_3O_2 \rightarrow H_2C_2H_3O_2^+ + HSO_4^-$$

Proton transfers can occur in all these solvents, and the Brønsted-Lowry concept of acids and bases is useful in giving these reactions a unified treatment. The self-ionization of the solvent is a typical protolytic reaction:

	acid(1)	+ base(2)	⇌ acid(2)	+ base(1)
in water:	H_2O	$+ H_2O$	$\rightleftharpoons H_3O^+$	$+ OH^-$
in ammonia:	NH_3	$+ NH_3$	$\rightleftharpoons NH_4^+$	$+ NH_2^-$
in acetic acid:	$HC_2H_3O_2$	$+ HC_2H_3O_2$	$\rightleftharpoons H_2C_2H_3O_2^+$	$+ C_2H_3O_2^-$
in sulfuric acid:	H_2SO_4	$+ H_2SO_4$	$\rightleftharpoons H_3SO_4^+$	$+ HSO_4^-$

Thus sodium amide in liquid ammonia, sodium acetate in acetic acid, and sodium hydrogen sulfate in sulfuric acid are bases analogous to sodium hydroxide in water. Neutralization of strong acid with strong base is the reverse of the above reactions. The reaction between NH_4Cl and $NaNH_2$ in liquid ammonia or between $HClO_4$ and $NaC_2H_3O_2$ in acetic acid is analogous with the reaction of hydrochloric acid and sodium hydroxide in water.

Acid-base reactions can be generalized to include solvents and substances that contain no protons as long as the four requirements of Sec. 11-1 are satisfied. For example, the indicator crystal violet turns from violet in excess sodium hydroxide to yellow in excess hydrochloric acid; the same color change occurs when boron trichloride is added to a solution of pyridine and crystal violet. Boron trichloride behaves as an acid even though it contains no hydrogen. According to G. N. Lewis, it is an acid because it accepts a share of the lone electron-pair in the pyridine. This is shown below together with some examples of more analytical significance:

Acid		Base		
Cl_3B	+	$:NC_5H_5$	$\rightarrow$	$Cl_3B:NC_5H_5$
Ag^+	+ 2	$:NH_3$	$\rightarrow$	$H_3N:Ag^+:NH_3$ or $Ag(NH_3)_2^+$
SO_3	+	$:O^{--}$	$\rightarrow$	$O:SO_3^{--}$ or SO_4^{--}
$FeCl_3$	+	$:O(C_2H_5)_2$	$\rightarrow$	$Cl_3Fe:O(C_2H_5)_2$

While the Lewis definitions help to systematize reactions and are very useful in organic chemistry, the Brønsted-Lowry concepts are better suited for our purposes.

11-8. The Approximate Calculation of the Concentrations of Ions and Molecules in Solutions of a Single Monoprotic Acid. Consider an acid HA with one ionizable proton. The ionization is represented by

$$HA \rightleftharpoons H^+ + A^- \qquad K_a = \frac{[H^+][A^-]}{[HA]} \qquad \qquad \textbf{4}$$

where the symbol H^+ is once again used as an abbreviation for H_3O^+. If the concentration of OH^- ion is negligible (Sec. 11-12), we can write

$$[H^+] = [A^-] \qquad \qquad \textbf{5}$$

because the equation shows that equal numbers of the two ions are produced. Let C moles of HA be dissolved to make a liter of solution. Some of this will remain as HA, and some will ionize and become A^- ions. Since there is no loss of A atoms in this process, material balance requires that (Sec. 4-13)

$$C = [HA] + [A^-] \qquad \qquad \textbf{6}$$

$$[HA] = C - [A^-] = C - [H^+] \qquad \qquad \textbf{7}$$

where use has been made of Eq. 5. When the expressions for $[HA]$ and $[A^-]$ are substituted in the acidity constant, we obtain

$$K_a = \frac{[H^+]^2}{C - [H^+]} \qquad \qquad \textbf{8}$$

$$[H^+]^2 + K_a[H^+] - CK_a = 0 \qquad \qquad \textbf{9}$$

This quadratic equation can be simplified if the extent of ionization is low, for then $[H^+]$ will be much less than C, and Eq. 8 takes the form

$$K_a \simeq [H^+]^2/C \qquad\qquad\qquad 10$$

$$[H^+] \simeq (CK_a)^{\frac{1}{2}} \qquad\qquad\qquad 11$$

For approximate calculations it will be sufficient to require that $[H^+]$ be less than 10% of C for the approximation in Eqs. 10 and 11 to be satisfactory.

EXAMPLE 1. Calculate the concentrations of ions and molecules in 0.1 M formic acid. It is important first to write the chemical equation and equilibrium constant expression to fix these clearly in mind:

$$HCHO_2 \rightleftharpoons H^+ + CHO_2^- \qquad K_a = \frac{[H^+][CHO_2^-]}{[HCHO_2]} = 1.8 \times 10^{-4}$$

Then if $[OH^-]$ is negligible, $[H^+] = [CHO_2^-]$, and by material balance $[HCHO_2] = 0.1 - [CHO_2^-] = 0.1 - [H^+]$. Hence

$$\frac{[H^+]^2}{0.1 - [H^+]} = 1.8 \times 10^{-4}$$

We do not know offhand whether or not the simpler version

$$\frac{[H^+]^2}{0.1} = 1.8 \times 10^{-4}$$

will work, but let us try it:

$$[H^+] = (0.1 \times 1.8 \times 10^{-4})^{\frac{1}{2}} = 4.2 \times 10^{-3} \ M$$

The answer is less than 10% of 0.1, so the approximation is satisfactory.[4] The results of the calculation can be summarized as

$$[H^+] = [CHO_2^-] = \boxed{4.2 \times 10^{-3} \ M}$$

$$[HCHO_2] = 0.1 - 0.0042 = \boxed{0.096 \ M}$$

$$[OH^-] = K_w/[H^+] = \boxed{2.4 \times 10^{-12} \ M}$$

The concentration of hydroxide ion is negligible in comparison with the other concentrations.

EXAMPLE 2. Calculate the concentrations of the ions and molecules in 0.01 M monochloroacetic acid solution.

$$HC_2H_2ClO_2 \rightleftharpoons H^+ + C_2H_2ClO_2^- \qquad K_a = \frac{[H^+][C_2H_2ClO_2^-]}{[HC_2H_2ClO_2]} = 1.4 \times 10^{-3}$$

If we try the simplified version (Eq. 11), we find

$$[H^+] = (0.01 \times 1.4 \times 10^{-3})^{\frac{1}{2}} = 3.7 \times 10^{-3}$$

[4]Students are sometimes puzzled because $[H^+]$ in the denominator is dropped but not that in the numerator. A millionaire can give away a dime without scruple, for it is negligible in comparison with his total wealth. Thus too we cut $C - [H^+]$ to C when C is large and $[H^+]$ is small. But a hobo with ten cents to his name must not give it away or he will have none; in the numerator $[H^+]^2$ stands alone and cannot be dropped.

which is more than 10% of 0.01. It is necessary to solve the more accurate quadratic equation (Eq. 8 or 9):

$$\frac{[H^+]^2}{0.01 - [H^+]} = 1.4 \times 10^{-3}$$

$$[H^+]^2 + 1.4 \times 10^{-3}\,[H^+] - 1.4 \times 10^{-5} = 0 \qquad \textbf{12}$$

There are three ways of doing this.

Method A. Completing the square. This gives an accurate solution. When a quadratic equation is put in the form

$$x^2 + px = q \qquad \textbf{13}$$

the left-hand side is converted to a perfect square by addition of $(\tfrac{1}{2}p)^2$; i.e.,

$$x^2 + px + (\tfrac{1}{2}p)^2 = q + (\tfrac{1}{2}p)^2 \qquad \textbf{14}$$

or

$$(x + \tfrac{1}{2}p)^2 = q + (\tfrac{1}{2}p)^2$$

$$x = \pm (q + \tfrac{1}{4}p^2)^{1/2} - \tfrac{1}{2}p$$

By comparing Eqs. 12 and 13 we see that $\tfrac{1}{2}p$ is 0.7×10^{-3} and $(\tfrac{1}{2}p)^2$ is $4.9 + 10^{-7}$. Therefore

$$([H^+] + 7 \times 10^{-4})^2 = 1.4 \times 10^{-5} + 4.9 \times 10^{-7} = 1.45 \times 10^{-5}$$

$$[H^+] = + (14.5 \times 10^{-6})^{1/2} - 7 \times 10^{-4} = 3.1 \times 10^{-3}\ M$$

The positive root must be taken to obtain a positive value of $[H^+]$.

Method B. The quadratic formula. This too gives an accurate solution. For any quadratic equation

$$ax^2 + bx + c = 0 \qquad \textbf{15}$$

the general solution is

$$x = \frac{-b \pm (b^2 - 4ac)^{1/2}}{2a} \qquad \textbf{16}$$

In Eq. 12 $a = 1$, $b = 1.4 \times 10^{-3}$, and $c = -1.4 \times 10^{-5}$. Hence

$$[H^+] = \frac{-1.4 \times 10^{-3} \pm (1.96 \times 10^{-6} + 5.6 \times 10^{-5})^{1/2}}{2}$$

$$= 3.1 \times 10^{-3}\ M$$

Method C. Successive approximations. This method gives a succession of approximate answers that converge to the true value.

First approximation: Obtain a preliminary value of $[H^+]$ from Eq. 11:

$$[H^+]_1 = (1.4 \times 10^{-5})^{1/2} = 3.7 \times 10^{-3}$$

Second approximation: Insert $[H^+]_1$ in the denominator of Eq. 8 and solve for a second value of $[H^+]$:

$$\frac{[H^+]_2^2}{0.01 - 0.0037} = 1.4 \times 10^{-3}$$

$$[H^+]_2 = (1.4 \times 10^{-3} \times 0.0063)^{1/2} = 3.0 \times 10^{-3}$$

Third approximation: Insert $[H^+]_2$ in the denominator of Eq. 8 and solve for a third value, $[H^+]_3$

$$\frac{[H^+]_3^2}{0.01 - 0.0030} = 1.4 \times 10^{-3}$$

$$[H^+]_3 = (1.4 \times 10^{-3} \times 0.0070)^{1/2} = 3.1 \times 10^{-3}$$

The second and third values differ by only one in the second digit, sufficiently close for our purposes. As long as the first approximation is less than about half the total concentration, the approximations converge rapidly; if it is more than half, the successive values converge slowly or even diverge. Despite its cumbersome appearance, this method is rapid and less subject to arithmetical errors than the other methods. It is particularly recommended when calculations are made with a slide rule.[5]

From $[H^+] = 3.1 \times 10^{-3} \, M$ we can find the other concentrations in 0.01 M monochloroacetic acid solution:

$$[H^+] = [C_2H_2ClO_2^-] = \boxed{3.1 \times 10^{-3} \, M}$$

$$[HC_2H_2ClO_2] = 0.01 - 0.0031 = \boxed{0.0069 \, M}$$

$$[OH^-] = \frac{K_w}{[H^+]} = \boxed{3.2 \times 10^{-12} \, M}$$

EXAMPLE 3. Find the pH of 0.02 M pyridinium chloride. The ionization reaction is that of a cation acid:

$$C_5H_5NH^+ \rightleftharpoons C_5H_5N + H^+ \qquad K_a = \frac{[H^+][C_5H_5N]}{[C_5H_5NH^+]} = 5.0 \times 10^{-6}$$

This is also termed the hydrolysis of the pyridinium salt. Although the acid is a cation, the problem differs in no essential feature from the preceding ones. We neglect $[OH^-]$ and set

$$[H^+] = [C_5H_5N]$$
$$0.02 - [H^+] = [C_5H_5NH^+]$$

Hence

$$K_a = \frac{[H^+]^2}{0.02 - [H^+]} \simeq \frac{[H^+]^2}{0.2}$$

and $[H^+] = 3.2 \times 10^{-4}$. This is less than 10% of 0.02, so the approximation is satisfactory. Then $pH = -\log (3.2 \times 10^{-4}) = \boxed{3.50}$

11-9. Approximate Calculation of the Concentrations of Ions and Molecules in Solutions of Bases. The analysis of such problems follows the same pattern as that for acids, but $[OH^-]$ replaces $[H^+]$ and K_b replaces K_a in the formulas. For such solutions we can neglect $[H^+]$ unless they are exceedingly dilute.

EXAMPLE 1. Find the concentrations of the ions and molecules in 0.07 M methylamine. This is the conjugate base of $CH_3NH_3^+$, the methylammonium ion, and its basic ionization is represented by

$$CH_3NH_2 + H_2O \rightleftharpoons CH_3NH_3^+ + OH^-$$

and

$$K_b = \frac{[CH_3NH_3^+][OH^-]}{[CH_3NH_2]} = \frac{K_w}{K_a(CH_3NH_3^+)} = \frac{10 \times 10^{-15}}{2.4 \times 10^{-11}} = 4.2 \times 10^{-4}$$

[5]If your slide rule is of the conventional type with A, B, C, and D scales, set 14 on the right side of the A scale with the right-hand index of the B scale under it. No further movement of the slide is necessary. Read $(14)^{1/2} = 374$ on the D scale, round off to two figures, and estimate the decimal point: 3.7×10^{-3}. Subtract this from 0.01 to get 0.0063. Move the indicator until the hairline is over 63 on the B scale, and read the second approximation, 3.0×10^{-3}, on the D scale. Subtract 0.0030 from 0.01 to get 0.0070. Move the indicator until the hairline is over 70 on the B scale, and read the third approximation, 3.1×10^{-3}, on the D scale.

The concentrations of methylammonium and hydroxide ions will be equal if $[H^+]$ is negligible:

$$[CH_3NH_3^+] = [OH^-]$$

Material balance for nitrogen requires

$$0.07 = [CH_3NH_3^+] + [CH_3NH_2]$$

or

$$[CH_3NH_2] = 0.07 - [CH_3NH_3^+] = 0.07 - [OH^-]$$

Then

$$4.2 \times 10^{-4} = \frac{[OH^-]^2}{0.07 - [OH^-]} \simeq \frac{[OH^-]^2}{0.07}$$

This should be compared with Eqs. 8 and 10 for acids. The approximate solution is $[OH^-] = 5.4 \times 10^{-3} \ M$ and, since this is less than 10% of 0.07, no further approximations are required. The concentrations of the species in the solution are:

$$[OH^-] = [CH_3NH_3^+] = \boxed{5.4 \times 10^{-3} \ M}$$

$$[CH_3NH_2] = 0.07 - 0.0054 = \boxed{0.065 \ M}$$

$$[H^+] = \frac{K_w}{[OH^-]} = \boxed{1.9 \times 10^{-12} \ M}$$

EXAMPLE 2. Find the pH of a 0.02 M sodium benzoate solution. The basic ionization of benzoate ion is represented by

$$C_7H_5O_2^- + H_2O \rightleftharpoons HC_7H_5O_2 + OH^-$$

and

$$K_b = \frac{[HC_7H_5O_2][OH^-]}{[C_7H_5O_2^-]} = \frac{K_w}{K_a(HC_7H_5O_2)} = \frac{10 \times 10^{-15}}{6.3 \times 10^{-5}} = 1.6 \times 10^{-10}$$

This reaction is also called the hydrolysis of the benzoate ion. Aside from the fact that the base is an anion, there is no essential difference in the formulation of this and the preceding examples:

$$[HC_7H_5O_2] = [OH^-]$$
$$0.02 - [OH^-] = [C_7H_5O_2^-]$$
$$K_b = 1.6 \times 10^{-10} = \frac{[OH^-]^2}{0.02 - [OH^-]} \simeq \frac{[OH^-]^2}{0.02}$$
$$[OH^-] = 1.8 \times 10^{-6}$$
$$p\text{OH} = -\log (1.8 \times 10^{-6}) = 5.75$$
$$p\text{H} = 14.00 - 5.75 = \boxed{8.25}$$

11-10. Calculations Involving the Extent of Ionization. The extent of ionization is the fraction of the electrolyte that ionizes (Sec. 4-11). The relation between extent of ionization α and the ionization constant was derived in Sec. 7-11:

$$K = \frac{\alpha^2 C}{1 - \alpha} \qquad\qquad 17$$

If α is less than 0.1 (or 10% ionized), this simplifies to

$$\alpha \simeq (K/C)^{1/2} \qquad\qquad 18$$

EXAMPLE 1. Find the extent of ionization of 0.03 M propionic acid. The equilibrium is represented by

$$HC_3H_5O_2 \rightleftharpoons H^+ + C_3H_5O_2^- \qquad K_a = \frac{[H^+][C_3H_5O_2^-]}{[HC_3H_5O_2]} = 1.3 \times 10^{-5}$$

Let $\alpha =$ the extent of ionization. We can either solve for $[H^+]$ in the usual way and find α from $[H^+]/0.03$ or we can use Eqs. 17 or 18. Eq. 17 is based on the following relations:

$$0.03\,\alpha = [C_3H_5O_2^-] = [H^+]$$

$$0.03\,(1-\alpha) = [HC_3H_5O_2]$$

Then

$$1.3 \times 10^{-5} = \frac{0.03\alpha^2}{1-\alpha} \simeq 0.03\alpha^2$$

and

$$\alpha = 2.1 \times 10^{-2} \text{ or } \boxed{2.1\%}$$

The use of Eq. 18 was justified because the answer is less than 10%.

EXAMPLE 2. The pH of 0.01 M sodium lactate is 7.88 at 25°. Find the extent of ionization of lactate as a base (or its extent of hydrolysis) and K_a of lactic acid.

$$C_3H_5O_3^- + H_2O \rightleftharpoons HC_3H_5O_3 + OH^- \qquad K_b = \frac{K_w}{K_a} = \frac{[HC_3H_5O_3][OH^-]}{[C_3H_5O_3^-]}$$

$$pOH = 14.00 - pH = 6.12$$

$$[OH^-] = 7.6 \times 10^{-7} \ M$$

$$\alpha = \frac{[HC_3H_5O_3]}{0.01} = \frac{[OH^-]}{0.01} = 7.6 \times 10^{-5} \text{ or } \boxed{0.0076\%}$$

$$K_b = \frac{K_w}{K_a} = \frac{\alpha^2 C}{1-\alpha} = \frac{(7.6 \times 10^{-5})^2 (1 \times 10^{-2})}{1 - 0.000076} = 5.8 \times 10^{-11}$$

$$K_a = \frac{K_w}{K_b} = \frac{10 \times 10^{-15}}{5.8 \times 10^{-11}} = \boxed{1.7 \times 10^{-4}}$$

This does not agree exactly with the tabular value, because interionic forces have not been taken into account.

11-11. Approximate Calculation of the Concentrations in Solutions of Polyprotic Acids and Bases. Consider the important case of a C molar solution of hydrogen sulfide. The two ionization equilibria are represented by

$$H_2S \rightleftharpoons H^+ + HS^- \qquad K_a(H_2S) = K_1 = \frac{[H^+][HS^-]}{[H_2S]} = 1.0 \times 10^{-7} \qquad \textbf{19}$$

$$HS^- \rightleftharpoons H^+ + S^{--} \qquad K_a(HS^-) = K_2 = \frac{[H^+][S^{--}]}{[HS^-]} = 1.3 \times 10^{-13} \qquad \textbf{20}$$

It is important to note that $[H^+]$ has the same value in both expressions.

There are not two kinds of H^+, one for K_1 and the other for K_2; all H^+ ions are alike. The material balance condition for sulfur is

$$\text{MB (S): } C = [H_2S] + [HS^-] + [S^{--}] \qquad 21$$

which expresses the requirement that the total number of sulfur atoms in H_2S, HS^-, and S^{--} must be equal to the number that were put into solution. The electroneutrality condition is

$$\text{EN: } [H^+] = [OH^-] + [HS^-] + 2[S^{--}] \qquad 22$$

which expresses the requirement that the total positive charge must equal the total negative charge (Sec. 4-12).

It is possible to find the concentrations of the ions and molecules in this solution without elaborate calculations if some simplifying assumptions are made. As long as the concentration of hydrogen sulfide is not very low, the solution will be sufficiently acid so that $[OH^-]$ can be neglected. The small value of K_2 indicates that very few HS^- ionize to S^{--}, so $[S^{--}]$ will be small in comparison with $[HS^-]$. Eqs. 21 and 22 then reduce to

$$[H^+] \simeq [HS^-] \qquad 23$$

$$C \simeq [H_2S] + [HS^-] \text{ or } [H_2S] \simeq C - [H^+] \qquad 24$$

These are comparable with Eqs. 5 to 7, as might be expected, since we are ignoring the effect of the second ionization step on $[H^+]$ and $[HS^-]$.

EXAMPLE 1. Calculate the concentrations of ions and molecules in 0.1 M H_2S. From Eqs. 19, 23, and 24 we obtain

$$K_1 = 1.0 \times 10^{-7} = \frac{[H^+]^2}{0.1 - [H^+]} \simeq \frac{[H^+]^2}{0.1}$$

It is reasonable to try the approximation that $0.1 - [H^+]$ be reduced to 0.1 because C is fairly large and K_1 is small. Then

$$[H^+] = \boxed{1.0 \times 10^{-4}\ M} \simeq [HS^-]$$

$$[H_2S] = 0.1 - 0.001 \simeq \boxed{0.1\ M}$$

To find $[S^{--}]$ we must use K_2:

$$K_2 = \frac{[H^+][S^{--}]}{[HS^-]} = \boxed{1.3 \times 10^{-13}} = \frac{1 \times 10^{-4}[S^{--}]}{1 \times 10^{-4}} = [S^{--}]$$

Also

$$[OH^-] = \frac{K_w}{[H^+]} = \boxed{1.0 \times 10^{-10}\ M}$$

We are now able to test the approximations that were made in deriving Eqs. 23 and 24. From Eq. 21

$$\text{MB (S): } 0.1 = [H_2S] + 1.0 \times 10^{-4} + 1.3 \times 10^{-13}$$

$$[H_2S] = 0.1 - 0.0001 - 0.00000000000013$$

we see that it is satisfactory to approximate $[H_2S]$ by 0.1. From Eq. 22

$$\text{EN: } [H^+] = [HS^-] + 1.0 \times 10^{-10} + 2 \times 1.3 \times 10^{-13}$$

$$= [HS^-] + 0.0000000001 + 0.00000000000026$$

we see that it is also satisfactory to set $[H^+] = [HS^-]$.

The same analysis can be made of solutions of triprotic acids such as H_3PO_4 or of bases such as CO_3^{--}.

EXAMPLE 2. Calculate the pH, concentrations of solute species, and extent of ionization (or hydrolysis) of carbonate ion as a base for a 0.2 M solution of Na_2CO_3. The equilibria are

$$CO_3^{--} + H_2O \rightleftharpoons HCO_3^- \times OH^-$$

$$K_b(CO_3^{--}) = \frac{K_w}{K_a(HCO_3^-)} = \frac{[HCO_3^-][OH^-]}{[CO_3^{--}]} = 2.1 \times 10^{-4}$$

$$HCO_3^- + H_2O \rightleftharpoons H_2CO_3 + OH^-$$

$$K_b(HCO_3^-) = \frac{K_w}{K_a(H_2CO_3)} = \frac{[H_2CO_3][OH^-]}{[HCO_3^-]} = 2.3 \times 10^{-8}$$

Here again the second stage has a much smaller constant than the first and will occur to a negligible extent. Therefore,

$$[HCO_3^-] \simeq [OH^-]$$

$$[CO_3^{--}] = 0.2 - [OH^-] \simeq 0.2$$

$$\frac{[OH^-]^2}{0.2} \simeq K_b(CO_3^{--}) = 2.1 \times 10^{-4}$$

$$[OH^-] = \boxed{6.5 \times 10^{-3} \ M} \simeq [HCO_3^-]$$

$$[CO_3^{--}] = 0.2 - 0.0065 \simeq \boxed{0.2 \ M}$$

$$pH = 14.00 - pOH = \boxed{11.82}$$

The concentration of molecular acid (or, more accurately, of H_2CO_3 and CO_2) is virtually equal to the second constant

$$K_b(HCO_3^-) = \frac{\cancel{6.5 \times 10^{-3}}[H_2CO_3]}{\cancel{6.5 \times 10^{-3}}} = [H_2CO_3] = \boxed{2.3 \times 10^{-8} \ M}$$

The extent of ionization or hydrolysis is given by the total concentration of ionized (or hydrolyzed) carbonate over the initial concentration:

$$\alpha = \frac{[HCO_3^-] + [H_2CO_3]}{0.2} = \frac{6.5 \times 10^{-3} + 2.3 \times 10^{-8}}{0.2}$$

$$= 3.2 \times 10^{-2} \text{ or } \boxed{3.2\%}$$

11-12. A More General Treatment of Ionization Constant Problems. Ionization does not occur in a vacuum but in the presence of, and through the agency of, water. If water plays an apparently minor role in solutions of ordinary concentration, it steps forward in exceedingly dilute solutions to take over the leading part. Suppose, for example, that a solution of HCN is diluted with more and more water. The extent of ionization of the acid increases (Sec. 2-16) but never rises to more than 0.4% in any solution of HCN in water at 25°. This is because it is impossible to prepare such a solution with a $[H^+]$ that is less than 10^{-7}, the value for pure water. If a drop of any acid is diluted with a lake full of pure water, the extent of ionization of the acid is limited by the hydrogen ion concentration established by the water. We can express this quantitatively, using HCN as a convenient example:

$$\alpha = \frac{\text{concentration of HCN that ionizes}}{\text{total concentration of HCN}} = \frac{[CN^-]}{[HCN] + [CN^-]}$$

$$= \frac{[CN^-]}{[H^+][CN^-]/K_a + [CN^-]}$$

where $[HCN] = [H^+][CN^-]/K_a$. We can cancel the common factor $[CN^-]$ and simplify still further by multiplying numerator and denominator by K_a. These operations lead to

$$\alpha = \frac{K_a}{K_a + [H^+]} \qquad\qquad 25$$

Thus at high dilutions when $[H^+] = 10^{-7}$ or 1000×10^{-10}, the maximum extent of ionization of HCN ($K_a = 4 \times 10^{-10}$) is

$$\alpha = \frac{4 \times 10^{-10}}{4 \times 10^{-10} + 1000 \times 10^{-10}} = 4 \times 10^{-3} \text{ or } 0.4\%$$

This discussion shows that for very dilute solutions a more general approach than that developed in Secs. 11-8 to -11 is needed. This more general approach is also useful in examining the approximations used in the preceding sections and as a basis for the treatment of more complex equilibria in later chapters. Consider for example a C molar solution of a weak acid HA. The principles of material balance and electroneutrality take the form

$$\text{MB } (A): C \;\;\;= [HA] + [A^-] \qquad\qquad 26$$

$$\text{EN: } [H^+] = [A^-] \;+ [OH^-] \qquad\qquad 27$$

If C is known, these two relations contain four unknown concentrations. They can be combined by addition or subtraction to eliminate one of these, e.g., $[A^-]$:

$$\text{MB } - \text{ EN: } C - [H^+] = [HA] - [OH^-]$$

$$[HA] = C - [H^+] + [OH^-] \qquad\qquad 28$$

This together with

$$[A^-] = [H^+] - [OH^-] \qquad\qquad 29$$

obtained by rearranging the electroneutrality condition, are accurate versions of Eqs. 5 and 7. They differ from the earlier equations only in including $[OH^-]$. At ordinary concentrations of acid, this concentration is negligible, but it becomes important for very dilute solutions.

Equations 28 and 29 are exact ones but they are insufficient in themselves to enable us to calculate the concentrations of the ions and molecules. To solve for the four unknown concentrations we need four equations, or two more than we have considered thus far. We have available expressions for the equilibrium constants K_w and K_a of the acid, i.e.,

$$K_w = [\text{H}^+][\text{OH}^-] \qquad\qquad\qquad 30$$

$$K_a = \frac{[\text{H}^+][A^-]}{[\text{H}A]} \qquad\qquad\qquad 31$$

It is possible to combine the four relations so as to eliminate all but one concentration, e.g., $[\text{H}^+]$:

$$K_a = \frac{[\text{H}^+]\{[\text{H}^+] - K_w/[\text{H}^+]\}}{C - [\text{H}^+] + K_w/[\text{H}^+]} = \frac{[\text{H}^+]^3 - K_w[\text{H}^+]}{C[\text{H}^+] - [\text{H}^+]^2 + K_w}$$

This can be rearranged to

$$[\text{H}^+]^3 + K_a[\text{H}^+]^2 - (CK_a + K_w)[\text{H}^+] - K_wK_a = 0 \qquad 32$$

No approximation has been made in deriving this relation; it is exact. It is fortunately hardly ever necessary to solve this cubic equation. At ordinary concentrations, the fourth term K_wK_a is much smaller than the rest, and also K_w is smaller than CK_a. Equation 32 then reduces to $[\text{H}^+]^3 + K_a[\text{H}^+]^2 - CK_a[\text{H}^+] \simeq 0$ which is readily rearranged to give Eq. 8. The still simpler Eq. 10 is obtained from the first and third terms on the left-hand side of Eq. 32. The relative importance of the terms changes with dilution, and in very dilute solutions the first term may become negligible in comparison with the other three.

The same approach can be used for solutions of a diprotic acid. Equations 19 to 22 can be combined with K_w to give

$$[\text{H}^+]^4 + K_1[\text{H}^+]^3 + (K_1K_2 - CK_1 - K_w)[\text{H}^+]^2$$
$$- K_1(2CK_2 + K_w)[\text{H}^+] - K_1K_2K_w = 0 \qquad 33$$

This is a quartic equation, whereas the one for a monoprotic acid (Eq. 32) was a cubic; the order of the expression for $[\text{H}^+]$ is one more than the number of equilibrium constants. At high concentrations only the first and third terms are important; Example 1, Sec. 11-11, was solved on this basis. At lower concentrations but when C is much greater than $(K_1K_2)^{1/2}$, the first three terms give

$$[\text{H}^+] = \frac{K_1}{2} + \left(\frac{K_1^2}{4} + K_1(C - K_2) + K_w\right)^{1/2} \qquad 34$$

11-13. Corrections for Interionic Forces in Ionization Constant Calculations. The effect of interionic forces on acidity constants was discussed in Sec. 7-16. The methods of Secs. 10-14 to -16 can be used to correct for this effect. If values of K_a are obtained at various ionic strengths, the results can be extended to obtain the activity constant K_a^0 at a concentration so low that interionic forces are negligible. The activity and concentration constants are related by

$$K^0 = KY \qquad 35$$

where Y is the activity coefficient factor (Sec. 10-14). If Y is known and K_a^0 can be found in a table, the concentration constant K_a required for the calculations of this chapter can be calculated.

EXAMPLE 1. Calculate the pH of a 0.01 M solution of carbonic acid in 1 M sodium chloride at 0°. The activity constant K_1^0 for the first step in the ionization

$$H_2CO_3 \rightleftharpoons H^+ + HCO_3^- \qquad K_1^0 = \frac{[H^+][HCO_3^-]}{[H_2CO_3]} Y$$

is 2.64×10^{-7} at 0°, and Y is 0.376. The second stage of the ionization can be neglected. Then

$$K_a = \frac{2.64 \times 10^{-7}}{0.376} = \frac{[H^+][HCO_3^-]}{[H_2CO_3]} \simeq \frac{[H^+]^2}{0.01}$$

$$[H^+] = 8.4 \times 10^{-5}$$

$$pH = \boxed{4.08}$$

Had K^0 been used without making the correction for interionic forces, the apparent pH would have been 4.29 or more than 0.2 unit higher.

Some important conclusions can be reached by dividing Y into activity coefficient contributions from the ions and molecules and applying the Debye-Hückel theory. For acetic acid

$$K^0 = \frac{a_{H^+} a_{C_2H_3O_2^-}}{a_{HC_2H_3O_2}} = K \frac{y_{H^+} y_{C_2H_3O_2^-}}{y_{HC_2H_3O_2}} \qquad 36$$

The molecules of un-ionized acid bear no charge and in very dilute solutions will behave as ideal solutes; we can write $y_{HC_2H_3O_2} \simeq 1$. The activity coefficients of the ions can be estimated for very dilute solutions with the Debye-Hückel limiting law (Eq. 17, Sec. 10-16):

$$\log y_{ion} = -z^2 S \sqrt{I} \qquad 37$$

where z is the valence of the ion and S is the constant 0.509 at 25°. If we write Eq. 36 in logarithmic form and use Eq. 37 to express the logarithm of the ionic activity coefficients, we obtain

$$\log K^0 = \log K - S \sqrt{I} - S \sqrt{I}$$

$$\log K = \log K^0 + 2S \sqrt{I} \qquad 38$$

A graph of log K against $\sqrt{I}$ should be a straight line with intercept log K^0 and slope $2S$. The same result is predicted for any molecular acid HA. For an anion acid such as $H_2PO_4^-$,

$$\log K^0 = \log K + \log y_{H^+} + \log y_{HPO_4^{--}} - \log y_{H_2PO_4^-}$$
$$= \log K - S\sqrt{I} - 4S\sqrt{I} + S\sqrt{I}$$
$$\log K = \log K^0 + 4S\sqrt{I} \qquad\qquad 39$$

Thus a linear relation is again obtained but with a slope twice as great. Interionic forces are particularly large because of the presence of the doubly charged anion. For a cation acid such as the ammonium ion NH_4^+ $\rightleftharpoons NH_3 + H^+$

$$\log K^0 = \log K + \log y_{NH_3} + \log y_{H^+} - \log y_{NH_4^+}$$
$$= \log K - S\sqrt{I} + S\sqrt{I}$$
$$\log K \simeq \log K^0 \qquad\qquad 40$$

This assumes that the activity coefficient of neutral ammonia molecules is 1. In the ionization of the cation acid, one positive ion is replaced by another, so interionic forces are not much changed by ionization and their effects cancel. The extent to which Eqs. 38 to 40 represent the behavior of the three types of acid in sodium chloride solutions is shown in Fig. 11-2. As we must expect, the behavior is close to that predicted only in very dilute solutions.

Activity coefficient corrections can be estimated using Eq. 37 or, better still, the more accurate version

$$\log y_+ y_- = \frac{-2S\sqrt{I}}{1 + \sqrt{I}} \qquad\qquad 41$$

EXAMPLE 2. Calculate the hydrogen ion concentration of 0.01 M acetic acid with correction for interionic forces. The equilibrium is represented by

$$HC_2H_3O_2 \rightleftharpoons H^+ + C_2H_3O_2^-$$

$$K_a^0 = \frac{[H^+][C_2H_3O_2^-]}{[HC_2H_3O_2]} \frac{y_{H^+} y_{C_2H_3O_2^-}}{y_{HC_2H_3O_2}} = 1.75 \times 10^{-5}$$

We can find $[H^+]$ from

$$\frac{[H^+]^2}{0.01 - [H^+]} = K_a$$

if we know K_a. This means that we have to estimate the activity coefficients, for

$$K_a = K_a^0 / y_{H^+} y_{C_2H_3O_2^-}$$

where the activity coefficient of the molecular acid is assumed to be unity. The activity coefficients are found from Eq. 41, but the ionic strength is required for this. Since

$$I = \tfrac{1}{2}([H^+] + [C_2H_3O_2^-] + [OH^-]) = [H^+]$$

which is the very concentration we want to calculate, it would appear that we had reached a dead end. Fortunately, the hydrogen ion concentration is low, so the activity coefficient factor must be close to 1. Let us then make a preliminary estimate of $[H^+]$ by using

$$\frac{[H^+]^2}{0.01 - [H^+]} \simeq K_a^0$$

From this we find $[H^+] = 4.1 \times 10^{-4} = I$ and $I^{1/2} = 2.0 \times 10^{-2}$. When this is used with Eq. 41, we find $y_{H^+} y_{C_2H_3O_2^-} = 0.96$, so $K_a = 1.82 \times 10^{-5}$, which leads to $[H^+] = \boxed{4.2 \times 10^{-4}\ M}$

Because 4.2×10^{-4} differs so slightly from the preliminary estimate, 4.1×10^{-4}, we need carry the calculation no further. If the two values had differed appreciably, we would have had to go through the calculations again, using the second value of $[H^+]$ for the ionic strength. Thus, by a series of successive approximations, the true value of $[H^+]$ could be found.

FIG. 11-2. The effect of sodium chloride on the ionization constants of three acids at 25°. Molecular acid, acetic acid; anion acid, dihydrogen phosphate ion; cation acid, glycinium ion. The dotted lines show the behavior predicted by Eqs. 38 through 40. The behavior of the glycinium ion is comparable with that of the ammonium ion.

Data from: H. Harned and F. Hickey, *J. Am. Chem. Soc.*, **59**, 1284 (1937) (acetic acid); M. Alpert, Dissertation, Yale University (1944) (dihydrogen phosphate ion); E. King, *J. Am. Chem. Soc.*, **67**, 2178 (1945) (glycinium ion).

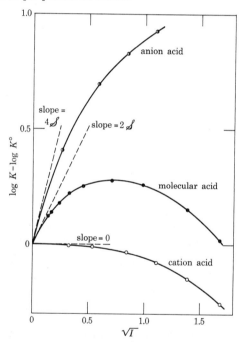

If the weak acid or base is not molecular but is an ion of a salt, the ionic strength can be calculated from the concentration of the salt.

SUPPLEMENTARY READING

T. R. Hogness and W. C. Johnson, *Qualitative Analysis and Chemical Equilibrium*, 4th ed., Holt, New York, 1954, Chapter 7, pp. 180–85, and Chapter 10.

T. Moeller, *Qualitative Analysis*, McGraw-Hill, New York, 1958, Chapters 5 and 6.

E. Kelsey and H. Dietrich, *Fundamentals of Semimicro Qualitative Analysis*, rev. ed., Macmillan, New York, 1951, Chapter 4.

R. P. BELL, *Acids and Bases*, Wiley, New York, 1952, Chapters 1, 2, 3, 4, and 7. A brief, readable summary of definitions of acid and base, equilibria in water and nonaqueous solvents, and the effect of interionic forces.

G. CHARLOT, *Qualitative Inorganic Analysis*, Wiley, New York, 1954, Chapter 4.

L. P. HAMMETT, *Introduction to the Study of Physical Chemistry*, McGraw-Hill, New York, 1952, Chapter 14.

L. POKRAS, "On the Species Present in Aqueous Solutions of 'Salts' of Polyvalent Metals," *J. Chem. Educ.*, **33**, 152, 223, 282 (1956).

J. C. BAILAR, ed., *The Chemistry of the Coordination Compounds*, Reinhold, New York, 1956, Chapters 12 and 13.

EXERCISES

11-1. Define "acid" and "base" in the Brønsted-Lowry sense. What experimental criteria must be satisfied by acids and bases, however defined?

11-2. What is meant by "conjugate" base and acid? How are K_a and K_b related? Compare the basic strengths of NO_2^-, SO_3^{--}, NO_3^-, and SO_4^{--}.

11-3. Classify the following as Brønsted-Lowry acids, bases, or ampholytes: (a) CN^-, (b) NH_4^+, (c) HCl, (d) H_2O, (e) NH_3, (f) HCO_3^-, (g) $Cr(OH)(H_2O)_5^{++}$, (h) $Zn(H_2O)_4^{++}$, (i) $Cu(NH_3)_4^{++}$, (j) H_3O^+, (k) S^{--}, (l) OH^-.

11-4. Why is it impossible to measure the intrinsic ability of an acid to give off a proton? What does K_a measure? What does K_b measure?

11-5. Explain why the hydrolysis of ammonium chloride and of potassium cyanide can be described as ionization reactions.

11-6. Which of the following metal ions are cation acids in the hydrated condition? Li^+, Co^{++}, Pb^{++}, K^+, Ba^{++}, Cr^{+++}, Mg^{++}, Be^{++}, Sr^{++}, Na^+, Cs^+, Mn^{++}, Fe^{+++}, Al^{+++}, Sn^{++}.

11-7. Explain the difference in acid strength of (a) Be^{++} and Mg^{++}, (b) Fe^{++} and Fe^{+++}, (c) Fe^{+++} and Al^{+++}, (d) Mg^{++} and Na^+.

11-8. What is the structure of $Fe_2(OH)_2^{+4}$? Suggest a possible structure for $Bi_6(OH)_{12}^{+6}$.

11-9. A mercury(II) nitrate solution is always prepared by dissolving the salt in nitric acid, but a zinc nitrate solution is prepared from the salt and water. Account for the difference. If both solutions are diluted with water, a precipitate is obtained from one. Which one? Write the equation for the reaction.

11-10. When an unknown solution to be analyzed for Cation Group 2 is diluted with water, a white precipitate forms. It redissolves on addition of hydrochloric acid. Suggest two compounds that might be in this precipitate and write equations for their formation.

11-11. When an iron(III) chloride solution is evaporated to dryness, blue litmus held in the escaping vapors turns red. The residue is not completely soluble in water but dissolves in hydrochloric acid. Suggest an explanation. Write equations for the reactions.

11-12. Consider 0.1 M solutions of the following salts. (a) KCN, (b) NH_4NO_3, (c) $C_5H_5NHClO_4$, (d) $FeCl_3$, (e) Na_3PO_4, (f) $KAl(SO_4)_2$, (g) $BaCl_2$, (h) K_2CO_3, (i) $ZnSO_4$, (j) KNO_3, (k) NaI, (l) $Co(NO_3)_2$.

(1) Which salts have cation acids, which have anion bases, and which have no ions with appreciable acidic or basic properties? (Consider the sulfate ion to have negligible basic properties.)

(2) Write an equation for the principal protolysis reaction, if any, in each salt solution. Omit ions that do not take part. Omit secondary stages.

(3) Predict the effect of each solution on litmus.

11-13. The following salts contain either an ampholyte or both a cation acid and an anion base. (a) NH_4CN, (b) $NaHS$, (c) $KHSO_4$, (d) $Zn(C_2H_3O_2)_2$, (e) $(NH_4)_2S$, (f) KH_2PO_4, (g) Na_2HPO_4, (h) $(NH_4)_2CO_3$, (i) $KHC_4H_4O_6$, (j) $Al(C_2H_3O_2)_3$, (k) $Ba(HSO_3)_2$, (l) KHC_2O_4.

(1) Write equations for the two ionization reactions.

(2) From the constants for these reactions determine the effect of each solution on litmus.

11-14. The pH of the sodium salts NaA and NaB in 0.1 M solutions are measured. Which of the following statements are true if that of the NaA solution is the higher? (a) NaA is more highly hydrolyzed than NaB, (b) NaA is more highly ionized than NaB, (c) HA is a stronger acid than HB, (d) The hydrolysis constant of NaA is larger than that of NaB.

11-15. Prove that if a solution contains a salt with a weakly acidic cation and a weakly basic anion having acidity constants K_1 and $K_2 = K_w/K_b$, the solution is acid if K_1K_2 is greater than K_w and basic if the product is less than K_w.

11-16. Hydrochloric acid is not a strong acid in ethyl alcohol. Account for this and write an equation for the reaction between HCl gas and C_2H_5OH. Sodium ethylate, NaC_2H_5O, is a strong base in alcohol. Why is $C_2H_5O^-$ analogous with OH^- in water solutions?

11-17. Give an illustration of the leveling effect of the solvent on base strength.

11-18. Calculate the pH and concentrations of all ionic and molecular species (except H_2O) in these solutions. (a) 0.2 M acetic acid, (b) 0.01 M hydrocyanic acid, (c) 0.3 M ammonia solution, (d) 0.01 M nitrous acid, (e) 10^{-4} M formic acid, (f) 0.2 M sodium lactate, (g) 0.02 M pyridine (C_5H_5N), (h) 0.02 M calcium acetate, (i) 0.05 M hydrogen sulfide, (j) 0.01 M carbonic acid, (k) 0.05 M sodium carbonate, (l) 0.2 M sulfurous acid, (m) 0.5 M sulfuric acid (Hint: Assume complete ionization to HSO_4^- but partial ionization to SO_4^{--}).

11-19. Calculate the pH and concentration of carbonate ion in 1.5×10^{-5} M carbonic acid. This is the approximate concentration of acid in ordinary distilled water that has come to equilibrium with the carbon dioxide in air.

11-20. Calculate the pH of an eye wash solution prepared by dissolving 2.00 grams of boric acid in enough water to make 100 ml of solution.

11-21. Calculate the concentrations of hydrogen and hydroxide ions in a solution prepared by dissolving 0.945 g of monochloroacetic acid in enough water to make 10 ml of solution.

11-22. Calculate the concentration of benzoate ion in a saturated solution of the acid if it contains 1 g of acid to 300 ml of solution.

11-23. The extent of ionization of an acid HA in 0.05 M solution is 5.8%. What is its extent of ionization in 0.2 M solution?

11-24. The ionization constant of lactic acid is 1.4×10^{-4}. What is its extent of ionization (a) in 1 M solution, (b) in 0.01 M solution?

11-25. The pH of 0.01 M anilinium chloride ($C_6H_5NH_3Cl$) is 3.24. Find the extent of ionization of the anilinium ion and K_b of aniline, its conjugate base.

11-26. Determine the extent of ionization and pH of each of the following acids: (a) 0.2 M monochloroacetic acid, (b) 0.5 M ammonium chloride, (c) 0.05 M ammonium chloride, (d) 0.1 M aluminum chloride, (e) 0.05 M zinc perchlorate.

11-27. Determine the extent of ionization and pH of each of the following bases. (a) 0.2 M ammonia solution, (b) 0.1 M potassium cyanide, (c) 0.1 M sodium sulfide, (d) 0.1 M calcium nitrite.

11-28. Calculate the pH of the following solutions, some of which contain acids, and others bases. (a) 0.01 M triethanolamine $(C_2H_4OH)_3N$, (b) 0.05 M barium acetate, (c) 0.1 M iron(III) nitrate, (d) 0.05 M glycinium chloride, $^+NH_3CH_2CO_2HCl$, (e) 0.3 M sodium oxalate.

11-29. Prove that the pH of a C molar solution of a weak acid HA is given by $pH = \frac{1}{2} pK_{HA} - \frac{1}{2} \log C$. List all approximations used.

11-30. Prove that the pH of a C molar solution of a weak base B (conjugate acid BH^+) is given by $pH = \frac{1}{2}(pK_w + pK_{BH^+} + \log C)$.

11-31. Prove that the pH of a C molar solution of KCN is given by $pH = \frac{1}{2}(pK_w + pK_{HCN} + \log C)$. List all approximations used.

11-32. Prove that for a solution of a weak base $K_b = [OH^-]^2/(C - [OH^-])$.

11-33. Derive Eq. 17 for a solution of a weak base B (conjugate acid BH^+).

11-34. Prove that in a solution of H_3PO_4 the concentration of HPO_4^{--} is approximately equal to K_2.

11-35. Calculate the concentrations of the ions and molecules in 0.1 M solutions of (a) phosphoric acid, (b) citric acid.

11-36. Prove that the extent of ionization of a base is given accurately by either (a) $K_b/(K_b + [OH^-])$ or (b) $[H^+]/([H^+] + K_a)$.

11-37. Calculate the maximum extent of ionization of sulfamic acid, acetic acid, and the ammonium ion, each in aqueous solutions at 25°.

11-38. A student attempted to prepare a solution having a pH value of 8 by diluting 1 M HCl with water. What is the fallacy?

11-39. Prove the following relations by using the principles of electroneutrality and material balance or some combination of them.

(a) $[C_2H_3O_2^-] = [H^+] - [OH^-]$ for 0.1 M acetic acid
(b) $[HCN] = 0.05 - [H^+] + [OH^-]$ for 0.05 M hydrocyanic acid
(c) $[H_2CO_3] = 0.01 - [H^+] + [OH^-] + [CO_3^{--}]$ for 0.01 M carbonic acid
(d) $[HCN] = [OH^-] - [H^+]$ for 0.2 M potassium cyanide
(e) $[NH_4^+] = 0.05 - [H^+] + [OH^-]$ for 0.05 M ammonium chloride
(f) $[HPO_4^{--}] = [OH^-] - [H^+] - 2[H_2PO_4^-] - 3[H_3PO_4]$ for 0.05 M trisodium phosphate
(g) $[HSO_4^-] = 0.1 - [H^+] + [OH^-]$ for 0.05 M sulfuric acid

11-40. Prove that for a C molar solution of ammonia
$$[OH^-]^3 + K_b[OH^-]^2 - (CK_b + K_w)[OH^-] - K_wK_b = 0$$

11-41. Prove that for a C molar solution of ammonia the neglect of two terms of the equation in Ex. 11-40 leads to $[OH^-] = (CK_b)^{1/2}$.

11-42. Prove that if the first term on the left-hand side of Eq. 32 is negligible, $[H^+] = 0.5C + (K_w + 0.25C^2)^{1/2}$. Use this to calculate the hydrogen ion concentration of a 10^{-7} M solution of an acid with $K_a = 10^{-5}$.

11-43. Calculate the magnitude of the various terms in Eq. 32 when (a) the solution is a 0.1 M solution of an acid with $K_a = 10^{-7}$ and $[H^+] = 10^{-4}$, (b) the solution is a 10^{-7} M solution of an acid with $K_a = 10^{-7}$ and $[H^+] = 1.6 \times 10^{-7}$.

11-44. Derive Eq. 34 from Eq. 33.

11-45. For very dilute solutions of boric acid in 0.725 molal NaCl (simulated sea water), $-\log Y = 0.41$. Calculate the pH of 0.001 M boric acid in this solution.

11-46. For very dilute solutions of the glycinium ion, $^+NH_3CH_2CO_2H$, which ionizes to H^+ and $^+NH_3CH_2CO_2^-$, in 3 M NaCl Y is 1.80. Calculate the hydrogen ion concentration of 0.01 M solution of glycinium ion in the salt solution.

11-47. Derive expressions for the relation between K^0, K, and I for (a) boric acid (b) the hydrogen carbonate ion (c) the pyridinium ion. Which K is most affected by changes in ionic strength? Which is least affected?

11-48. The equilibrium $2FeOH^{++} \rightleftharpoons Fe_2(OH)_2^{+4}$ is very sensitive to changes in ionic strength. Derive an expression relating K^0, K, and I, and compare it with Eqs. 38 to 40. Is the sensitivity predicted by the theory?

11-49. Calculate the hydrogen ion concentration of 0.02 M formic acid. Use Eq. 41 to estimate activity coefficient corrections.

11-50. Calculate the hydroxide ion concentration of 0.01 M ammonia. Use Eq. 41 to estimate activity coefficient corrections.

CHAPTER TWELVE

The Common Ion Effect Buffer Solutions Indicators

12-1. Introduction. The Common Ion Effect. Ionization is repressed, but not extinguished, by increasing the concentration of one of the products of the ionization reaction (Sec. 2-16). The addition of hydrochloric acid to solutions of acetic acid, ammonium chloride, and sodium dihydrogen phosphate represses the ionization reactions

$$HC_2H_3O_2 \rightleftharpoons H^+ + C_2H_3O_2^-$$

$$NH_4^+ \rightleftharpoons H^+ + NH_3$$

$$H_2PO_4^- \rightleftharpoons H^+ + HPO_4^{--}$$

because it supplies an excess of H^+, the common ion. A similar repression can be obtained by increasing the concentration of the other product, viz., $C_2H_3O_2^-$, NH_3, and HPO_4^{--}, although one of these is molecular, not ionic. The ionization of bases can be repressed in a similar way by addition of a strong base such as sodium hydroxide.

We learned in the preceding chapter how to calculate the concentrations of the ions and molecules in a solution of a weak acid or base alone and shall now deal with solutions containing the acid or base in the presence of a common ion. Many such mixtures are buffer solutions, and their usefulness in qualitative analysis and other branches of chemistry makes it necessary to discuss in some detail their mode of action, preparation, and application. Finally, the use of indicators in conjunction with buffer solutions to measure pH is discussed.

12-2. Mixtures of Weak and Strong Acids or Bases. Calculations for such mixtures are comparatively simple. Because the ionization of the weak electrolyte is repressed, the concentration of hydrogen or hydroxide ion is almost altogether determined by the strong acid or base. This will be particularly true when the concentration of the strong acid or base is high and when the weak acid or base is very weak (small K_a or K_b).

EXAMPLE 1. Calculate the concentrations of the various species in a solution that is 0.05 M in H_2S and 0.3 M in HCl. The ionization equilibria are represented by

$$H_2S \rightleftharpoons H^+ + HS^- \qquad K_1 = \frac{[H^+][HS^-]}{[H_2S]} = 1 \times 10^{-7}$$

$$HS^- \rightleftharpoons H^+ + S^{--} \qquad K_2 = \frac{[H^+][S^{--}]}{[HS^-]} = 1.3 \times 10^{-13}$$

If practically all the hydrogen ions come from the strong acid, we can write

$$[H^+] \simeq [Cl^-] = 0.3 \ M$$

Almost all the sulfide will be in the form of molecular H_2S because its ionization is repressed, so $[H_2S] \simeq 0.05 \ M$. To find $[HS^-]$ we use these values in K_1:

$$\frac{0.3 \ [HS^-]}{0.05} = 1 \times 10^{-7} \qquad\qquad [HS^-] = \boxed{1.7 \times 10^{-8} \ M}$$

To find $[S^{--}]$ we use K_2 and the known values of $[H^+]$ and $[HS^-]$:

$$\frac{0.3 \ [S^{--}]}{1.7 \times 10^{-8}} = 1.3 \times 10^{-13} \qquad\qquad [S^{--}] = \boxed{7.4 \times 10^{-21} \ M}$$

The concentration of hydroxide ion is found from $K_w/[H^+]$ and is

$$[OH^-] = \boxed{3.3 \times 10^{-14} \ M}$$

The extent of ionization is the ratio of the total concentration of hydrogen sulfide in ionized form to the total concentration in all forms:

$$\alpha = \frac{[HS^-] + [S^{--}]}{0.05} = 3.4 \times 10^{-7} \text{ or } 0.000034\%$$

This very low extent of ionization is a consequence of the presence of the common ion, for 0.05 M H_2S alone is 0.14% ionized.

This is an appropriate point at which to review the various calculations we have made for solutions of hydrogen sulfide. In Chapter 10 we used the expression

$$K_{ip} = [H^+]^2[S^{--}] = 1.3 \times 10^{-21}$$

to calculate the concentration of sulfide ion. This relation presupposes that $[H_2S] = 0.1 \ M$, which is the value for a solution saturated with hydrogen sulfide at 25° and 1 atm pressure. We could have used this expression in the preceding example if we had cut the value of K_{ip} in half, since $[H_2S] = 0.05 \ M$. In Chapter 11 we used the expressions

$$\frac{[H^+]^2}{0.05} = K_1 \qquad \text{and} \qquad [S^{--}] = K_2$$

These are based on the assumption that $[H^+] = [HS^-]$, which is true in a solution of hydrogen sulfide alone. In the presence of hydrochloric acid $[H^+]$ is much larger than $[HS^-]$ and $[S^{--}]$ is much smaller than K_2.

Student papers sometimes put forward a still different and erroneous relation

$$\frac{x^2}{1.7 \times 10^{-8}} = K_2 \quad \text{or} \quad x = 4.7 \times 10^{-11}$$

where 1.7×10^{-8} is the concentration of HS^- found in the above example. The unknown x apparently stands for $[H^+] = [S^{--}]$ (careful students will always define x explicitly), but this implies that there is one kind of H^+ ion in equilibrium with S^{--} which is different from those from HCl and from the first stage in the ionization of H_2S. As we have emphasized many times before, all H^+ ions are alike, and in equilibrium constant expressions $[H^+]$ is always the total concentration of hydrogen ion, the sum of the contributions from all sources. If we use $[H^+] = 0.3$ with K_1, we must also use it with K_2.

EXAMPLE 2. Calculate the concentrations of the various ionic and molecular species in a mixture that is $0.10\ M$ in Na_2CO_3 and $0.05\ M$ in $NaOH$. The basic ionization (or hydrolysis) of the carbonate ion is represented by

$$CO_3^{--} + H_2O \rightleftharpoons HCO_3^- + OH^-$$

$$K_1 = K_b\ (CO_3^{--}) = \frac{[HCO_3^-][OH^-]}{[CO_3^{--}]} = 2.1 \times 10^{-4}$$

$$HCO_3^- + H_2O \rightleftharpoons H_2CO_3 + OH^-$$

$$K_2 = K_b\ (HCO_3^-) = \frac{[H_2CO_3][OH^-]}{[HCO_3^-]} = 2.3 \times 10^{-8}$$

If the strong base represses these ionization reactions, almost all the carbonate will remain as CO_3^{--}:

$$0.10 \simeq [CO_3^{--}]$$

and the hydroxide ions will come almost entirely from the strong base:

$$0.05 \simeq [OH^-]$$

To find $[HCO_3^-]$ we use K_1:

$$\frac{0.05[HCO_3^-]}{0.10} = 2.1 \times 10^{-4}$$

$$[HCO_3^-] = \boxed{4.2 \times 10^{-4}\ M}$$

To find $[H_2CO_3]$ (actually we always mean by this the sum of the concentrations of H_2CO_3 and CO_2; see Sec. 2-21) we use K_2:

$$\frac{0.05[H_2CO_3]}{4.2 \times 10^{-4}} = 2.3 \times 10^{-8}$$

$$[H_2CO_3] = \boxed{1.9 \times 10^{-10}\ M}$$

The hydrogen ion concentration is found from $K_w/[OH^-]$ and is

$$\boxed{2 \times 10^{-13}\ M}$$

The extent of ionization (hydrolysis) of carbonate

$$\alpha = \frac{[HCO_3^-] + [H_2CO_3]}{0.1} = 0.0042 \text{ or } \boxed{0.42\%}$$

This is less than one-tenth as large as that for $0.1\ M\ Na_2CO_3$ in the absence of a strong base.

The addition of strong acid to solutions of cation acids is often used to suppress their ionization. Laboratory stock solutions of iron(III) chloride, tin(II) chloride, bismuth chloride, antimony(III) chloride, mercury(I) nitrate, and others always contain excess acid to prevent precipitation of partially or completely hydrolyzed products such as $BiOCl$ and Fe_2O_3 (Sec. 11-6).

12-3. Mixtures of Weak Acids and Their Conjugate Bases. Such mixtures are important as buffer solutions (Sec. 12-6). They may contain any molecular acid with a highly ionized salt of the acid as the source of the conjugate base, e.g., $HC_2H_3O_2$ and $NaC_2H_3O_2$. Or the weak acid may be a cation and the conjugate base a molecule, e.g., NH_4^+ from NH_4Cl together with NH_3. Or the acid and base may both be anions, e.g., $H_2PO_4^-$ (acid) and HPO_4^{--} (base) in mixtures of KH_2PO_4 with Na_2HPO_4.

EXAMPLE 1. Calculate the pH and extent of ionization of acetic acid for a mixture that is $0.10\ M$ in the acid and $0.05\ M$ in sodium acetate. The equilibrium is represented by

$$HC_2H_3O_2 \rightleftharpoons H^+ + C_2H_3O_2^- \qquad K_a = \frac{[H^+][C_2H_3O_2^-]}{[HC_2H_3O_2]} = 1.8 \times 10^{-5}$$

Because the acetate represses the ionization of the acid, we assume

$$[HC_2H_3O_2] \simeq 0.10 \qquad \text{and} \qquad [C_2H_3O_2^-] \simeq 0.050$$

Thus

$$K_a = 1.8 \times 10^{-5} \simeq [H^+]\frac{0.050}{0.10}$$

$$[H^+] = 3.6 \times 10^{-5}\ M$$

$$pH = \boxed{4.44}$$

The extent of ionization of the acid

$$\alpha = \frac{3.6 \times 10^{-5}}{0.10} = 3.6 \times 10^{-4} \text{ or } \boxed{0.036\%}$$

This is much smaller than 1.3%, the extent of ionization of $0.10\ M$ acetic acid alone.

EXAMPLE 2. Calculate the pH, concentration of hydroxide ion, and extent of ionization of ammonia in a mixture that is $0.020\ M$ in NH_4Cl and $0.030\ M$ in ammonia. There are two possible ways to formulate the equilibrium:

$$NH_4^+ \rightleftharpoons NH_3 + H^+ \qquad K_a = \frac{[H^+][NH_3]}{[NH_4^+]} = 5.7 \times 10^{-10}$$

$$NH_3 + H_2O \rightleftharpoons NH_4^+ + OH^- \qquad K_b = \frac{[NH_4^+][OH^-]}{[NH_3]} = 1.8 \times 10^{-5}$$

Either expression can be used, although the first is more convenient for finding the pH. Either ionization is repressed, the first by the excess of ammonia, the second by the excess of ammonium ion. Hence we assume

$$[NH_4^+] \simeq 0.020 \quad \text{and} \quad [NH_3] \simeq 0.030$$

Thus if we use K_a to find $[H^+]$

$$5.7 \times 10^{-10} = [H^+] \frac{0.030}{0.020}$$

$$[H^+] = \boxed{3.8 \times 10^{-10} \ M}$$

$$pH = \boxed{9.42}$$

The hydroxide ion concentration can be found from $K_w/[H^+]$ or from K_b:

$$1.8 \times 10^{-5} = [OH^-] \frac{0.020}{0.030}$$

$$[OH^-] = \boxed{2.6 \times 10^{-5} \ M}$$

and the extent of ionization of ammonia

$$\alpha = \frac{[OH^-]}{0.030} = 8.7 \times 10^{-4} \text{ or } \boxed{0.087\%}$$

The method of calculation used in these examples can now be generalized. For a mixture that contains any weak acid at molar concentration **A** and its conjugate base at molar concentration **B**,

$$[H^+] \simeq K_a \frac{\mathbf{A}}{\mathbf{B}} \qquad\qquad 1$$

For satisfactory buffer action the concentrations **A** and **B** must be large in comparison with $[H^+]$ and $[OH^-]$. Eq. 1 is an excellent approximation, unless K_a is very large or very small.

EXAMPLE 3. Calculate the pH of a buffer that is 0.025 M in KH_2PO_4 and 0.025 M in NaH_2PO_4. The acid is $H_2PO_4^-$, and, by Eq. 1,

$$[H^+] = K_a(H_2PO_4^-) \frac{0.025}{0.025} = 6.3 \times 10^{-8}$$

$$pH = \boxed{7.20} = pK_a$$

The measured value of this pH is 6.86, but this includes a correction for interionic forces. The ionization of HPO_4^{--} to PO_4^{---} need not be taken into account, for it is almost exactly balanced by hydrolysis of $H_2PO_4^-$ to H_3PO_4.

12-4. A More General Treatment of These Mixtures. In the preceding sections we have made somewhat freely simplifying assumptions about the concentrations, and it is time to verify them and show how a more general treatment can be made. The principles of material balance and electroneutrality are our guides.

EXAMPLE 1. (Sec. 12-2) 0.05 M H_2S + 0.3 M HCl. The principles of material balance and electroneutrality have the forms

$$MB (S): \ 0.05 = [H_2S] + [HS^-] + [S^{--}]$$
$$EN: [H^+] = [Cl^-] + [HS^-] + 2[S^{--}] + [OH^-]$$

If the answers that were previously obtained are nearly correct, we should be able to verify the approximations. Thus

$$0.05 = [H_2S] + 1.7 \times 10^{-8} + 7.4 \times 10^{-21}$$
$$[H_2S] = 0.05 - 0.000000017 - 0.0000000000000000000074$$

which is virtually 0.05, as we had assumed. Also

$$[H^+] = 0.3 + 1.7 \times 10^{-8} + 2 \times 7.4 \times 10^{-21} + 3.3 \times 10^{-14}$$

or virtually 0.3, as we had assumed.

EXAMPLE 2. (Sec. 12-2) 0.10 M Na_2CO_3 + 0.050 M NaOH. The conditions of material balance and electroneutrality have the form

$$MB (C): \ 0.10 = [CO_3^{--}] + [HCO_3^-] + [H_2CO_3]$$
$$EN: [H^+] + [Na^+] = [OH^-] + [HCO_3^-] + 2[CO_3^{--}]$$

From the first of these and the answers already obtained we find

$$[CO_3^{--}] = 0.10 - 4.2 \times 10^{-4} - 1.9 \times 10^{-10}$$

so $[CO_3^{--}]$ is virtually 0.10, as we had assumed. A convenient expression for $[OH^-]$ is obtained by eliminating $[CO_3^{--}]$ between the material balance and electroneutrality conditions:

$$2MB - EN: [OH^-] = 0.05 + [H^+] + [HCO_3^-] + 2[H_2CO_3]$$

where we have also used 0.25 for the total sodium ion concentration. Hence

$$[OH^-] = 0.05 + 2 \times 10^{-13} + 4.2 \times 10^{-4} + 2 \times 1.9 \times 10^{-10}$$

and this is virtually 0.05, as we assumed.

If the assumptions do not hold, this is soon discovered by checking against the material balance and electroneutrality conditions. Consider a mixture of 0.10 M Na_2CO_3 that is also 0.01 M in NaOH. This low concentration of strong base does not suppress the basic ionization of carbonate sufficiently for us to assume that $[OH^-] = 0.01$. If we do make this assumption, we find $[HCO_3^-] = 2.1 \times 10^{-3}$, which is not small in comparison with 0.01. A more accurate calculation is based on the relations

$$[CO_3^{--}] = 0.10 - [HCO_3^-]$$
$$[OH^-] = 0.01 + [HCO_3^-]$$

where $[H^+]$ and $[H_2CO_3]$ are neglected because they are so small. The second relation indicates that the total concentration of hydroxide ion is the sum of that from NaOH and that from hydrolysis of Na_2CO_3. When these relations are combined with the equilibrium constant, we obtain

$$2.1 \times 10^{-4} = [HCO_3^-] \frac{0.01 + [HCO_3^-]}{0.10 - [HCO_3^-]}$$

This is a quadratic equation that can be solved by one of the usual methods (Sec. 11-8) to give $[HCO_3^-] = 1.76 \times 10^{-3}$.

Mixtures of a weak acid and its conjugate base can also be treated in a more general way by using the material balance and electroneutrality conditions. Consider a mixture of **A** moles of acid HA and **B** moles of its conjugate base A^- in the form of the completely ionized salt MeA. Then

$$\text{MB } (A): \quad \mathbf{A} + \mathbf{B} \quad = [A^-] + [HA] \qquad\qquad \mathbf{2}$$

$$\text{EN: } [H^+] + [Me^+] = [A^-] + [OH^-] \qquad\qquad \mathbf{3}$$

Because the salt is completely ionized, $[Me^+] = \mathbf{B}$, and the electroneutrality condition can be rearranged to read

$$[A^-] \;= \mathbf{B} + [H^+] - [OH^-] \qquad\qquad \mathbf{4}$$

When this is used to eliminate $[A^-]$ from Eq. 2, we obtain

$$[HA] = \mathbf{A} - [H^+] + [OH^-] \qquad\qquad \mathbf{5}$$

In Sec. 12-3 we neglected the concentrations of H^+ and OH^- in comparison with **A** and **B**. Since $[H^+] = K_a[HA]/[A^-]$ we obtain a more general version of Eq. 1 by using Eqs. 4 and 5:

$$[H^+] = K_a \frac{\mathbf{A} - [H^+] + [OH^-]}{\mathbf{B} + [H^+] - [OH^-]} \qquad\qquad \mathbf{6}$$

It can be shown that this holds also for mixtures of a cation acid and its conjugate molecular base.

In accurate calculations, according to Eq. 6, we must make corrections for the concentrations of hydrogen and hydroxide ions. Actually, as long as **A** and **B** are large, and K_a is neither very small nor very big, these corrections are negligible. As an illustration, consider Example 1 in Sec. 12-3. For this mixture that was $0.10 \; M$ in $HC_2H_3O_2$ and $0.050 \; M$ in $NaC_2H_3O_2$ we found $[H^+] = 3.6 \times 10^{-5}$ and $[OH^-] = 2.8 \times 10^{-10}$. Both of these are negligible in comparison with 0.10 and 0.05, so Eq. 1 was a satisfactory approximation.

As an illustration of a mixture for which Eq. 6 must be used, consider a solution that is $0.01 \; M$ in both monochloroacetic acid and its sodium salt. These concentrations are low and K_a, which is 1.4×10^{-3}, is moderately large. Thus when we use Eq. 1

$$[H^+] = 1.4 \times 10^{-3} \frac{0.01}{0.01} = 1.4 \times 10^{-3} \; M$$

the value of $[H^+]$ so obtained is more than 10% of **A** or **B**. For this acid solution $[OH^-]$ is negligible, and Eq. 6 takes the form

$$[H^+] = 1.4 \times 10^{-3} \frac{0.01 - [H^+]}{0.01 + [H^+]} \qquad\qquad \mathbf{7}$$

$$[H^+]^2 + (0.01 + 0.0014)[H^+]^2 - 1.4 \times 10^{-5} = 0$$

This quadratic equation can be solved by completing the square or by using the quadratic formula (Sec. 11-8) to give $[H^+] = 1.1 \times 10^{-3} \; M$. The same result can be obtained very easily by successive approximations, using Eq. 7.

The preliminary value (first approximation) of 1.4×10^{-3} is inserted for $[H^+]$ in the ratio on the right-hand side:

$$[H^+] = 1.4 \times 10^{-3} \frac{0.01 - 0.0014}{0.01 + 0.0014} = 1.08 \times 10^{-3} \, M$$

A third approximation can be obtained by inserting this value in Eq. 7:

$$[H^+] = 1.4 \times 10^{-3} \frac{0.01 - 0.00108}{0.01 + 0.00108} = 1.12 \times 10^{-3} \, M$$

This value is sufficiently close to the second to make further approximations unnecessary.

Equation 6 holds for solutions of a monoprotic acid and its conjugate base. The treatment of diprotic or triprotic acids and their conjugate bases is more difficult, and only one relation will be quoted. For a mixture of salts MeH_2A and Me'_2HA

$$[H^+] = \frac{K_2(\mathbf{A} - K_3) + K_w}{\mathbf{B} + K_2 - K_w/K_1} \tag{8}$$

where K_1, K_2, and K_3 are the successive ionization constants of the tribasic acid H_3A. This is applicable to the phosphate buffer in Example 3, Sec. 12-3. Here $\mathbf{A}$ and $\mathbf{B}$ are $0.025 \, M$, which is large in comparison with the constants; so Eq. 8 reduces to $[H^+] = K_2\mathbf{A}/\mathbf{B}$, and this was the relation that was used in solving the problem.

12-5. The Effect of Interionic Forces. We have neglected the effect of interionic forces on the ionization equilibria. If activity coefficient corrections are introduced, Eq. 1 becomes

$$[H^+] = K_a^0 \frac{\mathbf{A}}{\mathbf{B}} \frac{y_{HA}}{y_{H^+} \, y_{A^-}} \tag{9}$$

for mixtures of a molecular acid HA and its conjugate base A^-. In dilute solutions molecules of HA will behave ideally, and we shall assume that $y_{HA} = 1$; then

$$[H^+] = K_a^0 \frac{\mathbf{A}}{\mathbf{B}} \frac{1}{y_{H^+} \, y_{A^-}} \tag{10}$$

The activity coefficients depend on the ionic strength and can be varied by (1) diluting the mixture or (2) adding a neutral salt. As the solution is diluted the ratio $\mathbf{A}/\mathbf{B}$ remains unchanged as long as $\mathbf{A}$ and $\mathbf{B}$ are large compared with $[H^+]$ and $[OH^-]$ (see Eq. 6). But dilution decreases the ionic strength and decreases the activity coefficients, so it will cause a slight increase in $[H^+]$. Addition of a neutral salt has the opposite effect because it increases the ionic strength and decreases the activity coefficients. The addition of a small amount of potassium chloride, for example, to a mixture of acetic acid and sodium acetate causes a slight increase in hydrogen ion concentration, the equivalent of a decrease in pH of a few hundredths of a unit.

The Debye-Hückel theory can be used to estimate the effect of interionic forces. The activity coefficients can be calculated with the relation (Secs. 10-16 and 11-13)

$$\log y_{H^+} y_{A^-} = \frac{-2S \sqrt{I}}{1 + \sqrt{I}} \qquad \qquad \textbf{11}$$

The ionic strength I must be less than 0.1 for this relation to be valid. If no other salts are present, I will be approximately equal to **B** when A^- ions are added in the form of a salt such as NaA or KA.

EXAMPLE. Calculate the hydrogen ion concentration of a mixture that is 0.05 M in sodium acetate and 0.02 M in acetic acid. By Eq. 11 with $I = 0.05$

$$\log y_{H^+} y_{C_2H_3O_2^-} = \frac{-2 \times 0.509\sqrt{0.05}}{1 + \sqrt{0.05}} = -0.186$$

$$y_{H^+} y_{C_2H_3O_2^-} = 0.65$$

Hence, from Eq. 10,

$$[H^+] = 1.75 \times 10^{-5} \frac{0.02}{0.05} \frac{1}{0.65} = \boxed{1.08 \times 10^{-5} \ M}$$

If we define pH by $-\log [H^+]$, this corresponds to a pH value of 4.97 as against 5.15 without the activity coefficient corrections.[1]

12-6. Buffer Solutions and Their Mode of Action. A *buffer solution* is any solution that maintains an approximately constant pH value despite small additions of acid or base. Many laboratory experiments, ranging from measurements of the rate of chemical reactions to the study of the growth of bacteria, require media of constant pH maintained by buffer action. In qualitative separations buffers are used to control the hydrogen ion concentration and thus indirectly to regulate the concentration of hydroxide, sulfide, carbonate, or chromate ion. Processes occurring in living cells are very sensitive to changes in pH, and buffering is essential if the cell is to survive. The pH of human blood is maintained within the narrow limits 7.35 to 7.45 by buffer action. The principal buffer system in blood plasma is H_2CO_3—HCO_3^- but phosphates and proteins are also involved. Sea water is weakly buffered by low concentrations of bicarbonate, carbonate, boric acid, and borates.

Typical buffer solutions include moderately concentrated solutions of strong acids or bases as well as mixtures of a weak acid and its conjugate base. Thus either 0.2 M HCl or 0.2 M NaOH is a good buffer, although 0.002 M HCl and 0.00005 M NaOH are not. The mixture in which acetic

---

[1]Actually $[H^+]$ and $-\log [H^+]$ are not as useful in equilibrium calculations as $a_{H^+} = [H^+]y_{H^+}$ and pH $= -\log a_{H^+}$. The practical pH scale corresponds closely to this definition. Certain reasonable but arbitrary assumptions have to be made in establishing the scale, because the activity coefficient of the hydrogen ion (or of any other single ionic species) cannot be determined. These subtleties are discussed by R. G. Bates in *Electrometric pH Determinations*, Wiley, New York, 1954. This book gives much useful information about buffers and the measurement of pH.

acid and sodium acetate are each at a concentration of 0.2 M is a good buffer; either component alone is not. To understand why we must examine the mode of action of buffers.

The buffer action of 0.2 M HCl or 0.5 M KOH is easily understood. These solutions already contain such a high concentration of hydrogen or hydroxide ions that addition of a little acid or base causes only a minor change in [H$^+$] or the pH. This is illustrated schematically in Fig. 12-1.

FIG. 12-1. Buffer action of 0.2 M hydrochloric acid. In (a) the con-centration of H$^+$ ion in the solu-tion is represented by a large rectangle. In (b) and (c) the effects of small additions of strong acid and base are shown.

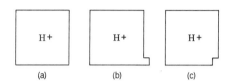

EXAMPLE 1. Calculate the change in pH that results when 1 drop (0.05 ml) of 0.2 M sodium hydroxide is added to 10 ml of 0.2 M HCl. Initially there were 10 ml $\times$ 0.2 mmole/ml or 2 mmoles of H$^+$ in 10 ml of 0.2 M HCl. One drop of the NaOH solution contains (0.2 mmole/ml) $\times$ 0.05 ml = 0.01 mmole of OH$^-$. This neutralizes an equal amount of H$^+$ leaving 2.00 $-$ 0.01 = 1.99 mmoles of H$^+$ in 10.05 ml or [H$^+$] = 0.199. Then

$$\text{final } pH = -\log 0.199 = 0.701$$
$$\text{initial } pH = -\log 0.200 = 0.699$$
$$\overline{}$$
$$\text{change in } pH = 0.002$$

Because this is small, 0.2 M HCl is a good buffer.

EXAMPLE 2. Repeat the calculation for 10 ml of 0.002 M HCl. Initially there is 0.02 mmole of H$^+$ and addition of 0.01 mmole of NaOH neutralizes half of this leaving 0.01 mmole in 10.05 ml. The final [H$^+$] is thus 0.001 M. Then

$$\text{final } pH = -\log 0.001 = 3.000$$
$$\text{initial } pH = -\log 0.002 = 2.699$$
$$\overline{}$$
$$\text{change in } pH = 0.301$$

Because this change is large, 0.002 M HCl is not a good buffer.

The buffer action of a mixture of acetic acid and sodium acetate is best understood by reference to the acidity constant, which can be written in the form

$$[\text{H}^+] = K_a \frac{[\text{HC}_2\text{H}_3\text{O}_2]}{[\text{C}_2\text{H}_3\text{O}_2^-]} \qquad 12$$

or more conveniently as

$$pH = pK_a - \log \frac{[\text{HC}_2\text{H}_3\text{O}_2]}{[\text{C}_2\text{H}_3\text{O}_2^-]} \qquad 13$$

If [H$^+$] and the pH are to remain the same, the buffer ratio of acid to con-jugate base must be no more than slightly altered by addition of small amounts of acid or base. If a small amount of sodium hydroxide is added, this is taken care of by converting some molecular acid to the ion

$$HC_2H_3O_2 + OH^- \rightarrow C_2H_3O_2^- + H_2O$$

Small amounts of acid are removed by converting the basic anion into the molecular acid

$$H^+ + C_2H_3O_2^- \rightarrow HC_2H_3O_2$$

These changes will have only a minor effect on the buffer ratio and hence on the pH if both numerator and denominator of the ratio are large to start with. This is illustrated schematically in Fig. 12-2. Such buffers have reserve supplies both of weak acid to counteract the added base and of conjugate weak base to counteract added acid.

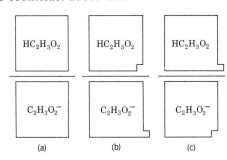

(a)   (b)   (c)

FIG. 12-2. The effect on the buffer ratio of adding small amounts of acid and base to an acetic acid-sodium acetate buffer. (a) Initial ratio. (b) Ratio after addition of a small amount of NaOH. (c) Ratio after addition of a small amount of HCl.

In a solution of acetic acid alone, the concentration of acetate ion is small. There are no reserves to resist the inroads of even small quantities of added acid. The ratio of concentrations will show a relatively large change upon addition of acid or base.

EXAMPLE 3. Calculate the change in pH of a buffer mixture that is 0.2 M in both acetic acid and sodium acetate upon addition of 1 drop of 0.2 M NaOH to 10 ml of the solution. Initially there are 2 mmoles of both $HC_2H_3O_2$ and $C_2H_3O_2^-$ and the buffer ratio is 1.00. The added 0.01 mmole of OH^- converts 0.01 mmole of $HC_2H_3O_2$ to $C_2H_3O_2^-$ making the buffer ratio $(2.00 - 0.01)/(2.00 + 0.01)$ or 0.99. From Eq. 13

$$pH_2 - pH_1 = -\log 0.99 - (-\log 1.00) = 0.004$$

Because this change is small the mixture is a good buffer.

EXAMPLE 4. Repeat the calculation of Example 3 for a mixture in which the concentrations are 0.002 M. The buffer ratio changes from $0.02/0.02 = 1$ to $(0.02 - 0.01)/(0.02 + 0.01) = 1/3$, and the corresponding change in pH is 0.48 unit. This mixture is not a good buffer.

EXAMPLE 5. Calculate the change in pH caused by the addition of 1 drop of 0.2 M NaOH to 10 ml of a mixture that is 0.39 M in $HC_2H_3O_2$ and 0.01 M in $NaC_2H_3O_2$. The total concentration of acid and salt is 0.40 as it was in Example 3, but the buffer ratio is 39/1 instead of 1/1. After addition of base, the buffer ratio becomes $(3.9 - 0.01)/(0.1 + 0.01) = 35/1$ and the change in pH is 0.045 units. This is about ten times as large a change as that found in Example 3.

The results of these calculations can be generalized. Effective buffer action is obtained if (1) the concentrations **A** and **B** of weak acid and conjugate base are large (0.01 M or more) and (2) the buffer ratio **A/B** is near 1:1. The first requirement ensures that a large reservoir of both weak acid and base will be present to take care of small additions of other acid or base. The second requirement is based on the fact that the added acid or base causes the least change in the ratio when **A/B** is 1. At this point, as Eq. 13 indicates, the pH is equal to $pK_a = -\log K_a$. In practice it is found that effective buffer action is obtained over a range of 1 to 1.5 pH units on either side of pK_a. For acetic acid $pK_a = 4.76$, and acetic acid–sodium acetate buffers are satisfactory in the range from pH 3.7 to 5.6. The pH ranges of some other buffer systems are given in Table 12-1.

12-7. The Preparation of Buffer Solutions. Buffer mixtures of a weak acid and its conjugate base can be prepared in three ways: (1) by mixing the weak acid and the conjugate base, (2) by mixing an excess of the weak acid with a

TABLE 12-1.

Some Useful Buffer Solutions

Acid	Conjugate base	pK_a at 25°	Useful pH range
$H_2C_8H_4O_4$	$HC_8H_4O_4^-$, hydrogen phthalate ion	2.95	2.2 — 4.0
$HCHO_2$	CHO_2^-, formate ion	3.76	2.8 — 4.6
$HC_2H_3O_2$	$C_2H_3O_2^-$, acetate ion	4.76	3.7 — 5.6
$HC_8H_4O_4^-$	$C_8H_4O_4^{--}$, phthalate ion	5.41	4.0 — 6.2
$H_2PO_4^-$	HPO_4^{--}, hydrogen phosphate ion	7.20	5.8 — 8.0
$(C_2H_4OH)_3NH^+$	$(C_2H_4OH)_3N$, triethanolamine	7.77	7.0 — 8.5
H_3BO_3	$B_4O_7^{--}$, tetraborate ion	9.24	7.0 — 9.2
NH_4^+	NH_3, ammonia	9.24	8.3 — 9.2
HCO_3^-	CO_3^{--}, carbonate ion	10.33	9.2 — 11.0
HPO_4^{--}	PO_4^{---}, phosphate ion	12	11.0 — 12.0

limited amount of a strong base, and (3) by mixing an excess of the conjugate base with a limited amount of strong acid. The choice of a particular method is largely a matter of convenience. There are standard recipes in handbooks and other reference works for the preparation of buffer solutions of almost any required pH value.

The following problems cover various aspects of the preparation of buffers.

EXAMPLE 1. Calculate the volume of standard 0.50 M NH_3 to be mixed with 10 g of NH_4Cl to give a buffer containing equimolar quantities of ammonia and ammonium chloride. Let this volume be V. In 10 g of NH_4Cl there is

N: 14	
4 H: 4	
Cl: 35.5	
———	
53.5	

$$\frac{10 \text{ g}}{53.5 \text{ g/mole}} = 0.187 \text{ mole or } 187 \text{ mmoles}$$

Then the volume of 0.5 M NH_3 is found by

$$V \text{ ml} \times 0.5 \text{ mmole/ml} = 187 \text{ mmole}$$

$$V = \boxed{374 \text{ ml}}$$

The concentration of hydrogen ion allowed by this buffer is equal to K_a of NH_4^+ because $A/B = 1$. The pH should be about 9.2.

EXAMPLE 2. Calculate the weights of pure, dry KH_2PO_4 and Na_2HPO_4 required to give 100 ml of a buffer that is 0.025 M in each salt. We require 0.1×0.025 or 0.0025 mole of each salt. The weights of salts are

K: 39	2 Na: 46
2 H: 2	H: 1
P: 31	P: 31
4 O: 64	4 O: 64
———	———
136	142

$$136 \times 0.0025 = \boxed{0.340 \text{ g } KH_2PO_4}$$

$$142 \times 0.0025 = \boxed{0.355 \text{ g } Na_2HPO_4}$$

EXAMPLE 3. Find the volume of 0.24 M sodium hydroxide that should be mixed with 2.0 ml of 0.50 M $NaHCO_3$ to give a buffer containing 2 moles of HCO_3^- per mole of CO_3^{--}. Let the required volume be V ml. We start with 2.0 ml $\times$ 0.50 mmole/ml = 1.0 mmole of HCO_3^-. If one-third of this is converted to carbonate by addition of sodium hydroxide, the buffer ratio will be 2:1 as required. Hence, we must add 0.33 mmole of sodium hydroxide:

$$V = \frac{0.33 \text{ mmole}}{0.24 \text{ mmole/ml}} = \boxed{1.38 \text{ ml}} \text{ or } 27.5 \text{ drops}$$

EXAMPLE 4. What weight of potassium acid phthalate ($KHC_8H_4O_4$) must be added to 50.0 ml of 0.136 M HCl to give a buffer containing 0.80 mole of phthalic acid to 1.00 mole of acid phthalate?
We start with $50.0 \times 0.136 = 6.80$ mmoles of HCl. We must add enough salt to convert this to phthalic acid:

K: 39
5 H: 5
8 C: 96
4 O: 64
———
204

$$H^+ + HC_8H_4O_4^- \rightarrow H_2C_8H_4O_4$$

and still more to establish the ratio of 1.00 mole of salt to 0.80 mole of acid. The total amount of potassium acid phthalate required is

$$6.80 + 6.80 \frac{1.00}{0.80} = 15.30 \text{ mmoles}$$

$$15.30 \text{ mmoles} \times 204 \text{ mg/mmole} = 3120 \text{ mg or } \boxed{3.12 \text{ g}}$$

EXAMPLE 5. Find the approximate pH of a buffer prepared by mixing 20 ml of 0.50 M acetic acid and 10 ml of 0.40 M sodium hydroxide. We start with $20 \times 0.50 = 10$ mmoles of acid and $10 \times 0.40 = 4.0$ mmoles of base. Neutralization produces sodium acetate in amount determined by the quantity of sodium hydroxide (Sec. 4-7). Thus after neutralization, there are 6.0 mmoles of acetic acid and 4.0 mmoles of sodium acetate. Then

$$K_a = 1.8 \times 10^{-5} = \frac{[H^+][C_2H_3O_2^-]}{[HC_2H_3O_2]} = [H^+] \frac{4 \text{ mmoles}}{6 \text{ mmoles}}$$

$$[H^+] = 2.7 \times 10^{-5}$$

$$pH = \boxed{4.57}$$

It will be noted that the ratio of acetate to acetic acid has been expressed in millimoles directly rather than in molarities or millimoles per milliliter. The ratio of molarities is equal to the ratio of the millimoles, because the volume factor cancels. This calculation could also have been done with Eq. 13 in the form

$$pH = pK_a - \log \frac{\text{mmoles } HC_2H_3O_2}{\text{mmoles } C_2H_3O_2^-} = 4.76 - 0.08 = 4.58$$

EXAMPLE 6. It is proposed to separate zinc from iron by precipitating zinc sulfide in a solution buffered at pH 3.00. How many drops of 6 M NaOH should be added to 40 drops of 2 M formic acid to prepare such a buffer? Let D be the number of drops of sodium hydroxide solution. Then since

$$pH = pK_a - \log \frac{[HCO_2H]}{[HCO_2^-]} = pK_a - \log \frac{A}{B}$$

we can find the buffer ratio at the required pH:

$$3.00 = 3.76 - \log \frac{A}{B}$$

$$\log \frac{A}{B} = 0.76$$

$$\frac{A}{B} = 5.75$$

The quantity of formate ion produced is measured by $6D$ and the quantity of formic acid left by $40 \times 2 - 6D$. Therefore

$$\frac{A}{B} = \frac{40 \times 2 - 6D}{6D} = 5.75$$

$$D = \boxed{2 \text{ drops}}$$

In finding the buffer ratio we did not need to convert to either molarity or mmole units as long as the units were the same in numerator and denominator.

12-8. Applications of Buffer Action to Qualitative Analysis.   There are a number of analytical separations that depend for their effectiveness on buffer action. That of magnesium from aluminum is a typical example. The solubility equilibria of the hydroxides are expressed by

$$Mg(OH)_2 \downarrow \rightleftharpoons Mg^{++} + 2OH^- \qquad K_{sp} = [Mg^{++}][OH^-]^2 = 1.1 \times 10^{-11}$$

$$Al(OH)_3 \downarrow \rightleftharpoons Al^{+++} + 3OH^- \qquad K_{sp} = [Al^{+++}][OH^-]^3 = 1.4 \times 10^{-34}$$

The large difference in solubility products makes it possible to separate the two metals by control of the hydroxide ion concentration. If $[OH^-]$ is kept low, but not too low, $Al(OH)_3$ will precipitate and $Mg(OH)_2$ will not. It would be impracticable to establish the required $[OH^-]$ by addition of a strong base. Only an exceedingly small amount could be added at once, and repeated addition of this amount would be necessary to precipitate any reasonable amount of aluminum hydroxide. In a buffer mixture of ammonia and ammonium chloride this separation goes smoothly, for the $[OH^-]$ is kept low by the common ion effect and is maintained approximately constant. Removal of hydroxide ions to give the precipitate disturbs the equilibrium

$$NH_3 + H_2O \rightleftharpoons NH_4^+ + OH^-$$

but, as long as a large reserve of NH_3 is present, more will ionize to restore equilibrium. This buffer is used in the precipitation of Cation Groups 3 and 4.

EXAMPLE 1. Calculate the minimum concentration of NH_4Cl that must be present in a solution that contains 5 mg/ml each of Mg^{++} and Al^{+++} if no $Mg(OH)_2$ is to precipitate when the solution is made 0.01 M in NH_3. The equilibria are represented by

$$NH_3 + H_2O \rightleftharpoons NH_4^+ + OH^- \qquad K_b = \frac{[NH_4^+][OH^-]}{[NH_3]} = 1.8 \times 10^{-5}$$

$$Mg(OH)_2 \downarrow \rightleftharpoons Mg^{++} + 2OH^- \qquad K_{sp} = [Mg^{++}][OH^-]^2 = 1.1 \times 10^{-11}$$

The basic ionization constant of ammonia is used rather than K_a, because $[OH^-]$ is then a linking concentration between the two equilibria. If no magnesium hydroxide is to precipitate, the maximum concentration of $[OH^-]$ is given by

$$[OH^-] = (K_{sp}/[Mg^{++}])^{1/2} = (1.1 \times 10^{-11}/0.21)^{1/2} = 7.2 \times 10^{-6} \ M$$

where $[Mg^{++}] = (5 \ \text{mg/ml})/(24 \ \text{mg/mmole})$. Using $[OH^-]$ in K_b we find

$$1.8 \times 10^{-5} = \frac{[NH_4^+] \ 7.2 \times 10^{-6}}{0.01}$$

$$[NH_4^+] = \boxed{2.5 \times 10^{-2} \ M}$$

In this same solution the concentration of aluminum ion is $(5 \ \text{mg/ml})/(27 \ \text{mg/mmole})$ or 0.19 M. Since $[OH^-] = 7.2 \times 10^{-6}$,

$$Q = [Al^{+++}][OH^-]^3 = 0.19 \times (7.2 \times 10^{-6})^3 = 7.1 \times 10^{-17}$$

This is much larger than $K_{sp} = 1.4 \times 10^{-34}$, so precipitation of aluminum hydroxide will occur (Sec. 8-8).

Sulfides can be selectively precipitated by controlling the hydrogen ion concentration. It is possible to separate zinc sulfide from the other sulfides of Cation Group 3 by precipitating it in acid solution. Numerical calculations are uncertain because of our lack of knowledge of the solubility products of the freshly precipitated sulfides (Sec. 9-13).

EXAMPLE 2. If a solution that is 0.1 M in zinc nitrate, 0.5 M in formic acid, and 0.1 M in sodium formate is saturated with hydrogen sulfide at 1 atm pressure and 25°, what concentration of zinc remains unprecipitated? Assume as a rough approximation that the solubility product of freshly precipitated zinc sulfide is 1×10^{-21}. The equilibria and constants are

$$ZnS \downarrow \rightleftharpoons Zn^{++} + S^{--} \qquad K_{sp} = [Zn^{++}][S^{--}] = 1 \times 10^{-21}$$

ionization of H_2S in saturated solution: $K_{ip} = [H^+]^2[S^{--}] = 1.3 \times 10^{-21}$

$$HCHO_2 \rightleftharpoons H^+ + CHO_2^- \qquad K_a = \frac{[H^+][CHO_2^-]}{[HCHO_2]} = 1.8 \times 10^{-4}$$

The first two are linked by $[S^{--}]$ and the second two by $[H^+]$. From the data for the buffer we can find the $[H^+]$, from this the $[S^{--}]$, and finally the $[Zn^{++}]$. The last is the molar concentration of zinc ions in solution at equilibrium after precipitation ceases and thus represents the concentration of zinc left unprecipitated.

$$[H^+]\frac{0.1}{0.5} = 1.8 \times 10^{-4}$$

$$[H^+] = 9 \times 10^{-4} \, M$$

$$(9 \times 10^{-4})^2[S^{--}] = 1.3 \times 10^{-21}$$

$$[S^{--}] = 1.6 \times 10^{-15} \, M$$

$$[Zn^{++}] \times 1.6 \times 10^{-15} = 1 \times 10^{-21}$$

$$[Zn^{++}] = \boxed{6 \times 10^{-7} \, M}$$

The solution initially contained 0.1 mmole of Zn^{++} per milliliter. Therefore the number of millimoles of zinc that precipitated was $0.1 - 6 \times 10^{-7}$ or 0.0999994 from each milliliter of solution.

The separation of barium from strontium with chromate is another illustration of buffer action. The chromate ion concentration is controlled by the equilibria

$$2CrO_4^{--} + 2H^+ \rightleftharpoons 2HCrO_4^- \rightleftharpoons Cr_2O_7^{--} + H_2O$$

The solubility product of barium chromate is much less than that of strontium chromate, and it can be precipitated from a weakly acid solution in which the chromate ion concentration is low. The precipitation removes chromate ions and forces the above equilibria to the left. This necessarily increases the concentration of hydrogen ion. But if the solution becomes too acid, precipitation of barium chromate will cease. A buffer mixture of acetic acid and ammonium acetate establishes the low concentration of hydrogen ion required for the separation and maintains this level despite production of hydrogen ions as barium chromate precipitates.

12-9. Indicators. The use of vegetable dyes to detect the presence of acids and bases and to follow neutralization reactions was introduced by Robert Boyle in 1663. John Quincy (d. 1722), medical writer and apothecary, wrote: "Liquids and substances are called acids, which being composed of pointed particles, affect the taste in a sharp and piercing manner. The common way of trying, whether any particular liquor hath in it any particles of this kind, is by mixing it with syrup of violets, which it will turn of a red colour; but if it contains alkaline or lixivial particles, it changes that syrup green."[2] James Watt, a chemist as well as the inventor of the reciprocating steam engine, first suggested (1784) the coloring matter of red cabbage as a wintertime substitute for extracts of flower petals. The most familiar vegetable dye still used as an indicator is litmus, which is obtained from certain lichens. Most indicators now in use are complex organic compounds synthesized in the laboratory. For our purposes the complexities of their structures need not be considered. Acid-base indicators are weak acids of such nature that the acid ($HInd$) and its conjugate base (Ind^-) have different colors. The equilibrium between acid and base is of the familiar type

$$HInd \rightleftharpoons H^+ + Ind^-$$

A strong acid converts most of the indicator to the molecular form and the color of $HInd$ is called the "acid color." A base converts most of the indicator to the anion Ind^- with the "alkaline color." The acid and alkaline colors of some common acid-base indicators are given in Table 12-2.[3]

We can write for the indicator equilibrium the usual expression for the ionization constant:

$$K_{HInd} = \frac{[H^+][Ind^-]}{[HInd]} \qquad \textbf{14}$$

This can be put in two, more convenient forms

$$[H^+] = K_{HInd} \frac{[HInd]}{[Ind^-]} = K_{HInd} \frac{[\text{form with acid color}]}{[\text{form with alkaline color}]} \qquad \textbf{15}$$

$$pH = pK_{HInd} - \log \frac{[\text{form with acid color}]}{[\text{form with alkaline color}]} \qquad \textbf{16}$$

[2]This quotation is in Samuel Johnson's famous dictionary (2nd ed., 1755). A similar entry under *alkalizate* is quoted from Newton: "The colour of violets seems to be of that order, because their syrup, by acid liquors, turns red, and, by urinous and alkalizate, turns green."

[3]Some indicators are cation or anion acids. This does not alter the argument.

These relations show that the color of a given indicator in any solution will be a mixture of alkaline and acid colors in a proportion determined by the pH. The color ratio is 1:1 when $pH = pK_{HInd}$ (or $[H^+] = K_{HInd}$), and the color of the solution is then a mixture of equal parts of the acid and alkaline colors. Bromthymol blue, for example, has a yellow acid color, a blue alkaline color, and a green color at $pH = 7.0 = pK_{HInd}$.

TABLE 12-2.

Properties of Some Common Acid-Base Indicators

Indicator	Acid color	Alkaline color	pK	pH range
Methyl violet	yellow	violet		0 - 2
Bromphenol blue	yellow	blue	4.0	3.0 - 4.6
Methyl orange	red	yellow	3.7	3.1 - 4.4
Bromcresol green	yellow	blue	4.7	3.8 - 5.4
Methyl red	red	yellow	5.1	4.2 - 6.2
Bromcresol purple	yellow	purple	6.3	5.2 - 6.8
Bromthymol blue	yellow	blue	7.0	6.0 - 7.6
Meta-cresol purple	yellow	purple	8.3	7.4 - 9.0
Phenolphthalein	colorless	red	9.7	8.0 - 9.8

The change of an indicator from acid to alkaline color is not abrupt but goes through intermediate mixed colors. The gradations can be observed most strikingly in a "standard series." A set of buffer solutions covering a suitable range of pH values in equally spaced steps is made, and equal amounts of indicator are put in equal volumes of the solutions. The difference in color of successive solutions is most striking near $pH = pK$, i.e., for color ratios near 1:1. As a rough general rule, the human eye cannot distinguish less than one part of one color in the presence of ten parts of the other. This means that all solutions of bromthymol blue containing more than 10 parts of acid form to 1 of alkaline look equally yellow, and those containing more than 10 parts of alkaline form to 1 of acid look equally blue to the human eye. The useful range of color ratios is thus from 1/10 to 10/1; i.e., the range in the logarithm of the ratio is from -1 to 1. Thus, by Eq. 16, the maximum pH value at which the indicator is useful is about $pK_{HInd} + 1$, and the minimum is about $pK_{HInd} - 1$. The useful range of an indicator is about 2 pH units. It can be extended further by using objective photoelectric comparisons to determine the color ratio. The pK values and pH ranges of some common indicators are given in Table 12-2. It is worth noting that the acid color is displayed at any pH below the minimum value in the range and the alkaline color is displayed at any pH above the maximum value. The acid color of phenolphthalein is exhibited not only in acid solutions but in solutions of pH between 7.0 and 8.3, which are alkaline. The alkaline color of methyl orange is exhibited not only in strong alkalies but also in weakly acid solutions with pH greater than 4.4.

12-10. Measurement of pH with Indicators. Measurement of pH is one of the most common laboratory tests. It may be as crude as a litmus test or it may entail the use of elaborate equipment such as a spectrophotometer or a pH meter (Chapter 15). It is easy to determine the pH within 1 or 2 units by means of an indicator. Somewhat more care is required to pin down the value to the nearest 0.1 of a unit.

Suppose that we are given a solution of unknown pH. First we determine with bromthymol blue whether the pH is above or below 7. If a small portion of it turns the indicator yellow, the solution is acid. Next a succession of indicators can be tried on separate portions of the solution. Suppose that bromcresol purple turns yellow, methyl red turns orange, and bromphenol blue remains blue. Inspection of Table 12-2 shows that the pH of the solution must be about 5.

This rather lengthy procedure can be avoided by use of a mixture of indicators. A mixture of phenolphthalein, bromthymol blue, and methyl red produces a series of color changes between pH 4 and 10. A drop of this "universal" indicator in our unknown solution would produce a red color corresponding to pH 5. Paper strips impregnated with universal indicator are very convenient. The color produced by touching some of the solution to the strip is matched against the color standards printed on the box. Such measurements fix the pH only to the nearest 1 or 2 units.

To measure the pH more accurately, we must make careful measurements with a single indicator. If the approximate pH is 5, methyl red with a range from 4.2 to 6.3 would be a good choice; bromcresol green, range 3.8 to 5.4 is less desirable because the pH of the solution is close to the upper end of its range where color differences are not easily detected. Having decided on the indicator, we prepare a standard series of equal amounts of the indicator in a series of buffer solutions that cover the pH range in steps of 0.2 unit. The same concentration of indicator is prepared in the unknown solution and the color of this is matched against those of the standards. If its color falls between those of standards with pH 5.2 and 5.4, the pH of the unknown is about 5.3. The color comparisons must be made in tubes of uniform size so equal depths of solution are examined. For greater accuracy the transmittancy of the solutions can be determined photoelectrically.

The measurement of pH with indicators is subject to a number of errors: the presence of neutral salts and changes in temperature and solvent alter the extent of ionization of the indicator and its color ratio; the indicator can be destroyed by oxidizing or reducing agents, and colloids may remove the indicator by adsorption. For rapid, rough measurements, however, indicators are very useful. Accurate values of the pH are generally obtained by the more elaborate electrical method described in Chapter 15.

SUPPLEMENTARY READING

E. KELSEY and H. DIETRICH, *Fundamentals of Semimicro Qualitative Analysis,* rev. ed., Macmillan, New York, 1951, pp. 78–81, 87–89.

E. GILREATH, *Qualitative Analysis,* McGraw-Hill, New York, 1954, pp. 68–75.

T. HOGNESS and W. JOHNSON, *Qualitative Analysis and Chemical Equilibrium,* 4th ed., Holt, New York, 1954, pp. 215–20.

D. DEFORD, "The Brønsted Concept in Calculations Involving Acid-Base Equilibria," *J. Chem. Educ.,* **27,** 554 (1950).

EXERCISES

12-1. Calculate the pH of each of the following mixtures.

(a) 0.6 M in HCl and 0.1 M in H_2S
(b) 0.1 M in H_3BO_3 and 0.1 M in HNO_3
(c) 20 ml of 0.5 M HCl mixed with 30 ml of 0.1 M $NaC_2H_3O_2$
(d) 0.2 M in NaOH and 0.01 M in NH_3
(e) 0.07 M in NaOH and 0.07 M in $NaC_2H_3O_2$
(f) 10 ml of 0.3 M NaOH mixed with 10 ml of 0.1 M NH_4NO_3

12-2. Calculate the required concentration in each part.

(a) $[HCO_3^-]$ in a mixture that is 0.1 M in Na_2CO_3 and 0.5 M in NaOH.
(b) $[AlOH^{++}]$ in a mixture that is 0.2 M in $AlCl_3$ and 0.2 M in HCl
(c) $[S^{--}]$ in a mixture that is 0.1 M in H_2S and 0.4 M in HCl
(d) $[B(OH)_4^-]$ in a mixture that is 0.1 M in HNO_3 and 0.02 M in H_3BO_3

12-3. Calculate the pH of each mixture.

(a) 0.1 M in acetic acid and 1 M in potassium acetate
(b) 0.1 M in ammonium chloride and 0.2 M in ammonia
(c) 0.01 M in sodium bicarbonate and 0.02 M in carbonic acid
(d) 0.01 M in sodium bicarbonate and 0.02 M in sodium carbonate
(e) 0.04 M in sodium tartrate ($Na_2C_4H_4O_6$) and 0.01 M in potassium acid tartrate
(f) 0.01 M borax (Hint: In dilute solution the tetraborate ion breaks down as shown by $B_4O_7^{--} + 7H_2O \rightarrow 2B(OH)_4^- + 2H_3BO_3$)

12-4. Calculate the required quantity. Assume that the total volume of each mixture is the sum of the volumes taken.

(a) $[OH^-]$ in a mixture of equal volumes of 1 M NH_4Cl and 0.2 M NH_3
(b) the pH of a mixture of 20 ml of 0.05 M NH_4Cl and 30 ml of 0.20 M NH_3
(c) $[H^+]$ of a mixture of 100 g of solid $NaHCO_3$, 500 ml of 0.01 M H_2CO_3 and enough water to make a total volume of 1 liter
(d) $[H^+]$ for a mixture of 40 ml of 1 M propionic acid and 60 ml of 0.1 M NaOH

(e) [OH⁻] for a mixture of 35 ml of 0.2 M NH₃ and 15 ml of 0.067 M HCl

(f) [OH⁻] for a mixture of 70 ml of 0.10 M NH₄Cl and 30 ml of 0.033 M NaOH

(g) the pH of a mixture of 10 ml of 1 M NaOH and 50 ml of 0.3 M anilinium chloride

(h) the pH of 1 drop of 1 M formic acid mixed with 4 drops of 0.5 M sodium formate

12-5. Calculate the change in pH that results when

(a) 1 drop of 0.1 M nitric acid is added to 10 ml of pure water,

(b) 1 drop of 0.1 M nitric acid is added to 10 ml of 0.5 M hydrochloric acid,

(c) 1 drop of 0.2 M sodium hydroxide is added to 10 ml of a buffer containing both acetic acid and sodium acetate at 1 M concentration.

12-6. Calculate the pH of a mixture that contains 10.0 g each of KH₂PO₄ and Na₂HPO₄ in sufficient water to make a liter of solution at 25°. Repeat the calculation for a temperature of 0° if pK of H₂PO₄⁻ at this temperature is 7.31.

12-7. Write material balance and electroneutrality conditions for a mixture that is 0.02 M in NH₄Cl and 0.03 M in NH₃. With these prove that Eq. 6 holds for this mixture.

12-8. Prove that Eq. 6 holds for a solution of a weak acid alone ($B = 0$).

12-9. Explain why the pH of a mixture that is 0.1 M in sodium acetate, acetic acid, and sodium chloride is less than that of the mixture without the sodium chloride.

12-10. Calculate the hydrogen ion concentration of a buffer that is 0.01 M in formic acid and 0.04 M in sodium formate. Use Eq. 11 to estimate the activity coefficients.

12-11. Criticize the following statement: "A mixture of acetic acid and sodium acetate is a buffer because it contains acetic acid, which can remove added base, and acetate ion, which can remove added acid."

12-12. Why is 0.2 M nitric acid a good buffer while 0.2 M formic acid is not?

12-13. Why is a mixture of 0.1 M NH₄NO₃ and 0.1 M NH₃ a better buffer than either 0.1 M NH₄NO₃ alone or 0.1 M NH₃ alone?

12-14. Calculate the molar concentrations of iron(III) and magnesium left unprecipitated by a mixture that is 1 M in NH₄Cl and 0.1 M in NH₃. What is the significance of the results?

12-15. Calculate the number of grams of solid ammonium chloride that must be added to 100 ml of 0.05 M ammonia if iron(II) hydroxide is not to precipitate when the mixture is added to 100 ml of 0.02 M iron(II) chloride solution. Assume a final volume of 200 ml and do not neglect the changes in concentration that result from mixing the two solutions: e.g., [Fe⁺⁺] = 0.01, not 0.02.

12-16. Magnesium and hafnium, initially present at 0.1 M concentration, are to be separated by an ammonia–ammonium chloride buffer. Within what limits must the ratio [NH₄⁺]/[NH₃] be kept in order that only HfO(OH)₂ shall precipitate and that not more than 0.01 mg of HfO⁺⁺ per ml shall be left in solution? $K_{sp} = [\text{HfO}^{++}][\text{OH}^-]^2 = 1 \times 10^{-23}$.

12-17. Can a buffer that is 0.1 M in triethanolamine and 0.5 M in triethanol-ammonium nitrate separate Mn⁺⁺ from Cr⁺⁺⁺ by precipitation of one hydroxide and not the other? Prove by appropriate calculations. Assume 0.05 M concentrations of the metal ions and assume that for a successful separation not more than 0.01 mg Cr/ml must be left in solution.

12-18. Find the approximate concentration of zinc ion left unprecipitated if a 0.1 M solution of a zinc salt is made 1 M in monochloroacetic acid and 0.5 M in the sodium salt of the acid and is saturated with hydrogen sulfide at 1 atm pressure and 25°. Assume that the solubility product of freshly precipitated zinc sulfide is about 1×10^{-21}.

12-19. If an equimolar mixture of acetic acid and sodium acetate that is 0.5 M in $FeCl_2$ is saturated with hydrogen sulfide at 1 atm and 25°, will any FeS precipitate? Prove by appropriate calculations.

12-20 It is found by experiment that CdS will precipitate from a 0.01 M solution of a cadmium salt upon saturation with hydrogen sulfide if the pH is greater than 0.22 and that ZnS will precipitate under similar conditions if the pH is greater than 1.15. Which of the following buffers would be most suitable for establishing the required pH level to separate cadmium and zinc?

(a) 1 M $HC_2H_3O_2$ + 0.1 M $NaC_2H_3O_2$
(b) 1 M $H_2C_2O_4$ + 0.1 M $NaHC_2O_4$
(c) 0.1 M $NaNH_2SO_3$ + 0.5 M NH_3SO_3 (sulfamic acid)
(d) 0.1 M Na_2SO_4 + 0.1 M $KHSO_4$.

12-21. The indicator bromcresol purple is a weak acid with characteristics given in Table 12-2.

(a) What is the color of the indicator in a buffer solution of pH 3?
(b) Would this indicator be suitable for measuring the pH of an acetic acid-sodium acetate buffer?

12-22. The pK value of the indicator cresol red is 8.3. What percentage of the indicator is in the acid form at (a) pH 7.0, (b) pH 8.0, (c) pH 9.0?

12-23. Explain why indicators have a useful range of only about 2 pH units.

12-24. You are given an unknown solution.

(a) How would you prove that the pH of the solution was about 6?
(b) What further work would you do to prove that the pH was 6.4?

12-25. The indicator bromcresol green has a pK value of 4.7. Five drops of a solution of this indicator are added to a buffer solution, and the mixture is divided between two tubes of uniform diameter of 1 cm. Two drops of the indicator solution are added to 0.2 M HCl in another such tube, and three drops of indicator are added to 0.2 M NaOH in a fourth tube. The color viewed through a depth of 2 cm of buffer matches the sum of colors viewed through the other two tubes held one behind the other. What is the pH of the buffer?

CHAPTER THIRTEEN

Solutions Containing Several Weak Acids and Bases

13-1. Introduction. Many systems contain more than one weak acid or base. A solution of formic acid saturated with hydrogen sulfide contains two weak acids. Many salts contain both an acidic cation and a basic anion, e.g., ammonium formate, zinc acetate, and ammonium carbonate. Solutions of these salts can also be produced by combining equivalent quantities of a weak acid and a weak base. In still other solutions one ionic species may act both as an acid and as a base. Such ampholytes are found, for example, in solutions of sodium bicarbonate and glycine.

For these more complicated equilibria exact calculations are possible but rarely necessary. Simple expressions for the hydrogen ion concentration give reasonably good results as long as the concentration of electrolyte is relatively high. The relations developed in this chapter are generally valid to within 10% if the concentration is above 0.01 M, and they will frequently hold at concentrations as low as 0.001 M. Concentrations below this are rarely encountered. In Sec. 13-4 a more general treatment is described for one type of system.

13-2. Solutions Containing Two Weak Acids or Bases. Suppose that a solution contains the weak acids HAx and HAy at concentrations **X** and **Y**, respectively. The equilibria are represented by

$$HAx \rightleftharpoons H^+ + Ax^- \qquad K_x = \frac{[H^+][Ax^-]}{[HAx]}$$

$$HAy \rightleftharpoons H^+ + Ay^- \qquad K_y = \frac{[H^+][Ay^-]}{[HAy]}$$

The conditions of electroneutrality and material balance take the form

$$\text{EN: } [H^+] = [OH^-] + [Ax^-] + [Ay^-]$$
$$\text{MB } (Ax): \quad \mathbf{X} = [HAx] + [Ax^-]$$
$$\text{MB } (Ay): \quad \mathbf{Y} = [HAy] + [Ay^-]$$

By combining the material balance conditions with the ionization constants we obtain

$$[Ax^-] = K_x(X - [Ax^-])/[H^+]$$
$$[Ay^-] = K_y(Y - [Ay^-])/[H^+]$$

When these relations and $[OH^-] = K_w/[H^+]$ are combined with the electro-neutrality condition we find

$$[H^+] = \frac{K_w}{[H^+]} + \frac{K_x(X - [Ax^-])}{[H^+]} + \frac{K_y(Y - [Ay^-])}{[H^+]}$$
$$= \sqrt{K_x(X - [Ax^-]) + K_y(Y - [Ay^-]) + K_w} \qquad 1$$

This is not very useful as it stands, because the concentrations of the anions are not known. If we confine our attention, as we have so frequently done before, to solutions in which the ionization of the two acids is feeble, i.e., when X and Y are large and K_x and K_y are small, Eq. 1 simplifies to

$$[H^+] \simeq \sqrt{K_xX + K_yY + K_w} \qquad 2$$

This relation is the basis for the calculations that follow. It is comparable with $[H^+] = (CK)^{1/2}$ for a solution of a single weak acid (Eq. 11, Chapter 11) and with $[H^+] = K_w^{1/2}$ for pure water.

EXAMPLE 1. Find the *p*H of a mixture that is 0.05 *M* in acetic acid and 0.01 *M* in benzoic acid. The ionization constants are, respectively, 1.8×10^{-5} and 6.3×10^{-5}. By Eq. 2

$$[H^+] = (0.05 \times 1.8 \times 10^{-5} + 0.01 \times 6.3 \times 10^{-5} + 1 \times 10^{-14})^{1/2} = 1.24 \times 10^{-3}$$

$$pH = \boxed{2.91}$$

It will be noted that K_xX and K_yY are about the same and are so much larger than K_w that the latter can be neglected.

EXAMPLE 2. Calculate the *p*H and concentration of sulfide ion in 0.2 *M* formic acid saturated with hydrogen sulfide at 25° and 1 atm. The ionization constants of formic acid and hydrosulfuric acid are, respectively, 1.8×10^{-4} and 1×10^{-7}, and the concentration of hydrogen sulfide in the saturated solution is 0.1 *M*. By Eq. 2

$$[H^+] = (0.2 \times 1.8 \times 10^{-4} + 0.1 \times 1 \times 10^{-7} + 1 \times 10^{-14})^{1/2} = 6.0 \times 10^{-3}$$

$$pH = \boxed{2.22}$$

Here one ionization constant is larger than the other. The concentration of hydrogen ion is almost entirely determined by the formic acid. The contribution of K_w is again negligible.

The concentration of sulfide ion can be obtained from K_{i_p} of H_2S because the solution is saturated with the gas and the hydrogen ion concentration is known:

$$(6.0 \times 10^{-3})^2[S^{--}] = 1.3 \times 10^{-21}$$

$$[S^{--}] = \boxed{3.6 \times 10^{-17} \ M}$$

If the solubility product of freshly precipitated zinc sulfide is about 1×10^{-21}, zinc sulfide will precipitate from this acid mixture as long as the concentration of zinc ion is greater than about $10^{-4} \ M$.

The approximation on which Eq. 2 is based is readily verified. If we use $[H^+] = 6.0 \times 10^{-3}$ and rearrange the acidity constant expression for formic acid, we obtain

$$\frac{[CHO_2^-]}{[HCHO_2]} = \frac{K_a}{[H^+]} = \frac{1.8 \times 10^{-4}}{6.0 \times 10^{-3}} = 0.03$$

Because this is small, we are justified in neglecting $[CHO_2^-]$ in comparison with 0.2; most of the formic acid is in the molecular form. If this approximation is not valid, a check of this sort will disclose the fact. Thus for a mixture which is 0.1 M in monochloroacetic acid and 0.01 M in oxalic acid, $[H^+]$ as given by Eq. 2 is 2.3×10^{-2}, and this leads to a ratio $[HC_2O_4^-]/[H_2C_2O_4]$ of 1.65; i.e., most of the acid is in the anionic form. This problem may be solved by successive approximations to give $[H^+] = 1.6 \times 10^{-2}$.

13-3. An Approximate Treatment of Salts of Weak Acids and Weak Bases. Solutions of such salts can be prepared by combining equivalent quantities of a weak acid HA and a weak base B. The salt contains the acid cation BH^+ conjugate to B and the basic anion A^- conjugate to HA. The equilibria in such solutions were considered briefly in Sec. 11-5. They can be expressed by

$$BH^+ \rightleftharpoons B \ + H^+ \qquad K_a = K_{BH^+} = \frac{[H^+][B]}{[BH^+]}$$

$$A^- + H_2O \rightleftharpoons HA + OH^- \qquad K_b = \frac{K_w}{K_{HA}} = \frac{[OH^-][HA]}{[A^-]}$$

If K_a is greater than K_b (or $K_{BH^+}K_{HA} > K_w$), the solution is acid; if the opposite relation holds, the solution is alkaline.

The material balance and electroneutrality conditions are

$$\text{MB } (A \text{ or } B): C = [BH^+] + [B] = [HA] + [A^-]$$
$$\text{EN}: [BH^+] + [H^+] = [OH^-] + [A^-]$$

where C is the concentration of the salt. These can be combined to give

$$[BH^+] = [A^-] \ + [OH^-] - [H^+] \qquad\qquad 3$$
$$[B] = [HA] - [OH^-] + [H^+] \qquad\qquad 4$$

It is customary to make the following approximations:

$$[BH^+] \simeq [A^-] \qquad\qquad 5$$
$$[B] \simeq [HA] \qquad\qquad 6$$

These would be exact relations if both ionization reactions went to an equal extent, for then an excess of neither H$^+$ or OH$^-$ would be produced and $[OH^-] - [H^+] = 0$. It is still possible for Eqs. 5 and 6 to be good approximations if $[OH^-] - [H^+]$ is small in comparison with the other concentrations. For this to be true, neither ionization reaction should occur to a large extent. If the concentration of salt is not lower than 0.01 M and if K_a or K_b is in the range from 10^{-3} to 10^{-11}, Eqs. 5 and 6 will be satisfactory approximations. Most monoprotic acids and bases have constants in this range.

For calculation of the hydrogen ion concentration the most convenient combination of constants is

$$K_{BH^+}K_{HA} = \frac{[H^+][B]}{[BH^+]} \frac{[H^+][A^-]}{[HA]}$$

which because of Eqs. 5 and 6 takes the simple forms

$$K_{BH^+}K_{HA} \simeq [H^+]^2$$

$$[H^+] \simeq (K_{BH^+}K_{HA})^{\frac{1}{2}}$$

7

The extent of reaction of each ion can be found once the hydrogen ion concentration is known. For the acidic cation it is given by

$$\alpha_{BH^+} = \frac{\text{moles of } BH^+ \text{ per liter that changed to } B}{\text{total moles of } BH^+ \text{ and } B} = \frac{[B]}{[BH^+] + [B]}$$

8

It must be emphasized that, for this type of salt, the molar quantity of BH^+ that undergoes reaction is not measured by $[H^+]$, for most of the H^+ ions are tied up with OH^- ions or with the anion base. Only $[B]$ correctly measures the molar quantity of BH^+ ions that reacted. Since $[BH^+] = [B][H^+]/K_{BH^+}$, we can use this to eliminate both $[B]$ and $[BH^+]$ from Eq. 8, and we obtain

$$\alpha_{BH^+} = \frac{K_{BH^+}}{K_{BH^+} + [H^+]}$$

9

It can be shown by a similar procedure that the extent of reaction of A^- to HA is given by

$$\alpha_{A^-} = \frac{[HA]}{[HA] + [A^-]} = \frac{[H^+]}{K_{HA} + [H^+]}$$

10

Equations 9 and 10 are both exact relations if $[H^+]$ is known accurately. When $[H^+]$ is found from Eq. 7, the same extent of ionization is obtained from both equations; for Eq. 7 is based on the supposition that the two reactions occur to the same extent.

EXAMPLE 1. Find the pH and extent of reaction of 0.01 M ammonium formate. The equilibrium constants are

$$K_{NH_4^+} = \frac{[H^+][NH_3]}{[NH_4^+]} = 5.7 \times 10^{-10}$$

$$K_{HCHO_2} = \frac{[H^+][CHO_2^-]}{[HCHO_2]} = 1.8 \times 10^{-4}$$

The product of the constants is equal to 1×10^{-13}, which is greater than K_w, so the solution is acid. By Eq. 7

$$[H^+] = (1 \times 10^{-13})^{1/2} = 3.2 \times 10^{-7} \, M$$

$$pH = \boxed{6.50}$$

The extent of reaction is given by either Eq. 9 or Eq. 10:

$$\alpha = \frac{K_{NH_4^+}}{K_{NH_4^+} + [H^+]} = \frac{5.7 \times 10^{-10}}{5.7 \times 10^{-10} + 3.2 \times 10^{-7}}$$

$$= 1.8 \times 10^{-3} \text{ or } \boxed{0.18\%}$$

The extent of reaction of ammonium formate, although low, is larger than that of 0.01 M ammonium chloride (0.024%) or that of 0.01 M sodium formate (0.075%). Salts of weak acids and weak bases are generally more extensively hydrolyzed than salts of other types because the two reactions help each other along. If Eq. 7 holds, the extent of reaction is also independent of the concentration of the salt. According to Eq. 7, $[H^+]$ does not depend on C and α will vary with C only if $[H^+]$ does. The extent of hydrolysis of a salt of a weak base and strong acid (ammonium chloride) or of a strong base and weak acid (sodium formate) increases when the solution is diluted.

The use of Eq. 7 for 0.01 M ammonium formate is readily justified. We have to verify that Eqs. 5 and 6 are satisfactory approximations. From $[H^+] = 3.2 \times 10^{-7} \, M$ and $\alpha = 1.8 \times 10^{-3}$ we find

$$[OH^-] = \frac{K_w}{[H^+]} = 0.32 \times 10^{-7}$$

$$[OH^-] - [H^+] = -2.9 \times 10^{-7}$$

$$[HCHO_2] = 1.8 \times 10^{-3} \, C = 1.8 \times 10^{-5}$$

$$[CHO_2^-] = 0.01 - 1.8 \times 10^{-5} \text{ or virtually } 0.01$$

Then by Eq. 3

$$[NH_4^+] = 0.01 - 2.9 \times 10^{-7}$$

so both $[NH_4^+]$ and $[CHO_2^-]$ do not differ appreciably from 0.01 M. By Eq. 4

$$[NH_3] = 1.8 \times 10^{-5} + 2.9 \times 10^{-7} = 1.8_3 \times 10^{-5}$$

so $[NH_3]$ and $[HCHO_2]$ differ by less than 2%, which we shall take to be negligible. Equations 5, 6, and 7 are thus satisfactory approximations for this solution.

13-4. A More Accurate Treatment of Salts of Weak Acids and Weak Bases. In the other sections of this chapter the treatment is an approximate one that is usually satisfactory as long as the concentration of electrolyte is high. In this section a more general method of attack is considered which leads to relations that are more accurate at high concentrations and are even satisfactory at very low concentrations. This procedure is so general that it can be used, after adaptation, for the treatment of any type of salt.

There are six unknowns: $[BH^+]$, $[B]$, $[HA]$, $[A^-]$, $[H^+]$, and $[OH^-]$. The material balance and electroneutrality conditions and the three equilibrium constants constitute six equations connecting these unknowns:

$$\text{MB } (B): C = [BH^+] + [B]$$
$$\text{MB } (A): C = [A^-] + [HA]$$
$$\text{EN}: [BH^+] + [H^+] = [A^-] + [OH^-]$$
$$K_{BH^+} = [H^+][B]/[BH^+]$$
$$K_{HA} = [H^+][A^-]/[HA]$$
$$K_w = [H^+][OH^-]$$

Because the number of equations matches the number of unknowns, it is possible to obtain an expression for any one unknown that involves only C and the constants. Let us choose $[H^+]$ as this unknown. From the material balance conditions: $[B] = C - [BH^+]$ and $[HA] = C - [A^-]$. These are combined with the expressions for the ionization constants to obtain explicit relations for $[BH^+]$ and $[A^-]$:

$$K_{BH^+} = [H^+](C - [BH^+])/[BH^+]$$
$$[BH^+] = C[H^+]/(K_{BH^+} + [H^+])$$
$$K_{HA} = [H^+][A^-]/(C - [A^-])$$
$$[A^-] = CK_{HA}/(K_{HA} + [H^+])$$

These expressions together with $[OH^-] = K_w/[H^+]$ can be used to eliminate all unknowns but $[H^+]$ from the electroneutrality condition:

$$\frac{C[H^+]}{K_{BH^+} + [H^+]} + [H^+] = \frac{K_w}{[H^+]} + \frac{CK_{HA}}{K_{HA} + [H^+]}$$

Then by multiplying through by $(K_{BH^+} + [H^+])(K_{HA} + [H^+])[H^+]$ to clear denominators, we obtain

$$C[H^+]^2 K_{HA} + C[H^+]^3 + K_{BH^+}K_{HA}[H^+]^2 + [H^+]^4 + K_{HA}[H^+]^3 + K_{BH^+}[H^+]^3$$
$$= K_w K_{BH^+}K_{HA} + K_w K_{HA}[H^+] + K_w K_{BH^+}[H^+] + K_w[H^+]^2$$
$$+ CK_{HA}K_{BH^+}[H^+] + CK_{HA}[H^+]^2$$

The explicit relation for $[H^+]$ in its final form is obtained by collecting terms in the same power of the hydrogen ion concentration:

$$[H^+]^4 + (C + K_{HA} + K_{BH^+})[H^+]^3 + (K_{BH^+}K_{HA} - K_w)[H^+]^2$$
$$-(CK_{HA}K_{BH^+} + K_w K_{HA} + K_w K_{BH^+})[H^+] - K_w K_{BH^+}K_{HA} = 0 \qquad \textbf{11}$$

This relation is exact for any conceivable values of C and the constants.[1] In spite of its formidable appearance, this quartic equation is not usually

---

[1]The equilibrium constants are the concentration constants; if the values from tables are the activity constants (K^0), activity coefficients have to be introduced ($K = K^0/Y$) for accurate calculations.

difficult to solve. It will frequently reduce to a simple quadratic equation, as in Example 1 which follows. Even when this is not possible, as in Example 2, it is not difficult to obtain an answer.

EXAMPLE 1. Calculate the pH and extent of reaction of the ions for 0.001 M ammonium formate.

Step 1. Compute the coefficients of the powers of [H$^+$] in Eq. 11. In each coefficient drop all terms that are less than 1 % of the largest. Thus

$C + K_{HA} + K_{BH+} = 10^{-3} + 1.8 \times 10^{-4} + 5.7 \times 10^{-10}$
$$\text{simplifies to } 1.18 \times 10^{-3}$$

$K_{HA}K_{BH+} - K_w = 1.0 \times 10^{-13} - 1.0 \times 10^{-14}$ simplifies to 9.0×10^{-14}

$CK_{HA}K_{BH+} + K_wK_{HA} + K_wK_{BH+} = 1.0 \times 10^{-16} + 1.8 \times 10^{-18} + 5.7 \times 10^{-24}$
$$\text{simplifies to } 1.0 \times 10^{-16}$$

The quartic equation then becomes
$$[H^+]^4 + 1.18 \times 10^{-3}[H^+]^3 + 9.0 \times 10^{-14}[H^+]^2$$
$$- 1.0 \times 10^{-16}[H^+] - 1.0 \times 10^{-27} = 0 \qquad \textbf{11a}$$

Step 2. Estimate the approximate value of [H$^+$]. Equation 7 can be used for this:
$$[H^+] = (K_{NH_4+}K_{HCHO_2})^{\frac{1}{2}} = 3.2 \times 10^{-7} M$$

Step 3. Calculate the left-hand side (LHS) of Eq. 11a using simple powers of ten for [H$^+$] on either side of the approximate value.

Try [H$^+$] = 10^{-6}: LHS = $10^{-24} + 1.18 \times 10^{-21} + 9 \times 10^{-26}$
$$-1.0 \times 10^{-22} - 1.0 \times 10^{-27} = +1.1 \times 10^{-21}$$

Try [H$^+$] = 10^{-7}: LHS = $10^{-28} + 1.18 \times 10^{-24} + 9 \times 10^{-28}$
$$-1.0 \times 10^{-23} - 1.0 \times 10^{-27} = -0.9 \times 10^{-23}$$

Since one value of LHS is positive and the other is negative, the true value of [H$^+$], which would make LHS = 0, must lie between 10^{-6} and 10^{-7}. These calculations show that only the second and fourth terms are large; the others are much smaller.

Step 4. Solve the quadratic obtained by retaining only the large terms in Eq. 11a:
$$1.18 \times 10^{-3}[H^+]^3 - 1.0 \times 10^{-16}[H^+] = 0$$
$$[H^+] = (1.0 \times 10^{-16}/1.18 \times 10^{-3})^{\frac{1}{2}}$$
$$= 2.9 \times 10^{-7} M$$
$$pH = \boxed{6.54}$$

This result should be compared with 6.50 or [H$^+$] = 3.2×10^{-7} obtained with the approximate Eq. 7. The extents of reaction of the ions are calculated with Eqs. 9 and 10:

$$\alpha_{NH_4+} = \frac{5.7 \times 10^{-10}}{2.9 \times 10^{-7}} = 2.0 \times 10^{-3} \text{ or } \boxed{0.20\%}$$

$$\alpha_{CHO_2-} = \frac{2.9 \times 10^{-7}}{1.8 \times 10^{-4}} = 1.6 \times 10^{-3} \text{ or } \boxed{0.16\%}$$

Thus the two salt ions do not react to an equal extent, but the difference is very small.

EXAMPLE 2. Calculate the pH and extent of reaction of the ions in 10^{-4} M ammonium cyanide solution.

Step 1. Compute the coefficients of the powers of [H$^+$] in Eq. 11. The ionization constants are $K_{NH_4^+} = 5.7 \times 10^{-10}$ and $K_{HCN} = 4 \times 10^{-10}$. When all terms less than 1 % of the largest in each coefficient are dropped, the quartic equation becomes

$$[H^+]^4 + 10^{-4}[H^+]^3 - 10^{-14}[H^+]^2 - 3.25 \times 10^{-23}[H^+] - 2.28 \times 10^{-33} = 0 \quad \textbf{11b}$$

Step 2. Estimate the approximate value of [H$^+$]. By Eq. 7 we find
$$[H^+] = (22.8 \times 10^{-20})^{1/2} = 4.8 \times 10^{-10}$$

Step 3. Calculate LHS of Eq. 11b using simple powers of ten on either side of the approximate value for [H$^+$]:

Try $[H^+] = 10^{-10}$: LHS $= 10^{-40} + 10^{-34} - 10^{-34}$
$$- 3.25 \times 10^{-33} - 2.3 \times 10^{-33} = -5.6 \times 10^{-33}$$

Try $[H^+] = 10^{-9}$: LHS $= 10^{-36} + 10^{-31} - 10^{-32}$
$$- 3.25 \times 10^{-32} - 2.3 \times 10^{-33} = +5.5 \times 10^{-32}$$

The true value for which LHS $= 0$ must lie between 10^{-9} and 10^{-10}. Only the first term is negligibly small, and when it is dropped, a cubic equation remains.

Step 4. Solve the remaining equation. One method, which is less tedious than it may appear, is to make a succession of guesses which come closer and closer to the true answer. If we guess that $[H^+] = 5 \times 10^{-10}$, half way between the extreme values, we find LHS $= -0.87 \times 10^{-32}$. For $[H^+] = 7 \times 10^{-10}$, the next guess, LHS $= +0.43 \times 10^{-32}$, so the answer must lie between 5 and 7×10^{-10}. For $[H^+] = 6 \times 10^{-10}$, LHS $= -0.38 \times 10^{-10}$, and the answer must lie between 6×10^{-10} and 7×10^{-10}. If we try 6.5×10^{-10}, we find LHS $= -0.02 \times 10^{-32}$, which is sufficiently close to zero for our purposes. This same answer can be obtained by plotting some of the values of LHS against [H$^+$]; a curve drawn through the points intersects LHS $= 0$ at $[H^+] = 6.5 \times 10^{-10}$. Newton's method could also be used to solve the cubic equation; it is described in algebra books.

From $[H^+] = 6.5 \times 10^{-10}$ M we find a pH value of $\boxed{9.19}$

whereas from Eq. 7 we would obtain 9.32. The extent of reaction of ammonium ion, as calculated from Eq. 9, is $\boxed{47\%}$

and that of the cyanide ion, from Eq. 10, is $\boxed{62\%}$

These values are large and far from equal, so Eq. 7 cannot be used.

It is not difficult to derive more accurate relations than Eq. 7, but even these formulas will hold only under restricted conditions. Since the formulas are rather elaborate and the restrictions are frequently forgotten, it is better to rely on the more general approach presented above.

13-5. Salts of a Weak Base and a Weak Diprotic Acid. Salts of the type $(BH)_2A$ include such common laboratory reagents as ammonium oxalate, ammonium carbonate, and ammonium sulfide. Their solutions contain the species B, BH^+, A^{--}, HA^-, H_2A, H^+, and OH^-. The material balance and electroneutrality conditions are

$$\text{MB } (B): 2C = [B] + [BH^+]$$
$$\text{MB } (A): C = [A^{--}] + [HA^-] + [H_2A]$$
$$\text{EN}: [BH^+] + [H^+] = [OH^-] + [HA^-] + 2[A^{--}]$$

The $[H^+]$ and $[OH^-]$ can be neglected in the electroneutrality condition as a first approximation. If we assume further that the concentration of molecular H_2A, which is formed in the second stage of the reaction of A^{--}, is very small, we can derive the following quadratic equation:

$$[H^+]^2 - K_a[H^+] - 2K_2K_a = 0 \qquad\qquad 12$$

where K_a is the acidity constant for BH^+ and K_2 is the second ionization constant of H_2A. The solution of this equation is given by the quadratic formula

$$[H^+] = (K_a/2) + [(K_a/2)^2 + 2K_2K_a]^{\frac{1}{2}} \qquad\qquad 13$$

To this approximation the pH of the solution is independent of the concentration of salt. Eq. 13 holds with an accuracy of 10% for solutions in which the salt concentration is $0.01\ M$ or more. It is valid for cations as weakly acidic as the ammonium ion ($K_a = 5.7 \times 10^{-10}$) and for anions as strongly basic as the sulfide ion or as weakly basic as the oxalate ion.

When the basic anion is as strongly basic as the sulfide ion, the term $2K_2K_a$ is very small in comparison with $(K_a/2)^2$, and Eq. 13 reduces to $[H^+] = K_a$. There is a simple interpretation of this. In a solution of ammonium sulfide, for example, the reaction

$$NH_4^+ + S^{--} \rightleftharpoons NH_3 + HS^-$$

goes to such a large extent that the salt is effectively transformed to an equimolar mixture of NH_4HS and NH_3. With $[NH_4^+] = [NH_3]$, it follows that

$$\frac{[H^+][NH_3]}{[NH_4^+]} = K_a = [H^+]$$

EXAMPLE 1. Find the pH and concentrations of the various species in $0.1\ M$ ammonium sulfide solution. The equilibrium constants are

$$K_a = 5.7 \times 10^{-10}$$
$$K_2 = \frac{[H^+][S^{--}]}{[HS^-]} = 1.3 \times 10^{-13}$$
$$K_1 = \frac{[H^+][HS^-]}{[H_2S]} = 1 \times 10^{-7}$$

By Eq. 13

$$[H^+] = 5.7 \times 10^{-10}\ M$$
$$p\text{H} = \boxed{9.24}$$

From K_2,

$$\frac{[S^{--}]}{[HS^-]} = \frac{K_2}{[H^+]} = 2.3 \times 10^{-4}$$

and from K_1,

$$\frac{[H_2S]}{[HS^-]} = \frac{[H^+]}{K_1} = 5.7 \times 10^{-3}$$

From the small values of these ratios we can conclude that most of the sulfide is in the form of HS^- ions. If we take $[HS^-] = 0.1$, from the ratios we find $[S^{--}] = 2.3 \times 10^{-5}$ and $[H_2S] = 5.7 \times 10^{-4}$ M. This sulfide ion concentration is more than sufficient to precipitate the sulfides of Cation Group 3.

EXAMPLE 2. Find the pH and concentration of carbonate ion in 0.1 M ammonium carbonate. The principal constants are

$$K_a = 5.7 \times 10^{-10}$$

$$K_2 = \frac{[H^+][CO_3^{--}]}{[HCO_3^-]} = 4.7 \times 10^{-11}$$

From Eq. 13

$$[H^+] = (5.7 \times 10^{-10}/2) + (8.1 \times 10^{-20} + 5.4 \times 10^{-20})^{\frac{1}{2}} = 6.5 \times 10^{-10}$$

$$pH = \boxed{9 \cdot 19}$$

We can write $[HCO_3^-] = 0.1 - [CO_3^{--}]$ if we neglect the concentration of $[H_2CO_3]$; and from K_2,

$$\frac{[CO_3^{--}]}{[HCO_3^-]} = \frac{K_2}{[H^+]} = \frac{4.7 \times 10^{-11}}{6.5 \times 10^{-10}} = \frac{[CO_3^{--}]}{0.1 - [CO_3^{--}]}$$

$$[CO_3^{--}] = \boxed{6.7 \times 10^{-3} \ M}$$

This concentration is high enough to precipitate $MgCO_3$ if $[Mg^{++}]$ is much greater than 0.01 M.

In the precipitation of Cation Group 4 ammonium carbonate is used in conjunction with ammonium chloride and ammonia. The equilibria can be summarized approximately by the equation

$$NH_4^+ + CO_3^{--} \rightleftharpoons NH_3 + HCO_3^-$$

Ammonium chloride provides an excess of ammonium ions, and the concentration of carbonate ion that can be maintained in equilibrium with a high concentration of ammonium ions is too low to precipitate magnesium carbonate. The danger, in fact, is that the carbonate ion concentration will be so low that the carbonates of Cation Group 4 will not be completely precipitated. Ammonia is added to prevent the reduction in carbonate ion concentration from going too far. Because the precipitation is carried out at an elevated temperature, the equilibrium constants will have different values from those we have used, and the loss of ammonia and carbon dioxide as gases would make numerical calculations unreliable. Ammonium carbonate solutions always contain considerable quantities of ammonium carbamate,

$NH_4CO_2NH_2$. These complications make calculations or a detailed discussion very difficult.

13-6. Salts of Metal Hydroxides and Weak Acids.

It will be recalled that practically all metal ions in the hydrated state can give off protons and function as acids (Sec. 11-6). Thus salts of metal hydroxides, except the strong basic hydroxides, and weak acids contain an acidic cation and a basic anion. Some typical examples are copper(II) sulfide, aluminum benzoate, zinc carbonate, and iron(III) acetate. The presence of the basic anion can so increase the ionization of the cation as to form complex ions such as $FeOH^{++}$ and $Fe_2(OH)_2^{+4}$. The precipitation of basic salts, i.e., salts such as $Fe(OH)_2C_2H_3O_2$ or $Al(OH)_2C_6H_5CO_2$ that contain both the anion of the acid and hydroxide ions, can be used in analytical separations.

Quantitative calculations for solutions of such salts will be restricted to a few very limited situations.

The calculation of the hydrogen ion concentration of a zinc acetate solution is similar to that for ammonium formate (Sec. 13-3) except that the molar concentration of the anion is twice that of the cation.

EXAMPLE. Calculate the solubility of zinc sulfide in water. Both ions of this salt interact with water:

$$Zn^{++} + H_2O \rightleftharpoons ZnOH^+ + H^+ \qquad K_a = 2.5 \times 10^{-10}$$

$$S^{--} + H_2O \rightleftharpoons HS^- + OH^- \qquad K_b = 7 \times 10^{-2}$$

Let X be the solubility or moles of zinc sulfide per liter of saturated solution. The material balance conditions take the form

$$X = [Zn^{++}] + [ZnOH^+] = [S^{--}] + [HS^-]$$

The small value of K_a indicates that X is an adequate measure of $[Zn^{++}]$, but the large value of K_b shows that it is certainly incorrect to put $X = [S^{--}]$. We cannot, therefore, write $K_{sp} = X^2$ which would correspond to a solubility $X = 8.9 \times 10^{-13}$ M. The zinc sulfide will actually be much more soluble than this because sulfide ions are removed to a large extent to give HS^- thus displacing the equilibrium

$$ZnS \rightleftharpoons Zn^{++} + S^{--} \qquad K_{sp} = 8 \times 10^{-25}$$

to the right.

An approximate calculation of X is based on the low solubility of zinc sulfide. If X is very small the quantity of hydroxide ions produced by the basic reaction of the sulfide will not materially change the hydrogen ion concentration of water. Then taking $[H^+] = 10^{-7}$ we find

$$\frac{[HS^-]}{[S^{--}]} = \frac{[H^+]}{K_{HS^-}} = \frac{1 \times 10^{-7}}{1.3 \times 10^{-13}} = 7.7 \times 10^5$$

$$\frac{[ZnOH^+]}{[Zn^{++}]} = \frac{K_{Zn^{++}}}{[H^+]} = \frac{2.5 \times 10^{-10}}{1 \times 10^{-7}} = 2.5 \times 10^{-3}$$

These ratios confirm our suspicion that almost all the sulfide is in the form of HS⁻ ions but that only a small part of the zinc is changed to $ZnOH^+$ ions. From the material balance conditions,

$$[Zn^{++}] = X - [ZnOH^+] \simeq X$$
$$[HS^-] = X - [S^{--}] \simeq X$$

Hence

$$[S^{--}] = \frac{[HS^-]}{7.7 \times 10^5} = 1.3 \times 10^{-6} X$$

From the solubility product expression,

$$K_{sp} = [Zn^{++}][S^{--}] = 8 \times 10^{-25} = 1.3 \times 10^{-6} X^2$$

$$X = \boxed{7.5 \times 10^{-10} \ M}$$

Thus solubility of zinc sulfide is almost 1000 times as great as we would expect from the square root of the solubility product, i.e., when no allowance is made for the acidic or basic character of the ions. The concentrations of sulfide and $ZnOH^+$ ions can also be found:

$$[S^{--}] = 1.3 \times 10^{-6} X = 1.0 \times 10^{-15} \ M$$
$$[ZnOH^+] = 2.6 \times 10^{-3} X = 2 \times 10^{-12} \ M$$

These concentrations are very much smaller than X.

13-7. Ampholytes of the Type NaHA. There are a number of substances that can either gain or lose protons (Sec. 11-3). The most familiar of these ampholytes, aside from water itself, are anions of polyprotic acids, e.g., HCO_3^- as in $NaHCO_3$, $H_2PO_4^-$ as in $Ca(H_2PO_4)_2$, or $HC_4H_4O_6^-$ as in $KHC_4H_4O_6$ (potassium hydrogen tartrate). Here, as in the earlier sections of this chapter, we shall not attempt a complete treatment of the equilibria but shall restrict consideration to approximate relations that are accurate within 10 to 15% at concentrations of salt above 0.001 M.

Consider a C molar solution of an ampholyte of the type NaHA formed by partial neutralization of the weak acid H_2A. The concentrations of Na⁺, H⁺, HA^-, A^{--}, OH⁻, and H_2A are connected by the usual relations:

$$\text{MB } (A \text{ or Na}): C = [Na^+] = [H_2A] + [HA^-] + [A^{--}]$$

$$\text{EN}: [H^+] + [Na^+] = [OH^-] + [HA^-] + 2[A^{--}]$$

$$K_1 = \frac{[H^+][HA^-]}{[H_2A]} \qquad K_2 = \frac{[H^+][A^{--}]}{[HA^-]}$$

The material balance and electroneutrality conditions can be combined to eliminate [Na⁺] and [HA^-]:

$$[H_2A] + [H^+] = [OH^-] + [A^{--}] \qquad\qquad 14$$

Now, as in Sec. 13-3, let us make the approximation

$$[H_2A] \simeq [A^{--}] \qquad\qquad 15$$

In effect this is based on the assumption that the two reactions

$$HA^- + H_2O \rightleftharpoons H_2A + OH^-$$
$$HA^- \rightleftharpoons A^{--} + H^+$$

occur to the same extent. Even when this is not strictly valid the concentrations of H^+ and OH^- ions can be negligible if the concentration of salt is high (1 M or more). Combining the constants as in Sec. 13-3, we obtain

$$K_1K_2 = \frac{[H^+]^2[A^{--}]}{[H_2A]} \simeq [H^+]^2$$

$$[H^+] \simeq (K_1K_2)^{1/2} \qquad \qquad \textbf{16}$$

This relation fails at concentrations much lower than 1 M if one constant is very large or very small, e.g., $NaHC_2O_4$ ($K_1 = 3.8 \times 10^{-2}$) or NaHS ($K_2 = 1.3 \times 10^{-13}$).

A better approximation can be derived in the following way. Starting with Eq. 14, we eliminate all concentrations but $[H^+]$ and $[HA^-]$:

$$\frac{[H^+][HA^-]}{K_1} + [H^+] = \frac{K_w}{[H^+]} + \frac{[HA^-]K_2}{[H^+]}$$

The denominators can be cleared by multiplying through by $K_1[H^+]$ with the result

$$[H^+]^2[HA^-] + [H^+]^2K_1 = K_wK_1 + K_1K_2[HA^-]$$

$$[H^+] = \sqrt{\frac{K_1K_2[HA^-] + K_wK_1}{[HA^-] + K_1}}$$

This relation is still an exact one. Let us now assume that the reaction of HA^- to give either A^{--} or H_2A is relatively small so that we can set $[HA^-] \simeq C$. Then

$$[H^+] \simeq \sqrt{\frac{CK_1K_2 + K_wK_1}{C + K_1}} \qquad \qquad \textbf{17}$$

This equation is valid for solutions of such salts as $NaHCO_3$, $NaHSO_3$, NaHS, and $NaHC_4H_4O_4$ (sodium hydrogen succinate) at concentrations as low as 0.001 M with an accuracy of 10% and for the acid salts of oxalic and tartaric acids with an accuracy of 15%. Note that when CK_2 is large in comparison with K_w and C is large in comparison with K_1, Eq. 17 reduces to Eq. 16.

EXAMPLE. Calculate the pH of 0.01 M sodium hydrogen sulfide.
By Eq. 16: $[H^+] \simeq (1 \times 10^{-7} \times 1.3 \times 10^{-13})^{1/2} = 1.1 \times 10^{-10}$
By Eq. 17: $[H^+] \simeq [(1.3 \times 10^{-22} + 1 \times 10^{-21})/(10^{-2} + 10^{-7})]^{1/2}$
$= 3.4 \times 10^{-10}$

$$pH = \boxed{9.47}$$

13-8. Other Ampholytes. A similar treatment of acid salts of triprotic acids can be given. We shall content ourselves with crude approximations valid at concentrations above 0.1 M. For salts such as KH_2AsO_4, NaH_2PO_4, or $NaH_2C_6H_5O_7$ (sodium dihydrogen citrate)

$$[H^+] \simeq (K_1K_2)^{1/2} \qquad\qquad 18$$

and for salts such as Na_2HPO_4

$$[H^+] \simeq (K_2K_3)^{1/2} \qquad\qquad 19$$

These relations can be compared with Eq. 16. At concentrations lower than 0.1 M, Eq. 18 gives too high a value for $[H^+]$, and Eq. 19 gives too low a value.

Amino acids, peptides, and proteins are important ampholytes present in living cells. The treatment of a simple amino acid such as glycine is similar to that of the acid salts in Sec. 13-7. The glycinium ion, $^+NH_3CH_2CO_2H$, has two acidic groups: $-NH_3^+$ (similar to the ammonium ion) and $-CO_2H$ (like that in acetic acid). The second of these groups gives off a proton more readily than the first just as acetic acid ($K_a = 1.8 \times 10^{-5}$) is a stronger acid than the ammonium ion ($K_a = 5.7 \times 10^{-10}$):

$$^+NH_3CH_2CO_2H \rightleftharpoons {}^+NH_3CH_2CO_2^- + H^+ \qquad K_1 = 4.5 \times 10^{-3}$$
$$^+NH_3CH_2CO_2^- \rightleftharpoons NH_2CH_2CO_2^- + H^+ \qquad K_2 = 1.7 \times 10^{-10}$$

Glycine is the intermediate ampholyte, $^+NH_3CH_2CO_2^-$. The molecule as a whole is electrically neutral, but it contains separate positive and negative charge centers and has a large dipole moment (about 15 debyes). Such particles are called *dipolar ions*.

The hydrogen ion concentration of solutions of glycine and other simple amino acids is given by Eq. 16, or, more accurately, by Eq. 17.

EXAMPLE. Calculate the pH of 0.01 M glycine.

By Eq. 16: $[H^+] \simeq (4.5 \times 10^{-3} \times 1.7 \times 10^{-10})^{1/2} = 8.7 \times 10^{-7}$

$$pH = \boxed{6.06}$$

By Eq. 17: $[H^+] = [(7.65 \times 10^{-13} + 4.5 \times 10^{-17})/(10^{-2} + 4.5 \times 10^{-3})]^{1/2}$

$$pH = \boxed{6.14}$$

The simplifying assumption on which Eq. 16 is based is $[H_2A] = [A^{--}]$. For glycine this takes the form

$$[^+NH_3CH_2CO_2H] = [NH_2CH_2CO_2^-] \qquad\qquad 20$$

This condition defines the *isoionic point* of the amino acid, for a solution in which this condition holds contains equal concentrations of positively and negatively charged amino acid ions. In a more acidic solution glycine will be largely in the form of the cation. If an electric current is passed through such a solution, the glycine travels toward the cathode. In a basic solution the glycine is in the form of the negative glycinate ion and migrates to the anode.

At the *isoelectric point* there is no net migration of glycine in either direction. For glycine and for other amino acids containing only two ionizing groups, the isoionic and isoelectric points are the same. It is seen from the example above that the *p*H at the isoelectric point (6.06) is close to, but not identical with, the *p*H of the amino acid in pure water (6.14).

SUPPLEMENTARY READING

T. HOGNESS and W. JOHNSON, *Qualitative Analysis and Chemical Equilibrium*, 4th ed., Holt, New York, 1954, pp. 233–40.

J. NORDMANN, *Qualitative Testing and Inorganic Chemistry*, Wiley, New York, 1957, pp. 159–65.

B. PARK, "The Hydrogen Ion Concentration of Weak Monobasic Acids and Their Salts," *J. Chem. Educ.*, **30**, 257 (1953).

D. DAVIDSON, "Amphoteric Molecules, Ions, and Salts," *J. Chem. Educ.*, **32**, 550 (1955).

J. RICCI, *Hydrogen Ion Concentration*, Princeton University Press, Princeton, N.J., 1952, Chapter 8. This book is an admirable exposition of the solution of acid-base equilibria problems. It is difficult to read unless you are prepared to spend some time mastering the special symbols, e.g., H for $[H^+]$, A for K_a, B for K_b, W for K_w, D for $[H^+] - [OH^-]$, and others (a list is given in the front of the book).

EXERCISES

13-1. Calculate the *p*H of a mixture that is 0.1 *M* in acetic acid and 0.05 *M* in propionic acid.

13-2. Calculate the *p*H of a mixture that is 0.01 *M* in hydrocyanic acid and 0.2 *M* in ammonium chloride.

13-3. Find the number of moles of lactic acid that must be added to a liter of 0.1 *M* acetic acid to bring the *p*H of the solution to 2.5. Assume that no change in volume occurs.

13-4. Calculate the *p*H and concentration of sulfide ion in 0.01 *M* acetic acid saturated with hydrogen sulfide at 25° and 1 atm. Will any zinc sulfide precipitate if the solution contains 0.1 mg of zinc per milliliter?

13-5. Calculate the *p*H of a 0.01 *M* aluminum nitrate solution that is 0.2 *M* in ammonium nitrate.

13-6. Does Eq. 2 hold for a mixture that is 0.01 *M* in lactic acid and 0.1 *M* in acetic acid? Prove by suitable calculations.

13-7. Calculate the *p*H and extent of reaction of the ions in 0.01 *M* ammonium cyanide solution.

13-8. Calculate the *p*H of 0.1 *M* ammonium propionate.

13-9. Calculate the *p*H and extent of reaction of 0.1 *M* ammonium lactate.

13-10. Calculate the *p*H and extent of reaction of 0.001 *M* anilinium propionate.

13-11. Calculate the *p*H and concentration of molecular acetic acid in 0.001 *M* methylammonium acetate.

13-12. Prove that the pH of the salt of a weak acid and weak base is given approximately by $pH = \frac{1}{2}(pK_{BH+} + pK_{HA})$.

13-13. Prove that if Eq. 7 holds, Eqs. 9 and 10 give the same result.

13-14. Prove that $\alpha_{BH+} - \alpha_{A-} = ([H^+] - [OH^-])/C$.

13-15. Calculate the pH and concentration of sulfide ion in 0.01 M ammonium sulfide.

13-16. Calculate the pH and concentration of carbonic acid in 0.01 M ammonium carbonate.

13-17. Calculate the pH of 0.05 M ammonium sulfite.

13-18. Calculate the pH of 0.03 M anilinium sulfide.

13-19. Calculate the pH and concentration of oxalate ion in 0.01 M ammonium oxalate.

13-20. Calculate the pH of 0.1 M zinc formate.

13-21. Calculate the solubility of copper(II) sulfide in moles per liter (a) assuming that the ions do not react with water and (b) assuming that the copper(II) ion behaves as an acid ($K_a = 5 \times 10^{-9}$) and the sulfide ion as a base.

13-22. Calculate the solubility of iron(II) sulfide in moles per liter (a) assuming that the ions do not react with water and (b) assuming that the iron(II) ion behaves as an acid ($K_a = 5 \times 10^{-9}$) and the sulfide ion as a base.

13-23. Calculate the pH and concentration of carbonate ion in 0.01 M sodium bicarbonate.

13-24. Calculate the pH of 0.1 M sodium acid sulfide.

13-25. Calculate the pH and ratio of succinate ion to hydrogen succinate ion in 0.01 M sodium hydrogen succinate.

13-26. Calculate the pH and concentrations of sulfite ion and sulfurous acid in 0.1 M soidum hydrogen sulfite.

13-27. Calculate the pH of 0.2 M sodium hydrogen tartrate.

13-28. Calculate the pH of 0.1 M solutions of sodium monohydrogen phosphate and potassium dihydrogen phosphate.

13-29. Calculate the pH of 0.05 M glycine.

13-30. Prove that at the isoelectric point the pH is given by $pH = \frac{1}{2}(pK_1 + pK_2)$.

13-31. The concentration ionization constants of glycine at very low concentration in sodium chloride solutions have been measured [E. J. King, $J.$ $Am.$ $Chem.$ $Soc.$, **73**, 155 (1951)]. For 0.3 M NaCl solutions at 25° $K_1 = 4.36 \times 10^{-3}$ and $K_2 = 2.64 \times 10^{-10}$. Calculate the pH of the isoelectric point.

13-32. This question is a review of various calculations in the last few chapters. On the left are given five relations; on the right are six solutions. For each relation find one or more of the solutions to which the relation applies.

Relations	*Solutions*
(1) $[H^+] = [HS^-]$	(a) 0.05 M H_2S
(2) $[H^+] = K_{H_2S}$	(b) 0.1 M Na_2S
(3) $[S^{--}] = K_{HS^-}$	(c) 0.1 M NaHS
(4) $[S^{--}] = [H_2S]$	(d) 0.5 M HCl that is 0.1 M in H_2S
(5) $[S^{--}] = K_{ip}/[H^+]^2$	(e) 0.1 M H_2S that is 0.1 M in NaHS
	(f) 0.1 M NaHS that is 0.1 M in Na_2S

The following exercises are based on Sec. 13-4.

13-33. Calculate the pH and extent of reaction of each ion in 0.001 M and in 1 M ammonium sulfamate.

13-34. Prove that for 0.001 M ammonium cyanide the hydrogen ion concentration is between 10^{-9} and 10^{-10} and that the first, third, and fifth terms on the left-hand side of Eq. 11 are negligible.

13-35. Prove that, if only the second and fourth terms of Eq. 11 are large, the hydrogen ion concentration is given by

$$[H^+] \simeq \sqrt{\frac{CK_{HA}K_{BH+} + K_wK_{HA} + K_wK_{BH+}}{C + K_{HA} + K_{BH+}}}$$

13-36. When the concentration of salt is very low, only the first and last terms on the left-hand side of Eq. 11 can be neglected. Solve the quadratic equation that remains for $[H^+]$. Use the quadratic formula.

13-37. Derive an equation analogous to Eq. 11 for an acid salt NaHA.

CHAPTER FOURTEEN

The Dissociation of Complex Ions

14-1. Introduction. The earlier discussion of complex ions (Chapter 6) dwelt on proofs of their existence and the details of their internal structure. Their dissociation also was described briefly, and they were classified as labile or inert (Sec. 6-6). Most of the ions used in analytical separations are in the first class, e.g., $Ag(NH_3)_2{}^+$, $Cd(CN)_4{}^{--}$, and $Zn(OH)_4{}^{--}$. They rapidly come to equilibrium with free metal ions and ligands. The inert complexes, such as $Fe(CN)_6{}^{----}$, not only are very weakly dissociated but also require a long time to come to equilibrium. It would be meaningless to apply equilibrium principles to their dissociation. In this chapter we shall be concerned with a quantitative treatment of the equilibria in solutions of labile complexes.

14-2. The Stepwise Dissociation of Complex Ions. A complex will lose its ligands one by one just as molecules of H_2S or H_3PO_4 lose their protons. For the diammine silver complex, the dissociation equilibria are represented by

$$Ag(NH_3)_2{}^+ \rightleftharpoons AgNH_3{}^+ + NH_3 \qquad K_2 = \frac{[AgNH_3{}^+][NH_3]}{[Ag(NH_3)_2{}^+]} = 1.3 \times 10^{-4} \qquad 1$$

$$AgNH_3{}^+ \rightleftharpoons Ag^+ + NH_3 \qquad K_1 = \frac{[Ag^+][NH_3]}{[AgNH_3{}^+]} = 4.8 \times 10^{-4} \qquad 2$$

The constants are numbered according to the number of ligands in the complex on the left-hand side of the chemical equation. In recent years the practice of writing the chemical equations in the reverse direction from those above has gained favor. The *formation constants* are the reciprocals of the *dissociation constants* given in Eqs. 1 and 2.

Until recently few dissociation constants were available for the separate steps, and it was customary to summarize the equilibria by

$$Ag(NH_3)_2{}^+ \rightleftharpoons Ag^+ + 2NH_3 \qquad K_{inst} = K_1 K_2 = \frac{[Ag^+][NH_3]^2}{[Ag(NH_3)_2{}^+]} = 6.3 \times 10^{-8} \qquad 3$$

This equilibrium constant is called the *instability constant* of the complex. The chemical equation must not be interpreted to mean that in a solution of

$Ag(NH_3)_2NO_3$ the concentration of ammonia is twice that of silver ion. Because of the stepwise dissociation, in a 0.01 M solution of the complex the concentration of silver ion is actually only about one-fifth, not one-half, that of ammonia. The instability constant is the product of the dissociation constants, a purely algebraic relation, and remains valid as long as we do not introduce any factitious relations such as $[NH_3] = 2[Ag^+]$.[1]

The dissociation of complex ions differs in an important respect from the ionization of polyprotic acids. The constant for the second step of such ionization is usually about 10^{-5} as large as that of the first step (Sec. 7-12). With complex ions the constants are relatively close together. Note that for the silver ammine complex, the constant for the second step is actually larger than that for the first. This makes calculations for the dissociation equilibria difficult. The second stage in the dissociation of $Ag(NH_3)_2^+$ cannot be neglected in comparison with the first. It was just this approximation that made possible a simple treatment of the ionization of hydrogen sulfide.

14-3. Dissociation of Complexes in the Presence of an Excess of Complexing Agent. In spite of the difficulties indicated in the preceding section, it is possible to make useful calculations for the dissociation of complexes. This is because in our laboratory work, complex ions are almost always formed in the presence of an excess of complexing agent, e.g., ammonia, hydroxide ion, or cyanide ion. We shall make the following simplifying assumptions in our calculations:

Assumption A: Most of the metal ion is tied up in the complex with the highest coordination number. The concentrations of free metal ion and intermediate complexes are very much smaller.

Assumption B: The concentration of free ligand is determined largely by the excess of complexing agent. The contribution of free ligands from dissociation of the complex is neglected.

EXAMPLE 1. Calculate the concentrations of silver and cadmium ions in a solution prepared by dissolving 0.010 mole each of $AgNO_3$ and $Cd(NO_3)_2$ in a liter of buffer solution that is 2 M in both ammonia and ammonium nitrate. The concentration instability constants of the complexes are known for 2 M ammonium nitrate solutions at 30°:

$$Ag(NH_3)_2^+ \rightleftharpoons Ag^+ + 2NH_3 \qquad K = \frac{[Ag^+][NH_3]^2}{[Ag(NH_3)_2^+]} = 9.3 \times 10^{-8}$$

$$Cd(NH_3)_4^{++} \rightleftharpoons Cd^{++} + 4NH_3 \qquad K = \frac{[Cd^{++}][NH_3]^4}{[Cd(NH_3)_4^{++}]} = 7.6 \times 10^{-8}$$

---

[1]Similar remarks were made in Sec. 9-4, footnote 2 on the combination of the ionization constants of hydrogen sulfide.

According to Assumption A

$$0.01 \simeq [Ag(NH_3)_2^+] = [Cd(NH_3)_4^{++}]$$

and by Assumption B

$$2 \simeq [NH_3]$$

The metal ion concentrations are obtained by combining these values with the instability constants:

$$[Ag^+] = \frac{9.3 \times 10^{-8} \times 0.01}{2^2} = \boxed{2.3 \times 10^{-10}\ M}$$

$$[Cd^{++}] = \frac{7.6 \times 10^{-8} \times 0.01}{2^4} = \boxed{4.8 \times 10^{-11}\ M}$$

The concentration of cadmium ion is lower than that of silver mainly because of the higher power to which $[NH_3]$ is raised in its instability constant expression. These concentrations are far too low to permit the precipitation of Ag_2O or $Cd(OH)_2$. The concentration of hydroxide ion is established by the buffer mixture:

$$[OH^-] = \frac{2}{2} K_b(NH_3) = 1.8 \times 10^{-5}\ M$$

The concentrations of metal ions required to give saturated solutions of the oxide and hydroxide are

$$[Ag^+] = \frac{K_{sp}(Ag_2O)}{[OH^-]} = \frac{2.6 \times 10^{-8}}{1.8 \times 10^{-5}} = 1.4 \times 10^{-3}\ M$$

$$[Cd^{++}] = \frac{K_{sp}(Cd(OH)_2)}{[OH^-]^2} = \frac{2.8 \times 10^{-14}}{(1.8 \times 10^{-5})^2} = 8.7 \times 10^{-5}\ M$$

These are much larger than those maintained by the complex ions, so precipitation of the hydroxides cannot occur.

Let us examine the original assumptions. The material balance condition for silver is

$$\text{MB for Ag: } 0.01 = [Ag^+] + [AgNH_3^+] + [Ag(NH_3)_2^+]$$

$$[Ag(NH_3)_2^+] = 0.01 - [Ag^+] - [AgNH_3^+]$$

The concentration of free silver ion is clearly negligible in comparison with 0.01. The concentration of the intermediate complex can be estimated using either K_1 ($= 1.5 \times 10^{-4}$) or K_2 ($= 6.3 \times 10^{-4}$); it is about $7.5 \times 10^{-7}\ M$ and this is also negligible in comparison with 0.01. The excess of ammonia has forced almost all the silver into the form of $Ag(NH_3)_2^+$; Assumption A is justified. Ammonia in the solution will be either free or in the form of the complexes. The ionization of ammonia is repressed by the high concentration of ammonium nitrate. To convert 0.01 mole each of Ag^+ and Cd^{++} to the complexes requires a total of 0.06 mole of ammonia. The concentration of free ammonia that remains is $1.94\ M$, which does not differ appreciably from 2, the value used above.

EXAMPLE 2. Calculate the solubility of silver chloride in a liter of 0.5 M ammonia solution. Let S be the number of moles of silver chloride that dissolve per liter. The material balance conditions are

$$MB(Cl): S = [Cl^-]$$
$$MB(Ag): S = [Ag^+] + [Ag(NH_3)_2^+]$$
$$\simeq [Ag(NH_3)_2^+] \quad \text{(Assumption A)}$$
$$MB(N): 0.5 = [NH_3] + [NH_4^+] + 2[Ag(NH_3)_2^+]$$
$$\simeq [NH_3] \quad \text{(Assumption B)}$$

These values are used in the instability constant and solubility product:

$$K = 6.3 \times 10^{-8} = \frac{[Ag^+](0.5)^2}{S}$$

$$K_{sp} = [Ag^+][Cl^-] = 1.8 \times 10^{-10} = [Ag^+] S$$

These are two equations in two unknowns and the silver ion concentration can be eliminated between them:

$$[Ag^+] = \frac{1.8 \times 10^{-10}}{S} = \frac{6.3 \times 10^{-8} S}{(0.5)^2}$$

$$S^2 = \frac{(0.5)^2 1.8 \times 10^{-10}}{6.3 \times 10^{-8}}$$

$$S = 2.7 \times 10^{-2} M$$

A more accurate answer can be obtained by correcting the concentration of free ammonia for the amount removed to give the complex. From the material balance relation for nitrogen

$$[NH_3] = 0.5 - 2S \simeq 0.446$$

if we use $2S = 0.054$ (the concentration of ammonium ion formed by ionization of the ammonia is negligible). When 0.446 is used in the calculation, we obtain $S = \boxed{0.024 \ M}$ This is equivalent to 3.4 g AgCl per liter.

EXAMPLE 3. When a zinc salt is added to an ammonia–ammonium nitrate buffer, some of the zinc ions are removed to form the hydroxide complex and some to form the ammonia complex. If the buffer is 0.5 M in both ammonia and ammonium nitrate, calculate the ratio of concentrations of the two complexes. The equilibria are represented by

$$Zn(OH)_4^{--} \rightleftharpoons Zn^{++} + 4\,OH^- \qquad K_{Zn(OH)_4^{--}} = \frac{[Zn^{++}][OH^-]^4}{[Zn(OH)_4^{--}]} = 3.3 \times 10^{-16}$$

$$Zn(NH_3)_4^{++} \rightleftharpoons Zn^{++} + 4\,NH_3 \qquad K_{Zn(NH_3)_4^{++}} = \frac{[Zn^{++}][NH_3]^4}{[Zn(NH_3)_4^{++}]} = 1.1 \times 10^{-10}$$

We might suppose at first glance that, because the hydroxide complex has the smaller constant, most of the zinc would be in this form. But the buffer contains a relatively low concentration of hydroxide ions and a high concentration of ammonia molecules. As long as the total concentration of zinc is small, the formation of the complexes will not greatly disturb the buffer equilibrium and we can write

$$0.5 = [NH_3] = [NH_4^+]$$

$$[OH^-] = K_b \frac{0.5}{0.5} = 1.8 \times 10^{-5} M$$

The unknown concentration of free zinc ion can be eliminated by taking the ratio of the instability constants, and the required ratio of concentrations of the complexes is obtained by rearrangement:

$$\frac{K_{Zn(OH)_4^{--}}}{K_{Zn(NH_3)_4^{++}}} = \frac{[OH^-]^4 \, [Zn(NH_3)_4^{++}]}{[NH_3]^4 \, [Zn(OH)_4^{--}]}$$

$$\frac{[Zn(NH_3)_4^{++}]}{[Zn(OH)_4^{--}]} = \frac{[NH_3]^4}{[OH^-]^4} \frac{K_{Zn(OH)_4^{--}}}{K_{Zn(NH_3)_4^{++}}}$$

$$= \frac{(0.5)^4 \times 3.3 \times 10^{-16}}{(1.8 \times 10^{-5})^4 \times 1.1 \times 10^{-10}} = \boxed{1.8 \times 10^{12}}$$

This large value shows that practically all the zinc is in the form of the ammonia complex. The hydroxide complex is generally obtained only by adding an excess of a strong base such as sodium hydroxide.

Zinc hydroxide cannot precipitate under the conditions of this experiment. When the hydroxide ion concentration is 1.8×10^{-5}, the concentration of zinc ion in a saturated solution is

$$[Zn^{++}] = \frac{K_{sp}}{[OH^-]^2} = \frac{7 \times 10^{-18}}{(1.8 \times 10^{-5})^2} = 2.2 \times 10^{-8} \, M$$

The concentration allowed by the ammonia complex is only 1.8×10^{-11}, so the solution is unsaturated in zinc hydroxide.

EXAMPLE 4. A 0.1 M solution of cadmium nitrate is treated with enough potassium cyanide to give a total cyanide ion concentration of 0.5 M. Will any cadmium sulfide precipitate from this mixture if it is made 0.001 M in sulfide ion by addition of a soluble sulfide? The equilibria are expressed by

$$Cd(CN)_4^{--} \rightleftharpoons Cd^{++} + 4 \, CN^- \qquad K_{Cd(CN)_4^{--}} = \frac{[Cd^{++}][CN^-]^4}{[Cd(CN)_4^{--}]} = 7.8 \times 10^{-18}$$

$$CdS \downarrow \rightleftharpoons Cd^{++} + S^{--} \qquad K_{sp} = [Cd^{++}][S^{--}] = 7 \times 10^{-27}$$

The material balance conditions are

MB (Cd) : $0.1 = [Cd^{++}] + [Cd(CN)_4^{--}] \simeq [Cd(CN)_4^{--}]$ (Assumption A)
MB (CN): $0.5 = [CN^-] + [HCN] + 4[Cd(CN)_4^{--}]$

If we neglect the hydrogen cyanide formed by ionization of CN^- as a base and take the concentration of the complex to be about 0.1 M,

$$[CN^-] = 0.5 - 4[Cd(CN)_4^{--}] = 0.5 - 0.4 = 0.1 \, M$$

The concentration of cadmium ion can now be found:

$$K_{Cd(CN)_4^{--}} = 7.8 \times 10^{-18} = \frac{[Cd^{++}](0.1)^4}{0.1}$$

$$[Cd^{++}] = 7.8 \times 10^{-15}$$

The product of concentrations

$$Q = [Cd^{++}][S^{--}] = 7.8 \times 10^{-15} \times 10^{-3} = 7.8 \times 10^{-18}$$

is larger than K_{sp} and precipitation of CdS will occur.

14-4 The Determination of Dissociation Constants. Consider a mixture containing a metal ion Me^{++} at total concentration C_1 and a ligand L^- at total concentration C_2. Suppose, for simplicity, that they form only one complex, MeL^+. The solution contains the following species: Me^{++}, L^-, MeL^+, HL (if L^- is a basic anion), H^+, and OH^-. The concentrations of these six species together with the value of K,

$$K = \frac{[Me^{++}][L^-]}{[MeL^+]}$$

constitute seven unknowns. There are six relations among them: (1) material balance for Me, (2) material balance for L, (3) electroneutrality, (4) K for the complex, (5) K_a for HL, and (6) K_w. A seventh relation is required if the value of K is to be found. This is obtained if one concentration can be measured. Some of the methods of doing this may be summarized:

1. Measurement of pH or [H⁺]. This is convenient when the ligand is a base, e.g., NH_3, citrate ion, or ethylenediaminetetraacetate ion.

2. Measurement of [Me⁺⁺]. An electrical method is generally used. It will be discussed in Chapter 15.

3. Distribution Measurements. If L or the complex is molecular and soluble in an organic solvent that does not mix with water, the concentration of L or the complex can be established by using the distribution constant

$$K_D = [L]_o/[L]_w$$

The concentration of L in the organic layer $[L]_o$ is measured and $[L]_w$ is calculated if K_D is known.

4. Optical Measurements. If the complex has a spectrum sufficiently different from that of Me^{++} and L^-, spectrophotometric measurements can be used to find $[MeL^+]$.

5. Solubility Measurements. This is Example 2 of the preceding section in reverse; the solubility is measured and used to calculate K.

The determination of the dissociation constant is usually made difficult by the necessity of taking into account interionic forces and the formation of more than one complex. The first difficulty is often dealt with by making measurements in the presence of a high concentration of an indifferent salt, e.g., $NaClO_4$ or NH_4NO_3 (Example 1). If this is at high concentration, variations in activity coefficients become negligible, but the dissociation constant is valid only for this high ionic strength.

The work of Fulton and Swinehart on zinc hydroxide complexes[2] can be used to illustrate the determination of instability constants when several complexes are present. They measured the solubility S of zinc hydroxide in

[2]J. Fulton and D. Swinehart, *J. Am. Chem. Soc.*, **76**, 864 (1954). They write $Zn(OH)_3^-$ and $Zn(OH)_4^{--}$ as the less hydrated versions $HZnO_2^-$ and ZnO_2^{--}. The analysis of the data is not altered by changes in hydration of the ions. Their method of numbering the constants has been retained; the constants K_2 to K_4 refer to equilibria that are not considered here. Fulton and Swinehart used activity coefficients in their analysis of the data and we have omitted these for simplicity.

sodium hydroxide solutions of various concentrations. They considered that the only species containing zinc were molecular $Zn(OH)_2$, $Zn(OH)_3^-$, and $Zn(OH)_4^{--}$ ions. The equilibria were represented by

$$Zn(OH)_2 \text{ (solid)} \rightleftharpoons Zn(OH)_2 \text{ (in solution)}$$
$$K_1 = [Zn(OH)_2]$$
$$Zn(OH)_2 \text{ (solid)} + OH^- \rightleftharpoons Zn(OH)_3^-$$
$$K_5 = [Zn(OH)_3^-]/[OH^-]$$
$$Zn(OH)_2 \text{ (solid)} + 2OH^- \rightleftharpoons Zn(OH)_4^{--}$$
$$K_6 = [Zn(OH)_4^{--}]/[OH^-]^2$$

The material balance condition for zinc is

$$\text{MB (Zn): } S = [Zn(OH)_2] + [Zn(OH)_3^-] + [Zn(OH)_4^{--}]$$
$$= K_1 + K_5[OH^-] + K_6[OH^-]^2$$

This expression shows that S approaches K_1 as the concentration of sodium hydroxide is decreased. A graph of S against the concentration of base was constructed, and the curve was extended to zero concentration of sodium hydroxide to obtain $K_1 = 4 \times 10^{-6}$. The other two constants K_5 and K_6 were chosen so that the sum of the three terms on the right-hand side of the material balance condition matched the measured solubility. It was necessary to assume the presence of both complexes. If it was supposed that only one complex existed, e.g., $Zn(OH)_3^-$, then no matter what value of K_5 was chosen the total solubility S could not be accounted for by $K_1 + K_5[OH^-]$ alone. The existence of both complex ions is supported by the fact that the solid compounds $NaZn(OH)_3$ and $Na_2Zn(OH)_4$ are known.

SUPPLEMENTARY READING

T. HOGNESS and W. JOHNSON, *Qualitative Analysis and Chemical Equilibrium*, 4th ed., Holt, New York, 1954, pp. 268–76.

T. MOELLER, *Qualitative Analysis*, McGraw-Hill, New York, 1958, pp. 164–73, 184–88.

J. NORDMANN, *Qualitative Testing and Inorganic Chemistry*, Wiley, New York, 1957, Chapter 9.

G. CHARLOT, *Qualitative Inorganic Analysis*, Wiley, New York, 1954, Chapters 5 and 6.

J. BAILAR, ed., *The Chemistry of the Coordination Compounds*, Reinhold, New York, 1956, Chapter 18 (physical methods in coordination chemistry).

J. FULTON and D. SWINEHART, "The Equilibria of Crystalline Zinc Hydroxide in Dilute Hydrochloric Acid and Sodium Hydroxide at 25°. The First and Second Acidic Dissociation Constants of Zinc Hydroxide," *J. Am. Chem. Soc.*, **76**, 864 (1954).

W. VOSBURGH and G. COOPER, "Complex Ions. I. The Identification of Complex Ions in Solution by Spectrophotometric Measurements," *J. Am. Chem. Soc.*, **63**, 437 (1941).

EXERCISES

14-1. Calculate the concentration of silver ion in a mixture that is 0.2 M in $KAg(CN)_2$ and 0.2 M in KCN.

14-2. Calculate the concentrations of Cu^+ and Cd^{++} in a solution in which both $Cu(CN)_3^{--}$ and $Cd(CN)_4^{--}$ are at 0.05 M concentration if the solution is also 0.5 M in KCN. Will Cu_2S or CdS precipitate when the mixture is made 0.001 M in sulfide ion by addition of a soluble sulfide?

14-3. If a small amount of a zinc salt is dissolved in a buffer that is 0.5 M in ammonia and 0.1 M in ammonium nitrate, what is the ratio of concentrations of the two complexes?

14-4. If a very small amount of mercury(II) nitrate is added to a solution that is 0.5 M in chloride ion and 0.001 M in iodide ion, what percentage of the mercury will be in the form of the chloride complex?

14-5. How many grams of silver iodide will dissolve in a liter of 10 M ammonia?

14-6. How many grams of silver bromide will dissolve in a liter of 10 M ammonia?

14-7. How many grams of sodium chloride must be added to a liter of a mixture that is 0.1 M in $Ag(NH_3)_2^+$ and 0.2 M in ammonia in order that silver chloride shall just begin to precipitate? Repeat the calculation for 0.1 M complex and 1 M ammonia.

14-8. Will any silver bromide precipitate if 12 mg of potassium bromide is added to 500 ml of a solution prepared by mixing 0.1 mole of silver nitrate and 5 moles of ammonia with sufficient water?

14-9. How many moles of potassium iodide must be added to a liter of mixture that is 1 M in hydrogen ion and 0.1 M in mercury(II) nitrate if mercury(II) sulfide is to be kept from precipitating when the mixture is saturated with hydrogen sulfide at 25° and 1 atm?

14-10. Fulton and Swinehart found $K_5 = 1.20 \times 10^{-3}$ and $K_6 = 2.20 \times 10^{-2}$. The solubility product of zinc hydroxide is 7×10^{-18}. Using these data prove that the over-all instability constant of $Zn(OH)_4^{--}$ has the value used in Example 3, Sec. 14-3.

14-11. The reaction between tin(IV) sulfide and sodium hydroxide has been expressed by the equation

$$SnS_2 \text{ (solid)} + OH^- \rightleftharpoons (SnS_2OH^-)$$

for which the equilibrium constant has the value 1.4. Calculate the solubility of the sulfide in 0.2 M sodium hydroxide.

14-12. At 30° the equilibrium constant for the reaction

$$Al(OH)_3 \text{ (solid)} + OH^- \rightleftharpoons Al(OH)_4^-$$

has been reported to be 13. Calculate the solubility of aluminum hydroxide in 0.5 M sodium hydroxide. If the solubility product of aluminum hydroxide is 1.9×10^{-32} at this temperature, what is the instability constant for $Al(OH)_4^- \rightleftharpoons Al^{+++} + 4 OH^-$?

14-13. Calculate the solubility of zinc sulfide in 0.5 M sodium hydroxide. Neglect the basic ionization of sulfide ion.

14-14. Repeat the calculation of Ex. 14-13 but take the basic ionization of sulfide into account.

14-15. Prove that in a solution of $Ag(NH_3)_2NO_3$, in which stepwise dissociation of $Ag(NH_3)_2^+$ occurs, the concentrations of silver ion and ammonia are related by

$$[Ag^+] = \frac{4.8 \times 10^{-4}[NH_3]}{9.6 \times 10^{-4} + [NH_3]}$$

CHAPTER FIFTEEN

Electric Cells

15-1. Introduction. The concepts of oxidation and reduction and the ion-electron method of balancing redox equations were discussed in Chapter 3. A typical redox reaction such as the oxidation of iodide by iodate in acid solution can be represented by the sum of two partial equations:

Reduction: $2IO_3^- + 12H^+ + 10e^- \rightarrow I_2 + 6H_2O$

Oxidation: $10I^- \rightarrow 5I_2 + 10e^-$

_____

Over-all: $IO_3^- + 6H^+ + 5I^- \rightarrow 3I_2 + 3H_2O$

This procedure was adopted because it provides an easy and reliable method of balancing redox equations. It should be understood that the way the reaction happens is not correctly represented by the partial equations. It is very improbable that an iodate ion should gain five electrons all at once. Electrons are generally transferred one at a time (Sec. 7-4), so reduction probably proceeds through a series of steps. The equation merely summarizes the over-all change. While the partial equations do not represent the mechanism of the reaction, there are experiments in which they have physical meaning. These are experiments with electric cells.

An *electric cell* (or galvanic cell, after Luigi Galvani) consists of two electrodes that dip into a solution, or more commonly, into two solutions that make contact with each other. Two types can be prepared: (1) chemical cells that use a spontaneous redox reaction as a source of electrical energy and (2) concentration cells that use the spontaneous transfer of solute from high to low concentration as the source of energy. We shall be concerned in this chapter principally with cells of the first type. A chemical cell could be constructed which used the oxidation of iodide by iodate. The two reagents are separated in the cell so direct transfer of electrons cannot occur from iodide to iodate but takes place through the external electrical circuit. The reduction reaction occurs at one electrode of the cell and the oxidation at the other. The partial equations that we have written represent the two electrode reactions, and it is in this context that they have physical significance.

A study of electric cells, as we shall see, gives information about the relative strengths of oxidizing or reducing agents, the equilibrium constants for redox reactions, the pH of solutions, ionization constants, solubility products, instability constants, and activity coefficients.

15-2. The Cycle of Changes in Typical Cells. The design and operation of cells is best understood by reference to specific examples. The cycle of operations in a cell is described by starting at an arbitrary point and stating how the current passes through cell and external wires back to this point. In choosing the starting point we are not pretending to decide what starts the flow of electricity; this question is at least as old as the dispute between Volta and Galvani.[1]

Cell 1. The cell represented in Fig. 15-1 uses as its source of electrical energy the spontaneous reduction of silver chloride by hydrogen:

$$H_2 + 2AgCl \downarrow \rightarrow 2Ag \downarrow + 2H^+ + 2Cl^-$$

A cycle in the operation of the cell can be divided into four parts.

1. Molecules of hydrogen at the left-hand electrode (tube B) lose electrons under the influence of the catalyst, platinum black, and go into solution as hydrated protons:

$$H_2 \rightarrow 2H^+ + 2e^-$$

The electrons that are released are left behind on the platinum electrode and confer on it a negative charge.

2. Electrons spew from the platinum electrode into the wire of the external circuit and travel toward the right-hand electrode. This flow of electrons constitutes an electric current and can be made to do electrical work, e.g., heat a coil of wire, run a motor, or light an incandescent lamp. The current can also be used to electrolyze water or a solution. The electrical work required to displace the equilibrium $2H_2O \rightleftharpoons 2H_2 + O_2$ to the right is thus obtained at the expense of the approach of the cell reaction to its equilibrium state (Sec. 9-2).

3. Electrons coming on to the right-hand electrode (tube C), a silver ball coated with silver chloride, reduce some of the silver ions of silver chloride to free silver. The chloride ions are released and enter the solution:

$$2e^- + 2AgCl \downarrow \rightarrow 2Ag \downarrow + 2Cl^-$$

Because of this reaction, electrons cannot accumulate on the right-hand electrode, and this electrode is positive with respect to the other one.

4. Current is carried through solution by migration of the ions. The electrode reactions have caused an accumulation of positive charge in the

---

[1]Galvani caused a frog's leg to contract by touching it with a combination of two metals. In publishing his results (1791) he asserted that the electricity came from the animal tissue. Volta claimed that the electricity originated in the metals.

form of H+ ions about the left-hand electrode and an accumulation of **nega-tive** charge in the form of Cl⁻ ions about the right-hand electrode. **Unless** electroneutrality is restored in solution, these charge layers about the **elec-**trodes will resist the formation of more H+ and Cl⁻ ions, and current **will** cease. To restore electroneutrality the ions must migrate. If the electrolyte is a mixture of hydrochloric acid and sodium chloride, the hydrogen **and** sodium ions will move away from the left-hand electrode and travel to the

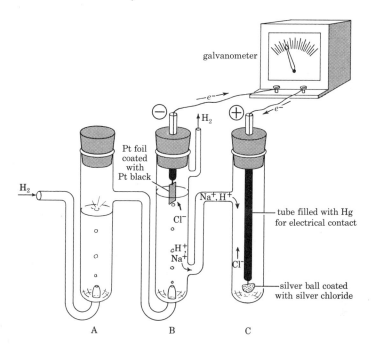

FIG. 15-1. Cell 1. Hydrogen flows first through chamber A containing some of the cell solution, so it becomes saturated with water vapor before it bubbles into chamber B. If this were not done, hydrogen would sweep water out of B and change the composition of the solution. In accurate work the cell is placed in a water bath maintained at constant temperature and the e.m.f. is measured with a potentiometer (Sec. 15-5).

right while the chloride ions will migrate from right to left. The positive ions are thus moving toward the positive electrode; migration occurs to restore electroneutrality, not because of a long-range attraction between the ions and some distant electrode. For current to exist it is not necessary for a particular ion near the left-hand electrode actually to reach the right-hand electrode. Water may flow through a pipe for a long time before a molecule at one end reaches the other end. Ions move slowly in solution, only a few millimeters an hour in this cell, but the number of ions is so large that a considerable current can pass. A river can pour a large volume of water per hour over a dam, even though the current is sluggish, if the river and dam are very wide.

It will be convenient to define the *anode* as the electrode at which oxidation occurs and the *cathode* as the one at which reduction occurs. These definitions apply either to cells that generate current (galvanic cells such as the one we have just described) or to cells into which current must be forced from outside (electrolysis cells). Cations will always migrate to the cathode, which will be positive in the discharge of a galvanic cell and negative in charging or electrolysis. In Cell 1 the hydrogen electrode is the anode and the silver–silver chloride electrode the cathode.[2]

Cell 2. The cell illustrated in Fig. 15-2 uses the spontaneous displacement of copper by zinc as the source of electrical energy:

Anode reaction (oxidation): $Zn \rightarrow Zn^{++} + 2e^-$
Cathode reaction (reduction): $2e^- + Cu^{++} \rightarrow Cu$

Cell reaction: $Zn + Cu^{++} \rightarrow Zn^{++} + Cu$

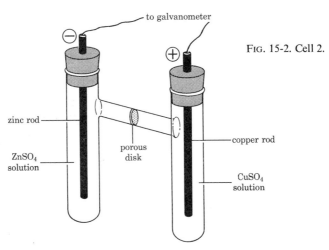

Fig. 15-2. Cell 2.

The experimental arrangement of this cell is somewhat different from that of Cell 1, because the copper(II) ions must be kept away from the zinc electrode. If they were to come in contact with the zinc metal, transfer of electrons directly from the electrode to the ions could occur. If the electrons are not transferred through the wires of the external circuit, the ability of the cell to do electrical work is decreased. The copper(II) sulfate solution is separated

---

[2]It is possible to define the anode as the positive electrode and the cathode as the negative one. Then, in a galvanic cell, oxidation occurs at the cathode, while in electrolysis the reaction would be reduction. There is no general agreement as to which definition is to be preferred. The definition used in this text has the advantage of fixing attention on the electrode reactions rather than on the superficial charge on the electrode.

from the zinc sulfate solution by a porous disk. The two solutions meet in the pores of this disk to form a *liquid junction*. Diffusion of Cu^{++} ions across this junction is inevitable, but ionic diffusion is always very slow and is opposed in this cell by the electrical migration of the cations in the direction of the copper electrode. A cell containing such a junction is stable for a sufficiently long time so that measurements can be made on it before any extensive mixing of the solutions takes place.

   Cell 3.   The cell illustrated in Fig. 15-3 uses the spontaneous oxidation of iron(II) ion by chlorine as a source of electrical energy:

Anode reaction (oxidation):	$2Fe^{++} \rightarrow 2Fe^{+++} + 2e^-$
Cathode reaction (reduction):	$Cl_2 + 2e^- \rightarrow 2Cl$

Cell reaction: $Cl_2 + 2Fe^{++} \rightarrow 2Fe^{+++} + 2Cl^-$

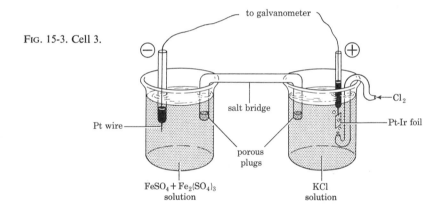

FIG. 15-3. Cell 3.

The chlorine gas must be kept away from the iron(II) ions or direct reaction will occur. In this cell a *salt bridge* is used to make electrical contact between the two solutions. The bridge is a U-shaped tube filled with concentrated potassium chloride or ammonium nitrate solution and fitted with porous plugs at each end to prevent the escape of the solution during preparation of the cell. The anode is a shiny platinum wire dipping into the solution containing the iron(II) and iron(III) ions. The platinum is inert and merely serves as a collector of the electrons given up by the oxidation of the iron(II) ions. The cathode is similar to a hydrogen electrode (tube B in Fig. 15-1). Chlorine gas saturated with water vapor is bubbled over a catalytically active, yet chemically inert, strip of platinum-iridium alloy.

   These are three typical chemical cells. They use spontaneous redox reactions as the source of electrical energy. A reaction such as the displacement of zinc by copper is not suitable, for it will not occur spontaneously at ordinary concentrations of the ions. To make copper displace zinc, the reverse of the reaction in Cell 2, we must put electrical energy into the cell, i.e., electrolyze it. In searching for reactions suitable as a source of electrical energy in chemical cells, we look for redox reactions that occur spontaneously. If the cell is to be a practicable source of electrical energy, the cell reaction must also occur rapidly. If it involves a gas that comes to equilibrium with the solution slowly, a catalyst is put on the electrode surface if one is known. The cell must be constructed so that substances that could react with each other directly are kept apart, either by a liquid junction or a salt bridge.

15-3. The Schematic Representation of Cells. It is not practicable to draw a picture of each cell we wish to discuss. It is convenient to use a more schematic representation. The rules are:

1. The anode is written on the left, cathode at the right. Electrons then pass from left to right through an external circuit which is not shown.

2. Vertical bars represent boundaries between electrodes and solutions.

3. A double vertical bar stands for a salt bridge.

4. A broken vertical line shows a liquid junction.

5. The solutes in each solution are listed in any convenient order, and their concentrations are given in parentheses after the formulas.

The schematic representations of Cells 1, 2, and 3 will illustrate these rules:

Cell 1: (Pt) H_2 (1 atm) | HCl (0.01 M), NaCl (0.1) M | AgCl, Ag

Cell 2: Zn | $ZnSO_4$ (0.1 M) ⦙ $CuSO_4$ (0.1 M) | Cu

Cell 3: Pt | $Fe_2(SO_4)_3$ (0.005 M), $FeSO_4$ (0.01 M) ‖ KCl (0.1 M) | Cl_2(1 atm)(Pt-Ir)

15-4. Types of Electrode Systems, or Half Cells. The principal types of electrodes have been illustrated in Cells 1, 2, and 3. They are

1. A metal dipping into a solution containing the metal ion.

EXAMPLE: Zn | Zn^{++}; electrode reaction $Zn \rightarrow Zn^{++} + 2e^-$

2. An inert electrode (Pt, Au, or C) dipping into a solution containing a substance in two different oxidation states.

EXAMPLES: Pt | I_2, I^-; electrode reaction $2I^- \rightarrow I_2 + 2e^-$
Pt | Ce^{++++}, Ce^{+++}; electrode reaction $Ce^{+++} \rightarrow Ce^{++++} + e^-$
(Pt) H_2 | H^+; electrode reaction $H_2 \rightarrow 2H^+ + 2e^-$

3. A metal coated with an insoluble salt or oxide of the metal dipping into a solution containing the anion of the salt or hydroxide ions.

EXAMPLES: Ag, AgCl | Cl⁻; electrode reaction $Ag + Cl^- \rightarrow AgCl + e^-$

Hg, Hg₂Cl₂ | Cl⁻; electrode reaction $2Hg + 2Cl^- \rightarrow Hg_2Cl_2 + 2e^-$

Hg, HgO | OH⁻; electrode reaction $Hg + 2OH^- \rightarrow HgO + H_2O + 2e^-$

The mercury–mercury(I) chloride electrode is commonly used in *pH* meters and other instruments. It is usually called the *calomel electrode* after the old name for mercury(I) chloride.

These electrode systems have been written as anodes. When represented with the metal on the right side, they can equally well serve as cathodes, e.g., I⁻, I₂ | Pt; electrode reaction $I_2 + 2e^- \rightarrow 2I^-$.

15-5. Fundamental Electrical Concepts.   In the operation of an electric cell, electrons flow in the external circuit, and ions migrate through the cell solution. The flow of charge constitutes a current and can be measured as the number of coulombs passing a plane in the wire or solution per unit time. A current of one ampere transports a charge of one coulomb per second. The flow of electric charge is analogous to that of water. The current of water can be measured as the number of liters (or gallons) that pass through a given plane in a pipe per second.

It is helpful to pursue the analogy further. The flow of water over a dam is a spontaneous fall from a high potential energy to a low one. The energy that a unit mass of water possesses because of its position above the lower level is called its "gravitational potential." The difference in potential of water at the bottom and top of the dam is measured by the work required to transport a unit mass of water from the bottom to the top. It will of course depend on the height of the dam. Water flows over the dam spontaneously from high to low potential. As it flows it can be made to do work equivalent at most to the difference in potential multiplied by the total mass of water that falls.

The concept of potential can be extended to electrical circuits. The flow of electric charge will occur spontaneously from a high potential energy to a low one. The potential energy per unit charge at some point in the circuit is defined as the electrical *potential* at that point. The difference in potential between two points is then the work required to transport a unit charge from one point to the other. The difference in potential between the two electrodes of a cell is called the *electromotive force*, generally abbreviated to e.m.f. and symbolized in equations by $\mathcal{E}$. The work required to bring a charge from one electrode to the other is the product of the e.m.f. and the charge. It is convenient to express the charge in faradays (Sec. 4-12). If a reaction produces one gram equivalent weight of product, the transfer of one faraday, or 96,500 coulombs, of electricity is required. For Cell 2 the formation of each Zn^{++} ion and Cu atom requires the transfer of two electrons, and two faradays are transferred in the formation of a mole each of Zn^{++} and Cu. Let *n* be the number of faradays (or number of electrons in the chemical equation) and let $\mathcal{F}$ represent one faraday of charge. Then the total electrical work is

$$W = n\mathcal{F}\mathcal{E} \qquad\qquad 1$$

A cell will do work when electrons flow spontaneously from a high electrical potential at the anode to a low one at the cathode. Let W and $\mathcal{E}$ be positive numbers when this spontaneous discharge of the cell occurs but negative numbers when energy has to be added to cause the reaction to go. Thus $\mathcal{E}$ will normally be positive for Cells 1 to 3. For the cell

$$\text{Cu} \mid \text{CuSO}_4 \mathbin{\vdots} \text{ZnSO}_4 \mid \text{Zn}$$

with a cell reaction $\text{Cu} + \text{Zn}^{++} \rightarrow \text{Zn} + \text{Cu}^{++}$, $\mathcal{E}$ will be negative because work must be done on the cell to make copper displace zinc. Reversing the direction of a reaction thus reverses the sign of the e.m.f. associated with it.

All conductors by their very nature offer some resistance to the flow of electrons or ions (Sec. 2-14). This resistance limits the current that will be produced for a given e.m.f. By Ohm's law the current I varies directly with the e.m.f. and inversely with the resistance R:

$$I = \frac{\mathcal{E}}{R} \qquad\qquad 2$$

When the e.m.f. is expressed in volts and the current in amperes, the resistance is in ohms.

Consider some implications of Ohm's law for electric cells. Suppose that two cells like Cell 2 are made in different sizes. It is an experimental fact that if they are otherwise just alike and are at the same temperature, the two cells will have the same e.m.f. when this is measured without drawing an appreciable amount of current. The larger cell will have somewhat lower resistance because of the larger electrodes used, and it can pass more current according to Eq. 2. The larger cell also contains larger quantities of chemicals and will last longer than the small cell. But both have the same e.m.f., for this is determined not by the physical size of the cell but by the temperature, the nature of the cell reaction, and the concentrations of the substances involved in the reaction. A chemical study is necessarily focused on the cell reaction and hence on the e.m.f., and we shall not concern ourselves further with the current or resistance.

The values of e.m.f. in the following discussion have been measured in such a way that no appreciable current is drawn from the cell. This is necessary in order that no appreciable amount of chemical change will occur to disturb the condition of the cell, and that its resistance will not affect the measured e.m.f. Hence the electromotive forces obtained in this way are characteristic of the cell reaction and are not dependent on the measuring device. The measurements are made with an electrical instrument called a potentiometer.[3]

15-6. Electromotive Force and the Direction of Reversible Cell Reactions.   It is a generalization from experience that the e.m.f. measures the tendency of a cell reaction to occur for the conditions under which the cell operates. Thus

$$\left.\begin{array}{l} \mathcal{E} = 0 \text{ for equilibrium} \\ \mathcal{E} \text{ is positive for reaction from left to right} \\ \mathcal{E} \text{ is negative for reaction from right to left} \end{array}\right\} \qquad 3$$

The directions right and left refer as usual to the chemical equation for the cell reaction. For Cell 2 the cell reaction is represented by $Cu^{++} + Zn \rightarrow Zn^{++} + Cu$. When the ions are present at moderate concentration, the e.m.f. is large and positive (about 1.1 v) and the reaction proceeds spontaneously from left to right. As it does so, the concentration of cupric ion decreases and that of zinc ion increases; the e.m.f. of the cell gradually falls.

The same principle can be expressed in terms of the electrical work, for by Eq. 1 this is proportional to the e.m.f. *The tendency of the reaction to occur from left to right is measured by the electrical work that the cell can do.* As the cell reaction proceeds, the e.m.f. falls and its capacity to do work decreases until the reaction reaches equilibrium. Then the cell can do no work at all. These statements are consequences of the second law of thermodynamics (Chapter 9).

15-7. The Standard Electromotive Force.   A cell such as Cell 2 can be set up in any number of different ways, e.g., with all conceivable concentrations of zinc and copper(II) ions. It is convenient to single out one such cell and call its e.m.f. the standard e.m.f. ($\mathcal{E}^0$). This cell is taken to be one in which both ions are at unit activity:

$$Zn \mid Zn^{++}(a = 1) \mathrel{\vdots} Cu^{++}(a = 1) \mid Cu$$

We shall take unit activity to be, very roughly, unit concentration, although this is strictly true only for ideal solutes (Sec. 10-14). For gases the state of unit activity corresponds very closely to that at one atmosphere pressure. Pure solids and liquids are taken to be at unit activity. The standard e.m.f. of a cell measures the tendency of the cell reaction to occur when all substances are at unit activity. It was first introduced in Sec. 9-7.

15-8. The Nernst Equation.   The relation between the e.m.f. of a cell and

---

[3]Potentiometers are described in textbooks of physics and physical chemistry; see, for example, F. W. Sears and M. Zemansky, *College Physics*, 2nd ed., Addison-Wesley, Cambridge, Massachusetts, 1952, pp. 521–22; F. Daniels and R. Alberty, *Physical Chemistry*, Wiley, New York, 1955, pp. 415–16; or F. Miller, *College Physics*, Harcourt Brace, New York, 1959, pp. 342-43.

the concentrations of the substances involved in the cell reaction is given by the Nernst equation:[4]

$$\mathcal{E} = \mathcal{E}^0 - \frac{2.3RT}{n\mathcal{F}} \log Q \qquad\qquad 4$$

where R is a constant (Sec. 9-9), T is the absolute temperature, and Q is a concentration quotient having the same form as the equilibrium constant (Sec. 9-5). For accurate work Q must also include an activity coefficient factor; we shall ignore this for the moment. The meaning of the Nernst equation may be stated in words: the tendency of a cell reaction to occur depends on the temperature (expressed in $\mathcal{E}^0$ and T), the nature of the chemical substances that take part in the cell reaction (expressed in $\mathcal{E}^0$), and the concentrations of these substances (expressed in Q).

The coefficient $2.3RT/\mathcal{F}$ is in volts and has the value 0.0592 at 25°, 0.0542 at 0°, and 0.0740 at 100°. Hereafter, the discussion will be confined to measurements at 25°.

If the cell reaction is known, the form of the Nernst equation can be written down immediately.

EXAMPLE 1. *Cell 1*. The cell reaction is $H_2 + 2AgCl \rightarrow 2Ag + 2H^+ + 2Cl^-$. Two electrons are transferred, or $n = 2$. Thus

$$\mathcal{E}_{Cell\ 1} = \mathcal{E}^0_{Cell\ 1} - \frac{0.0592}{2} \log \frac{[H^+]^2[Cl^-]^2}{P_{H_2}}$$

where the pressure of hydrogen gas has been used as a convenient measure of its concentration (Sec. 7-19).

EXAMPLE 2. *Cell 2*. The reaction is $Zn + Cu^{++} \rightarrow Cu + Zn^{++}$, and again $n = 2$. The Nernst equation has the form

$$\mathcal{E}_{Cell\ 2} = \mathcal{E}^0_{Cell\ 2} - \frac{0.0592}{2} \log \frac{[Zn^{++}]}{[Cu^{++}]}$$

EXAMPLE 3. *Cell 3*. The reaction is $Cl_2 + 2Fe^{++} \rightarrow 2Fe^{+++} + 2Cl^-$, and again $n = 2$. The Nernst equation has the form

$$\mathcal{E}_{Cell\ 3} = \mathcal{E}^0_{Cell\ 3} - \frac{0.0592}{2} \log \frac{[Fe^{+++}]^2[Cl^-]^2}{[Fe^{++}]^2\, P_{Cl_2}}$$

15-9. The Relation Between Standard Electromotive Force and the Equilibrium Constant. When the cell reaction has come to equilibrium, Q becomes the equilibrium value K and the electromotive force is zero. Then Eq. 4 becomes

$$0 = \mathcal{E}^0 - \frac{2.3RT}{n\mathcal{F}} \log K$$

$$\mathcal{E}^0 = \frac{2.3RT}{n\mathcal{F}} \log K \qquad\qquad 5$$

[4]This is named after Walther Nernst (1864–1921), noted German physical chemist. He was awarded the Nobel prize in 1920 for his contributions to thermodynamics.

The proportionality between the standard e.m.f. and the logarithm of the equilibrium constant was used in Chapter 9 (Sec. 9-7). If the standard e.m.f. is known, the equilibrium constant can be calculated.

EXAMPLE 1. For Cell 2, $\mathcal{E}^0 = 1.10$ v at 25°. Hence

$$1.10 = (0.0592/2) \log K$$
$$\log K = (2.20/0.0592) = 37.2$$
$$K = \text{antilog } 37.2 = \boxed{1.6 \times 10^{37}}$$

This large value of K shows that the displacement of copper by zinc goes virtually to completion.

EXAMPLE 2. For the redox reaction $I_2 + 2Fe^{++} \rightarrow 2Fe^{+++} + 2I^-$ the standard e.m.f. is -0.24 v at 25°. Hence[5]

$$-0.24 = (0.0592/2) \log K$$
$$\log K = (-0.48/0.0592) = -8.1$$
$$K = \text{antilog } (-8.1) = \text{antilog } (0.9 - 9) = \boxed{8 \times 10^{-9}}$$

The small value of this equilibrium constant shows that the reaction of iodine with ferrous ion does not normally go to an appreciable extent.

15-10. The Relation Between Electromotive Force and Free Energy Change. In Sec. 9-9 the change in free energy was introduced as a measure of the tendency of a reaction to occur at constant temperature and pressure. It was defined by Eq. 10 of that section:

$$\Delta F = -2.3RT \log K + 2.3RT \log Q \qquad 6$$

The decrease in free energy $-\Delta F$ can be identified with the electrical work obtained from the reaction, for both are positive for reaction from left to right, negative for reaction from right to left, and zero at equilibrium; both are expressed in energy units. Thus

$$-\Delta F = W = n\mathcal{F}\mathcal{E} \qquad 7$$

Combination of Eqs. 6 and 7 leads to one form of the Nernst equation:

$$n\mathcal{F}\mathcal{E} = 2.3RT \log K - 2.3RT \log Q$$
$$\mathcal{E} = \frac{2.3RT}{n\mathcal{F}} \log K - \frac{2.3RT}{n\mathcal{F}} \log Q \qquad 8$$

Let us now single out one cell in which all substances are at unit activity (Sec. 15-7). For this cell $\mathcal{E} = \mathcal{E}^0$, $\Delta F = \Delta F^0$, and $Q = 1$; therefore

$$\frac{-\Delta F^0}{n\mathcal{F}} = \mathcal{E}^0 = \frac{2.3RT}{n\mathcal{F}} \log K \qquad 9$$

[5]The method of handling logarithms, particularly negative values, is discussed in Secs. 9-10 and 10-3.

which is Eq. 5. If this is combined with Eq. 8, we obtain the Nernst equation in its usual form (Eq. 4):

$$\mathcal{E} = \mathcal{E}^0 - \frac{2.3RT}{n\mathcal{F}} \log Q \qquad\qquad 10$$

The relation between standard free energy change and standard e.m.f. can be used to find the latter when direct measurements on cells cannot be made.

EXAMPLE. The oxidation of hydrogen by dichromate cannot be carried out in a cell because the reaction is too slow to come to equilibrium. The reaction is represented by

$$Cr_2O_7^{--} + 8H^+ + 3H_2 \rightarrow 2Cr^{+++} + 7H_2O$$

The standard free energies of formation can be obtained from thermal measurements. Then

$$\Delta F^0 = 2\Delta F_f^0(Cr^{+++}) + 7\Delta F_f^0(H_2O) - \Delta F_f^0(Cr_2O_7^{--}) - 8\Delta F_f^0(H^+)$$
$$= 2(-51.5) + 7(-56.69) - (-315.4) - 0$$
$$= -184.4 \text{ kcal}$$

In using this in Eq. 9 we must express the faraday in kcal/volt-equivalent if $\mathcal{E}^0$ is to be in volts; the value of the faraday in these units is 23.06. For this reaction $n = 6$ and hence

$$\mathcal{E}^0 = \frac{-\Delta F^0}{n\mathcal{F}} = \frac{+184.4}{6 \times 23.06} = \boxed{1.33 \text{ v}}$$

Although the rate of reaction is slow, the large positive e.m.f. indicates that when equilibrium is reached almost all the dichromate will be reduced.

15-11. Single Electrode Potentials. Up to this point we have considered only the e.m.f. of complete cells. It is convenient to divide the total e.m.f. into contributions from the two electrodes:

$$\mathcal{E}_{cell} = \mathcal{E}_{anode} + \mathcal{E}_{cathode} = \mathcal{E}_{ox} + \mathcal{E}_{red}$$

The anode potential is the potential of the solution with respect to the electrode. When the anode bears a negative charge as in Cells 1 to 3, the anode potential is positive; i.e., work is released in carrying positive charge from solution to the electrode. The cathode potential is the potential of the electrode with respect to the solution and is also positive; i.e., work is released in carrying a positive charge from the electrode to the solution.

The division of total e.m.f. into two electrode potentials is a matter of convenience only, for it is impossible to determine the potential of a single electrode. All that we can measure is the difference in potential of two electrodes.

It is unnecessary to tabulate both anode and cathode potentials. For any given electrode system the reaction when the electrode is used as a cathode is the reverse of that when it is used as an anode, and the two potentials differ only in sign; e.g., for a zinc electrode dipping into a solution of a zinc salt

anode: $Zn \rightarrow Zn^{++} + 2e^{-}$ $\mathcal{E}_{anode} = \mathcal{E}_{ox}$

cathode: $Zn^{++} + 2e^{-} \rightarrow Zn$ $\mathcal{E}_{cathode} = \mathcal{E}_{red} = -\mathcal{E}_{ox}$

Hence the total cell e.m.f. can be represented as the difference between two oxidation potentials or the difference between two reduction potentials. This will be illustrated for Cell 2.

Method A. Oxidation potentials. If both electrode reactions are written as oxidation processes

$$Zn \rightarrow Zn^{++} + 2e^{-} \qquad \mathcal{E}_{Zn \rightarrow Zn^{++}}$$
$$Cu \rightarrow Cu^{++} + 2e^{-} \qquad \mathcal{E}_{Cu \rightarrow Cu^{++}}$$

the over-all reaction is the difference of these partial equations and the e.m.f. of the cell is the difference of two oxidation potentials:

$$\mathcal{E}_{cell} = \mathcal{E}_{Zn \rightarrow Zn^{++}} - \mathcal{E}_{Cu \rightarrow Cu^{++}}$$

The oxidation potential of zinc is larger than that of copper, so the e.m.f. of the cell is positive.

Method B. Reduction potentials. Both electrode reactions are now written as reductions, the reverse of those above. The e.m.f. of the cell is given by

$$\mathcal{E}_{cell} = \mathcal{E}_{Cu^{++} \rightarrow Cu} - \mathcal{E}_{Zn^{++} \rightarrow Zn}$$

The reduction potential of copper is positive and larger than that of zinc, so the e.m.f. of the cell is still positive. Regardless of the system used for electrode potentials, they must combine to give the identical e.m.f. of the cell. The way the cell behaves is independent of man-made conventions.

Chemists can be divided into two groups: those who use oxidation potentials and those who use reduction potentials. Most American physical chemists are in the first class; almost everyone else is in the second. It will doubtless seem deplorable that the two groups cannot agree on a single convention, but the human race is made up of individualists and chemists are no exception. A committee of the International Union of Pure and Applied Chemistry has proposed a set of conventions in which reduction potentials are preferred. Until these are more widely accepted in the United States the student must be prepared to deal with both systems. Oxidation potentials are used in this text.

The Nernst equation can be applied to oxidation potentials. For a copper electrode dipping into a solution of a copper salt, the oxidation half-reaction is $Cu \rightarrow Cu^{++} + 2e^{-}$ and the Nernst equation takes the form

$$\mathcal{E}_{ox} = \mathcal{E}^{0}_{Cu \rightarrow Cu^{++}} - (0.0592/2) \log [Cu^{++}] \qquad 11$$

The activity of pure copper metal is unity, and the concentration of electrons is unknown but probably constant, so it is included in $\mathcal{E}^0$. For the reduction of copper(II) ions to copper the Nernst equation is

$$\mathcal{E}_{red} = \mathcal{E}^0_{Cu^{++} \to Cu} - (0.0592/2) \log \frac{1}{[Cu^{++}]}$$

$$= \mathcal{E}^0_{Cu^{++} \to Cu} + (0.0592/2) \log [Cu^{++}] \qquad \textbf{12}$$

Superficially Eqs. 11 and 12 differ only in the sign of the logarithmic term, but the sign of $\mathcal{E}^0$ will also differ: for oxidation it is -0.34 and for reduction, $+0.34$ v.

The Nernst equations for the oxidation potentials of some other electrode systems are given to illustrate the conventions:

$$Ag + Cl^- \to AgCl + e^- \qquad \mathcal{E}_{ox} = \mathcal{E}^0_{Ag \to AgCl} - 0.0592 \log \frac{1}{[Cl^-]}$$

$$Fe^{++} \to Fe^{+++} + e^- \qquad \mathcal{E}_{ox} = \mathcal{E}^0_{Fe^{++} \to Fe^{+++}} - 0.0592 \log \frac{[Fe^{+++}]}{[Fe^{++}]}$$

$$2Cl^- \to Cl_2 + 2e^- \qquad \mathcal{E}_{ox} = \mathcal{E}^0_{Cl^- \to Cl_2} - (0.0592/2) \log \frac{P_{Cl_2}}{[Cl^-]^2}$$

15-12. The Determination of Relative Oxidation Potentials.   In introducing oxidation potentials we noted that their absolute values cannot be determined. Consider the cell

$$Me \mid Me^{++} (0.01 \ M) \parallel Cu^{++} (0.01 \ M) \mid Cu$$

where Me stands for any metal and Me^{++} for its ion, although the latter need not be divalent. For this cell the e.m.f. is given by

$$\mathcal{E}_{cell} = \mathcal{E}_{Me \to Me^{++}} - \mathcal{E}_{Cu \to Cu^{++}}$$

If the metal is a better reducing agent than copper under these conditions, the cell reaction

$$Me + Cu^{++} \to Cu + Me^{++}$$

will go from left to right, and the e.m.f. will be positive. If the metal is less active than copper, the reaction will go from right to left, and the e.m.f. will be negative. Fig. 15-4 gives some values of the e.m.f. for various metals and hydrogen. The distances along the line represent differences in reducing power of the elements with copper as the standard. In this list zinc is the best reducing agent, and silver is the poorest. Note that the relative reducing power of the elements is not affected by the assignment of any particular e.m.f. as the standard. If that for copper is made 1.00 v arbitrarily, all other values are increased by the same amount. The relative reducing power as measured by the distance between the values is unaffected by the shift of the zero point.

Reducing agents other than metals can also be introduced into the series by using suitable anodes in the cell. For the iron(II) ion the cell would have the form

$$\text{Pt} \mid \text{Fe}^{++} (0.01 \ M), \text{Fe}^{+++} (0.01 \ M) \parallel \text{Cu}^{++} (0.01 \ M) \mid \text{Cu}$$

and the e.m.f. is about -0.44 v. This places iron(II) ion as a slightly better reducing agent than silver metal.

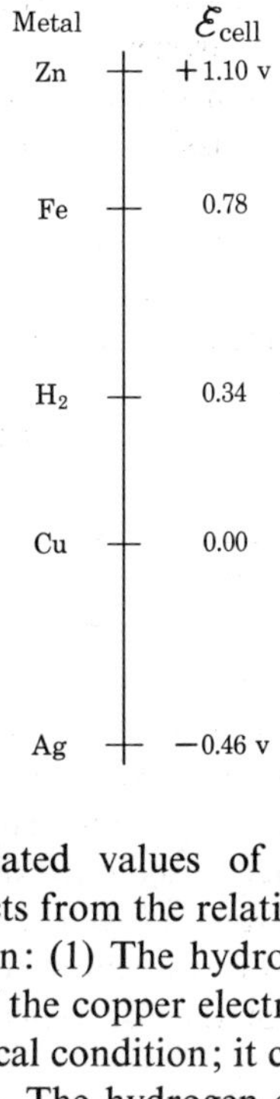

Metal	$\mathcal{E}^{\circ}_{cell}$
Zn	$+1.10$ v
Fe	0.78
H$_2$	0.34
Cu	0.00
Ag	-0.46 v

FIG. 15-4. Relative oxidation potentials of some metals. Standard metal: copper.

15-13. Standard Oxidation Potentials. Tabulated values of standard oxidation potentials differ in two important respects from the relative oxidation potentials introduced in the preceding section: (1) The hydrogen electrode is used as the standard electrode in place of the copper electrode. The potential of a metal electrode depends on its physical condition; it can sometimes be altered merely by bending the metal rod. The hydrogen electrode, although more troublesome to prepare and use, has a very reproducible potential. (2) All substances must be in their standard states rather than at 0.01 M concentration. Gases such as hydrogen are virtually in their standard states when their pressure is 1 atm. Solids and liquids are in their standard states when they are pure and in their most stable forms at the prevailing temperature and pressure. The standard state of solutes in solution is that in which they are at unit activity; for our purposes we shall take this to be very roughly at 1 M concentration, but in accurate work the activity includes a correction for interionic forces. The cell used in standard comparisons of oxidation potentials is thus

$$\text{Me} \mid \text{Me}^{++} (a = 1) \parallel \text{H}^{+} (a = 1) \mid \text{H}_2 (1 \text{ atm}) (\text{Pt})$$

in which the chemical reaction is $Me + 2H^+ \rightarrow Me^{++} + H_2$. Since all activities are unity, $Q = 1$ and the Nernst equation is

$$\mathcal{E}_{cell} = \mathcal{E}^0_{cell} = \mathcal{E}^0_{Me \rightarrow Me^{++}} - \mathcal{E}^0_{H_2 \rightarrow H^+} \qquad 13$$

By convention the standard hydrogen electrode in which both hydrogen gas and hydrogen ions are at unit activity is assigned the value

$$\mathcal{E}^0_{H_2 \rightarrow H^+} = 0.00000 \text{ v} \qquad 14$$

The e.m.f. of the cell is then the standard oxidation potential of Me relative to that of hydrogen.

Oxidation potentials and their applications were introduced in Sec. 9-8 and that discussion should now be considered if it was not earlier. It is worth emphasizing the limitations on the application of these values (Sec. 9-13): Accurate values of the potentials are often lacking for the particular temperature and solvent under study. The neglect of interionic forces, i.e., the use of concentrations in place of activities, is a serious limitation. Moreover, many redox reactions approach equilibrium slowly; standard oxidation potentials give no information about the rate of reaction.

15-14. Formal Oxidation Potentials. The actual reducing power of a substance such as iron(II) ion depends not only on the standard oxidation potential and the concentrations but also on interionic forces and complex formation. The oxidation of iron(II) ion to iron(III) ion is assisted by the fact that the product, iron(III) ion, because of its smaller size and higher charge is generally more strongly complexed and more sensitive to interionic forces than is the iron(II) ion. Thus the oxidation half-reaction $Fe^{++} \rightarrow Fe^{+++} + e^-$ goes further to the right than when both ions are at unit activity, or iron(II) ion is generally a better reducing agent than the standard oxidation potential would lead us to believe. Let us define a *formal oxidation potential* $\mathcal{E}^{0'}$ as the potential of the following half-cell with respect to the standard hydrogen electrode:

$$Pt \mid Fe^{++} (1 \ M), Fe^{+++} (1 \ M), X$$

where X stands for the other solute species in the solution. Some values of this formal oxidation potential when various acids are used for X are given in Table 15-1. The effect of complex formation is particularly notable with phosphoric, hydrofluoric, and acetic acids. In the presence of these, iron(II) ion is a much stronger reducing agent than the standard oxidation potential would lead us to expect.

15-15. A Summary. The e.m.f. of a cell that uses a reversible redox reaction as a source of electrical energy measures the tendency of the cell reaction to occur (Sec. 15-6, Eq. 3). The standard e.m.f. measures the tendency of the cell reaction to go when all substances are in their standard states

(Sec. 15-7). The standard e.m.f. can be calculated as the difference of two oxidation potentials from the table (Sec. 15-11). If the concentrations of the substances in a redox reaction differ from those of the standard state, the e.m.f. will differ from the standard value according to the Nernst equation (Sec. 15-8, Eq. 4). The equilibrium constant, the standard e.m.f., and the standard free energy change are related quantities that can be used to express the intrinsic reducing (or oxidizing) power of one substance relative to that of another (Secs. 15-9 and 15-11).

Some applications of e.m.f. measurements will be illustrated in the remaining sections of this chapter.

TABLE 15-1.

Formal Oxidation Potentials of the Iron(II)-Iron(III) Couple*

$[Fe^{++}] = [Fe^{+++}] = 1 \ M$; concentration of acids $= 1 \ N$; $\mathcal{E}^0 = -0.771$ v

Acid	$\mathcal{E}^{0\prime}$ in volts
$HClO_4$	-0.747
HNO_3	$- .729$
H_2SO_4	$- .679$
HCl	$- .700$
HBr	$- .728$
H_3PO_4	$- .438$
HF	$- .320$
$HC_2H_3O_2$	$- .408$
HCl + citric acid	$- .696$
HCl + tartaric acid	$- .698$
HCl + sulfosalicylic acid	$- .694$
HCl + Complexon B†	$- .535$
HCl + oxalic acid	$- .532$

*Data of R. Bock and M. Herrmann, *Z. anorg. u. allgem. Chem.*, **273**, 1 (1953).
†Complexon B is the complexing agent with the formidable chemical name: the sodium salt of (ethylenedinitrilo)tetraacetic acid.

15-16. Electrometric Determination of pH.   This is a particularly important application of e.m.f. measurements. As one example, consider Cell 1 in the form

$$(Pt) \ H_2 \ (1 \ atm) \ \mid \ \text{Solution} \ X \ \mid \ AgCl, \ Ag$$

where the pH of solution X is to be determined. It must contain chloride ion at a known concentration; let us suppose that the solution is 0.01 M in NaCl so $[Cl^-] = 0.01 \ M$. The Nernst equation has the form

$$\mathcal{E}_{cell} = \mathcal{E}^0_{H_2 \to H^+} - \mathcal{E}^0_{Ag \to AgCl} - 0.0592 \log \left([H^+][Cl^-]/P_{H_2}^{\frac{1}{2}} \right)$$

if activity coefficient corrections for interionic forces are neglected. Then since the standard oxidation potential of the hydrogen electrode is zero, and since the pressure of hydrogen gas is one atmosphere, the Nernst equation simplifies to

$$\mathcal{E}_{cell} = -\, \mathcal{E}^0_{Ag \to AgCl} - 0.0592 \log [H^+] - 0.0592 \log [Cl^-]$$

$$pH = -\log [H^+] = \frac{\mathcal{E}_{cell} + \mathcal{E}^0_{Ag \to AgCl}}{0.0592} + \log [Cl^-]$$

Suppose that the e.m.f. of this cell is measured and found to be 0.6000 v at 25°. The standard oxidation potential of the silver–silver chloride electrode is −0.2225 v. Hence

$$pH = (0.6000 - 0.2225)/0.0592 + \log 0.01 = \boxed{4.37}$$

In general, the electrometric determination of pH requires the measurement of the e.m.f. of a cell of the type

electrode sensitive to changes in [H⁺]	Solution X	reference electrode with a constant potential

In the preceding example the hydrogen electrode was the one sensitive to changes in the hydrogen ion concentration and the silver–silver chloride electrode was the constant reference electrode of known potential.

The commercial pH meter will be taken as a second example of a cell used to measure pH. The electrode sensitive to hydrogen ion is of rather curious design; it contains a thin membrane of glass that is permeable to protons. The potential difference across this membrane is proportional to the pH of the solution into which it dips. This glass membrane is more rugged than the hydrogen electrode and is unaffected by oxidizing and reducing agents in the solution. The reference electrode used with a pH meter is a calomel electrode (Sec. 15-4) that contains a salt bridge filled with saturated potassium chloride. Typical examples of these electrodes are shown in Fig. 15-5. The cell can be represented by the schematic diagram

Ag, AgCl | KCl, HCl ⦚ Solution X ‖ KCl (saturated) | Hg_2Cl_2, Hg
(glass electrode)   (calomel electrode)

where the wavy line indicates the glass membrane. The oxidation potential of the glass electrode is related to the pH by the expression

$$\mathcal{E}_{glass} = \mathcal{E}^0_{glass} + 0.0592 \, pH$$

The standard oxidation potential of the glass electrode is not constant but depends on the physical condition of the glass and varies from one electrode to another and even varies for a given electrode from day to day. The measurement of pH is therefore made by a comparison method. The e.m.f. of the cell ($\mathcal{E}_s$) is determined when it contains a buffer of known pH (pH_s). The solution X is substituted for the known buffer and the e.m.f. is redetermined

($\mathcal{E}_x$). The difference in the two readings is independent of the standard potential:

$$\mathcal{E}_x - \mathcal{E}_s = 0.0592\, p\mathrm{H}_x - 0.0592\, p\mathrm{H}_s$$

$$p\mathrm{H}_x = p\mathrm{H}_s + \frac{\mathcal{E}_x - \mathcal{E}_s}{0.0592}$$

The pH meter contains a potentiometer or vacuum tube voltmeter, and by proper standardization it can be made to read directly in pH units. If the measurements degenerate to pushing buttons and turning dials, the interpretation of the results is something else again. The precise meaning of pH

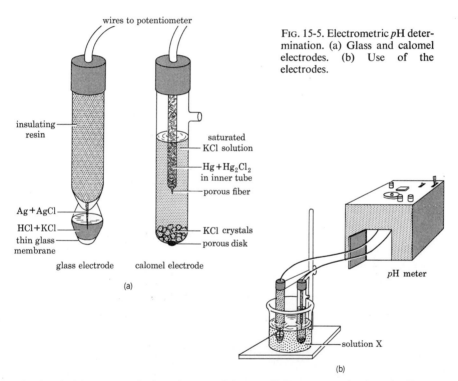

FIG. 15-5. Electrometric pH determination. (a) Glass and calomel electrodes. (b) Use of the electrodes.

is clouded by uncertainties about activity coefficient corrections and effects associated with the liquid junction between the salt bridge and solution X. When measurements are carefully done, the dial reading on a pH meter is a useful empirical indication of the acidity of the solution, but it cannot be simply interpreted as $-\log [\mathrm{H}^+]$ (Sec. 12-5, footnote 1).

15-17. Determination of Ionization Constants. This is an extension of the pH measurements. Suppose that we prepare a buffer solution of some weak acid HA at 0.02 M concentration and its sodium salt at 0.01 M concentration.

The buffer solution is put in Cell 1 and its pH is determined. For the purpose of illustration, let us suppose that the pH is found to be 4.37, or $[H^+] = 4.3 \times 10^{-5}$. Then

$$K_a = \frac{[H^+][A^-]}{[HA]} = 4.3 \times 10^{-5} \frac{0.01}{0.02} = 2.1 \times 10^{-5}$$

In accurate work the procedure is more elaborate because of the necessity of correcting for interionic forces.

15-18. Determination of Dissociation Constants of Complex Ions. The e.m.f. of the cell

Ag | KAg(CN)$_2$ (0.00625 M), KCN (0.025 M) || AgNO$_3$ (0.100 M) | Ag

is 1.100 v. The oxidation potential of the anode is for the reaction $Ag \rightarrow Ag^+ + e^-$ where the silver ions are in equilibrium with the complex

$$Ag(CN)_2^- \rightleftharpoons Ag^+ + 2CN^-$$

The Nernst equation for the anode is

$$\mathcal{E}_L = \mathcal{E}^0_{Ag \rightarrow Ag^+} - 0.0592 \log [Ag^+]_L$$

The oxidation potential for the right-hand electrode is

$$\mathcal{E}_R = \mathcal{E}^0_{Ag \rightarrow Ag^+} - 0.0592 \log [Ag^+]_R$$

The e.m.f. of the cell is the difference:

$$\mathcal{E}_{cell} = \mathcal{E}_L - \mathcal{E}_R = -0.0592 \log \frac{[Ag^+]_L}{[Ag^+]_R}$$

Because the two electrodes are identical, the standard oxidation potentials cancel and the e.m.f. of the cell depends only on the ratio of the silver ion concentrations. Now $[Ag^+]_R = 0.100\ M$ and the measured e.m.f. is 1.100 v. Hence we can find the concentration of silver ion in equilibrium with the complex:

$$1.100 = -0.0592 \log \frac{[Ag^+]_L}{0.1}$$

$$\log [Ag^+]_L = \frac{-1.100}{0.0592} + \log 0.1 = -19.58$$

$$[Ag^+]_L = 2.6 \times 10^{-20}$$

Then for dissociation of the complex

$$K_{inst} = \frac{[Ag^+][CN^-]^2}{[Ag(CN)_2^-]} = \frac{2.6 \times 10^{-20} (0.025)^2}{0.00625}$$

$$= \boxed{2.6 \times 10^{-21}}$$

Activity coefficient corrections should also be made here if an accurate result is required.

15-19. Determination of Activity Coefficients. Electromotive force measurements are important sources of activity coefficient values. The method will be illustrated by reference to Cell 1 in the form

$$(Pt) \; H_2 \; (1 \; atm) \; | \; HCl \; (1 \; m) \; | \; AgCl, \; Ag$$

The measured e.m.f. of this cell at 25° is 0.2335 v. The Nernst equation is written to include the activity coefficient factor:

$$\mathcal{E}_{cell} = \mathcal{E}^0_{H_2 \to H^+} - \mathcal{E}^0_{Ag \to AgCl} - 0.0592 \log \frac{[H^+][Cl^-]}{P_{H_2}^{\frac{1}{2}}} Y$$

where $Y = y_{H^+} y_{Cl^-}$. Then, since the pressure of hydrogen is 1 atm and the ions are at unit concentration, and since the oxidation potential of the hydrogen electrode is zero, we find

$$\log Y = \frac{\mathcal{E}_{cell} + \mathcal{E}^0_{Ag \to AgCl}}{0.0592} = \frac{-0.2335 + 0.2225}{0.0592} = -0.186$$

$$Y = \boxed{0.652}$$

It is customary to tabulate the square root of Y, called the (geometric) *mean activity coefficient*; for 1 molal hydrochloric acid this is 0.807.

SUPPLEMENTARY READING

H. B. STEINBACH, "Animal Electricity," *Sci. American*, **182**, 40 (1950).

J. NORDMANN, *Qualitative Testing and Inorganic Chemistry*, Wiley, New York, 1957, Chapter 11.

E. GILREATH, *Qualitative Analysis*, McGraw-Hill, New York, 1954. Chapter 9.

W. MELDRUM and A. DAGGETT, *A Textbook of Qualitative Analysis*, American Book Co., New York, 1946, Chapter 15.

H. FALES and F. KENNY, *Inorganic Qualitative Analysis*, 3rd ed., Appleton-Century-Crofts, New York, 1953, Chapter 7.

G. CHARLOT, *Qualitative Inorganic Analysis*, Wiley, New York, 1954, Chapters 3, 7, 8, and 13.

W. LATIMER, *The Oxidation States of the Elements and Their Potentials in Aqueous Solutions*, 2nd ed, Prentice-Hall, Englewood Cliffs, N.J., 1952. This book presents a wealth of data and many applications of oxidation potentials.

R. G. BATES, *Electrometric pH Determinations*, Wiley, New York, 1954, Chapters 7 to 9 (apparatus and techniques of *pH* determinations).

EXERCISES

15-1. Which of the following reactions are conceivable sources of electrical energy? Write the anode and cathode reactions for those that are.

(a) $Cr_2O_7^{--} + 14H^+ + 6Fe^{++} \rightarrow 6Fe^{+++} + 2Cr^{+++} + 7H_2O$
(b) $Cl_2 + 2Br^- \rightarrow Br_2 + 2Cl^-$
(c) $Ag^+ + Cl^- \rightarrow AgCl$
(d) $C + O_2 \rightarrow CO_2$
(e) $Ba^{++} + 2OH^- + 2H^+ + SO_4^{--} \rightarrow BaSO_4 + 2H_2O$
(f) $2Ag + Fe^{++} \rightarrow Fe + 2Ag^+$
(g) $Al + Bi^{+++} \rightarrow Al^{+++} + Bi$

15-2. Describe the cycle of operation of Cells 2 and 3.

15-3. Draw pictures of the experimental arrangements of each of the following cells:

(a) $H_2 \mid H_2SO_4 \parallel AgNO_3 \mid Ag$
(b) $Hg, Hg_2Cl_2 \mid KCl \parallel Ce_2(SO_4)_3, Ce(SO_4)_2 \mid Pt$

15-4. Show by schematic diagrams the arrangement of cells that use these reactions.

(a) $2Ag^+ + Cd \rightarrow 2Ag + Cd^{++}$
(b) $Ag + Cl^- + Fe^{+++} \rightarrow Fe^{++} + AgCl$

15-5. Write equations for the electrode reactions and over-all cell reactions.

(a) $Sn \mid Sn^{++} \parallel Ce^{++++}, Ce^{+++} \mid Pt$
(b) $Pb, PbSO_4 \mid H_2SO_4 \mid PbO_2, PbSO_4, Pb$
(c) $Pt \mid I_2, KI \parallel H_2SO_4, KIO_3, I_2 \mid Pt$

15-6. Why is a salt bridge or liquid junction not required for Cell 1?

15-7. Suppose that the chemical equation for Cell 1 is written

$$\tfrac{1}{2}H_2 + AgCl \rightarrow Ag + H^+ + Cl^-$$

Write the Nernst equation corresponding to this and compare it with that given in Example 1, Sec. 15-8. Which of the following are changed when the equation is written differently: $Q, n, \mathcal{E}^0, K, \mathcal{E}$?

15-8. Write the Nernst equations for the cells in Exercises 15-4 and 15-5.

15-9. Predict qualitatively the effect of an increase in the pressure of chlorine on the e.m.f. of Cell 3. What would be the effect of an increase in concentration of iron(III) sulfate?

15-10. The standard e.m.f. of the cell

$$Ag, AgCl \mid HCl \parallel Fe(ClO_4)_2, Fe(ClO_4)_3 \mid Pt$$

is 0.56 v at 25°. Calculate the equilibrium constant for the cell reaction and write the expression for this constant.

15-11. The standard e.m.f. of the cell

$$Ag \mid AgNO_3 \parallel Fe(ClO_4)_2, Fe(ClO_4)_3 \mid Pt$$

is -0.02 v at 25°. Calculate the equilibrium constant for the cell reaction and write the expression for this constant. Compare this result with that of Exercise 15-10 and account for the difference.

15-12. Calculate the equilibrium constant for the reaction in Cell 1 if the standard e.m.f. is 0.22 v at 25°.

15-13. Calculate the equilibrium constant for the reaction in Cell 3 if the standard e.m.f. is 0.58 v at 25°.

15-14. Show the division of the total e.m.f. of Cells 1 and 3 into (a) oxidation potentials and (b) reduction potentials.

15-15. Write the Nernst equation for the following electrode systems or half-cells.

(a) $Ag\,|\,Ag^+$; (b) $Ag^+\,|\,Ag$; (c) $Hg, Hg_2Cl_2\,|\,Cl^-$; (d) $Pt\,|\,Fe(CN)_6^{---}$; $Fe(CN)_6^{----}$.

15-16. We wish to set up a cell to measure approximately the relative oxidation potentials for the reactions $Zn \rightarrow Zn^{++} + 2e^-$ and $Ag \rightarrow Ag^+ + e^-$.

(a) Sketch a practical experimental arrangement for such a cell. From your knowledge of chemistry, decide which electrode would be negative.

(b) Write the chemical equation for the reaction giving rise to the electrical energy of this cell.

(c) Write the Nernst equation for the cell.

(d) Would the e.m.f. increase or decrease in magnitude if ammonia were added to the electrolyte in the silver but not in the zinc half of the cell?

15-17. The standard free energy of formation of Pu^{+++} ion relative to H^+ is estimated by Latimer to be -140.5 kcal/mole. Calculate the standard oxidation potential for $Pu \rightarrow Pu^{+++} + 3e^-$. Will plutonium metal dissolve in hydrochloric acid?

15-18. Calculate the relative oxidation potentials of copper electrodes in 0.1 M and 0.01 M copper(II) nitrate solutions. What is the change in potential for a ten-fold dilution? What would be the change for silver electrodes in silver nitrate solutions?

15-19. Give the meaning of the statement: "The standard oxidation potential of zinc is 0.76 v at 25°."

15-20. The potential of a silver electrode dipping into a solution saturated with silver chloride can be expressed by either $\mathcal{E} = \mathcal{E}^0_{Ag \rightarrow Ag^+} - 0.0592 \log [Ag^+]$ or $\mathcal{E} = \mathcal{E}^0_{Ag \rightarrow AgCl} - 0.0592 \log (1/[Cl^-])$.

(a) Prove that $\log K_{sp}(AgCl) = (\mathcal{E}^0_{Ag \rightarrow Ag^+} - \mathcal{E}^0_{Ag \rightarrow AgCl})/0.0592$.

(b) Calculate the solubility product if the first potential is -0.80 v and the second is -0.22 v.

15-21. From the tabular values of the standard oxidation potentials calculate the equilibrium constants of these reactions. (Some of these can also be calculated from the standard free energies of formation.)

(a) $Fe + 2Fe^{+++} \rightleftharpoons 3Fe^{++}$
(b) $SO_2 + 2H_2O + I_2 \rightleftharpoons 2I^- + HSO_4^- + 3H^+$
(c) $2Fe^{+++} + H_2S \rightleftharpoons 2Fe^{++} + S^0 + 2H^+$
(d) $2ClO_3^- + Mn^{++} \rightleftharpoons MnO_2 + 2ClO_2$

15-22. Calculate the e.m.f. of Cell 1 if it contains 0.01 m HCl. The measured value is 0.4641 v. The difference between observed and calculated values is caused by neglect of interionic forces. (Assume a hydrogen pressure of 1 atm and temperature of 25°.)

15-23. Use the data given in Exercise 15-22 to calculate the activity coefficient factor of 0.01 m hydrochloric acid.

15-24. Calculate the e.m.f. of the cell

$$\text{Ag} \mid \text{AgNO}_3 \ (0.01 \ M) \parallel \text{Cu(NO}_3)_2 \ (0.02 \ M) \mid \text{Cu}$$

15-25. Calculate the pH of the following solutions in Cell 1 if both are 0.01 M in NaCl and the temperature is 25° and hydrogen pressure is 1 atm. (a) Solution A, e.m.f. $= 0.400$ v, (b) Solution B, e.m.f. $= 0.800$ v.

15-26. The activity coefficient factor Y of zinc chloride can be obtained from measurements on the cell

$$\text{(Hg) Zn} \mid \text{ZnCl}_2(m) \mid \text{AgCl, Ag}$$

Prove that $\log Y = \dfrac{\mathcal{E}^0_{\text{cell}} - \mathcal{E}_{\text{cell}}}{0.0592/2} - \log 4m^3$

TABLE OF ATOMIC WEIGHTS (1957)

COMMON LOGARITHMS OF NUMBERS

PERIODIC CHART OF THE ELEMENTS

➡

TABLE OF ATOMIC WEIGHTS (1957)

	SYMBOL	ATOMIC NO.	ATOMIC WT.		SYMBOL	ATOMIC NO.	ATOMIC WT.
Actinium	Ac	89	..	Mercury	Hg	80	200.61
Aluminum	Al	13	26.98	Molybdenum	Mo	42	95.95
Americium	Am	95	..	Neodymium	Nd	60	144.27
Antimony	Sb	51	121.76	Neon	Ne	10	20.183
Argon	Ar	18	39.944	Neptunium	Np	93	..
Arsenic	As	33	74.91	Nickel	Ni	28	58.71
Astatine	At	85	..	Niobium	Nb	41	92.91
Barium	Ba	56	137.36	Nitrogen	N	7	14.008
Berkelium	Bk	97	..	Nobelium	No	102	..
Beryllium	Be	4	9.013	Osmium	Os	76	190.2
Bismuth	Bi	83	209.00	Oxygen	O	8	*16*
Boron	B	5	10.82	Palladium	Pd	46	106.4
Bromine	Br	35	79.916	Phosphorus	P	15	30.975
Cadmium	Cd	48	112.41	Platinum	Pt	78	195.09
Calcium	Ca	20	40.08	Plutonium	Pu	94	..
Californium	Cf	98	..	Polonium	Po	84	..
Carbon	C	6	12.011	Potassium	K	19	39.100
Cerium	Ce	58	140.13	Praseodymium	Pr	59	140.92
Cesium	Cs	55	132.91	Promethium	Pm	61	..
Chlorine	Cl	17	35.457	Protactinium	Pa	91	..
Chromium	Cr	24	52.01	Radium	Ra	88	..
Cobalt	Co	27	58.94	Radon	Rn	86	..
Copper	Cu	29	63.54	Rhenium	Re	75	186.22
Curium	Cm	96	..	Rhodium	Rh	45	102.91
Dysprosium	Dy	66	162.51	Rubidium	Rb	37	85.48
Einsteinium	Es	99	..	Ruthenium	Ru	44	101.1
Erbium	Er	68	167.27	Samarium	Sm	62	150.35
Europium	Eu	63	152.0	Scandium	Sc	21	44.96
Fermium	Fm	100	..	Selenium	Se	34	78.96
Fluorine	F	9	19.00	Silicon	Si	14	28.09
Francium	Fr	87	..	Silver	Ag	47	107.880
Gadolinium	Gd	64	157.26	Sodium	Na	11	22.991
Gallium	Ga	31	69.72	Strontium	Sr	38	87.63
Germanium	Ge	32	72.60	Sulfur	S	16	32.066
Gold	Au	79	197.0	Tantalum	Ta	73	180.95
Hafnium	Hf	72	178.50	Technetium	Tc	43	..
Helium	He	2	4.003	Tellurium	Te	52	127.61
Holmium	Ho	67	164.94	Terbium	Tb	65	158.93
Hydrogen	H	1	1.0080	Thallium	Tl	81	204.39
Indium	In	49	114.82	Thorium	Th	90	232.05
Iodine	I	53	126.91	Thulium	Tm	69	168.94
Iridium	Ir	77	192.2	Tin	Sn	50	118.70
Iron	Fe	26	55.85	Titanium	Ti	22	47.90
Krypton	Kr	36	83.80	Tungsten	W	74	183.86
Lanthanum	La	57	138.92	Uranium	U	92	238.07
Lead	Pb	82	207.21	Vanadium	V	23	50.95
Lithium	Li	3	6.940	Xenon	Xe	54	131.30
Lutetium	Lu	71	174.99	Ytterbium	Yb	70	173.04
Magnesium	Mg	12	24.32	Yttrium	Y	39	88.92
Manganese	Mn	25	54.94	Zinc	Zn	30	65.38
Mendelevium	Md	101	..	Zirconium	Zr	40	91.22

COMMON LOGARITHMS OF NUMBERS

NOS.	0	1	2	3	4	5	6	7	8	9	PROPORTIONAL PARTS 1	2	3	4	5	6	7	8	9
1	000	041	079	114	146	176	204	230	255	279	–	–	–	–	–	–	–	–	–
2	301	322	342	362	380	398	415	431	447	462	–	–	–	–	–	–	–	–	–
3	477	491	505	519	531	544	556	568	580	591	1	3	4	5	6	8	9	10	11
4	602	613	623	633	643	653	663	672	681	690	1	2	3	4	5	6	7	8	9
5	699	708	716	724	732	740	748	756	763	771	1	2	2	3	4	5	6	6	7
6	778	785	792	799	806	813	820	826	833	839	1	1	2	3	3	4	5	5	6
7	845	851	857	863	869	875	881	886	892	898	1	1	2	2	3	4	4	5	5
8	903	908	914	919	924	929	934	940	944	949	1	1	2	2	3	3	4	4	5
9	954	959	964	968	973	978	982	987	991	996	0	1	1	2	2	3	3	4	4

The common (Briggsian) logarithm p of any number x is the power to which 10 must be raised to give x:

$$10^p = x \qquad \log_{10}x = p$$

The logarithm can be divided into a decimal part, the *mantissa*, and a whole number, the *characteristic*. The table above contains mantissas with decimal points omitted. The characteristic when x is greater than 1 is positive and is one less than the number of digits to the left of the decimal point in x, e.g.,

$x = 2.0 = 2.0 \times 10^0 \qquad \log x = 0.301$

$x = 20.0 = 2.0 \times 10^1 \qquad \log x = 1.301$

$x = 200.0 = 2.0 \times 10^2 \qquad \log x = 2.301$

The examples demonstrate that if a number is expressed as a multiple of a power of ten with only one digit to the left of the decimal point, the characteristic is that power. When x is less than 1 the characteristic is negative and one larger than the number of zeros used to fix the decimal point, e.g.,

$x = 0.20 = 2.0 \times 10^{-1}$
$\log x = 0.301 - 1$

$x = 0.020 = 2.0 \times 10^{-2}$
$\log x = 0.301 - 2$

$x = 0.0020 = 2.0 \times 10^{-3}$
$\log x = 0.301 - 3$

Any of these could be written as a single, negative number, e.g., $0.301 - 3 = -2.699$, but the other notation is convenient because the mantissas given in the table are always positive.

The mantissa of the logarithm of a 3-digit number can be read directly from the table by adding the proportional part for the third digit to the appropriate value for the first two digits, e.g.,

$$\log 5.47 = 0.732 + 0.006 = 0.738$$

There may be an error of 1 or 2 in the third decimal place. In the first two rows the proportional part must be found by interpolation between two adjacent values, e.g.,

$$\log 1.32 = 0.114 + 0.2\,(0.146 - 0.114) = 0.120$$

Convenient Formulas

$$\log ab = \log a + \log b$$
$$\log (a/b) = \log a - \log b$$
$$\log (1/a) = - \log a$$
$$\log a^n = n \log a$$
$$10^x 10^y = 10^{x+y}$$
$$10^x \div 10^y = 10^{x-y}$$
$$(10^x)^n = 10^{nx}$$
$$\sqrt[n]{10^x} = 10^{x/n}$$

IA	IIA	IIIA	IVA	VA	VIA	VIIA			VIII
1 **H** 1.0080									
3 **Li** 6.940	4 **Be** 9.013								
11 **Na** 22.991	12 **Mg** 24.32								
19 **K** 39.100	20 **Ca** 40.08	21 **Sc** 44.96	22 **Ti** 47.90	23 **V** 50.95	24 **Cr** 52.01	25 **Mn** 54.94	26 **Fe** 55.85	27 **Co** 58.94	
37 **Rb** 85.48	38 **Sr** 87.63	39 **Y** 88.92	40 **Zr** 91.22	41 **Nb** 92.91	42 **Mo** 95.95	43 **Tc** (99)	44 **Ru** 101.1	45 **Rh** 102.91	
55 **Cs** 132.91	56 **Ba** 137.36	57 *** La** 138.92	72 **Hf** 178.50	73 **Ta** 180.95	74 **W** 183.86	75 **Re** 186.22	76 **Os** 190.2	77 **Ir** 192.2	
87 **Fr** (223)	88 **Ra** (226)	89 †**Ac** (227)							

*LANTHANUM SERIES

58 **Ce** 140.13	59 **Pr** 140.92	60 **Nd** 144.27	61 **Pm** (147)	62 **Sm** 150.35	63 **Eu** 152.0

†ACTINIUM SERIES

90 **Th** (232)	91 **Pa** (231)	92 **U** 238.07	93 **Np** (237)	94 **Pu** (242)	95 **Am** (243)

( ) Numbers in parentheses indicate mass number of most stable or best known isotope.

Atomic weights corrected to conform with 1957 international committee values.

THE ELEMENTS

IB	IIB	IIIB	IVB	VB	VIB	VIIB	INERT GASES

						1 **H** 1.0080	**2** **He** 4.003	2
		5 **B** 10.82	**6** **C** 12.011	**7** **N** 14.008	**8** **O** 16.000	**9** **F** 19.00	**10** **Ne** 20.183	2 8
		13 **Al** 26.98	**14** **Si** 28.09	**15** **P** 30.975	**16** **S** 32.066	**17** **Cl** 35.457	**18** **Ar** 39.944	2 8 8
28 **Ni** 58.71	**29** **Cu** 63.54	**30** **Zn** 65.38	**31** **Ga** 69.72	**32** **Ge** 72.60	**33** **As** 74.91	**34** **Se** 78.96	**35** **Br** 79.916	**36** **Kr** 83.80	2 8 18 8
46 **Pd** 106.4	**47** **Ag** 107.880	**48** **Cd** 112.41	**49** **In** 114.82	**50** **Sn** 118.70	**51** **Sb** 121.76	**52** **Te** 127.61	**53** **I** 126.91	**54** **Xe** 131.30	2 18 18 8
78 **Pt** 195.09	**79** **Au** 197.0	**80** **Hg** 200.61	**81** **Tl** 204.39	**82** **Pb** 207.21	**83** **Bi** 209.00	**84** **Po** (210)	**85** **At** (210)	**86** **Rn** (222)	2 8 18 32 18 8

64 **Gd** 157.26	**65** **Tb** 158.93	**66** **Dy** 162.51	**67** **Ho** 164.94	**68** **Er** 167.27	**69** **Tm** 168.94	**70** **Yb** 173.04	**71** **Lu** 174.99	2 8 18 32 9 2

96 **Cm** (247)	**97** **Bk** (249)	**98** **Cf** (251)	**99** **Es** (254)	**100** **Fm** (253)	**101** **Md** (256)	**102** **No** (253)		2 8 18 32 ? 9 2

Adapted from chart copyright by Fisher Scientific Company.

PERIODIC CHART OF THE ELEMENTS

COMMON LOGARITHMS OF NUMBERS

TABLE OF ATOMIC WEIGHTS (1957)

←

CHAPTER SIXTEEN

The Laboratory Work in Qualitative Analysis

16-1. An Introduction to Qualitative Analysis. What is qualitative analysis? Suppose that you are given something to examine. It may be a rock, a white powder, some metal turnings, or a pink solution. After performing a qualitative analysis, you can state what elements are in it. The white powder, for example, might contain sodium, calcium, aluminum, carbon as carbonate, sulfur as sulfate, and phosphorus as phosphate. Your analysis will give you only a rough idea of how much of each is present; it is the task of quantitative analysis to determine accurately the percentage of each. Nor does the qualitative analysis tell how the pieces fit together, e.g., whether the calcium goes with the carbonate, sulfate, or phosphate. Sometimes an intelligent guess can be made when the origin of the sample is known. If the sample is a baking powder, it is reasonable to expect it to contain sodium aluminum sulfate, calcium sulfate, calcium acid phosphate, and sodium bicarbonate. Microscopic and x-ray methods can also be used to identify the salts. Our concern in this course is only to learn to identify the elements.

How are substances identified? Some property of the substance is used that sets it apart from other substances, e.g., the deep blue color that cupric ion gives when it reacts with ammonia, the pleasant odor produced by converting acetate ion to ethyl acetate, or the low solubility and crystalline character of the white precipitate that forms when a soluble sulfate is added to a solution containing barium ion. Few of the reagents used in these tests are *specific* in the sense that they give unequivocal tests for the elements in the presence of all other elements. Most are *general* reagents that react with a large number of other elements. Ammonia, for example, not only converts Cu^{++} to blue $Cu(NH_3)_4^{++}$ but also forms a blue complex with Ni^{++} and precipitates many insoluble hydroxides. A soluble sulfate will precipitate not only $BaSO_4$, but also $PbSO_4$, $SrSO_4$, and often $CaSO_4$. All of these are white, crystalline solids which are hard to tell apart by superficial examination. Before identifying an ion, it is almost always necessary to separate it from other interfering ions.

How are interfering ions removed? There are many ways of doing this. Some ions such as carbonate can be converted to volatile compounds and

339

are driven off as gases. Some can be converted to a form that is more soluble in an organic solvent than in water and are removed by extraction. If iodide, for example, is oxidized to free iodine, most of it can be removed from an aqueous solution by shaking the solution with some carbon tetrachloride which dissolves the iodine. Some ions can be *sequestered* or their interference *masked* without removing them from the solution. Thus ferric ion, which interferes with the test for cobalt, is sequestered by converting it to the stable, colorless FeF_6^{---} complex ion.

Precipitation is the most common method of separation used in this course. An elaborate scheme has been worked out for the analysis of metals whereby the metal ions (cations) are first separated into small groups. Then the ions of each group are separated further. More and more specific properties of the ions are used until some final precipitation or color reaction is obtained for each ion that is present. In this course only a limited number of cations is studied. The first group to be precipitated consists of Ag^+, Hg_2^{++}, and Pb^{++}, the common ions that form insoluble chlorides. The *group reagent* that is used to precipitate them is hydrochloric acid. The chlorides are removed and another group is precipitated. The sequence of separations that is used to divide the 23 metals into five groups can be summarized most conveniently in a block outline (p. 341).

The analysis of anions also requires separations, but an elaborate scheme is not used in this text.

No system of analysis is a sure solution to all analytical problems. The traditional set of metals selected for introductory work does not include many elements, some of which, such as titanium, are very common ones. Drastic modification of the scheme of analysis may be required to accommodate it for other elements. Nor is it satisfactory for the detection of traces; special techniques are required for this. The elaborate procedure outlined above is not always necessary or efficient; short cuts and modifications may be appropriate for special samples. The scheme of analysis, in short, is not a substitute for thought. Any analytical procedure must be used intelligently and resourcefully.

What is semimicro analysis? The sample for analysis may weigh several hundred grams or less than a pencil mark. In this course five to ten drops (0.25 to 0.5 ml) of solutions and 15-25 mg of solids will be used. This scale of analysis between macro and micro is called semimicro. It does not deal with low concentrations but with low amounts. The concentrations of the ions will generally be greater than 0.01 M. The analysis of traces, substances at concentrations below 0.0001 M, requires exacting techniques. The small scale of semimicro analysis has several advantages. It is a greater challenge and more demanding in its techniques than macro analysis. It is more rapid to carry out and requires fewer chemicals and less apparatus.

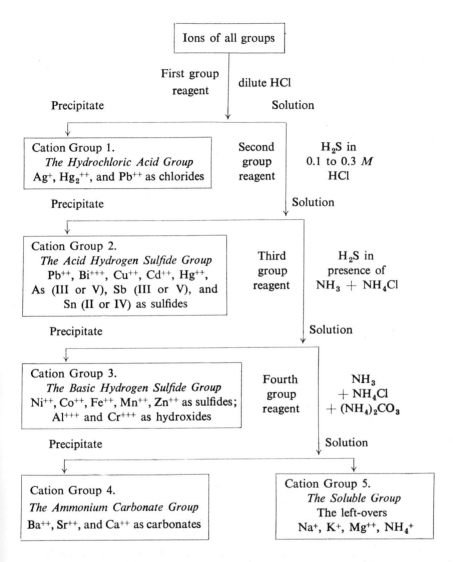

What kind of apparatus is used? Much of the equipment consists of small scale versions of familiar macro apparatus: test tubes, stirring rods, casseroles, crucibles, flasks, spatulas, burners. A few items such as capillary pipets are specifically designed for semimicro work. Most of the reagents that you require are contained in a small kit. Less commonly used reagents are set out on the side shelf.

Why is the laboratory work valuable? There is nowhere a more elegant demonstration of the triumphs as well as the inadequacies of the theories of electrolytic solutions than that provided by qualitative analysis. The laboratory work thus provides first-hand experience with the practical implications of the theories. The relation between theory and fact and the distinction between observations and conclusions are then very important and are appreciated when an accurate and immediate record of each experiment is kept. More laboratory experience will be derived from this course, so that it is excellent preparation for any kind of scientific work. Some of the analytical techniques, e.g., those dealing with precipitation, are of general application. On the other hand, it is not the purpose of this course to turn out a Complete Analyst capable of dealing with all conceivable kinds of material. Wider knowledge and more practical experience are required for that. During this course you will begin to acquire experience with inorganic substances and their behavior. You will learn which ions form insoluble sulfides and the appearance of these. You will learn to distinguish at a glance between a chromate, a dichromate, and a chromic salt; and you will learn how to convert any one of these into the others. Such facts may not seem important in themselves, but in the aggregate they constitute a valuable reservoir of knowledge. There is no substitute for such first-hand experience with inorganic substances. Such experience is required for interpretation of results, whether they are given by a semimicro analysis or by the elaborate instruments to which analytical chemists are becoming addicted. In part, such experience makes the difference between those who, according to G. E. F. Lundell, are "analysts" and those who are "determinators." The latter follow directions, push buttons, read dials—and are helpless when confronted with an unfamiliar situation.

How is the laboratory work organized?   Your instructor will inform you of the exact details of what you are to do and the scheduling of time. The first task is to check in your desk and do the preliminary work described in the next section. Then usually the analysis of the cations is taken up a group at a time. For each group you may do a certain number of preliminary experiments that acquaint you with the inorganic chemistry of the ions or with difficult analytical techniques. Then you analyze a solution of known composition for practice. An "unknown" covering the ions of one or two groups is done next. After the cation groups have been studied, general unknowns covering all the groups may be analyzed. The analysis for anions can be taken up first, interwoven with that of the cations, or done at the end.

16-2. Preliminary Work.   The following work should require one or, at most, two periods. Items marked with an asterisk may be unnecessary in some laboratories.

a. Check in.   After you have been assigned a desk, check the equipment in it against the apparatus list, and replace missing items. Inspect all glass and porcelain ware for chips, cracks, or bad scratches. If the apparatus and desk are dirty, some housecleaning is in order.

b. Prepare reagent kit.

*(1) Label the bottles with the formulas of the reagents (a list is given in the Appendix). Glass stoppered bottles are usually used for the concentrated acids, polyethylene bottles for the strong bases, and amber bottles for reagents such as $AgNO_3$, $KMnO_4$, and H_2O_2 that are affected by light. Attach the labels neatly at a uniform level. Make sure that they are high enough to be seen when the bottles are in the rack.

(2) Arrange the bottles in some systematic order, e.g., alphabetically, and keep them that way. A satisfactory arrangement for the larger bottles is shown below:

BACK

NH_3 6M	KOH 0.5M	H_2SO_4 18M	$HC_2H_3O_2$ 6M	HNO_3 6M	HNO_3 16M
NH_3 15M	NaOH 6M	Thioacet- amide	HCl 2M	HCl 6M	HCl 12M

FRONT

The most commonly used reagents are in front. The ammonia solutions are separated as far as possible from nitric and hydrochloric acids, because the ammonia and acid fumes combine to give unsightly white deposits of ammonium salts on the bottles.

*(3) Fill the bottles between one-half and two-thirds full of reagents.

*c. Make six glass rods. Cut rod with a diameter of 2 mm into suitable lengths as shown in Fig. 16-1. Fire polish each end most carefully because sharp edges will scratch test tubes and make them susceptible to breakage at inopportune times. Handles may be made on some of the rods as illustrated.

*d. Make four or more capillary pipets. These are used for withdrawing and transferring solutions from test tubes and centrifuge tubes. The small end takes up less room in a narrow tube than an ordinary medicine dropper would.

(1) Cut convenient lengths—about 15 cm (6 in.)—of 7 or 8 mm soft glass tubing. Too long a piece is hard to handle; too short a piece will place your fingers too close to the flame for comfort.

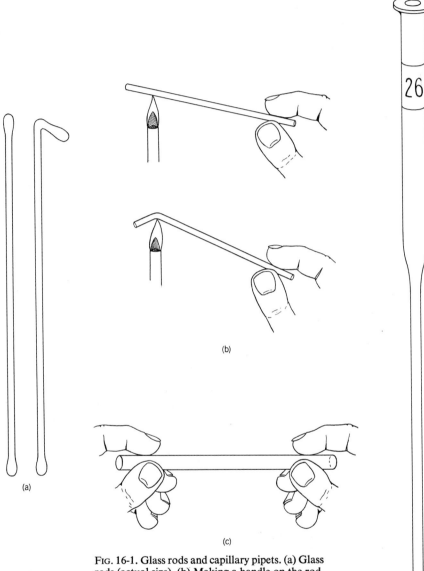

FIG. 16-1. Glass rods and capillary pipets. (a) Glass rods (actual size). (b) Making a handle on the rod. (c) Position of fingers around glass tube. Rotating motion is imparted by each thumb and forefinger. (d) Capillary pipet (actual size).

(2) Light the large bunsen burner and adjust gas and air intakes to give a medium-sized flame with a well-defined inner cone. Do *not* use a wing top.

(3) Hold the tubing near the ends between thumb and forefinger of each hand (Fig. 16-1c). Rotate it slowly using both hands, so that the middle of the tube is heated uniformly by the hottest part of the flame (above the inner cone). One complete rotation every 2 seconds is fast enough. Continue heating until the tube is red-hot and keep it at that temperature for a minute or so.

(4) Remove the tube from the flame and pull *slowly* at first, then more and more rapidly as the glass cools. If the tube was held in the flame long enough to get well heated, it should not be necessary to pull quickly at first. The slow drawing gives a thicker, stronger capillary.

(5) Put a slight constriction in the center of the capillary by lowering it into the hot region *above* the flame and pulling it out. Break the two pipets apart at this constriction.

(6) Let the glass cool. Remember that it does not have to be red-hot to burn.

(7) Cut the broad ends to convenient lengths. Heat until the glass softens and then press down squarely on a heat-resistant surface (asbestos pad or bottom of the spot plate). This gives a flange to make a snug fit with the rubber bulb. Attach the bulb after the flange has cooled.

(8) Calibrate the pipet by counting the number of drops it delivers into a 10 ml graduated cylinder. Deliver at least 2 ml of water. Label the shank of the pipet with the number of drops per milliliter; it should deliver between 20 and 40.

16-3. The Techniques of Semimicro Qualitative Analysis. While some of these techniques are peculiar to work using small-scale equipment, most are of general application and, with some adaptations, are used in other chemistry courses. Read through the description of these techniques before starting the laboratory work. Then reread them as reference is made to them in the directions for analysis.

Sampling. Technique 1. It is essential that the sample taken for analysis from a large quantity of material be a representative one; i.e., it must contain all of the constituents in the material. For a solution it is necessary only that the solution be mixed well before the sample is removed. If it contains suspended matter, shake thoroughly and withdraw the sample quickly before the solids have time to settle. Solid materials may be far from homogeneous. Even after they have been carefully mixed, separation of the constituents may occur after the mixture is bottled if they differ considerably in density. Examine the material under a hand lens for evidence of inhomogeneity and mix thoroughly before taking a sample.

Dissolving the Sample. Technique 2. This subject is treated in more detail in Chapter 24. Here only the simpler situations that occur with the earlier unknowns are considered. The most desirable solvent is water. Test the solubility of a small amount (less than 20 mg) in water. If solution does not take place rapidly at room temperature after adequate stirring, try warming for several minutes in the water bath. Add more water if the first few drops appear to dissolve some but not all of the sample. If there is a residue insoluble in water, test its solubility in 6 M nitric or hydrochloric acid. Allow plenty of time for solution to take place. Some salts hydrolyze extensively in water to give precipitates. It is often easier to dissolve them directly in acid than it is to try to dissolve the precipitate that forms by hydrolysis. Concentrated acids and aqua regia (3:1 HCl-HNO_3) can sometimes be used to advantage but should be avoided if possible, for the excess acid would have to be neutralized or removed by evaporation. Some salts are also remarkably insoluble in concentrated acids.

Measurement of Quantity. Technique 3.

(a) The quantity of *solutions* is measured in drops or milliliters. One standard drop is 0.05 ml; thus there are 20 such drops per milliliter. It is sufficient to assume for most work that the droppers of the reagent kit deliver drops of this size. The volume of a drop will vary not only with the size of the dropper but with the reagent; we shall usually ignore such variations. When a more accurate measurement of volume is required, use calibrated capillary pipets.

(b) The quantity of *solids* is best measured with a balance. A triple beam balance sensitive to 10 mg (0.01 g or 0.1 cg) is satisfactory for most work. Weigh by difference: find the weight of an empty test tube or micro beaker, and weigh the sample into it. When measurement of an exact quantity is not important, a spatula may be used. A heaping spatula-full of the size pictured in Fig. 16-2 contains about 0.1 to 0.15 g of inorganic salts.

Addition of Reagents. Technique 4.

(a) It is imperative that reagents be preserved against contamination. Droppers of reagent bottles should always be held above tubes and other vessels and not be allowed to touch them (Fig. 16-2).

(b) Sometimes, particularly in neutralization, it is desirable to add less than one drop of reagent. Give the dropper bulb the slightest squeeze, and remove the fraction of a drop that emerges first to a clean stirring rod and then to the solution.

Mixing. Technique 5. Because of the narrow bore of test tubes and centrifuge tubes this is one of the most critical and difficult operations of semimicro analysis. Yet the first rule of analysis must be to mix thoroughly before drawing any conclusions. If mixing is done by shaking the tube while

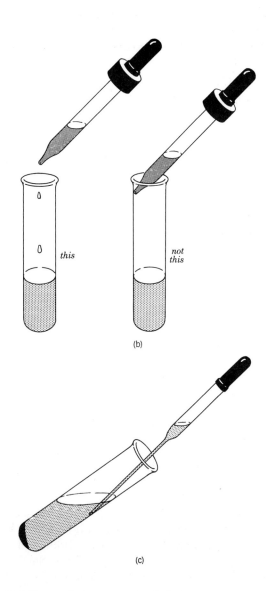

FIG. 16-2. Techniques of measurement and pipetting. (a) Semimicro spatula (actual size). (b) Addition of reagents. Correct and incorrect techniques. (c) Separation of solution from precipitate with a capillary pipet.

this

not
this

(b)

(c)

(a)

it is closed with a finger or cork, contamination of the solution will very likely occur. The following techniques are better.

(a) If the solution fills no more than half of the test tube, it can be well mixed by grasping the top firmly between thumb and forefinger of one hand and flicking the bottom of the tube with the forefinger of the other hand. This will not work as well with centrifuge tubes because of their tapered bottoms.

(b) If the test tube is more than half full, it is best to mix by pouring the contents from one tube to another or from tube to casserole or micro beaker.

(c) Mixing can also be done efficiently by sucking up a portion of the solution with a capillary pipet (not all the way up to the bulb) and expelling at the bottom of the tube. Repeat at least twice.

(d) Stirring may be done with a glass rod, using a combination of up and down and circulatory motions. This is the least efficient of the four techniques. Glass rods are more useful for such purposes as testing with litmus or loosening a cake of precipitate than for stirring.

Heating Solutions. Technique 6.   Solutions in casseroles can be heated directly over a free flame. This is unsatisfactory for solutions in test tubes and centrifuge tubes because of the tendency of steam bubbles to form at the bottom of the tube and expel solution as they rise and expand. Always heat solutions in tubes by setting them in a hot water bath. A simple bath can be made from a 250 ml beaker and a metal cover containing three or more holes (Fig. 16-3a). If a rubber band is wrapped around the top of the tube, it will be easier to lift out.

Evaporation of Solutions. Technique 7.   Casseroles are the most convenient vessels for evaporating several milliliters of solution. An inch or two of heavy rubber tubing slipped halfway up the handle will make the casserole easier to hold when it is hot. Micro crucibles can be used for the evaporation of a few drops. Construct a simple holder (Fig. 16-3b) by burning off half the fuzz from a pipecleaner and twisting the bare wire into a loop. The crucible should fit two thirds of the way down into the loop. Small beakers (5 or 10 ml) can also be used for evaporations but should not be heated over a direct flame.

Evaporations must be carried out so that material will not be lost by spattering. Usually it is undesirable to overheat a residue left after complete evaporation, for the residue is often volatile or it changes to a less soluble form on baking. The following techniques will help you avoid these difficulties.

(a) Use a microburner and adjust it to give a flame not more than $\frac{1}{2}$ inch high. If necessary, use a screw clamp on the burner tubing to make this adjustment. This will be referred to in the analytical procedures as a *microflame.*

(b) During evaporations in casseroles, keep the contents agitated by a swirling motion. As dryness approaches, the center of the bottom will go dry first. Keep it moist as long as possible by swirling and tilting motions. Before complete dryness is reached, withdraw the casserole from the flame, and let the heat of the dish complete the evaporation. This will avoid overheating.

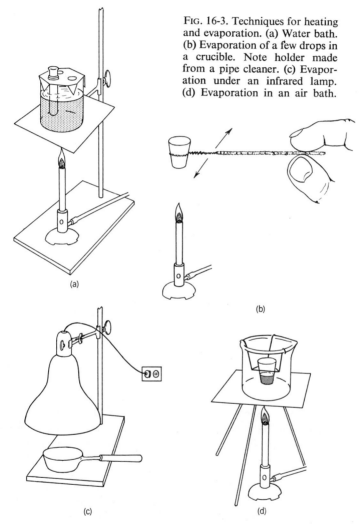

FIG. 16-3. Techniques for heating and evaporation. (a) Water bath. (b) Evaporation of a few drops in a crucible. Note holder made from a pipe cleaner. (c) Evaporation under an infrared lamp. (d) Evaporation in an air bath.

(c) Very smooth evaporations can be obtained with a minimum of attention by using the heat of an infrared lamp pointed down at the solution from above (Fig. 16-3c).

(d) Slow, uniform evaporation can also be obtained by setting the beaker or crucible in an air bath. This is constructed from a dry beaker and a Nichrome triangle (Fig. 16-3*d*).

(e) Evaporations can be carried out on a wire gauze if a small flame is used and if the dish is set off-center from the flame. The gauze will conduct enough heat to cause slow evaporation.

Centrifugation. Technique 8.   This is much quicker than filtration for the separation of small quantities. A centrifuge subjects an object to a force far in excess of that of gravity. If *d* is the distance from the axis of rotation to the precipitate, the force acting on the precipitate is proportional to *d* multiplied by the square of the speed of rotation. When *d* is 11 cm and the speed of rotation is 1650 rpm, the force is about 330 times that of gravity. The precipitate will settle 330 times faster in the centrifuge than it would if allowed to settle in a test tube placed in a rack. The following points should be observed in using centrifuges.

(a) The revolving head must be carefully balanced. Always balance the tube containing the sample with another one containing an equal volume of water; place them opposite each other in the head. Balance centrifuge tube against centrifuge tube and test tube against test tube. Even though they contain equal volumes of water, centrifuge tube and test tube will not balance because the latter contains more glass. An unbalanced centrifuge will wobble or "walk" on the desk. This may damage the centrifuge and endanger bystanders.

(b) Centrifuge only a few seconds at top speed. At a force 330 times that of gravity a precipitate that normally settles in 10 minutes will settle in less than 2 seconds. You share the use of the centrifuge with others; do not monopolize it.

(c) Test tubes are satisfactory for most centrifugations and are preferable to centrifuge tubes in general use, because solutions are more easily mixed in tubes with a wide bottom. If the precipitate is small or does not pack down tightly in a test tube, a cleaner separation is obtained in a centrifuge tube. Some centrifuges can be braked with the hand or a mechanical device after the motor is turned off. If this is done too abruptly, the precipitate may be redispersed in a test tube.

Separation of Supernatant Solution from Precipitate. Technique 9.   The clear solution obtained by centrifugation can be separated most simply from the precipitate by decantation or pouring off the solution. A more complete separation even when the precipitate does not pack down tightly is obtained by drawing off the solution with a capillary pipet. *Before* inserting the pipet in the solution, squeeze the bulb to expel air. You will find it easiest at first to draw off the solution in several portions rather than all at once. Move the tip of the pipet farther down the tube each time. If the centrifuge has an angled head, the precipitate will be banked against one side of the tube. When the tube is held as shown in Fig. 16-2c, it is easy to separate the precipitate from the last of the solution. Some precipitates cling to the walls of the tube and will not settle further. This does no harm as long as the precipitate remains on the walls during the pipetting. Other precipitates are light and float even after centrifugation. If there is any danger that they may get drawn into the pipet, wrap a wisp of cotton about the tip so that the solution is filtered through it. Very little cotton is required; take about a tenth as much as you believe is necessary.

Washing of Precipitates. Technique 10.   Even after the removal of the supernatant liquid, all precipitates will be wet with a small amount of the solution. The precipitate may also adsorb ions from solution to its surface. To remove these and increase the purity of the precipitate, it is washed. The wash liquid is usually water, but sometimes it is advantageous to wash with a very dilute solution of the reagent used for precipitation. The chlorides of Cation Group 1, for example, are washed with very dilute hydrochloric acid because their solubility is lower in the presence of excess chloride ion.

Washing is carried out by adding the wash liquid to the precipitate. A stirring rod is used to break up the caked precipitate and disperse it in the liquid. After the centrifugation the wash liquid may be added to the first solution if it contains an appreciable amount of ions or it may be discarded.

As a general rule it is more efficient to wash with two small portions of wash fluid than with one portion of the same total volume. Let V be the volume of each small wash and $2V$ be the volume of the single washing. Suppose that v is volume of solution left with the precipitate after removal of the supernatant solution. If C_0 represents the concentration of solute in the original solution, a single wash with volume V leaves liquid of concentration C_1 around the precipitate where $C_1 = C_0 v/(v + V)$. Two successive washes leave a solution of concentration C_2 where

$$C_2 = \frac{v}{v + V} C_1 = \left(\frac{v}{v + V}\right)^2 C_0$$

A single wash with a volume $2V$ leaves a concentration $C_1^* = C_0 v/(v + 2V)$. If V is 10 drops and v is 2, $C_2 = C_0/36$ while $C_1^* = C_0/11$. This shows that two washes each of 10 drops remove three times as much contaminant as one wash of 20 drops. Such calculations assume that washing is merely a matter of dilution. Thorough mixing of precipitate and wash solution is necessary if the full benefits of the washing are to be realized. Even then, removal of adsorbed impurities requires more washings than the above calculations would lead us to expect.

Transfer of Precipitates. Technique 11.   Sometimes it is necessary to transfer a precipitate from one tube to another. The volume of solution may have been such that precipitation was carried out in two or three tubes, and the precipitates must be combined before going further. To do this, add water to one precipitate, disperse it in the water by squirting the mixture in and out with a pipet several times, then suck up and transfer quickly to the other tube. Clean the pipet carefully afterwards.

Testing the Acidity. Technique 12.   Indicator papers are most useful for this purpose. Several kinds are available ranging from familiar litmus papers to wide range papers. The latter are impregnated with a mixture of indicators and show a succession of color changes over a wide range of *p*H values. Indicators can be added directly to the solution, but this is not generally desirable because they frequently become adsorbed on the surfaces of precipitates and obscure useful colors. The theory of acid-base indicators is discussed in Sec. 12-9.

To use an indicator paper, dip a rod into the solution under test, withdraw it carefully, and touch it to the paper. In withdrawing the rod keep it away from the sides of the tube. Frequently, through inadequate mixing, the upper walls of the tube may be wet with acid or base. If the rod touches this, a false test may be obtained. Most of the errors committed by beginners in this test can be avoided by thorough mixing. Do not dip the test paper into the solution. This soaks up solution, a serious disadvantage when there are only a few drops, and it contaminates the solution with indicator and fibers from the paper.

Generation of Hydrogen Sulfide. Technique 13.   This is most conveniently done by hydrolysis of thioacetamide (Sec. 7-7 and Outline 3, Cation Group 2). The solution must be acidic or basic, and hot. Allow plenty of time for reaction to occur; usually this will be less than five minutes. Gaseous hydrogen sulfide can also be used with a few slight modifications of the procedure. It is generated by the action of dilute hydrochloric acid on iron(II) sulfide in a small Kipp generator or by heating a mixture of paraffin, asbestos, and sulfur. The gas is bubbled into the solution under test through a drawn-out tube similar to a capillary pipet. Several of these tubes should be prepared, for one soon becomes dirty and can contaminate a solution.

16-4. General Remarks About the Laboratory Work.

a. Plan your work.   Study what you are to do before you come to the laboratory. Make a tentative plan for each period: what work you hope to accomplish, what to do first, and so forth.

b. Organize your working space.   Some systematic arrangement of the equipment on top of your desk is necessary if you are to work efficiently. The exact arrangement must be determined by the area available, position of the sink and gas outlets, and shelf space. One such arrangement is shown in Fig. 16-4. The reagents are easily visible and accessible yet are not in the way.

Flames and the hot water bath are kept away from the reagent racks; several reagents are adversely affected by heat. Pipets and rods must be kept clean and off the desk top; they may be kept on a folded towel, or in a wire rack, a box lined with filter paper or cotton, or a beaker of distilled water.

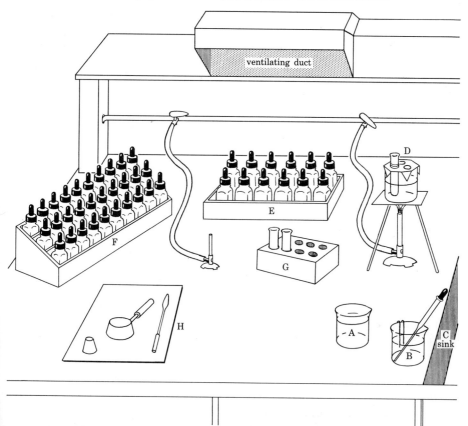

FIG. 16-4. The desk top. A possible arrangement of the working space. A, B, beakers containing distilled water, rods, and pipets; C, sink; D, water bath; E, large reagent bottles in rack; F, small reagent bottles in rack; G, test tube rack; H, folded towel on which rest crucible, casserole, spatula, etc.

c. Cleanliness is of the utmost importance.

(1) Pipets. Develop the habit of rinsing a pipet immediately after use and before even setting down a test tube. Rinse twice with distilled water from one beaker (A in Fig. 16-4) and once from another (B); squirt each rinse into the sink or a pan, bowl, or waste beaker. Change the water in beaker A as it becomes contaminated. If particles of precipitate remain in the pipet, remove the rubber bulb and loosen them with a pipe cleaner. Rinse with distilled

water before replacing the bulb. Store and use pipets with the glass tips pointed down so that solutions do not flow back into the bulbs; rinse out the bulbs now and then to avoid contamination from this part of the pipet.

(2) Rods. Rinse rods after each use. Beware of a film of solids that often adheres and will not wash off. Wipe it off with a clean towel, a piece of filter paper, or a wisp of cotton.

(3) Test tubes and centrifuge tubes. Do not let dirty tubes accumulate. Use time while heating solutions or centrifuging to clean tubes. Small test tube brushes are convenient, but if the tip of the brush is a bare wire, take care that it does not scratch the bottom of the tube. Pipe cleaners can be used if one end is formed into a loop for cleaning test tubes and the other end is doubled back a short distance for reaching the bottoms of centrifuge tubes. Rinse tubes three times with distilled water. Note that a sharp flick of the wrist is required to dislodge water from the bottom of a centrifuge tube.

(4) Reagent bottles. Wash off dirt and the white film of ammonium salts now and then. Not only do clean bottles look better, but there is also less risk of contamination of the contents.

(5) Discarding chemicals. Wash solutions down the sink with plenty of water. Soluble solids can be disposed of in a similar fashion. Put insoluble solids, broken glass, and waste paper (litmus, labels, etc.) into the waste crock. Never return excess reagent to the stock bottle.

(6) Desk tops. Clean up spills immediately with a sopping wet sponge. Do not use your towel for this or it will soon become full of holes and worse than useless.

d. Safety.

(1) Many chemicals in this work are poisonous. Keep food out of the laboratory. Do not use beakers for drinking glasses. Wash your hands thoroughly before leaving and dry them on a clean towel.

(2) Many chemicals are corrosive. Beware particularly of the concentrated acids and ammonia. But treat *all* chemicals as potentially harmful. Make it a rule to wash off immediately with plenty of water *any chemical* that is spilled on the skin. Do not delay until the skin begins to smart or sting.

(3) Wear sensible clothes and protect them with a coat or apron.

(4) Many schools require that either goggles or glasses be worn in the laboratory. This is a nuisance to those who are not used to them, but it is preferable to the loss of an eye.

(5) Report all burns and cuts to the instructor no matter how trivial they seem.

16-5. The Laboratory Notebook. An accurate record of experimental results and conclusions is an indispensable part of scientific work. In industrial laboratories a notebook must be kept so that it can be admitted as evidence in court should a dispute arise as to the priority of patentable discoveries. Each page is dated and the significant results are witnessed. We shall not need to take such elaborate precautions, but they may serve to emphasize that a laboratory notebook is not a private diary. Since it is subject to the scrutiny of others, it must be (1) intelligible to anyone conversant with the subject and (2) in such form as to leave no doubt of its honesty and reliability. Consult your instructor about the type of notebook he requires. The following rules are suggested.

1. A date should appear at the top of each right-hand page.

2. The pages should be numbered consecutively.

3. A bound, not a loose-leaf, notebook should be used.

4. Notes should be taken in ink.

5. Record observations and conclusions on the right-hand page. Save the left-hand page for calculations and corrections.

6. A page on no account is to be removed. Cross out the information on it with a large X if it is to be discarded.

7. Mistakes should be crossed out, never erased. In the interest of legibility, draw a single line through a mistake, and write above it or beside it but not on top of it.

8. Use underlined headings frequently to make clear the organization of the work, e.g., Introductory Experiments, Group 1 or Analysis of Unknown No. 25. Carry these headings from one page to the next if the experiment takes more than one.

9. The use of standard abbreviations is permissible. Some of those used by *Chemical Abstracts* are given in Table 16-1. Avoid private abbreviations, for these make the notebook intelligible only to you—and on occasion, not even to you.

10. *If notes are to be of any value, they must be recorded immediately.* When they are written hours or even days after the experiment was done, they are unreliable as records of what actually happened. The tendency, which may be altogether subconscious, to suppress observations that do not square with a worker's preconceptions or to edit them to reinforce this bias increases after he leaves the laboratory. The requirement that notes be taken as soon as the experiment or one stage of it is finished offends the aesthetic sensibilities of some students. They prefer to synthesize a neat set of notes from scribbles on loose scraps of paper. Or when required to enter notes directly in the note-book, they will spend hours recopying them at home. Only the original, un-edited record has any scientific significance. It may be full of blots, crossed-out mistakes, nitric acid stains, and the like, but it is at least an honest record of

the experiments. Neatness and some care in taking notes are not to be minimized, for the notes must be intelligible, but they are less important than an immediate record of the experiment.

TABLE 16-1.

Selected Abbreviations Used in *Chemical Abstracts*

addn	addition	M	molar (concn)
alk	alkaline	max	maximum
amt	amount (noun)	mg	milligram
anhyd	anhydrous	min	minimum
approx	approximate or approximately	ml	milliliter
bp	boiling point	mm	millimeter
compd	compound	mol	molecular
concd	concentrated	no.	number
concn	concentration	powd	powdered
cryst	crystalline	ppm	parts per million
decomp	decompose	ppt	precipitate
det	determine	pptd	precipitated
detn	determination	pptn	precipitation
dil	dilute	prepd	prepared
dild	diluted	resp	respectively
equil	equilibrium, equilibria	sat	saturate
evap	evaporate	satd	saturated
evapn	evaporation	sec	second
examd	examined	sepn	separation
expt	experiment (noun)	sol	soluble
ext	extract	soln	solution
extn	extraction	TA*	thioacetamide
hr	hour	temp	temperature
insol	insoluble	vol	volume
l	liter	wt	weight
		xs*	excess

*Not in *Chemical Abstracts*, but useful.

Convenient forms are given in Table 16-2 for recording results. The first is for introductory experiments, and space is provided for equations and answers to questions that are given in the text. The second is appropriate for describing the analysis of practice solutions and "unknowns." When it has been carefully prepared, this outline of the analysis can be used to locate errors responsible for incorrect results. In this way a student can learn to correct mistakes. Note that in the column headed "Substance" reference is made to precipitates and solutions from preceding steps. Under "Results" informative statements are made; the phrase "no result" does not make clear what you were looking for: no white precipitate, no blue color, no gas evolved? The last two columns are used for the formulas of important solutes or precipitates. A formula is appropriate when a solution or precipitate is carried over to the next step or when it is used to identify an ion. A question mark can be used after the formula when the identity of the substance has not yet been established.

16-6. The Plan of the Following Chapters. Before studying the chapters that deal with the analysis, it is helpful to know how they are organized. The

TABLE 16-2.

Sample Forms for Recording Results

Introductory Experiments

Experiment	Operations	Observations	Equations	Conclusions and answers to questions
1.	Excess KOH was added to $AgNO_3$ soln	Brown ppt formed, insol in excess KOH	$2Ag^+ + 2OH^- \rightarrow$ $Ag_2O \downarrow + H_2O$	Silver oxide is insoluble and not amphoteric.
2.	KCl was added to Ag_2O	White ppt formed in place of brown one	$Ag_2O + 2Cl^- +$ $H_2O \rightarrow 2AgCl \downarrow$ $+ 2OH^-$	AgCl is less sol than Ag_2O. The concn of Ag^+ in equil with AgCl is less than that in equil with Ag_2O

Practice or Unknown Solutions

Step	Substance	Reagent	Result	Inference	Precipitate	Solution
1.	Unknown no. 231	HCl	cryst white ppt	ions of Group 1 present	chlorides of Group 1	
2.	Washed ppt from 1	hot H_2O	ppt completely dissolves	Pb^{++} probably present; Ag^+, Hg_2^{++} absent		Pb^{++}, Cl^-?
3.	Soln from 2	$HC_2H_3O_2$ K_2CrO_4	yellow ppt	Pb^{++} present	$PbCrO_4$	

five chapters on the cations are divided into descriptive and experimental parts. The first comprises a discussion of the properties of the metals and ions, both those of general and those of analytical importance, a list of cross references to the theoretical part of the text, and a set of chemical equations for reactions that are used in the analysis. The laboratory directions begin with introductory experiments designed to direct attention to certain reactions and techniques. Then the analytical procedure is given for the analysis of known and unknown mixtures. Suggestions for further work and review exercises complete the chapter.

Analytical procedures are given largely in outline form. All outlines start with the treatment of a sample, and the directions for this up to centrifugation or division of the sample form a rectangle. An arrow leads from this to separate rectangles in which subsequent treatment of the precipitate and solution is described. The succession of rectangles continues until all ions have been separated and identified. The rectangles in which the final identifications are described are set at the right side or bottom of the outline and are shaded to distinguish them from the rest. To conserve space and keep the organization of the analysis clearly in view the directions are as condensed as possible. The abbreviations in Table 16-1 are used. Explanations, precautions, and special instructions are relegated to the notes that follow each outline; these are referred to by number in the outline. Common techniques have been described in Sec. 16-3 and references are made to these, e.g., T-8 refers to Technique 8.

The work on anions is organized differently. There are separate chapters on properties (Chapter 22) and analytical details (Chapter 23).

SUPPLEMENTARY READING

Qualitative Analysis: These works are more comprehensive or more specialized than the usual introductory text.

A. A. NOYES and E. H. SWIFT, *A Course of Instruction in Qualitative Chemical Analysis of Inorganic Substances*, 10th ed., Macmillan, New York, 1942.

G. CHARLOT, *Qualitative Inorganic Analysis*, Wiley, New York, 1954.

R. MCALPINE and B. SOULE, *Prescott and Johnson's Qualitative Chemical Analysis*, Van Nostrand, New York, 1933.

G. E. LUNDELL and J. HOFFMAN, *Outlines of Methods of Chemical Analysis*, Wiley, New York, 1938.

W. HILLEBRAND and G. LUNDELL, *Applied Inorganic Analysis*, 2nd ed., Wiley, New York, 1953.

P. WENGER and R. DUCKERT, eds., *Reagents for Qualitative Inorganic Analysis*, Elsevier, New York, 1948.

F. FEIGL, *Spot Tests*, 5th ed., Van Nostrand, New York, 1958, Vol. I—Inorganic Applications.

Inorganic Chemistry: These works are more comprehensive than the usual text-book of general chemistry but less so than the giant treatises of Mellor, Abegg, and Gmelin.

W. LATIMER and J. HILDEBRAND, *Reference Book of Inorganic Chemistry*, 3rd ed., Macmillan, New York, 1951.

T. MOELLER, *Inorganic Chemistry*, Wiley, New York, 1952.

N. SIDGWICK, *The Chemical Elements and Their Compounds*, Clarendon Press, London, 1950, 2 vols.

H. REMY, *Treatise on Inorganic Chemistry*, Van Nostrand, New York, 1956, 2 vols.

P. THORNE and E. ROBERTS, eds., *Ephraim's Inorganic Chemistry*, 6th ed., Interscience, New York, 1955.

M. SNEED and R. BRASTED, *Comprehensive Inorganic Chemistry*, Van Nostrand, New York, 1955-, several vols.

CHAPTER SEVENTEEN

Cation Group 1
The Hydrochloric Acid Group

Ag^+, Pb^{++}, Hg_2^{++}

17-1. Introduction.[1]   The ions of this analytical group are precipitated as insoluble chlorides by addition of a slight excess of hydrochloric acid. The positions in the Periodic Table of these elements and of the less common members of the Hydrochloric Acid Group are shown at the right. The Roman numeral in parentheses stands for the oxidation number of the element in the insoluble chloride. Although they resemble each other in forming insoluble chlorides, the ions in other reactions show an interesting diversity of behavior. Thus once the group has been precipitated, it is easy to separate and identify the ions by using their more specific characteristics.

		IIIB	IVB
IB	IIB		
29 Cu (I)			
47 **Ag** (I)			
79 Au (I)	80 **Hg** (I)	81 Tl (I)	82 **Pb** (II)

THE PROPERTIES OF THE IONS

17-2. Electronic Structures.   The diversity of behavior of these ions is a consequence of differences in their electronic structures. The number of electrons in the outer shells of the atoms and ions is given in Table 17-1. All electrons in a shell do not have the same energy; they may be classified in four subshells designated by the letters s, p, d, and f.[2] The electrons with lowest energy are those in the s subshells and the p electrons are next. Thus

[1]See Sec. 16-6 for a description of the general plan of this and the following chapters.

[2]Other subshells, viz. g, h, i, etc., can be occupied by electrons with abnormally high energies. Only the first four occur in atoms that are in their normal, or ground, states.

the s electrons are most difficult to remove from an atom or ion. They spend more time closer to the nucleus than do other electrons in the same shell. The s and p electrons are the only types we shall be concerned with at present; the d and f electrons will be discussed in connection with later groups. There can be at most only two s electrons and six p electrons in any one shell. The full quota of eight electrons is the inert gas octet found, for example, in Ar atoms and S^{--}, Cl^-, K^+, and Ca^{++} ions.

TABLE 17-1.

The Electronic Structures of the Atoms and Ions of Cation Group 1

Atom or ion	Total number of electrons in		
	4th shell	5th shell	6th shell
Ag^0	18	1	
Ag^+	18		
Ag^{++}	17		
Pb^0	32	18	4
Pb^{++}	32	18	2
$[Pb^{++++}]*$	32	18	
Hg^0	32	18	2
$[Hg^+]*$	32	18	1
Hg^{++}	32	18	

*Hypothetical ions; see text.

A silver atom has a single valence electron, and this must be of the s type which has the lowest energy. It is convenient to refer to it as a $5s$ electron where the number 5 indicates that it occurs in the fifth shell. A lead atom has two s electrons and two p electrons in the sixth shell. Its outer electronic configuration is written $6s^2 6p^2$ where the superscripts indicate the number of electrons of each kind. This electronic arrangement has a lower energy than either $6s 6p^3$ or $6p^4$ and is more stable.

17-3. Silver and Its Ions.

a. Oxidation States of Silver.   In all its common compounds silver has an oxidation number of $+1$. This corresponds to the loss of the single $5s$ electron to give Ag^+ ion. The outer shell of this ion contains 18 electrons and is a stable electronic structure. Removal of an electron from Ag^+ to give Ag^{++} breaks into this shell and leaves the less stable configuration of 17 electrons. Removal of the $5s$ electrons from silver atoms requires 174.6 kcal/g-atom whereas removal of the second electrons to give Ag^{++} ions requires 495.1 kcal —almost three times as much energy. The energy invested in forming the bivalent ions can be repaid if energy is released in formation of very stable crystals. The compounds AgO and AgF_2 in which Ag^{++} ions are combined with the small O^{--} and F^- ions are known, but they are easily reduced to the compounds of Ag(I). There are a few complexes of silver in which its oxidation number is $+3$; and in one peculiar substance, Ag_2F, its oxidation number is $+\frac{1}{2}$. In the latter there are Ag-Ag bonds similar to those in metallic silver.

b. Properties of Ag^+ Ion. Its radius is 1.13 A which is intermediate between the radii of Na^+ (0.98) and K^+ (1.33), two other singly charged ions. Like these ions it is unaffected by visible light and forms colorless (white) fluoride, chloride, nitrate, acetate, and sulfate. The compound AgF_2 is brown owing to the incompleteness of the outer shell of Ag^{++}, which makes it easy for the outer electrons to absorb light energy.

The Ag^+ ion differs from the Na^+ and K^+ ions in the strength of its attraction for other ions and molecules. In its outer shell of 18 electrons some electrons are more loosely held than are those in the outer shells of 8 electrons in Na^+ and K^+ ions. This is evident when the energies required to remove an electron from the ions are compared: Ag^+, 495 kcal/mole; K^+, 733; Na^+, 1090. As an Ag^+ ion approaches another ion or molecule X, the more loosely held electrons can be attracted towards X (polarization) and perhaps even shared to some extent with X (formation of partially covalent bond). As a result of this added attraction, the silver ion forms many complex ions and many precipitates. Some of the latter are highly colored as a result of the electron loosening.

A number of the reactions of silver ion are summarized in Table 17-2. All these reactions are reversible because of the appreciable solubility of the precipitates or the measurable dissociation of the complex ions. They differ in the extent to which silver ions are removed. After precipitation of a fairly soluble compound such as $Ag_2C_2O_4$, a comparatively high concentration of silver ion is left in solution; whereas the precipitation of Ag_2S, the most insoluble silver compound, removes almost all silver ions from solution. The order of listing in the table is then one of increasing removal of silver ion. That being so, any of the first 14 products will be converted to silver sulfide by treatment with a soluble sulfide, for silver ions are thereby removed to a greater extent; e.g.,

$$Ag_2CrO_4 \downarrow + S^{--} \rightarrow Ag_2S \downarrow + CrO_4^{--}$$

Likewise, all the compounds but silver sulfide can be converted to the cyanide complex by an excess of potassium cyanide; e.g.,

$$AgI \downarrow + 2CN^- \rightarrow Ag(CN)_2^- + I^-$$

These examples are only two out of 105 that can be predicted from the positions of the reactions in the table. Taking these together with the 15 reactions actually given in Table 17-2, we see that there are 120 reactions stored in the small confines of this table.

TABLE 17-2.

Reactions of the Silver Ion

Reactions are listed in order of increasing removal of silver ion; least at the top, greatest at the bottom

Typical reagents*	Equations	Color of product
$H_2C_2O_4$, $Na_2C_2O_4$	$2Ag^+ + C_2O_4^{--} \rightleftharpoons Ag_2C_2O_4 \downarrow$	white
K_2CO_3, $NaHCO_3$, *not* $(NH_4)_2CO_3$	$2Ag^+ + CO_3^{--} \rightleftharpoons Ag_2CO_3 \downarrow$	white
K_2CrO_4	$2Ag^+ + CrO_4^{--} \rightleftharpoons Ag_2CrO_4 \downarrow$	purplish red
Na_2HAsO_4	$3Ag^+ + HAsO_4^{--} \rightleftharpoons Ag_3AsO_4 \downarrow + H^+$	reddish brown
$NaOH$, $Ba(OH)_2$	$2Ag^+ + 2OH^- \rightleftharpoons Ag_2O \downarrow + H_2O$	brownish black
HCl, NH_4Cl†	$Ag^+ + Cl^- \rightleftharpoons AgCl \downarrow$	white
1 M NH_3	$Ag^+ + 2NH_3 \rightleftharpoons Ag(NH_3)_2^+$	colorless
$K_4Fe(CN)_6$	$4Ag^+ + Fe(CN)_6^{----} \rightleftharpoons Ag_4Fe(CN)_6 \downarrow$	white
NH_4SCN, $KSCN$†	$Ag^+ + SCN^- \rightleftharpoons AgSCN \downarrow$	white
KBr†	$Ag^+ + Br^- \rightleftharpoons AgBr \downarrow$	pale yellow
KCN†	$Ag^+ + CN^- \rightleftharpoons AgCN \downarrow$	white
KI†	$Ag^+ + I^- \rightleftharpoons AgI \downarrow$	yellow
$Na_2S_2O_3$ in excess	$Ag^+ + 2S_2O_3^{--} \rightleftharpoons Ag(S_2O_3)_2^{---}$	colorless
KCN in excess	$Ag^+ + 2CN^- \rightleftharpoons Ag(CN)_2^-$	colorless
H_2S, Na_2S, $(NH_4)_2S$	$2Ag^+ + S^{--} \rightleftharpoons Ag_2S \downarrow$	black

*Common laboratory reagents are given. Other soluble reagents such as the potassium, sodium, and ammonium salts could be used unless the ammonium compound furnishes sufficient ammonia to give the ammonia complex as is true for ammonium carbonate.
†These reagents redissolve the precipitates if used in excess.

This method of systematizing the reactions of an ion is not without flaws, and we must be aware of these if we are to use the table intelligently. No attempt has been made to space the reactions according to the *extent* of removal of silver ion. If this were done, the three reactions at the bottom should be widely spaced and the three at the top, which do not differ greatly, should be close together. The table gives the correct order of reactions but does not give any quantitative indication of the relative extents. The concentrations of the reagents also affect the extent of reaction. The conversion of silver carbonate to silver chromate

$$Ag_2CO_3 \downarrow + CrO_4^{--} \rightleftharpoons Ag_2CrO_4 \downarrow + CO_3^{--}$$

is favored by a high concentration of chromate but reversed by a high concentration of carbonate. The position of $Ag(NH_3)_2^+$ in the table is sensitive to the concentration of ammonia. Silver chloride is readily soluble in 1 *M* ammonia, but silver bromide is only slightly soluble. In 15 M ammonia, silver bromide dissolves, but silver iodide does not. An increase in concentration of ammonia thus lowers the position in the table of the reaction forming $Ag(NH_3)_2^+$.

c. Compounds of Silver.   The nitrate is the only common soluble salt, but the fluoride, chlorate, and perchlorate are also soluble. Silver acetate, nitrite, and sulfate are sparingly soluble and can be precipitated from concentrated solutions. Silver salts of weak acids are dissolved by a strong acid such as nitric acid; e.g.,

$$Ag_2CO_3 \downarrow \; + 2H^+ \rightarrow 2Ag^+ + H_2O + CO_2 \uparrow$$
$$Ag_3AsO_4 \downarrow + 2H^+ \rightarrow 3Ag^+ + H_2AsO_4^-$$

Silver sulfide is dissolved by oxidizing the sulfide to free sulfur, a more effective way of removing sulfide ion than the formation of molecular hydrogen sulfide:

$$3Ag_2S \downarrow + 8H^+ + 2NO_3^- \rightarrow 6Ag^+ + 3S^0 \downarrow + 2NO + 4H_2O$$

The special affinity of silver for sulfur contrasts with its reluctance to combine with oxygen. The oxide is made not by direct union of the elements but by precipitation (Table 17-2). When heated, it decomposes to the elements

$$2Ag_2O \rightarrow 4Ag + O_2 \uparrow$$

There is no evidence that the solid hydroxide AgOH exists. Insofar as its meager solubility allows, silver oxide is a moderately strong base. Its solutions, which contain Ag^+ and OH^-, are basic and solutions of its salts do not contain an appreciable concentration of AgOH. The solubility of silver oxide is decreased by a small excess of alkali hydroxide because of the common ion effect but is abnormally large in strongly basic solutions. This increase in solubility has been attributed to the reaction of Ag_2O as an acid to give AgO^- (or $Ag(OH)_2^-$); other evidence of this amphoteric behavior is lacking, and caution is always required in interpreting solubility data in concentrated solutions.

d. Redox Reactions.   Silver is a noble metal and is not dissolved by hydrochloric or dilute sulfuric acid to an appreciable extent. The reverse reaction

$$H_2 + 2Ag^+ \rightarrow 2Ag \downarrow \; + 2H^+$$

does occur if a catalyst is present to activate the hydrogen. A metal such as zinc that displaces hydrogen from acids will also displace silver:

$$Zn \downarrow \; + 2Ag^+ \rightarrow Zn^{++} + 2Ag \downarrow$$

Some metals, such as copper, though not sufficiently active to displace hydrogen, can nevertheless displace silver:

$$Cu \downarrow \; + 2Ag^+ \rightarrow 2Ag \downarrow \; + Cu^{++}$$

All three of these reactions go virtually to completion, but theoretical calculations show that the concentration of silver ion remaining after reduction by zinc is smallest, and that left after reduction by copper is largest (though still minute). Thus zinc is the most powerful of these reducing agents.

These facts are expressed in another form in Table 17-3. It is convenient to speak of the reduced and oxidized forms of a substance as a redox *couple*. The couples in Table 17-3 are listed in such an order that the best reducing agent is at the top left, and the best oxidizing agent is at the bottom right. Any reducing agent (on the left) will reduce any oxidizing agent below it (on the right). Thus zinc, hydrogen, and copper will displace silver as we have seen. Silver metal will dissolve in nitric acid, because the silver couple lies

TABLE 17-3.

Redox Couples of Silver and Other Substances

	Reducing form (reducing agent)			Oxidized form (oxidizing agent)		
	Zn		$\rightleftharpoons$	Zn^{++}	$+$	$2e^-$
	$2Ag$	$+ \; S^{--}$	$\rightleftharpoons$	Ag_2S	$+$	$2e^-$
	Ag	$+ \; 2CN^-$	$\rightleftharpoons$	$Ag(CN)_2^-$	$+$	e^-
Reducing power	H_2		$\rightleftharpoons$	$2H^+$	$+$	$2e^-$
	Ag	$+ \; Cl^-$	$\rightleftharpoons$	$AgCl$	$+$	e^-
	Cu		$\rightleftharpoons$	Cu^{++}	$+$	$2e^-$
	Ag		$\rightleftharpoons$	Ag^+	$+$	e^-
	$2H_2O$	$+ \; NO$	$\rightleftharpoons$	$NO_3^- + 4H^+$	$+$	$3e^-$
	Ag^+		$\rightleftharpoons$	Ag^{++}	$+$	e^-

(The left margin is labeled "Reducing power" with an upward arrow; the right margin is labeled "Oxidizing power" with a downward arrow.)

above that for nitric acid. The instability of Ag^{++} ion is shown by its position at the bottom. The conversion of Ag(I) to Ag(II) is easier in basic solution because of the exceedingly low solubility of AgO; i.e., the couple

$$Ag_2O \downarrow + 2OH^- \rightarrow 2AgO \downarrow + H_2O + e^-$$

occupies a position slightly higher than that of the $Ag \rightarrow Ag^+ + e^-$ couple in Table 17-3. The reducing power of silver metal is increased by adding substances that combine with silver ion and drive the half-reaction $Ag \rightarrow Ag^+ + e^-$ to the right. The position of the Ag-AgCl, Ag-Ag(CN)$_2^-$, and Ag-Ag$_2$S couples shows once more that sulfide is the most effective and chloride the least effective of the three in removing silver ion (compare with the order in Table 17-2).

17-4. Lead and Its Ions.

a. Oxidation States of Lead. The lead atom has four valence electrons equally divided between *s* and *p* subshells. When ionization occurs, the two

p electrons are lost first, for they are less tightly bound than the s electrons. The lead(II) ion Pb^{++} has an outer structure represented by $6s^2$. The most common oxidation state of lead is $+2$ as in Pb^{++}, PbO, PbI_4^{--}, and $Pb(OH)_3^{-}$. Loss of the two $6s$ electrons to give Pb^{++++} ion requires a prohibitive amount of energy. Compounds of lead(IV)[3] are known, but in these lead shares electrons with four atoms and so attains the electronic structure of the inert gas radon. The most important compound of lead(IV) is lead dioxide PbO_2, a powerful oxidizing agent, readily reduced to lead(II). Other compounds include lead tetraacetate $Pb(C_2H_3O_2)_4$ and lead tetraethyl $Pb(C_2H_5)_4$, a constituent of antiknock gasoline. In these compounds lead forms four covalent bonds in the same way as the first member of Periodic Group IVB, carbon.

The stability of Pb^{++} ion led Sidgwick to dub the $6s^2$ electrons the "inert pair." Similar inert pairs are found in Sn^{++}, Sb^{+++}, and Bi^{+++} ions. Actually the prevalence of such ions is not so much an indication of the inertness of $5s$ or $6s$ electrons as it is of the instability of covalent bonds formed by Pb(IV), Sn(IV), Sb(V), and Bi(V). In a large atom such as that of lead, the valence electrons are far from the nucleus and wander about in comparatively large volumes. The diffuseness of their motions reduces their effectiveness in covalent binding; the electronic glue is too thin. Large atoms also contain many closed shells which repel other atoms and reduce the strength of covalent bonds. Thus the tendency to form such bonds decreases from carbon through the family to lead.

b. Properties of Pb^{++} Ion.   The lead and barium ions are both doubly charged and have about the same radius, viz., 1.21 A for Pb^{++} and 1.35 for Ba^{++}. Both form slightly soluble salts with anions such as SO_4^{--}, CrO_4^{--}, CO_3^{--}, and F^-. Lead and barium nitrates are both relatively insoluble in concentrated nitric acid. Both metal ions have stable electronic structures and normally give colorless compounds.

Lead(II) ion differs from Ba^{++} ion and resembles Ag^+ ion in forming polarized or partially covalent bonds with ions such as S^{--}, OH^-, Cl^-, Br^-, and I^-. Its compounds with the highly polarizable sulfide and iodide ions are colored. Like Ag^+ ion, it forms many complex ions, especially with the halides and hydroxide, but it gives no stable ammonia complex. The solid $Pb(NH_3)_2Cl_2$ can be prepared but the ammonia molecules are replaced by water when it dissolves:

$$Pb(NH_3)_2Cl_2 \downarrow + nH_2O \rightarrow Pb(H_2O)_n^{++} + 2NH_3$$

where n is the unknown hydration number of Pb^{++} ion. The maximum coordination number of Pb(II) is four as in PbI_4^{--}; complexes such as PbI_3^-, $Pb(OH)_3^-$, $PbOH^+$, and $Pb(C_2H_3O_2)_3^-$ in which the coordination number

---

[3]Note the use of Roman numerals to designate the oxidation state. Lead(IV) and Pb(IV) carry no implications as to the structure of lead in this oxidation state, whereas the symbol Pb^{++++} would imply incorrectly the existence of this ion.

is less than four may contain water molecules, e.g., $Pb(H_2O)I_3^-$ or $Pb(H_2O)_3(OH)^+$.

Because of its polarizing action, Pb^{++} forms many ion-pairs. Some of these in order of decreasing extent of dissociation are

$$PbNO_3^+ > PbCl^+ > PbBr^+ > PbI^+ > PbC_2H_3O_2^+ > PbOH^+$$

Some reactions of Pb^{++} ion are summarized in Table 17-4. The order from top to bottom is one of increasing removal of Pb^{++} ion. Thus any of the compounds is readily converted to the sulfide, and other reactions such as

$$PbSO_4 \downarrow + 3C_2H_3O_2^- \rightarrow Pb(C_2H_3O_2)_3^- + SO_4^{--}$$

or

$$PbCl_2 \downarrow + CrO_4^{--} \rightarrow PbCrO_4 \downarrow + 2Cl^-$$

are readily predicted.

TABLE 17-4.

Reactions of the Lead(II) Ion

Reagents*	Equations	Color of product
HCl, KCl, NH₄Cl†	$Pb^{++} + 2Cl^- \rightarrow PbCl_2 \downarrow$	white
KBr†	$Pb^{++} + 2Br^- \rightarrow PbBr_2 \downarrow$	white
NaF	$Pb^{++} + 2F^- \rightarrow PbF_2 \downarrow$	white
H₂SO₄, Na₂SO₄, (NH₄)₂SO₄	$Pb^{++} + SO_4^{--} \rightarrow PbSO_4 \downarrow$	white
KI†	$Pb^{++} + 2I^- \rightarrow PbI_2 \downarrow$	yellow
3 M NH₄C₂H₃O₂	$Pb^{++} + 3C_2H_3O_2^- \rightarrow Pb(C_2H_3O_2)_3^-$	colorless
Na₂HPO₄	$3Pb^{++} + 2HPO_4^{--} \rightarrow Pb_3(PO_4)_2 \downarrow + 2H^+$	white
(NH₄)₂CO₃, cold Na₂CO₃‡	$Pb^{++} + CO_3^{--} \rightarrow PbCO_3 \downarrow$	white
KOH†, NaOH†, NH₃	$Pb^{++} + 2OH^- \rightarrow Pb(OH)_2 \downarrow$	white
K₂CrO₄	$Pb^{++} + CrO_4^{--} \rightarrow PbCrO_4 \downarrow$	yellow
6 M KOH or NaOH	$Pb^{++} + 3OH^- \rightarrow Pb(OH)_3^-$	colorless
H₂S, Na₂S, (NH₄)₂S	$Pb^{++} + H_2S \rightarrow PbS \downarrow + 2H^+$	black

*Common laboratory reagents are given, but other soluble sources of the ion could be used.
†These reagents redissolve the precipitates if used in excess.
‡Hot Na_2CO_3 and K_2CO_3 precipitate the basic carbonate, "white lead," $Pb_3(OH)_2(CO_3)_2$.

c. Salts of Lead(II). Most lead salts are only slightly soluble in water. The most important exceptions, the nitrate and acetate, are common laboratory reagents. Other soluble salts include the nitrite and chlorate. The chloride is sparingly soluble in cold water, more soluble in hot water.

Solutions of lead salts are very weakly acidic because of removal of hydroxide ions from water:

$$Pb^{++} + H_2O \rightleftharpoons PbOH^+ + H^+$$

Soluble lead salts are prepared by treating the oxide or metal with the appropriate acid. The insoluble salts can be made by precipitation from lead nitrate or lead acetate solution.

Lead salts of weak acids can be dissolved by a stronger acid. Lead chromate, for example, is dissolved by nitric acid:

$$PbCrO_4 \downarrow \ + H^+ \rightarrow Pb^{++} + HCrO_4^-$$

but acetic acid is too weak to do so. Lead sulfide is practically insoluble in dilute hydrochloric and sulfuric acids. It dissolves in nitric acid by oxidation of sulfide to sulfur and in concentrated hydrochloric acid because of formation of hydrogen sulfide and chlorocomplexes of lead. Complex formation can be used to dissolve other lead salts, particularly those of strong acids:

$$PbSO_4 \downarrow \ + 3OH^- \rightarrow Pb(OH)_3^- + SO_4^{--}$$

$$PbI_2 \downarrow \quad + I^- \quad \ \rightarrow PbI_3^-$$

d. Oxides and Hydroxide of Lead.   There are three oxides of lead: (1) brownish-black lead dioxide, or lead(IV) oxide, PbO_2, (2) red lead(II, IV) oxide, Pb_3O_4, and (3) yellow or red lead monoxide, or lead(II) oxide, PbO, also called "litharge." The only hydroxide is that of lead(II), $Pb(OH)_2$.

Lead dioxide is prepared by oxidation of lead(II) salts. It has almost no basic properties other than slight solubility in concentrated nitric and sulfuric acids. When heated with basic oxides or alkali hydroxides, it gives salts such as Ca_2PbO_4 or $K_2Pb(OH)_6$, so that it shows acidic properties. Its most important reactions are those in which it acts as an oxidizing agent. These are discussed later.

Lead monoxide occurs in a yellow and a red form, an example of *polymorphism* (from Greek words meaning "many forms"). The red variety is more stable at room temperature, but the transformation of yellow to red is slow even at 100°. This oxide is much more basic than PbO_2 and readily dissolves in acids to give solutions of lead(II) salts:

$$PbO \downarrow \ + 2H^+ \rightarrow Pb^{++} + H_2O$$

As a weakly acidic oxide it dissolves to some extent in strong alkali hydroxides to give plumbites. The anion in plumbites can be formulated as $Pb(OH)_3^-$ or $HPbO_2^-$; the former is preferred in this text. Lead hydroxide reacts in the same way as the oxide with acids and bases. It loses water and decomposes to the oxide when heated.

The contrast in behavior of PbO_2 and PbO is typical of the oxides of many other elements. The acidic character of the oxides increases as the oxidation number of the element increases. When these acidic oxides react with strong bases, the metal ion coordinates with hydroxide ions as in $Pb(OH)_3^-$ and $Pb(OH)_6^{--}$. With increase in oxidation number, the metal ion becomes smaller and more highly charged, the very changes that promote stronger bonds with hydroxide ions and accentuate acidic behavior. Thus a

Pb(IV) ion has a radius about $\frac{2}{3}$ that of the Pb^{++} ion and a higher, though probably not double, positive charge; as a result PbO_2 is more acidic than PbO.

Lead(II, IV) oxide can be prepared by heating either of the other two oxides in air or by combining the oxides:

$$2PbO + PbO_2 \rightarrow Pb_3O_4$$

It contains two Pb(II) atoms to one of Pb(IV) and as a result has some of the properties of each simple oxide. It is, for example, both basic and acidic and is an oxidizing agent. Yet its crystals are not simple mixtures of the other oxides. Each Pb(II) is close to three oxygen atoms and each Pb(IV) atom is surrounded by six oxygen atoms. The formulas $2PbO \cdot PbO_2$ and $Pb_2(PbO_4)$ sometimes given for Pb_3O_4 clearly do not express its structure correctly.

e. Redox Reactions of Lead. These cover transitions between the oxidation states 0, +2, and +4. The position of the lead couples in comparison with more familiar ones is given in Table 17-5. Lead is seen to be a slightly better reducing agent than hydrogen and is capable of displacing hydrogen from acids:

$$Pb + 2H^+ \rightarrow Pb^{++} + H_2 \uparrow$$

The attack of the metal is usually slow because insoluble films of $PbCl_2$ or $PbSO_4$ protect the metal. Nitric acid is capable of dissolving lead:

$$3Pb + 8H^+ + 2NO_3^- \rightarrow 2NO \uparrow + 3Pb^{++} + 4H_2O$$

but the concentrated acid acts very slowly because of the insolubility of lead nitrate in this medium. The position of the $Pb-PbSO_4$ couple shows that removal of lead ions to give insoluble lead sulfate makes lead a more active reducing agent.

TABLE 17-5.

Some Redox Couples of Lead and Other Substances in Acid Solution

Change in oxidation number	Reduced form (reducing agent)			Oxidized form (oxidizing agent)	
		Zn	$\rightleftharpoons$	Zn^{++}	$+ 2e^-$
$0 \rightleftharpoons +2$	Pb +	SO_4^{--}	$\rightleftharpoons$	$PbSO_4 \downarrow$	$+ 2e^-$
$0 \rightleftharpoons +2$		Pb	$\rightleftharpoons$	Pb^{++}	$+ 2e^-$
		H_2	$\rightleftharpoons$	$2H^+$	$+ 2e^-$
		Cu	$\rightleftharpoons$	Cu^{++}	$+ 2e^-$
		Ag	$\rightleftharpoons$	Ag^+	$+ e^-$
	NO +	$2H_2O$	$\rightleftharpoons$	$NO_3^- + 4H^+$	$+ 3e^-$
$+2 \rightleftharpoons +4$	$Pb^{++} +$	$2H_2O$	$\rightleftharpoons$	$PbO_2 \downarrow + 4H^+$	$+ 2e^-$
		Ag^+	$\rightleftharpoons$	Ag^{++}	$+ e^-$

Oxidation of Pb^{++} to PbO_2 is considerably more difficult than oxidation of silver to Ag^+ ion. It can be carried out at the anode by electrolysis of a lead nitrate solution that is strongly acid with nitric acid:

$$Pb^{++} + 2H_2O \rightarrow PbO_2 \downarrow + 4H^+ + 2e^-$$

This reaction can be used to separate lead from other metals and determine its percentage in alloys. Oxidation of lead(II) to lead(IV) oxide can also be accomplished by chemical oxidizing agents such as chlorine or hypochlorite in basic solution. In acid solution it is a powerful oxidizing agent. It can oxidize concentrated hydrochloric acid:

$$4H^+ + 2Cl^- + PbO_2 \downarrow \rightarrow Pb^{++} + Cl_2 \uparrow + 2H_2O$$

and can do still more difficult things such as oxidizing manganese(II) to permanganate in nitric acid solution:

$$4H^+ + 2Mn^{++} + 5PbO_2 \downarrow \rightarrow 5Pb^{++} + 2H_2O + 2MnO_4^-$$

17-5. Mercury and the Mercury(I) Ion.

a. Oxidation States of Mercury.   A mercury atom has two $6s$ electrons, the inert pair (Sec. 17-4a). Its first ionization potential is unusually high (240.6 kcal/g-atom), and the loss of one electron does not give a stable Hg^+ ion. Two such ions combine together to give a dimer $[Hg:Hg]^{++}$ in which the remaining $6s$ electrons are paired and shared by the two atoms. Because the double positive charge is divided between two atoms, the average oxidation number of mercury in the ion is $+1$. The energy required to remove two electrons from gaseous Hg atoms to give Hg^{++} ions is slightly larger than that required to convert Ag atoms to Ag^{++} ions, namely 673.0 and 669.9 kcal/g-atom, respectively. Mercury frequently achieves the $+2$ oxidation state by sharing electrons and forming molecular substances such as $HgCl_2$ and complex ions such as HgI_4^{--}. Compounds of mercury(I) are more ionic, perhaps because the positive charge is spread over two mercury atoms. For further discussion of mercury(II) see Chapter 18.

b. Reactions and Compounds of Hg_2^{++} Ion.   The only important soluble salts of mercury(I) are the acetate and nitrate. Both are colorless, although the latter, $Hg_2(NO_3)_2 \cdot 2H_2O$, is often yellow as a result of decomposition. Soluble salts can be prepared by the action of an acid on mercury(I) carbonate, by reduction of the mercury(II) salt with metallic mercury, or by oxidation of mercury metal with a limited amount of oxidizing agent. The soluble salts hydrolyze extensively, and basic salts may form when the solid salt is dissolved in water:

$$Hg_2^{++} + NO_3^- + H_2O \rightleftharpoons Hg_2(OH)NO_3 \downarrow + H^+$$

The hydrolysis is repressed by addition of an excess of strong acid. Solutions of mercury(I) perchlorate and nitrate are acidic, but this is less a result of the above reaction than it is of the hydrolysis of Hg^{++} ions always present in solutions of mercury(I) salts.

Various slightly soluble mercury(I) compounds can be prepared by precipitation. These reactions are summarized in Table 17-6. Attempts to precipitate other compounds such as the oxide, sulfide, or cyanide invariably

TABLE 17-6.

Reactions of the Mercury(I) Ion

Precipitation Reactions
(listed in order of increasing removal of Hg_2^{++} ion)

Reagent	Equation	Color of product
H_2SO_4, $(NH_4)_2SO_4$, Na_2SO_4	$Hg_2^{++} + SO_4^{--} \rightleftharpoons Hg_2SO_4 \downarrow$	white
K_2CrO_4	$Hg_2^{++} + CrO_4^{--} \rightleftharpoons Hg_2CrO_4 \downarrow$	yellow to brown
Na_2HPO_4	$Hg_2^{++} + HPO_4^{--} \rightleftharpoons Hg_2HPO_4 \downarrow$	white
$NaHCO_3$, $BaCO_3$	$Hg_2^{++} + CO_3^{--} \rightleftharpoons Hg_2CO_3 \downarrow$	yellow
HCl, NH_4Cl, KCl	$Hg_2^{++} + 2Cl^- \rightleftharpoons Hg_2Cl_2 \downarrow$	white
KSCN, NH_4SCN	$Hg_2^{++} + 2SCN^- \rightleftharpoons Hg_2(SCN)_2 \downarrow$	gray
HBr, KBr	$Hg_2^{++} + 2Br^- \rightleftharpoons Hg_2Br_2 \downarrow$	white
HI, KI	$Hg_2^{++} + 2I^- \rightleftharpoons Hg_2I_2 \downarrow$	greenish yellow

Disproportionation Reactions

NaOH, KOH	$Hg_2^{++} + 2OH^- \rightleftharpoons Hg^0 \downarrow + HgO \downarrow + H_2O$	
KCN	$Hg_2^{++} + 2CN^- \rightleftharpoons Hg^0 \downarrow + Hg(CN)_2$	
KI in excess	$Hg_2I_2 \downarrow + 2I^- \rightleftharpoons Hg^0 \downarrow + HgI_4^{--}$	
NH_3	$Hg_2Cl_2 \downarrow + 2NH_3 \rightleftharpoons Hg^0 \downarrow + HgNH_2Cl \downarrow + NH_4^+ + Cl$	
H_2S, Na_2S, $(NH_4)_2S$	$Hg_2^{++} + S^{--} \rightleftharpoons Hg^0 \downarrow + HgS \downarrow$	

give mixtures of the mercury(II) compound with free mercury. Mercury(I) ions are always in equilibrium with free mercury and mercury(II) ions:

$$Hg_2^{++} \rightleftharpoons Hg^0 + Hg^{++}$$

In a solution saturated with mercury metal (3.0×10^{-7} M in Hg^0 at 25°) the concentration of Hg_2^{++} ion is always 83 times that of Hg^{++} ion. Generally, mercury(II) compounds are either more weakly ionized, more highly complexed, or more insoluble than the mercury(I) compounds. Thus the addition of sulfide, hydroxide, cyanide, iodide (in excess), and ammonia causes preferential removal of Hg^{++} ions and displaces the equilibrium to the right

$$Hg_2^{++} \to Hg^0 + Hg^{++}$$

This simultaneous oxidation and reduction of an ion is called a *disproportiona-tion* reaction. Some examples are given in Table 17-6.

   c. Redox Reactions of Mercury.   The position of various mercury couples in relation to more familiar ones is shown in Table 17-7. The Hg-Hg_2^{++} couple is below that of H_2-H^+, and mercury is not soluble in hydrochloric or dilute sulfuric acids. Mercury is easily displaced by copper, lead, or zinc. Silver and mercury are oxidized to the $+1$ state with equal ease. Subsequent oxidation of Hg_2^{++} to Hg^{++} is more difficult. Strong oxidizing agents such as nitric acid or hot concentrated sulfuric acid, if used in limited amount, will convert mercury to the mercury(I) salt. An excess of these oxidizing agents will oxidize all of the mercury to mercury(II). Since the Hg_2^{++}-Hg^{++} couple lies below the Hg-Hg_2^{++} couple, the mercury(II) ion is sufficiently active to oxidize mercury to Hg_2^{++} and, as we have seen, at equilibrium the concentra-tion of Hg_2^{++} ion is 83 times as large as that of Hg^{++} ion.

TABLE 17-7.

Some Redox Couples of Mercury and Other Substances

Change in oxidation number of Hg	Reduced form (reducing agents)		Oxidized form (oxidizing agents)		
	Zn	$\rightleftharpoons$	Zn^{++}	$+$	$2e^-$
	Pb	$\rightleftharpoons$	Pb^{++}	$+$	$2e^-$
	H_2	$\rightleftharpoons$	$2H^+$	$+$	$2e^-$
	$Sn^{++} + 6Cl^-$	$\rightleftharpoons$	$SnCl_6^{--}$	$+$	$2e^-$
$0 \rightleftharpoons +1$	$2Hg + 2Cl^-$	$\rightleftharpoons$	Hg_2Cl_2	$+$	$2e^-$
	Cu	$\rightleftharpoons$	Cu^{++}	$+$	$2e^-$
$+1 \rightleftharpoons +2$	$Hg_2Cl_2 + 6Cl^-$	$\rightleftharpoons$	$2HgCl_4^{--}$	$+$	$2e^-$
$0 \rightleftharpoons +1$	$\left\{\begin{array}{l} Ag \\ 2Hg \end{array}\right.$	$\rightleftharpoons$ $\rightleftharpoons$	Ag^+ Hg_2^{++}	$+$ $+$	$\left.\begin{array}{l} e^- \\ 2e^- \end{array}\right\}$
$+1 \rightleftharpoons +2$	Hg_2^{++}	$\rightleftharpoons$	$2Hg^{++}$	$+$	$2e^-$
	$NO + 2H_2O$	$\rightleftharpoons$	$NO_3^- + 4H^+$	$+$	$3e^-$

17-6. Discussion of the Analytical Procedure.

   a. Precipitation of the Group.   Two of the three chlorides, those of silver and mercury(I), have very low solubilities and can be precipitated almost completely by addition of a slight excess of hydrochloric acid. Lead(II) chloride is much more soluble and will not precipitate at all, unless the con-centration of Pb^{++} ion is high. Even at best enough lead is left in solution to give a precipitate of lead sulfide with Cation Group 2.

Hydrochloric acid, rather than ammonium chloride or another soluble chloride, is used to precipitate the group because it supplies hydrogen ions as well as chloride ions. The solution must be sufficiently acid to prevent the precipitation of the oxychlorides of bismuth(III) and antimony(III):

$$Bi^{+++} + Cl^- + H_2O \rightleftharpoons BiOCl\downarrow + 2H^+$$

A small excess of chloride is desirable, for it represses the solubility of the chlorides of Group 1 so that fewer metal ions are left in solution. But in the presence of a large excess of chloride the precipitates are all more soluble and may even be redissolved if too high a concentration of hydrochloric acid is used (see Fig. 8-1). The formation of weakly dissociated chlorocomplex ions decreases the concentration of the free metal ions to such an extent that the precipitates dissolve:

$$AgCl\downarrow + Cl^- \rightleftharpoons AgCl_2^-$$

$$PbCl_2\downarrow + Cl^- \rightleftharpoons PbCl_3^-$$

$$Hg_2Cl_2\downarrow + 2Cl^- \rightleftharpoons HgCl_4^{--} + Hg^0$$

b. Separation and Identification of the Ions. All the chlorides become more soluble as the temperature is raised, but the effect is noticeable only with lead chloride. At 100° 1 ml of water will dissolve ten times as much silver chloride as it does at 25°, but this is still only 0.021 mg of AgCl. The solubility of lead chloride only triples with this increase in temperature, but 1 ml of water dissolves over 30 mg of this more soluble precipitate at 100°. The lead chloride in the hot water extract of the group precipitate is readily converted to lead chromate, for the latter removes lead ions to a greater extent (Table 17-4). Silver is separated from mercury(I) by the action of ammonia. Silver chloride is dissolved to give the weakly dissociated ammonia complex of silver (Table 17-2). Silver chloride is reprecipitated from this solution by destroying the complex with nitric acid. Ammonia causes mercury(I) chloride to disproportionate, i.e., half of the mercury(I) is reduced to free mercury, which is black in the finely divided form, and half is oxidized to mercury(II) amidochloride $HgNH_2Cl$.[4] The formation of the black residue is usually sufficient indication of the presence of mercury(I). If confirmation is required, the residue can be dissolved in aqua regia and, after destruction of the nitrate, mercury is reprecipitated by reduction of the mercury(II) chloride in the solution to Hg_2Cl_2 or Hg^0 with tin(II) chloride.

17-7. Cross References. A number of sections in the theoretical part of the text deal with subjects more briefly mentioned in this chapter. These

---

[4]Mercury(I) chloride is a purgative known as "calomel," a name which comes from Greek words meaning "beautiful black." Since mercury(I) chloride is white, it has been supposed that the name may refer to the color produced by the action of ammonia.

references are collected here for your convenience; it is not necessary that you read most or all of them at this time.

Sec. 2-6 (ionic crystals: AgCl)
Sec. 2-7 (electronic structures of ions)
Sec. 2-8 (ionic radii)
Sec. 2-10 (layer lattices: $PbCl_2$)
Sec. 2-16 (equilibrium; common ion effect)
Sec. 2-18 (ion-pairs)
Sec. 2-20 (AgCl, $HgCl_2$ as electrolytes)
Sec. 2-23 (salts in solution)
Chapter 3 (ionic reactions and ionic equations)
Secs. 5-4, -5 (polarized and partially covalent bonds)
Sec. 5-7 (solubility of AgCl)
Sec. 6-9 (bonds in complex ions)
Sec. 6-10 (relation of complex formation to charge and radius)
Sec. 6-12 (s, p, d, and f electrons)
Sec. 6-14 (color)
Secs. 7-14, -21 (Hg_2^{++} vs. Hg^+)
Sec. 8-2 (solubility product principle)
Sec. 8-5 (common ion effect on solubility)
Sec. 8-17 (amphoteric hydroxides)
Sec. 11-6 (hydrolysis)
Secs. 14-2, -3 (dissociation of $Ag(NH_3)_2^+$)

17-8. The Successive Reactions of the Ions of Cation Group 1.   Rules for writing formulas are given in Sec. 3-5.

Lead

1. Precipitation of the group. Reagent: dilute hydrochloric acid
$$Pb^{++} + 2Cl^- \rightarrow PbCl_2 \downarrow$$

2. Separation from Ag and Hg(I). Reagent: hot water
$$PbCl_2 \downarrow \; \rightarrow Pb^{++} + 2Cl^-$$

3. Identification. Reagents: potassium chromate and acetic acid
$$Pb^{++} + CrO_4^{--} \rightarrow PbCrO_4 \downarrow$$

Silver

1. Precipitation of the group. Reagent: dilute hydrochloric acid
$$Ag^+ + Cl^- \rightarrow AgCl \downarrow$$

2. Separation from Pb. Reagent: hot water. No action on AgCl.

3. Separation from Hg(I). Reagent: ammonia solution
(a) $AgCl \downarrow \; + 2NH_3 \rightarrow Ag(NH_3)_2^+$
(b) $2AgCl \downarrow \; + 2Hg^0 \downarrow \; \rightarrow Hg_2Cl_2 \downarrow \; + 2Ag^0 \downarrow$

4. Confirmation. Reagent: nitric acid
$$Ag(NH_3)_2^+ + 2H^+ + Cl^- \rightarrow AgCl \downarrow + 2NH_4^+$$

5. Recovery from Residue 1-3 (Outline 1). Reagent: aqua regia
(a) $Ag^0 \downarrow + 2H^+ + Cl^- + NO_3^- \rightarrow AgCl \downarrow + NO_2 \uparrow + H_2O$
(b) $AgCl \downarrow + Cl^- \rightarrow AgCl_2^-$ (with excess reagent)
(c) $AgCl_2^- \rightarrow AgCl \downarrow + Cl^-$ (after dilution with H_2O)
(d) Identification of AgCl. Reagents: ammonia solution and nitric acid. Reactions are same as in Steps 3(a) and 4.

Mercury(I)

1. Precipitation of the group. Reagent: dilute hydrochloric acid
$$Hg_2^{++} + 2Cl^- \rightarrow Hg_2Cl_2 \downarrow$$

2. Separation from Pb. Reagent: hot water. No action on Hg_2Cl_2

3. Separation from Ag. Reagent: ammonia solution
$$Hg_2Cl_2 \downarrow + 2NH_3 \rightarrow HgNH_2Cl \downarrow + Hg \downarrow + NH_4^+ + Cl^-$$

4. Dissolution of Residue 1-3 (Outline 1). Reagent: aqua regia
$$Hg^0 \downarrow + 4H^+ + 4Cl^- + 2NO_3^- \rightarrow HgCl_4^{--} + 2NO_2 \uparrow + 2H_2O$$
$$2HgNH_2Cl \downarrow + 8H^+ + 6NO_3^- + 6Cl^- \rightarrow 2HgCl_4^{--} + N_2 \uparrow + 6NO_2 \uparrow + 6H_2O$$

5. Evaporation to remove nitrate. Mercury is unaffected unless evaporation is carried too far. The decomposition of nitrate is represented in part by
$$4H^+ + 3Cl^- + NO_3^- \rightarrow NOCl \uparrow + Cl_2 \uparrow + 2H_2O$$

6. Identification of Hg. Reagent: tin(II) chloride
$$2HgCl_4^{--} + Sn^{++} \rightarrow Hg_2Cl_2 \downarrow + SnCl_6^{--}$$
$$Hg_2Cl_2 \downarrow + Sn^{++} + 4Cl^- \rightarrow 2Hg^0 \downarrow + SnCl_6^{--}$$

EXPERIMENTAL PART

17-9. Introductory Experiments. These experiments are designed to draw your attention to important reactions, techniques, and sources of difficulty in the analysis. Consult the earlier sections of this chapter for discussion and equations. See Sec. 16-5 concerning the record that should be kept of these experiments. The record should include a chemical equation for each reaction.

1. Some ionic reactions of silver ions. Prepare some silver oxalate $(Ag_2C_2O_4)$ by adding a drop or two of $(NH_4)_2C_2O_4$ reagent to one drop of $AgNO_3$ reagent in a test tube (Techniques 4a and 5a).[5] Centrifuge (Technique 8); be careful to balance the test tube against another one containing an equal amount of water. Withdraw the solution with a capillary pipet (Technique 9) and discard it. Add to the precipitate a drop or two of K_2CrO_4

[5]These references are to the techniques described in Sec. 16-3.

reagent. Centrifuge; withdraw the solution and discard it. Wash the precipitate once with about 20 drops (1 ml) of distilled water[6] (Technique 10). Centrifuge and discard the washing water. Dissolve the precipitate in a few drops of 6M NH_3. Add a drop of KI solution (side shelf). Record your observations and write equations for the reactions. Arrange the silver compounds in order of increasing removal of silver ion and compare this order with that given in Table 17-2.

2. Further reactions of silver compounds. Prepare some silver oxide from a drop of $AgNO_3$ reagent. Without bothering to separate precipitates and solutions, add in succession 6 M $HC_2H_3O_2$ and 6 M HNO_3. A drop or two of each reagent should suffice. Record observations and equations. Why does the concentration of silver ion in solution increase during these transformations?

3. Some ionic reactions of lead(II) ion. Devise suitable experiments to verify the position of PbI_2 in Table 17-4. Your notebook record should indicate what reagents you used, your observations and conclusions, and equations for the reactions; but details such as the number of drops of the various solutions need not be given.

4. Preparation of lead chloride from lead(II) oxide. Weigh an empty test tube, add about 0.1 g of PbO, and reweigh to find the weight of sample. Add 5 drops of 6 M HCl and 1 ml of water. Warm and stir until reaction has ceased (a residue may remain). Remove the hot solution to another test tube; discard the residue. Allow the solution to cool undisturbed. If possible, examine some of the product under low magnification, and sketch the crystals in your notebook.

Calculate the volume of 6 M HCl required to react with the weight of PbO that was taken. Was an excess actually used?

5. Properties of lead(II, IV) oxide. Take about $\frac{1}{4}$ spatula-full (Technique 3b) of Pb_3O_4 in a test tube and add 5 drops of 6 M nitric acid. Warm, then centrifuge and transfer the solution to another tube. Verify that the solution contains Pb^{++} ions. Describe your test. Wash the residue in the first tube once with water and discard the washing. What evidence is there that the residue is not Pb_3O_4? Add concentrated hydrochloric acid to the residue and warm in a hot water bath (Technique 6). Hold moist starch-iodide paper in the vapors that rise in the tube. Write equations for all reactions.

6. Preparation and properties of mercury(I) nitrate. Obtain a drop of metallic mercury in a 5 ml beaker or casserole. Add 10 drops of 6 M HNO_3 and set the beaker on top of the hot water bath. After visible reaction ceases, there should still be mercury left. Pour the solution into another small, dry beaker and allow it to cool. Save the mercury for Experiment 7. If no crystals form in the cooled solution, rub the inside of the beaker with a stirring rod. If none

---

[6]Always use distilled water in all analytical experiments.

result from this, set the beaker on the hot water bath and evaporate the solution to smaller volume.

Test the action of water, 6 M HNO_3, and 6 M HCl on separate portions of the crystals. Write equations for all reactions.

7. Reduction of mercury(II) with mercury(0). Wash the remainder of the mercury from Experiment 6 with two portions of water containing a drop of 6 M HNO_3. Discard the washings. Add several drops of the standard solution of Hg^{++} ion (side shelf) and warm. Test the solution for Hg_2^{++} ion. Return unused mercury to a waste bottle on the side shelf. Write an equation for the reaction. Why is a little metallic mercury often added to solutions of mercury(I) salts?

8. Preparation of silver tetraiodomercurate(II). Polymorphism. To 1 drop of $HgCl_2$ solution add 0.1 M KI (side shelf) until the first precipitate just dissolves (if too much is added, the experiment will fail). Then add 2 drops of $AgNO_3$ reagent (from your kit) to precipitate Ag_2HgI_4. Write equations for the reactions.

This compound, like PbO and AgI, exists in two crystal forms. One is stable below 40°, but between 40 and 50.7° it changes into a second form. Verify this by warming the test tube containing the precipitate briefly in a water bath. Verify that the change is reversible.[7]

9. Detection of silver in the presence of large amounts of mercury. Mix 1 drop of the standard solution of Ag^+ ion with 10 drops of the standard solution of Hg_2^{++} ion.[8] Precipitate the chlorides by adding 3 drops of 6 M HCl. Centrifuge; withdraw and discard the solution. Treat the precipitate with several drops of 15 M NH_3 as directed under Precipitate 1-2 in Outline 1. Test the solution for silver as directed under Solution 1-3. Dissolve the residue in aqua regia and test for silver as directed under Precipitate 1-3, Note 14. Account for your results.

17-10. Analysis of Known and Unknown Solutions.

1. Use 5 drops of a *known* or *practice* solution that contains about 5 mg of Pb^{++}, 1 mg of Hg_2^{++}, and 2 mg of Ag^+ per milliliter. If this is not already prepared, mix 3 drops of the standard solution of Pb^{++}, 2 drops of the standard solution of Ag^+, and 1 drop of the standard solution of Hg_2^{++}.

2. The unknown may be (a) a solution containing the ions of this and possibly other groups. If it is basic, acidify with 6 M HCl. (b) a solid mixture. Take a representative sample (Technique 1, Sec. 16-3) and dissolve about 20 mg (Technique 3b) in water or 6 M HNO_3. The latter is better to prevent hydrolysis if Hg_2^{++} is present.

The directions for the analysis are given in Outline 1. The reference

---

[7] For a simple interpretation read E. Gould, *Inorganic Reactions and Structures*, Holt, New York, 1955, p. 191.

[8] The standard solutions contain 10 mg of ion per milliliter.

numbers in the instructions direct your attention to the notes that follow the outline for explanations, precautions, and further instructions. The symbols T-8, T-12, etc., refer to the techniques described in Sec. 16-3.

Consult Sec. 16-5 for a discussion of the type of notebook record to be kept for the analysis of known and unknown solutions.

17-11. Suggestions for Further Work.

1. Analyze known or unknown solutions by paper chromatography. The circular technique is convenient. Consult Chapter 25 for details.

2. Carry out a preparation of one or more of these inorganic compounds: $Pb(NO_3)_2$ from PbO, PbO_2, $[Ag(NH_3)_2]_2SO_4$, AgO, Cu_2HgI_4. The last of these is similar to Ag_2HgI_4 in being polymorphic, but the transition is sharper and more striking. Directions for making several grams of these compounds are given in texts of inorganic preparations.[9]

[9]Consult (1) H. Walton, *Inorganic Preparations*, Prentice-Hall, New York, 1948; (2) H. Biltz and W. Biltz, tr. W. Hall and A. Blanchard, *Laboratory Methods of Inorganic Chemistry*, 2nd ed., Wiley, New York, 1928; (3) A. Blanchard and J. Phelan, *Synthetic Inorganic Chemistry*, 3rd ed., Wiley, New York, 1922; (4) *Inorganic Syntheses*, several vols., McGraw-Hill, New York, 1939- .

OUTLINE I. The Systematic Analysis of Cation Group I

To a suitable sample (Sec. I7-I0) of known or unknown soln in a centrifuge tube add I drop[1] (T-3a, T-4a)[2] 6 M HCl and stir.[3] If a ppt forms,[4] allow it to settle and add another drop of HCl to test for completeness of pptn. Continue addn of HCl until no more ppt forms, but avoid a large xs.[5] Stir for I-2 minutes to give time for slow pptn of $PbCl_2$. Centrifuge using another centrifuge tube filled with an equal vol of water as a counterbalance (T-8a, b). Withdraw as much as possible of the clear soln with a capillary pipet (T-9). Transfer soln to a test tube and check again for completeness of pptn. Wash the residue (T-I0) with a few[6] drops very dil HCl.[7]   →   **Solution I-I. Ions of late groups, including Pb++, and H and Cl⁻.**

Precipitate I-I. AgCl, Hg₂Cl₂, PbCl₂. Add about 5 drops hot, distilled water.[8] Warm in hot water bath and stir occasionally for a few minutes. Centrifuge and separate soln from ppt quickly. Transfer soln to a test tube.   →   **Solution I-2. Pb++, PbCl+, Cl** Add I drop 6 M $HC_2H_3O_2$[9] and severa drops K_2CrO_4. Yellow ppt, $PbCrO_4$: **presence Pb.**[10]

Precipitate I-2. AgCl, Hg₂Cl₂, (PbCl₂). If Pb is found in Soln I-2, repeat extn of residue with hot water until extract gives only a faint turbidity with K_2CrO_4.[11]
To the Pb-free residue add several drops[6] of 15 M NH_3. Use a rod to disperse caked residue in the reagent. Centrifuge. Transfer soln to a test tube.[12]

Solution I-3. Ag(NH₃)₂+, Cl⁻, xs NH₃. Acidify with 6 M HNO_3. Verify with litmus (T-12).[13] White ppt, AgCl: **presence of Ag.**

Precipitate I-3. HgNH₂Cl, Hg⁰ (black (AgCl, Ag⁰). Black residue is usually sufficie indication of **presence of Hg(I).**[14]

Notes on Outline 1

1. Small quantities of reagents are usually required. One drop (0.05 ml) of 6 *M* HCl contains $6 \times 0.05 = 0.3$ mmole (Sec. 4-4). If a sample contains 20 mg of silver, a very large amount, this is equivalent to 0.19 mmole (Sec. 4-3). Thus 1 drop of 6 *M* HCl supplies more than enough chloride for complete precipitation.

2. Such references are to the techniques described in Sec. 16-3.

3. Thorough mixing is difficult in a centrifuge tube because of the narrow bottom (T-5). Work the glass rod up and down and rub the inner walls to induce crystallization of $PbCl_2$, which readily forms supersaturated solutions.

4. If no precipitate forms, Ag^+ and Hg_2^{++} ions are definitely absent, but Pb^{++} ion may be at too low a concentration to precipitate with Group 1 (it will then appear in Group 2) or $PbCl_2$ may have supersaturated. Supersaturation is overcome by vigorous stirring, rubbing the inner walls with the rod, and patient waiting. Allow five minutes before concluding that Group 1 is absent.

5. A large excess of reagent may dissolve the chlorides.

6. In these directions "a few" is taken to mean 1 or 2 drops and "several" to mean 2 to 4 drops. Learn to judge for yourself from the size of the precipitate how much reagent to add. Use the least amount of reagent that will produce the required result.

7. The residue is washed with very dilute HCl to minimize the loss of $PbCl_2$. Dilute 1 drop of 6 *M* HCl with about 10 drops (0.5 ml) of water in a test tube and mix well (T-5a).

8. Use water from a tube suspended in the water bath. Start heating it before beginning the analysis so that it will be ready when you need it. Do not use water directly from the water bath; if this has a lead top, enough lead is introduced to give a false test.

9. The acetic acid prevents precipitation of other chromates such as $CuCrO_4$ or $(BiO)_2CrO_4$ which may appear at this point through failure to wash the group precipitate carefully.

10. Centrifuge to determine the bulk of the precipitate. It is useful to observe the size of tests on known solutions, for these help you to distinguish between normal and trace amounts in unknowns. Traces are generally caused by contamination and should not be reported. In some courses you may be required to estimate whether the ions are present in small, medium, or large amounts.

When large amounts of bismuth are present, it may sometimes carry through to this point through careless technique. If this is suspected, test the solubility of the yellow precipitate in 6 *M* NaOH; $PbCrO_4$ will dissolve but $(BiO)_2CrO_4$ will not.

11. If lead is not almost completely removed from the precipitate, it can coat the chlorides with insoluble $Pb(OH)_2$ when ammonia is added and thus prevent their reaction with the reagent.

12. A test tube is better for the acidification of Solution 1-3 because of the ease of mixing in such tubes (T-5).

13. This is a more difficult operation than the beginner may realize. Silver is often missed through failure to mix solution and nitric acid well and to get a definite acid reaction. If you see a cloudy white layer floating on top of a clear one, mixing has not been vigorous enough. Note particularly as discussed in T-12 that a false acid reaction can be obtained if the stirring rod touches an upper part of the tube that is wet with acid. Mix as described in T-5a.

14. In the presence of large amounts of mercury, small amounts of silver can be lost by reduction of silver chloride to metallic silver. If the silver test is indecisive or negative or if confirmation of the presence of mercury is required, treat the black residue with 1 drop of 16 M HNO_3 and 3 drops of 12 M HCl (this combination is aqua regia). Warm in the hot water bath until reaction ceases and then transfer the mixture to a crucible. Evaporate the solution carefully almost to dryness (T-7) to destroy nitrate and remove excess HCl. Use a microflame (T-7a) and hold the crucible in a wire loop made from a pipe cleaner. Wave the crucible back and forth *above*, not in, the flame. Withdraw it momentarily if boiling becomes too vigorous. Stop heating when a drop or two of solution remains; further evaporation will occur as the crucible and solution cool.

Dilute the solution in the crucible with several drops of water, and transfer the mixture to a centrifuge tube. A turbidity or precipitate may be AgCl. Centrifuge and remove the solution to a test tube. Test the solubility of the precipitate in NH_3: AgCl should dissolve and be reprecipitated when the solution is acidified with HNO_3 (Solution 1-3). To the solution in the test tube add a few drops of $SnCl_2$ reagent. A white, gray, or black precipitate of Hg_2Cl_2 mixed with Hg^0 is confirmation of the presence of Hg(I).

EXERCISES

17-1. For each metal of this group give (a) its position in the Periodic Table, (b) its principal oxidation states, and (c) the reason for its occurrence in Cation Group 1.

17-2. Cite some evidence culled from the chemistry of this group to support the division of electrons in a shell into at least two classes, the s and p subshells.

17-3. The element thallium, atomic number 81, symbol Tl, lies between mercury and lead in the Periodic Table. Predict its oxidation states and write the electronic structures of the outer shell of its atoms and ions.

17-4. Write the electronic structures of the outer shells of K^+. Hg_2^{++}, Rn, Ag^+, Ba^{++}, and Pb^{++}.

17-5. What is meant by an "inert pair" of electrons?

17-6. Solid disilver fluoride (Ag_2F) has an unusually high electrical conductivity. Suggest an explanation.

17-7. Give the colors of Ag^+, $Pb(NO_3)_2$, Hg_2SO_4, PbO_2, $Ag(NH_3)_2^+$, AgF_2, $Hg_2(NO_3)_2 \cdot 2H_2O$, PbI_2, Ag_3AsO_4, Hg_2Cl_2, $PbCrO_4$, Ag_2O, $Pb(OH)_3^-$, Hg_2^{++}, Pb_3O_4, Ag_2S, and Ag_2CrO_4. Select examples from this list of substances that are (a) colorless because of stable electronic structures, (b) colored because of incomplete electronic configuration, (c) colored because of a colored anion, (d) colored because of polarization or partially covalent bond.

17-8. Classify the following as soluble, sparingly soluble, or almost insoluble: Ag_2SO_4, $Hg_2(NO_3)_2$, $Pb(C_2H_3O_2)_2$, AgF, PbS, Hg_2CrO_4, $AgBr$, $PbSO_4$, $AgCN$, $PbCrO_4$, Ag_2O, Ag_2CrO_4, Hg_2CO_3, $Pb(ClO_3)_2$.

17-9. Some silver chloride is dissolved in ammonia solution. When potassium iodide solution is added to this, a yellow precipitate forms. This precipitate is soluble in sodium thiosulfate solution. Sodium sulfide precipitates a black substance from the solution. From these observations alone deduce the relative solubilities of the three precipitates and the relative stabilities of the two complex ions.

17-10. A yellow solid (A) containing one of the ions of this group dissolves in dilute nitric acid with no evolution of gas to give a colorless solution. On cooling, this solution deposits colorless crystals of substance B. These crystals are readily soluble in water, and from this solution sodium hydroxide precipitates a gelatinous white substance C. When some of C is heated gently, it changes to A. The rest of C is dissolved in more sodium hydroxide to give a solution of a substance D. From this solution sodium sulfide precipitates a black solid (E). This is soluble in dilute nitric acid to give a colorless gas (F), a yellow solid (G), and a solution of substance B. Identify all the lettered substances.

17-11. Select the substance with the required characteristic.

(a) Most acidic: Ag_2O, PbO_2, Pb_3O_4, PbO

(b) Most unstable: Hg_2O, Ag_2O, PbO, PbO_2

(c) Best solvent for Ag^0: HCl, $HC_2H_3O_2$, HNO_3, H_2SO_4

(d) Forms strongest bonds with Pb^{++}: O, N, K, S

(e) Best solvent for Ag_2CrO_4: HCl, NaOH, HNO_3, NH_4Cl

(f) Gives saturated solution with lowest concentration of lead(II) ions: PbS, $Pb(NO_3)_2$, $PbCrO_4$, $PbCl_2$

(g) Best solvent for $Hg_2(NO_3)_2$: H_2O, HNO_3, HCl, NaOH

(h) Most soluble in KOH: Ag_2O, PbO, HgO, Hg_2O

(i) Best solvent for AgI: NH_3, KCN, dil. HNO_3, NaOH

(j) Best oxidizing agent: Zn^{++}, NO_3^-, PbO_2, Ag^+

17-12. Predict the direction of the following reactions. Assume that all ions are at about the same concentration.

(a) $2AgCN \downarrow + S^{--} \rightleftharpoons Ag_2S \downarrow + 2CN^-$

(b) $H_2 + 2AgCl \downarrow \rightleftharpoons 2Ag^0 \downarrow + 2H^+ + 2Cl^-$

(c) $2Ag \downarrow + Pb^{++} \rightleftharpoons Pb \downarrow + 2Ag^+$

(d) $PbCrO_4 \downarrow + 3C_2H_3O_2^- \rightleftharpoons Pb(C_2H_3O_2)_3^- + CrO_4^{--}$

(e) $Hg_2^{++} + 2Ag^+ \rightleftharpoons 2Ag^0 \downarrow + 2Hg^{++}$

(f) $Ag_2O \downarrow + H_2O + 2I^- \rightleftharpoons 2AgI \downarrow + 2OH^-$

17-13. Give a structural interpretation of the following; i.e., relate the observation to the structure of the atoms or ions:

(a) the similarity in solubilities of many barium and lead(II) salts,
(b) the existence of lead in two positive oxidation states,
(c) the formation of colored PbI_2 and Ag_2O from colorless ions,
(d) the instability of Ag^{++},
(e) the greater stability of complexes of silver as compared with those of potassium,
(f) the relative solubilities of silver chloride and sodium chloride,
(g) the relative acidic character of PbO and PbO_2.

17-14. What is an "analytical group"? Why is it desirable to separate cations into such groups before identifying them?

17-15. Explain why a slight excess of hydrochloric acid is used in precipitating the group. Why is a large excess to be avoided?

17-16. Write equations for the succesive reactions of the ions of this group (Sec. 17-8).

17-17. Balance the following skeleton equations either by the ion-electron method (Sec. 3-13) or by the oxidation number method (Sec. 3-14). All these reactions take place in acid solution.

(a) $Ag \downarrow + NO_3^- \rightarrow NO_2 + Ag^+$
(b) $Hg \downarrow + NO_3^- + Cl^- \rightarrow NO_2 + HgCl_4^{--}$
(c) $HgNH_2Cl \downarrow + NO_3^- + Cl^- \rightarrow HgCl_4^{--} + N_2 + NO_2$
(d) $NO_3^- + Cl^- \rightarrow NOCl + Cl_2$
(e) $HgCl_4^{--} + Sn^{++} \rightarrow SnCl_6^{--} + Hg_2Cl_2 \downarrow$
(f) $Hg_2Cl_2 \downarrow + Cl^- + Sn^{++} \rightarrow SnCl_6^{--} + Hg \downarrow$

17-18. Account for the following operations in the analysis by Outline 1:

(a) the addition of acetic acid before the identification of lead,
(b) the continued washing of the group precipitate with hot water,
(c) the addition of aqua regia to the mercury precipitate.

17-19. What reagent or mixture of reagents could you use to separate the substances in each pair in a single step? Give preference to separations actually used in the analytical procedure. (a) $Ca^{++} - Ag^+$, (b) $AgCl - PbCl_2$, (c) $Hg_2^{++} - Hg^{++}$, (d) $Hg_2Cl_2 - AgCl$, (e) $AgCl - CuCl_2$, (f) $Hg_2Cl_2 - PbCl_2$, (g) $Hg_2Cl_2 - HgCl_2$.

17-20. How would you distinguish between separate samples of the two substances in each part? (a) $Ag_2CrO_4 - PbCrO_4$, (b) $PbCrO_4 - (BiO)_2CrO_4$, (c) $PbO - PbO_2$, (d) $Pb(NO_3)_2 - Hg_2(NO_3)_2$, (e) $PbCO_3 - PbSO_4$, (f) $AgBr - AgI$, (g) $Pb(OH)_2 - PbF_2$, (h) $Ag_2O - PbO_2$.

17-21. A solid unknown may possibly contain $AgNO_3$, Hg_2Cl_2, or $Pb(C_2H_3O_2)_2$. From the observations decide which of these substances are definitely present or absent. There may not be sufficient evidence to permit a decision on all the substances.

(a) The unknown is completely soluble in water.
(b) When potassium chromate is added to the solution an orange-red precipitate forms.
(c) The addition of hydrochloric acid converts this precipitate to a white one.

17-22. The equation $NH_3 + Hg_2Cl_2 \rightarrow Hg + HgNH_2Cl + H^+ + Cl^-$ is balanced, and yet it is incorrect. Why are two moles of NH_3 required?

CHAPTER EIGHTEEN

Cation Group 2

The Acid Hydrogen Sulfide Group

$Hg^{++}, Cd^{++}, Cu^{++}, Pb^{++}, Sn^{++}, Sn(IV),$
$Bi^{+++}, Sb(III), Sb(V), As(III), As(V)$

18-1. Introduction. The eight elements of this group form sulfides that are precipitated by hydrogen sulfide or thioacetamide from solutions that are 0.1 to 0.3 M in hydrochloric acid. Of the chlorides only that of lead is sparingly soluble in dilute hydrochloric acid and precipitates with Cation Group 1 to an appreciable extent. Silver and mercury(I), had they not already been removed as chlorides, would precipitate as sulfides with Group 2.

The positions in the Periodic Table of these elements and of the others that form sulfides that are insoluble in 0.1 to 0.3 M acid are shown below.

								IIIB	IVB	VB	VIB
VIA	VIIA		VIII		IB	IIB					
					29 **Cu** (II)			32 Ge (II)	33 **As** (III,V)	34 (Se)* (IV)	
42 Mo (VI)	43 Tc	44 Ru (III)	45 Rh (III)	46 Pd (II)		48 **Cd** (II)		50 **Sn** (II,IV)	51 **Sb** (III,V)	52 (Te)* (IV)	
	75 Re (VII)	76 Os (IV)	77 Ir (III)	78 Pt (IV)	79 Au (III)	80 **Hg** (II)		82 **Pb** (II)	83 **Bi** (III)	84 Po	

*Se and Te are precipitated as the free elements, not the sulfides, by H_2S.

18-2. Some Features of the Group as a Whole. The most notable common characteristic of all these elements is their affinity for sulfur. This is shown not only by their precipitation together as a group but also by their occurrence in nature in sulfide ores: PbS, galena; $CuFeS_2$, chalcopyrite; CdS, greenockite;

HgS, cinnabar; FeAsS, arsenopyrite; Sb_2S_3, stibnite; and Bi_2S_3, bismuth glance.

None of the simple positive ions, Hg^{++}, Cd^{++}, Cu^{++}, Pb^{++}, Sn^{++}, Bi^{+++}, or Sb^{+++}, has inert gas structure. The first two ions have 18 electrons in their outer shell, Cu^{++} ion has 17, and the rest have outer shells of 18 electrons plus an inert pair. All have a strong polarizing effect on H_2O molecules and OH^-, HS^-, O^{--}, and S^{--} ions, the attraction being strongest for the highly polarizable sulfide ion. All of the ions but Cu^{++} contain paired electrons in stable configurations and normally give colorless compounds, unless the anion is colored as in yellow $PbCrO_4$ or highly polarizable as in the iodides, oxides, and sulfides (Table 18-1).

TABLE 18-1.

Colors of Iodides, Oxides, and Sulfides of Cation Group 2

Element	Iodide	Oxide	Sulfide
Cu(I)	white CuI	red Cu_2O	black Cu_2S
Cu(II)	*	black CuO	black CuS
Cd(II)	white CdI_2	brown to black CdO	yellow CdS
Hg(II)	red HgI_2	yellow or red HgO	red or black HgS
Sn(II)	orange SnI_2	black SnO	brown SnS
Sn(IV)	yellow to brown SnI_4	white SnO_2	yellow SnS_2
Pb(II)	yellow to red PbI_2	yellow or red PbO	black PbS
Pb(II, IV)		red Pb_3O_4	
Pb(IV)	*	brown-black PbO_2	*
As(II)	dark red AsI_2		red As_4S_4
As(III)	red AsI_3	white As_2O_3	yellow As_2S_3
As(V)	*	white As_2O_5	yellow As_2S_5*
Sb(III)	red or yellow SbI_3	white Sb_2O_3	yellow, orange, or red Sb_2S_3†
Sb(V)	*	yellow Sb_2O_5	orange-red Sb_2S_5*
Bi(III)	black BiI_3	yellow Bi_2O_3	dark brown Bi_2S_3†

*These iodides and sulfides either cannot be prepared or else decompose readily to the lower iodide or sulfide; e.g.,

$$2Cu^{++} + 4I^- \rightarrow 2CuI \downarrow + I_2; Sb_2S_5 \rightarrow Sb_2S_3 + 2S^0$$

†The more massive crystalline forms of these sulfides found in nature are lead gray in color. They can be prepared by heating the precipitated sulfides in the absence of air.

Arsenic(V), antimony(V), and tin(IV) do not exist as positive ions but attain inert gas structure by sharing electrons with oxide, hydroxide, sulfide, or halide ions. The chlorides, and hydrides of these three elements are typical molecular substances. These elements are on the borderline between metals and nonmetals in the Periodic Table. The oxides and sulfides of Cation Group 2 thus range from basic substances such as CdO and PbS, which have crystal structures like that of NaCl, to acidic substances such as antimony(III) oxide and arsenic(III) sulfide, which are composed of Sb_4O_6 and As_4S_6 molecules. The acidic and basic properties of the sulfides are used in subdividing the group.

The ions of the group will now be considered one at a time. Since the discussion of the ions of Cation Group 1 ended with mercury(I), it is appropriate to begin with mercury(II). Lead(II) was dealt with in Chapter 17 and will be considered only briefly here in connection with its congener, tin.

PROPERTIES OF THE IONS

18-3. The Mercury(II) Ion.

a. Characteristics of the +2 Oxidation State of Mercury. The mercury(II) ion has an outer shell of 18 electrons divided between s, p, and d subshells. Its ionic radius is 1.10 A, about the same as that of Sr^{++} ion and in between the radii of Cd^{++} and Pb^{++} ions. It differs radically from these ions in its tendency to form covalent bonds. The energy required to remove two electrons from a mercury atom is abnormally high, and in most compounds of mercury(II) the electrons are shared rather than lost completely to give Hg^{++} ions. Crystals of the chloride, for example, contain discrete $HgCl_2$ molecules, and its solution is a poor electrical conductor. The molecular character of the iodide in solution is indicated by the fact that it is more soluble in benzene, a nonpolar solvent, than it is in water. Mercury(II) also forms many complex ions in which four groups at most are coordinated to the mercury. In HgI_4^{--}, for example, the four ligands are arranged tetrahedrally about the central mercury atom:

and mercury acquires a share in an octet of electrons so that its electronic arrangement resembles that of the inert gas radon.[1] It also forms complexes in which its coordination number is less than four.

b. Reactions of Hg^{++} Ion. These are summarized in Table 18-2. The order is one of increasing removal of Hg^{++} ion and a quantitative indication of this is given by the equilibrium constants, which increase as the extent of removal of Hg^{++} by the reactions from left to right increases. This order will

---

[1] The effective atomic number of mercury is 86, the atomic number of radon. See Sec. 6-11.

hold only if the reagents are used at about the same concentration. Mercury(II) sulfide, for example, will not precipitate from a strongly acid solution saturated with hydrogen sulfide if a large excess of iodide is present; under these conditions the extent of removal of Hg^{++} ion to give the iodide complex is greater than that to give the sulfide.

Redox reactions of Hg^{++} ion were discussed in Sec. 17-5c.

TABLE 18-2.

Some Reactions of Hg^{++} Ion

Reagent*	Equation	K†
HCl, NaCl, NH_4Cl in excess	$Hg^{++} + 4Cl^- \rightleftharpoons HgCl_4^{--}$	10^{16}
HBr or KBr in excess	$Hg^{++} + 4Br^- \rightleftharpoons HgBr_4^{--}$	10^{21}
KSCN or NH_4SCN in excess	$Hg^{++} + 4SCN^- \rightleftharpoons Hg(SCN)_4^{--}$	10^{22}
NaOH or KOH (not NH_3)	$Hg^{++} + 2OH^- \rightleftharpoons HgO \downarrow + H_2O$	10^{25}
KI in excess	$Hg^{++} + 4I^- \rightleftharpoons HgI_4^{--}$	10^{30}
KCN in excess	$Hg^{++} + 4CN^- \rightleftharpoons Hg(CN)_4^{--}$	10^{41}
H_2S, $(NH_4)_2S$, CH_3CSNH_2	$Hg^{++} + S^{--} \rightleftharpoons HgS \downarrow$	10^{52}

*Common laboratory reagents are given. Other soluble, highly ionized sources of the required ion could be used.
†The equilibrium constant is given to the nearest power of ten. Some are not accurately known; the relative position of $HgBr_4^{--}$ and $Hg(SCN)_4^{--}$, for example, is uncertain.

c. Compounds of Mercury(II).

(1) The oxide HgO. There are two forms, yellow and red, that differ only in particle size. Priestley's classic preparation of oxygen by heating the oxide is testimony of its thermal instability. No hydroxide is known. Although the solubility of the oxide increases somewhat in concentrated alkali, there is no other evidence of acidic behavior. Were it to act as an acid, hydroxide complexes would form, but this is unlikely in view of the low affinity that mercury usually shows for oxygen.

(2) The sulfide HgS. Mercury has a very strong affinity for sulfur. Its sulfide is the most insoluble of those encountered in this course. It is polymorphic: the red form, known as the mineral cinnabar or the pigment vermilion, has a higher density than, slightly lower solubility than, and different crystal structure from, the black form, metacinnabarite. The latter is always precipitated by hydrogen sulfide, but cinnabar is obtained when thioacetamide in excess acts on mercury(II) in acid solution.[2] The precipitated cinnabar is frequently lighter in color than vermilion, contains smaller particles, and is probably somewhat more soluble in acid or alkali. It changes to the black form when heated with ammonium sulfide or a combination of

[2] The molar ratio of thioacetamide to mercury must be greater than 2:1. See J. F. Vozza, J. Chem. Educ., 35, 145 (1958).

ammonia and thioacetamide. Various light-colored mixed sulfides are known, e.g., white $2HgS \cdot Hg(NO_3)_2$ obtained by the action of concentrated nitric acid on black HgS.

Mercury(II) sulfide can be dissolved if the concentration of one or both of its ions is reduced by chemical action. The concentration of sulfide ion in its saturated solution is so low that neither the formation of H_2S nor the oxidation of S^{--} ion to S^0 can occur to an appreciable extent. Consequently, HgS is insoluble in dilute acids including HNO_3. It dissolves slowly in concentrated hydrochloric or nitric acid and is readily soluble in aqua regia, because mercury is removed to give weakly dissociated $HgCl_4^{--}$ ions and sulfide is oxidized to free sulfur.

The sulfide is acidic, unlike the oxide, and dissolves in alkali sulfides to give a thiocomplex ion:

$$HgS \downarrow + S^{--} \rightleftharpoons HgS_2^{--}$$

At equilibrium the concentration of complex is about four times that of simple sulfide ion, so that if the concentration of sulfide is made high, a considerable amount of HgS can be dissolved. It is not soluble in $(NH_4)_2S$ solution because this reagent supplies a relatively low concentration of sulfide ion owing to the equilibrium

$$NH_4^+ + S^{--} \rightleftharpoons NH_3 + HS^-$$

Potassium and sodium hydroxides do not dissolve appreciable amounts of HgS unless the sulfides of arsenic, antimony, and tin are present. The dissociation of the thioanions of these three elements, e.g.,

$$SnS_3^{--} \rightleftharpoons SnS_2 + S^{--}$$

apparently supplies enough sulfide to the solution to bring about the dissolution of some HgS. If 0.5 M KOH is used, the solubility of HgS is sufficiently small as to cause no serious trouble in the analysis of this group.

(3) Compounds with Hg(II)—N bonds. The action of ammonia on mercury(II) salts varies with the anion of the salt and the presence or absence of ammonium compounds. The action of ammonia on $HgCl_2$ gives the white mercury(II) amidochloride:

$$HgCl_2 + 2NH_3 \rightarrow HgNH_2Cl \downarrow + NH_4^+ + Cl^-$$

In the presence of an excess of ammonium chloride the ammonia coordinates without loss of a proton or displacement of a chloride to give $Hg(NH_3)_2Cl_2$ or

$$
\begin{array}{ccc}
Cl & & NH_3 \\
& \diagdown \diagup & \\
& Hg & \\
& \diagup \diagdown & \\
H_3N & & Cl
\end{array}
$$

Ammonia acts on yellow HgO to give Millon's base:

$$NH_3 + 2HgO \downarrow \rightarrow [OHg_2NH_2]OH$$

The iodide salt of this base is the brown precipitate that forms in the Nessler test for ammonium ion (Sec. 21-8). An ammine $Hg(NH_3)_4^{++}$ is also known but is of no importance in analysis.

(4) Soluble salts. These are divided into strong and weak electrolytes. The fluoride is a strong electrolyte because the high electronegativity of fluorine and low polarizability of fluoride ion favor the formation of ionic bonds. The crystal structure of mercury(II) fluoride resembles that of calcium fluoride (Fig. 2-6) with 8 fluoride ions about each Hg^{++} ion. In mercury(II) chloride, two chloride atoms are very close to each mercury atom as would be expected for Cl—Hg—Cl molecules. The fluoride crystal is more tightly bound together by the ionic forces and has the higher melting point: 645° for HgF_2 as compared with about 280° for $HgCl_2$. The bromide and iodide form layer lattices with each mercury surrounded by four halide ions and are less easily broken apart by water and less soluble than the fluoride and chloride.

The strongly ionized salts, which include the nitrate and perchlorate besides the fluoride, hydrolyze readily to precipitate yellow HgO or a basic salt:

$$Hg^{++} + H_2O \rightleftharpoons HgO \downarrow + 2H^+$$

The hydrolysis is repressed by strong acid. The basic nitrates $Hg(OH)NO_3$ and $Hg_3O_2(NO_3)_2 \cdot H_2O$ are unstable and react with water to give the oxide.

The ionization and hydrolysis of weakly ionized $HgCl_2$ was discussed in Sec. 2-20; the net effect is

$$HgCl_2 + H_2O \rightleftharpoons Hg(OH)Cl + H^+ + Cl^-$$

Because $HgCl_2$ is weakly ionized, the reaction can be reversed by addition of an excess of either H^+ or Cl^- just as the ionization of $HC_2H_3O_2$ can be repressed by an excess of either H^+ or $C_2H_3O_2^-$.

(5) Insoluble salts. These include the sulfide, oxalate, phosphate, ferrocyanide, and iodide. The bromide is intermediate in solubility between the iodide and chloride. The sulfate is sparingly soluble.

18-4. The Cadmium(II) Ion.

a. Characteristics of the $+2$ Oxidation State of Cadmium. This is the only important oxidation state of cadmium. The existence of Cd_2^{++}, analogous with Hg_2^{++}, has not been established. The Cd^{++} ion, like Hg^{++}, has an outer shell of 18 electrons. Its radius is 0.97 A or about equal to that of Ca^{++} ion.

Cadmium resembles zinc and copper(II) more closely than it does mercury(II). In comparison with the latter, its sulfide is more soluble, its salts are more highly dissociated and less hydrolyzed, and it forms an ammonia complex that is useful in analysis. These differences have their origin in the comparatively small size and high nuclear charge of Hg^{++} ions. This is brought out by comparing the differences in radii and nuclear charges of several pairs of ions:

Pair	Difference in radii	Difference in nuclear charge
$Sr^{++} - Ba^{++}$	0.21 A	18 units
$Zn^{++} - Cd^{++}$	0.18	18
$Cd^{++} - Hg^{++}$	0.13	32

The high nuclear charge and small radius of Hg^{++} are consequences of the occurrence of the lanthanides (rare-earth metals) between Groups IIIA and IVA of the third long period, and the effect is called the *lanthanide contraction*.

b. Reactions of Cd^{++} Ion. The important reactions are summarized in Table 18-3. It will be noted that cadmium forms a number of complex ions. They are more highly dissociated than those of mercury(II); e.g., the formation constant of HgI_4^{--} is 10^{30} and that of CdI_4^{--} is only 10^6. The coordination number of cadmium in its complexes varies from 1 to 4 and is occasionally 6. In complexes such as $Cd(CN)_4^{--}$ it shares an octet of electrons with the four cyanide ions and acquires the electronic configuration of xenon; i.e., its effective atomic number is 54.

The order of the reactions in Table 18-3 is that of their equilibrium constants. It is also the order of decreasing concentration of Cd^{++} if the equilibrium concentrations of reagents and complex ions are adjusted to some fixed value, e.g., 0.1 M. Under such conditions all of the first eight substances

TABLE 18-3.

Some Reactions of the Cd^{++} Ion

Reagents	Equations		Approximate K
HCl, NaCl, NH_4Cl in excess	$Cd^{++} + 3Cl^-$	$\rightleftharpoons CdCl_3^-$	10^3
KI in excess	$Cd^{++} + 4I^-$	$\rightleftharpoons CdI_4^{--}$	10^6
NH_3 in excess	$Cd^{++} + 4NH_3$	$\rightleftharpoons Cd(NH_3)_4^{++}$	10^7
$Na_2C_2O_4, H_2C_2O_4,$ $(NH_4)_2C_2O_4$	$Cd^{++} + C_2O_4^{--}$	$\rightleftharpoons CdC_2O_4 \downarrow$	10^8
$K_4Fe(CN)_6$	$Cd^{++} + \frac{1}{2}Fe(CN)_6^{----} \rightleftharpoons \frac{1}{2}Cd_2Fe(CN)_6 \downarrow$		10^8
$Na_2CO_3, K_2CO_3,$ $(NH_4)_2CO_3*$	$Cd^{++} + CO_3^{--}$	$\rightleftharpoons CdCO_3 \downarrow$	10^{11}
NaOH, KOH, NH_3*	$Cd^{++} + 2OH^-$	$\rightleftharpoons Cd(OH)_2 \downarrow$	10^{14}
KCN in excess	$Cd^{++} + 4CN^-$	$\rightleftharpoons Cd(CN)_4^{--}$	10^{19}
$H_2S, Na_2S, (NH_4)_2S$	$Cd^{++} + S^{--}$	$\rightleftharpoons CdS \downarrow$	10^{26}

*Soluble in excess reagent to give the ammonia complex ion.

could be transformed into the last one, CdS, by addition of a soluble sulfide. The action of a reagent such as NH_3 is critically dependent on its concentration: the 6 M reagent will dissolve all the precipitates but CdS.

c. Compounds of Cadmium(II).

(1) The oxide CdO and hydroxide $Cd(OH)_2$. Crystals of the oxide are composed of Cd^{++} and O^{--} arranged in the same pattern as the ions of NaCl (Fig. 2-5). Unlike mercury, cadmium forms a crystalline hydroxide which has a layer lattice (Fig. 2-9a). Both oxide and hydroxide are predominantly basic; i.e., they dissolve in acids to give Cd^{++} ions. They are slightly soluble in concentrated alkalies, and crystalline salts such as $Na_2Cd(OH)_4$, $Na_3Cd(OH)_5$, and $Sr_2Cd(OH)_6$ have been isolated from these solutions. From these facts we infer that strongly alkaline solutions of $Cd(OH)_2$ contain hydroxide complex ions but that the hydroxide is predominantly basic because its acidic reactions, e.g.,

$$Cd(OH)_2 \downarrow + 2OH^- \rightleftharpoons Cd(OH)_4^{--}$$

occur to an appreciable extent only in the presence of a high concentration of strong base.

(2) The sulfide CdS. It forms as a yellow precipitate from solutions that are saturated with hydrogen sulfide and not more than about 0.3 M in acid. The rate of its precipitation by thioacetamide when the hydrogen ion concentration exceeds 0.01 M is controlled by the rate of hydrolysis of the reagent. At lower acid concentrations thioacetamide reacts directly with Cd^{++} ions without requiring the intermediate hydrolysis step.

Cadmium sulfide is much more soluble than mercury(II) sulfide; they are, in fact, the most soluble and least soluble of the sulfides of Cation Group 2. Cadmium sulfide is readily soluble in dilute acids. It is not soluble in KCN, NH_3, KOH, $(NH_4)_2S$, or K_2S. Unlike HgS, it has no acidic properties.

(3) Soluble salts. These include the halides, thiocyanate, nitrate, sulfate, and acetate. A number of them form stable hydrates, e.g., $Cd(NO_3)_2 \cdot 4H_2O$. The halides form crystals with layer lattices (Fig. 2-9a). Their solutions are unusual in containing anion as well as cation complexes. Anion complexes are generally formed only with an excess of complexing agent. A salt such as $CdCl_2$ forms complex anions by itself:

$$CdCl_2 + CdCl_2 \rightleftharpoons CdCl_3^- + CdCl^+$$

and hence the process is called *auto-complex formation* (from the Greek *autos* meaning "self"). Because of the presence of such complex ions, the specific conductance, freezing point depression, and other electrolytic properties of solutions of the cadmium halides are abnormal in comparison with those of the halides of other bivalent metal ions such as calcium, nickel, or zinc.

(4) The insoluble salts. The principal ones are given in Table 18-3. All are soluble in dilute nitric acid.

d. Redox Reactions. Cadmium metal is about as active a reducing agent as iron and readily dissolves in acids. The Cd-Cd^{++} couple in Table 18-4 lies well above the H$_2$-H$^+$ and NO-NO$_3$$^-$ couples. The ion can be reduced to the free metal by zinc or aluminum if the solution is not too acid. In basic solution cadmium ions are removed by precipitation or complex formation, and the metal is potentially a better reducing agent than it is in acid solutions. Cadmium ion is removed to the greatest extent to form the sulfide (Table 18-3); thus the Cd-CdS couple is the highest in Table 18-4. The ammonia complex of cadmium, unlike that of copper, is not reduced by dithionite (S$_2$O$_4$$^{--}$).

TABLE 18-4.

Some Redox Couples of Cadmium and Other Substances

Acid Solutions				
Reduced form (reducing agent)		Oxidized form (oxidizing agent)		$\mathcal{E}^0$* at 25° in volts
Al	$\rightleftharpoons$	Al^{+++} $+$ $3e^-$		1.66
Zn	$\rightleftharpoons$	Zn^{++} $+$ $2e^-$		0.76
Fe	$\rightleftharpoons$	Fe^{++} $+$ $2e^-$		0.44
Cd	$\rightleftharpoons$	Cd^{++} $+$ $2e^-$		0.40
H$_2$	$\rightleftharpoons$	2H$^+$ $+$ $2e^-$		0.00
NO $+$ 2H$_2$O	$\rightleftharpoons$	NO$_3$$^-$ $+$ 4H$^+$ $+$ $3e^-$		-0.96
Basic Solutions				
S^{--} $+$ Cd	$\rightleftharpoons$	CdS $\downarrow$ $+$ $2e^-$		1.24
4CN$^-$ $+$ Cd	$\rightleftharpoons$	Cd(CN)$_4$$^{--}$ $+$ $2e^-$		1.09
2OH$^-$ $+$ Cd	$\rightleftharpoons$	Cd(OH)$_2$ $\downarrow$ $+$ $2e^-$		0.81
4NH$_3$ $+$ Cd	$\rightleftharpoons$	Cd(NH$_3$)$_4$$^{++}$ $+$ $2e^-$		0.61
4NH$_3$ $+$ 2H$_2$O $+$ S$_2$O$_4$$^{--}$	$\rightleftharpoons$	2SO$_3$$^{--}$ $+$ 4NH$_4$$^+$ $+$ $2e^-$		0.56

*The standard oxidation potential $\mathcal{E}^0$ (Sec. 9-8) measures the reducing power of a substance relative to hydrogen when all solutes are at approximately unit concentration. A large positive value indicates an active reducing agent, a large negative value a powerful oxidizing agent.

18-5. The Copper(II) Ion.

a. Electronic Structure and Oxidation States of Copper. Like silver and gold, the other members of Group IB, copper has oxidation states of $+1$, 2, and 3. The last of these occurs only in a few complex ions and will not be considered further. Unlike silver and gold, copper generally occurs in the $+2$ state. There is no completely satisfying explanation of this.

The copper atom has a $4s$ valence electron outside a complete shell of 18 electrons: configuration $3s^2 3p^6 3d^{10} 4s^1$. The Cu$^+$ ion is formed by loss of the

$4s$ electron and thus has an 18-electron outer shell like those of the Ag^+ and Cd^{++} ions. The Cu^{++} ion has the electronic configuration $3s^23p^63d^9$. Removal of a $3d$ electron from the Cu^+ ion is not comparatively easy, as is sometimes stated; the energy required (468 kcal/mole) is a little smaller than that for $Ag^+ \rightarrow Ag^{++}$ (495) but a good deal larger than that for $Ni^+ \rightarrow Ni^{++}$ (419). The Cu^{++} ion is smaller than the Ag^{++} ion, and hence more energy is released in formation of crystals of its salts and of its hydrated and complex ions. This is perhaps responsible in part for the greater stability of the Cu(II) compounds.

b. Compounds of Copper(I).   Copper in this oxidation state exists only in insoluble or weakly dissociated compounds. In solution free Cu^+ ions disproportionate:

$$2Cu^+ \rightleftharpoons Cu^0 + Cu^{++}$$

At equilibrium the ratio of molar concentrations $[Cu^{++}]/[Cu^+]^2$ is about 10^6; thus if Cu^+ could exist at 0.1 M concentration the Cu^{++} would have to be present at the impossible concentration of 10,000 M. Actually, if $[Cu^{++}] = 1$ M, $[Cu^+]$ can at most be no more than 0.001 M. Characteristic compounds of copper(I) include insoluble CuCl, CuBr, CuI, CuSCN, Cu_2S, and Cu_2O and such complex ions as $Cu(CN)_3^{--}$, $CuCl_2^-$, and $Cu(NH_3)_2^+$. The sulfide and oxide are colored; the other compounds are colorless because the Cu^+ ion contains a completed shell of 18 electrons (compare with the Ag^+ ion). At high temperatures compounds of copper(I) become more stable than those of copper(II).

c. Characteristics of Copper(II).   The radius of the Cu^{++} ion is about 0.7 A, not greatly different from those of Mg^{++}, Fe^{++}, Co^{++}, Ni^{++}, and Zn^{++}. The compounds of all these ions have similar solubilities and hydrations. There is a series of double salts, for example, known as Tutton salts or schönites [after the prototype $K_2Mg(SO_4)_2 \cdot 6H_2O$] with the general formula $M_2N(SO_4)_2 \cdot 6H_2O$, where M is a univalent ion and N is any bivalent ion with a radius of about 0.7 A. The stabilities of these crystals depend primarily on the charge and radius of the cation N and not on its electronic structure. A typical schönite containing Cu^{++} ion is the light blue $(NH_4)_2Cu(SO_4)_2 \cdot 6H_2O$.

Because of the incomplete electronic structure of Cu^{++} ion, its compounds are usually colored. The salts are blue in dilute solutions and in the solid hydrates, e.g., $CuSO_4 \cdot 5H_2O$. When water molecules in the hydrated cation are replaced by other molecules or ions the color changes, e.g., to green $(CuCl^+)$, brown $(CuBr^+)$, or indigo blue $[Cu(NH_3)_4^{++}]$. Anhydrous copper(II) salts range in color from white $[CuSO_4, CuF_2, Cu(NO_3)_2]$ to dark brown $(CuCl_2)$ and black $(CuBr_2)$. This runs parallel to a change from ionic to covalent binding. The dark chloride Cu_2Cl_3 contains both Cu(I) and Cu(II) and is formed by partial reduction of $CuCl_2$ in solution by metallic copper.

Many compounds that contain a metal in two oxidation states have deep colors.

d. Reactions of the Cu^{++} Ion. A number of important reactions of Cu^{++} ion are listed in Table 18-5 in the usual order. The effect of changes in concentration of reagents on the order is worth noting again. Both the oxide and hydroxide readily dissolve to give the ammonia complex if the concentration of ammonia is high enough. Several complex ions are given in the table. The usual maximum coordination number of copper(II) is 4 and such complexes contain the ligands at the corners of a square with the Cu^{++} ion in the center. In the oxalate complex two corners of the square are grasped by each oxalate ion; i.e., this is a chelate (see Sec. 6-8). The coordination number of copper is sometimes as high as 6, as in the $Cu(H_2O)_6^{++}$ ions found in $(NH_4)_2Cu(SO_4)_2 \cdot 6H_2O$. Such complexes are octahedral.

TABLE 18-5.

Some Reactions of the Cu^{++} Ion

Reagents	Equations	K	Color of product
HCl, NH$_4$Cl, KCl in excess	$Cu^{++} + 4Cl^- \rightleftharpoons CuCl_4^{--}$	10^4	green
K$_2$CrO$_4$	$Cu^{++} + CrO_4^{--} \rightleftharpoons CuCrO_4 \downarrow$	10^5	brownish red
KIO$_3$	$Cu^{++} + 2IO_3^- \rightleftharpoons Cu(IO_3)_2 \downarrow$	10^7	pale blue
(NH$_4$)$_2$C$_2$O$_4$ in excess	$Cu^{++} + 2C_2O_4^- \rightleftharpoons Cu(C_2O_4)_2^{--}$	10^8	greenish blue
K$_4$Fe(CN)$_6$	$Cu^{++} + \frac{1}{2}Fe(CN)_6^{----} \rightleftharpoons \frac{1}{2}Cu_2Fe(CN)_6 \downarrow$	10^8	very dusky red
NH$_3$ in excess	$Cu^{++} + 4NH_3 \rightleftharpoons Cu(NH_3)_4^{++}$	10^{12}	indigo blue
NaOH, KOH, limited NH$_3$*	$Cu^{++} + 2OH^- \rightleftharpoons Cu(OH)_2 \downarrow$	10^{19}	blue
hot NaOH, KOH	$Cu^{++} + 2OH^- \rightleftharpoons CuO \downarrow + H_2O$	10^{20}	black
H$_2$S, CH$_3$CSNH$_2$, (NH$_4$)$_2$S	$Cu^{++} + S^{--} \rightleftharpoons CuS \downarrow$	10^{35}	black

*Pale blue basic salts precipitate if less than 2 moles of base are added per mole of Cu^{++} ion.

e. Compounds of Copper(II).

(1) The oxide CuO and hydroxide $Cu(OH)_2$. Crystals of the oxide contain Cu^{++} and O^{--} ions in a cubic pattern that is a distorted version of that in the NaCl crystal. The blue hydroxide crystallizes in a layer lattice and is readily dehydrated to the black oxide by heat. Both compounds are predominantly basic and dissolve readily in acids:

$$CuO \downarrow + 2H^+ \rightarrow Cu^{++} + 2H^+$$

They are also soluble in aqueous ammonia and KCN to give complex ions. They are slightly acidic and dissolve in strong bases to give deep blue solutions from which solids such as $Na_2Cu(OH)_4$ and $Sr_2Cu(OH)_6$ have been isolated. At equilibrium

$$Cu(OH)_2 \downarrow\, + 2OH^- \rightleftharpoons Cu(OH)_4^{--}$$

the ratio of concentrations $[Cu(OH)_4^{--}]/[OH^-]^2$ is 0.0019; thus if $[OH^-] = 1\ M$, the concentration of the complex is only 0.0019 M. The solubility is appreciable only in concentrated solutions of NaOH.

(2) The sulfide CuS. This has a very low solubility product and is even precipitated by H_2S from solutions of Cu(II) salts that are as much as 6 M in HCl. It is readily dissolved by 3 M HNO_3 because of oxidation of S^{--} to S^0. It slowly dissolves in 12 M HCl but is insoluble in hot 3 M H_2SO_4. It dissolves in KCN solution to give the very stable complex of Cu(I), $Cu(CN)_3^{--}$. The sulfide is not acidic and does not dissolve in KOH or K_2S, but it is slightly soluble in $(NH_4)_2S$ solution.

(3) Soluble salts of Cu(II). These include the chloride, bromide, sulfate, nitrate, perchlorate, and acetate. The iodide and thiocyanate decompose to give the Cu(I) salts. Many of them form hydrates, e.g., $CuSO_4 \cdot 5H_2O$, that are blue and contain hydrated cupric ions. Dilute solutions are also blue because of these ions. It is not yet certain that solutions of the sulfate contain $Cu^{++}SO_4^{--}$ ion-pairs; the difficulty of distinguishing between ion-pair formation and strong interaction between highly charged but separate ions has given rise to a lively controversy. Hydrolysis, i.e.,

$$Cu^{++} + H_2O \rightleftharpoons CuOH^+ + H^+$$

is more pronounced than it is in solutions of cadmium salts but does not occur to a sufficient extent to precipitate the hydroxide.

The chloride and bromide contain partially covalent bonds. Crystals of the chloride are made of chains:

The chains are stacked together so that each copper is surrounded by six chlorides: four in its own chain and one each from a chain above and one below its own chain. In crystals of the hydrate $CuCl_2 \cdot 2H_2O$, the two water molecules are coordinated to the copper above and below the plane of the chain. Thus the coordination number of copper in these crystals is six.

(4) Insoluble salts of Cu(II). In addition to those given in Table 18-5, mention may be made of the oxalate, phosphate, and basic carbonates. Sodium and potassium carbonates, which are strongly alkaline reagents,

precipitate basic carbonates of variable composition. The beautiful minerals malachite, green $Cu_2(OH)_2CO_3$, and azurite, blue $Cu_3(OH)_2(CO_3)_2$, are well-defined basic carbonates.

f. Redox Reactions. The pertinent couples are given in Table 18-6. The metal is below hydrogen in activity but is readily oxidized to Cu^{++} ions by nitric acid. Active metals such as Zn or Fe will reduce the ions back to the metal. The Cu^+-Cu^{++} couple lies above the Cu-Cu^+ couple, and hence disproportionation will occur:

$$2Cu^+ \rightarrow Cu^0 + Cu^{++}$$

This is reversed if Cu^+ ions are removed to give the insoluble chloride:

$$Cu + Cu^{++} + 2Cl^- \rightarrow 2CuCl \downarrow$$

because the Cu-$CuCl$ couple lies above the $CuCl$-Cu^{++} couple. The Cu^{++} ion is a sufficiently active oxidizing agent to oxidize iodide:

$$2Cu^{++} + 4I^- \rightarrow 2CuI \downarrow + I_2$$

This reaction is used in the quantitative determination of copper. In ammoniacal solution the ammonia complex can be reduced to free copper by

TABLE 18-6.

Some Redox Couples of Copper and Other Substances

		Acid Solutions	
Change in oxidation number of Cu	Reduced form (reducing agent)	Oxidized form (oxidizing agent)	$\mathcal{E}^0$ at 25° in volts
	Zn $\rightleftharpoons$	Zn^{++} $+ 2e^-$	0.76
	Fe $\rightleftharpoons$	Fe^{++} $+ 2e^-$	.44
	H$_2$ $\rightleftharpoons$	2H$^+$ $+ 2e^-$	.00
$0 \rightarrow +1$	Cu + Cl$^-$ $\rightleftharpoons$	CuCl $\downarrow$ $+ e^-$	$-.14$
$+1 \rightarrow +2$	Cu$^+$ $\rightleftharpoons$	Cu^{++} $+ e^-$	$-.15$
$0 \rightarrow +2$	Cu $\rightleftharpoons$	Cu^{++} $+ 2e^-$	$-.34$
$0 \rightarrow +1$	Cu $\rightleftharpoons$	Cu$^+$ $+ e^-$	$-.52$
	2I$^-$ $\rightleftharpoons$	I$_2$ $+ 2e^-$	$-.54$
$+1 \rightarrow +2$	CuCl $\downarrow$ $\rightleftharpoons$	Cu^{++} + Cl$^-$ $+ e^-$	$-.54$
$+1 \rightarrow +2$	CuI $\downarrow$ $\rightleftharpoons$	Cu^{++} + I$^-$ $+ e^-$	$-.86$
	NO + 2H$_2$O $\rightleftharpoons$	NO$_3^-$ + 4H$^+$ $+ 3e^-$	$-.96$
		Basic Solutions	
	4NH$_3$ + 2H$_2$O + S$_2$O$_4^{--}$ $\rightleftharpoons$ 2SO$_3^{--}$ + 4NH$_4^+$ $+ 2e^-$		$+0.56$
$0 \rightarrow +2$	4NH$_3$ + Cu $\rightleftharpoons$ Cu(NH$_3$)$_4^{++}$ $+ 2e^-$		.06

dithionite ($S_2O_4^{--}$). Since the cadmium ammonia complex is not reduced (Sec. 18-4d), this reaction can be used to separate copper from cadmium.

18-6. The Ions of Tin.

a. Electronic Structure and Oxidation States of Tin. This element comes above lead in Group IVB and its atoms therefore have an outer shell with two $5s$ and two $5p$ electrons. Like lead its atoms can lose the $5p$ electrons to form simple Sn^{++} ions. Or they can acquire the electronic configuration of the inert gas xenon by sharing all four electrons with other atoms. In this way tin, like lead, forms an unstable hydride, stannane SnH_4, analogous with methane CH_4 and silane SiH_4, in which its oxidation number is -4. In its oxidation state of $+4$ tin atoms are bound covalently to atoms of electronegative elements such as oxygen, sulfur, and the halogens. When it uses the $5s$ and $5p$ electrons to form four bonds, tetrahedral molecules are obtained, and octahedral complexes such as $SnCl_6^{--}$ and $Sn(OH)_6^{--}$ are obtained by making use of two $5d$ orbitals:

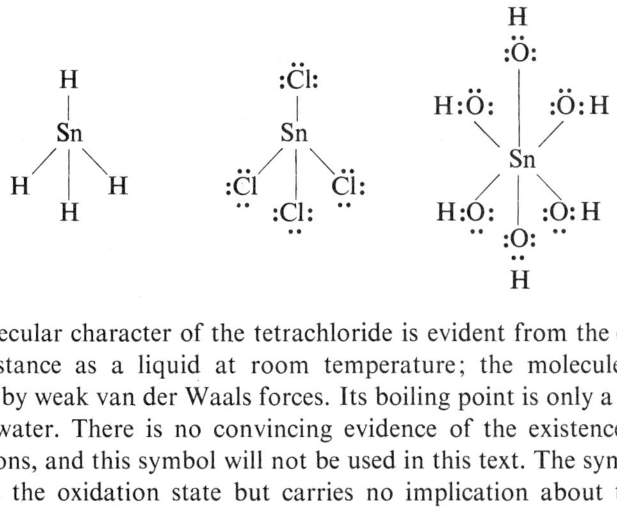

The molecular character of the tetrachloride is evident from the existence of this substance as a liquid at room temperature; the molecules are held together by weak van der Waals forces. Its boiling point is only a little above that of water. There is no convincing evidence of the existence of simple Sn^{++++} ions, and this symbol will not be used in this text. The symbol $Sn(IV)$ indicates the oxidation state but carries no implication about the type of bonds involved.

Compounds of tin are colorless except those with strongly polarizable ions: SnS, SnS_2, SnI_2, SnI_4, and SnO (Table 18-1).

b. Comparison of Tin with Lead. These are the most metallic elements of Group IVB of the Periodic Table; carbon and silicon are familiar nonmetals and germanium is a metalloid. In going up the group from lead to tin, it is thus logical to expect a decrease in "metallic" character. The ordinary allotrope, white tin, has metallic luster, ductility, and conductivity, but another form, gray tin, stable below 13.2°, is nonmetallic and has a crystal structure like that of diamond with each tin atom bonded to four others by covalent bonds. The less metallic character of tin is also evident in the greater stability of its $+4$ oxidation state; e.g., $SnCl_4$ is stable, whereas $PbCl_4$ readily breaks down to $PbCl_2$ and Cl_2. And the oxides and sulfides of tin are more acidic than those of lead.

c. Reactions and Compounds of Tin(II). Since little accurate information is available, no effort will be made to systematize the reactions of tin ions in the tabular form used for the preceding elements.

(1) The oxide SnO and hydroxide $Sn(OH)_2$. The white hydroxide is precipitated by the action of alkali metal hydroxides or carbonates on solutions of tin(II) salts. It is readily dehydrated to the oxide. Both compounds dissolve in acids and alkalies and are therefore amphoteric, e.g.,

$$\text{with HCl: } Sn(OH)_2 \downarrow + 2H^+ \rightleftharpoons Sn^{++} + 2H_2O$$

$$\text{with NaOH: } Sn(OH)_2 \downarrow + OH^- \rightleftharpoons Sn(OH)_3^-$$

The existence of the stannite ion, $Sn(OH)_3^-$, is supported by the isolation of solid salts such as $NaSn(OH)_3$.

(2) The sulfide SnS. This dusky brown precipitate results from the action of hydrogen sulfide or thioacetamide on solutions of tin(II) chloride if the concentration of HCl does not exceed about 1 M. The arrangement of the ions in its crystals is a distorted version of the pattern in crystals of NaCl or PbS.

The precipitated sulfide dissolves readily in dilute HCl with liberation of H_2S. It is oxidized by nitric acid to sulfur and white, insoluble SnO_2. It does not dissolve in $(NH_4)_2S$ and is only slightly soluble in KOH or K_2S: 2.1 g/l in 0.5 M KOH and 3.1 g/l in 2 M KOH. Polysulfides, which contain sulfur atoms combined with sulfide ions, oxidize it to a tin(IV) complex, e.g.,

$$S_2^{--} + SnS \downarrow \rightarrow SnS_3^{--}$$

(3) Soluble salts of tin(II). The most common salt is the colorless chloride $SnCl_2 \cdot 2H_2O$. The other halides are known, but the orange iodide is only sparingly soluble. The nitrate and sulfate can be prepared under exceptional conditions, and the former is very unstable. The hydrolysis of the chloride is complex. A white basic chloride precipitates:

$$Sn^{++} + Cl^- + H_2O \rightleftharpoons Sn(OH)Cl \downarrow + H^+$$

unless an excess of hydrochloric acid is added to suppress the hydrolysis. Solutions of tin(II) chloride contain chloride complexes ranging from $SnCl^+$ to $SnCl_4^{--}$ as well as polynuclear species such as $Sn_2(OH)_2^{++}$ and possibly $Sn_3(OH)_4^{++}$.

(4) Insoluble salts of tin(II). Mention has already been made of the sulfide, iodide, and basic chloride, and to these we may add the oxalate SnC_2O_4, soluble in excess $(NH_4)_2C_2O_4$, the white ferrocyanide $Sn_2Fe(CN)_6$,

and the cyanide $Sn(CN)_2$, unlike many heavy metal cyanides insoluble in excess KCN.

d. Reactions and Compounds of Tin(IV).

(1) The oxide SnO_2. This occurs in mineral form as cassiterite, the chief source of tin. It has the same crystal structure as rutile (Fig. 2-6c). There is no evidence that the hydroxide exists but two hydrated forms of the oxide can be made. The *alpha* form is precipitated by hydroxide or carbonate or by hydrolysis of tin(IV) salts at low temperatures. The *beta* form, also called "metastannic acid," is produced when the salts are hydrolyzed at high temperatures or by the action of nitric acid on tin. This is the form frequently obtained in qualitative analysis when a tin alloy is dissolved in that acid. It contains coarser particles than the *alpha* form and is not as soluble.

The hydrated oxide is readily dissolved by strong bases, and the presence of the stannate ion, $Sn(OH)_6^{--}$, is inferred from the existence of solid salts such as $CaSn(OH)_6$. Although the oxide dissolves in strong hydrochloric or sulfuric acids, this is perhaps more a result of complex formation than it is of the basic character of SnO_2. The oxide is definitely more acidic and less basic than SnO. These reactions are represented by the equations

$$SnO_2 \downarrow + 2H_2O + 2OH^- \rightleftharpoons Sn(OH)_6^{--}$$

$$SnO_2 \downarrow + 4H^+ + 6Cl^- \rightleftharpoons SnCl_6^{--} + 2H_2O$$

$$SnO_2 \downarrow + 2H_2SO_4 \rightleftharpoons SnSO_4^{++} + SO_4^{--} + 2H_2O$$

(2) The sulfide SnS_2. It comes down as a moderately yellow precipitate by the action of hydrogen sulfide or thioacetamide in 0.1 to 1 M HCl solutions. No precipitate is obtained if oxalate is present because tin(IV) is tied up in a stable complex, probably $Sn(C_2O_4)_3^{--}$. The precipitated sulfide is soluble in HCl; at $60°$ the solubilities in mg SnS_2/ml are: 77 in 1.86 M HCl, 251 in 3.12 M HCl, and 507 in 4.59 M HCl. The hydrochloric acid converts sulfide to H_2S and tin(IV) to the hexachlorostannate ion:

$$SnS_2 \downarrow + 4H^+ + 6Cl^- \rightarrow 2H_2S + SnCl_6^{--}$$

a reaction comparable with that between SnO_2 and HCl. Tin(IV) sulfide is more acidic than SnS and readily dissolves in K_2S, $(NH_4)_2S$, or KOH:

$$SnS_2 \downarrow + S^{--} \rightleftharpoons SnS_3^{--} \quad ; K_{eq} \sim 10^3$$

$$SnS_2 \downarrow + OH^- \rightleftharpoons SnS_2OH^-; K_{eq} \sim 2$$

The SnS_3^{--} ion is called the thiostannate ion.

(3) Other compounds of tin(IV). The tetrachloride is the only common one, but the other halides are known. All are molecular substances in the anhydrous condition. In solution they hydrolyze in a complex way with the liberation of hydrogen halide gas and the precipitation of hydrated tin(IV) oxide, i.e.,

$$SnCl_4 + (x + 2)H_2O \rightarrow SnO_2 \cdot xH_2O \downarrow + 4HCl \uparrow$$

The hydrolysis can be suppressed by excess HCl, but the resulting solution probably contains tin in the form of $SnCl_6^{--}$ ions rather than $SnCl_4$ molecules.

e. Redox Reactions of Tin.   The metal is slightly more active than lead:

$$Sn \rightarrow Sn^{++} + 2e^- \qquad \mathcal{E}^0 = +0.14 \text{ v}$$

and is readily attacked by hot HCl and H_2SO_4 with the liberation of hydrogen. Concentrated nitric acid converts it to insoluble metastannic acid while aqua regia gives both this and $SnCl_6^{--}$ ions.

The Sn-Sn^{++} couple lies above the Sn^{++}-Sn(IV) couple in acid solution. Active metals such as Zn or Al, used to reduce tin(IV) to tin(II), will also carry the reduction to the free metal. This redissolves in excess acid after the aluminum or zinc has been consumed:

$$Sn + 2H^+ \rightarrow Sn^{++} + H_2 \uparrow$$

The reaction between Sn^{++} ions and Hg(II) to give Hg_2Cl_2 and Hg^0 is used to identify both Hg and Sn and has been discussed in Sec. 17-6 (see also Table 17-7).

In acid solution the reaction

$$Sn + SnCl_6^{--} \rightleftharpoons 2Sn^{++} + 6Cl^-$$

comes to equilibrium with most of the tin in the form of Sn^{++} [or chloro-complexes of tin(II)]. Thus solutions of tin(II) salts, which are gradually oxidized by oxygen of the air, can be preserved by keeping a lump of metallic tin in the bottom of the bottle. In basic solution the position of the couples is reversed owing to the stability of the stannate ion $Sn(OH)_6^{--}$:

$$Sn(OH)_3^- + 3OH^- \rightleftharpoons Sn(OH)_6^{--} + 2e^- \qquad \mathcal{E}^0 = 0.93 \text{ v}$$
$$Sn + 3OH^- \rightleftharpoons Sn(OH)_3^- + 2e^- \qquad \mathcal{E}^0 = 0.91 \text{ v}$$

Hence the disproportionation reaction

$$2Sn(OH)_3^- \rightleftharpoons Sn \downarrow + Sn(OH)_6^{--}$$

occurs to an appreciable extent. Alkaline stannite solutions are usually freshly prepared because of this.

18-7. The Ions of Bismuth(III).

a. Electronic Structure and Oxidation States of Bismuth.   The bismuth atom has five valence electrons: two in the $6s$ subshell (the inert pair) and three in the $6p$ subshell. It can lose the less tightly bound $6p$ electrons to form simple Bi^{+++} ions or share three or five electrons with other atoms. The oxidation state of -3 is exhibited only in the unstable hydride bismuthine, BiH_3, analogous with NH_3. The three $6p$ electrons are used to form covalent bonds with the hydrogen atoms. The $+5$ or highest oxidation state of bismuth is very unstable and is found only in Bi_2O_5 and possibly in a few salts of uncertain composition. The pentoxide has recently been shown to be the active principle of "sodium bismuthate" prepared by the oxidation of Bi_2O_3 with sodium peroxide.

Bismuth in its $+3$ oxidation state forms only partially ionic bonds. Its reluctance to lose three electrons completely is indicated by its high ionization energy, 1200 kcal/mole. This is almost half again as large as that required to form La^{+++}, an ion of about the same size, and is almost equal to the ionization energy of aluminum although Al^{+++} ion is only half as large. The extent to which simple Bi^{+++} ions exist in solution is unknown, but it is probable that bismuth(III) is largely in complex form.

Bismuth compounds are generally colorless with exceptions noted in the subsequent discussion.

b. Compounds and Reactions of Bismuth(III).

(1) The oxide Bi_2O_3 and hydroxides $BiO(OH)$ and $Bi(OH)_3$. Alkali hydroxides and ammonia precipitate basic salts from solutions containing Bi(III). These gradually change to the white, gelatinous hydroxide $Bi(OH)_3$ and, upon boiling, to yellow $BiO(OH)$. Further dehydration gives the oxide. The existence of the three compounds is supported by x-ray diffraction measurements. The hydroxide is basic and dissolves in acids:

$$Bi(OH)_3 \downarrow \ + 3H^+ \rightarrow Bi^{+++} + 3H_2O$$

where the formula Bi^{+++} is used only for want of any better information. There is no ammine complex of bismuth and the hydroxide is insoluble in ammonia; because of this, bismuth can be separated from copper(II) and cadmium. The solubility of the oxide in 2.5 M NaOH is almost five times that in 0.5 M base but is still only 0.029 mg Bi_2O_3/ml. The increase in solubility has been attributed to the formation of BiO_2^- [or $Bi(OH)_4^-$] ions, but this is not yet supported by other evidence.

(2) The sulfide Bi_2S_3. The mineral form is lead-gray in color but the sulfide precipitated by H_2S or thioacetamide is dark brown. Precipitation is complete if the concentration of HCl is not much above 1 M. The sulfide is insoluble in dilute HCl but dissolves in the hot concentrated acid to give H_2S and chlorocomplexes such as $BiCl_4^-$. It is easily dissolved by 3 M HNO_3 because of oxidation of sulfide to sulfur. It is insoluble in $(NH_4)_2S$ but dissolves slightly in K_2S, possibly by formation of a BiS_2^- ion.

(3) Salts and complexes of Bi^{+++} ion. Of the trihalides the most ionic is BiF_3; it is also the least soluble. The action of concentrated acids on the oxide can be used to prepare $BiCl_3$, $Bi(NO_3)_3$, $Bi_2(SO_4)_3$, and $Bi(ClO_4)_3$. None of these gives a clear solution unless excess acid is present, for they all hydrolyze with precipitation of basic salts, e.g.,

$$BiCl_3 + H_2O \rightleftharpoons BiOCl \downarrow \ + 2H^+ + 2Cl^-$$

These are much more complex reactions than the equation indicates. Solutions of bismuth trichloride in excess HCl undoubtedly contain such complexes as $BiCl_4^-$, $BiCl_6^{---}$, $BiOH^{++}$, $Bi(OH)_2^+$, and possibly polynuclear species such as $Bi_6(OH)_{12}^{+6}$. Other important complexes include $Bi(SCN)_6^{---}$, $Bi(NO_2)_6^{---}$, and yellow BiI_4^-.

(4) **Basic bismuth(III) salts.** These are often called *bismuthyl* compounds after the BiO^+ radical that they contain. No such simple ion exists in the solid state. The chloride, for example, has a layer lattice, the sequence of layers being Bi, O, Cl, Bi, O, Cl, etc. Each bismuth atom is surrounded most closely by three oxygen and three chlorine atoms and is not bonded to any one oxygen. The bismuthyl ion BiO^+ may exist to some extent in solution; the complex $Bi(OH)_2^+$ is a hydrated form of it.

Bismuthyl chloride or bismuth oxychloride is the most familiar bismuth salt. It is more soluble than the sulfide, and the transformation

$$2BiOCl\downarrow + 3H_2S \rightarrow Bi_2S_3\downarrow + 2H_2O + 2H^+ + 2Cl^-$$

occurs without difficulty. The basic carbonate $(BiO)_2CO_3$ is a common reagent. The basic chromate $(BiO)_2CrO_4$ sometimes precipitates with $PbCrO_4$. It is only slightly soluble in 2 N acetic acid but, unlike $PbCrO_4$, it is insoluble in hot $NH_4C_2H_3O_2$ or NaOH. All of the basic bismuth salts are dissolved by strong acids but the reaction is sometimes slow.

c. Redox Reactions. Bismuth is less active than hydrogen; the order of couples is

$$H_2 \rightarrow 2H^+ + 2e^- \qquad \mathcal{E}^0 = \quad 0.00$$
$$4Cl^- + Bi \rightarrow BiCl_4^- + 3e^- \qquad \mathcal{E}^0 = -0.16$$
$$H_2O + Bi \rightarrow BiO^+ + 2H^+ + 3e^- \qquad \mathcal{E}^0 = -0.32$$

The metal is attacked by nitric and hot concentrated sulfuric acids. Reduction of bismuth(III) to bismuth(0) is conveniently done in strongly alkaline solution with stannite ion as the reducing agent: the Bi-$Bi(OH)_3$ couple ($\mathcal{E}^0$ about 0.4) lies well below the $Sn(OH)_3^-$-$Sn(OH)_6^{--}$ couple ($\mathcal{E}^0 = 0.93$). "Sodium bismuthate" (impure Bi_2O_5) is a very active oxidizing agent ($\mathcal{E}^0$ about -1.6) and is used in Cation Group 3 for the difficult oxidation of Mn^{++} ion to MnO_4^- ion.

18-8. The Ions of Antimony.

a. Electronic Structure and Oxidation States of Antimony. Atoms of antimony, like those of bismuth, have two s and three p valence electrons. The common oxidation states of antimony are thus -3, $+3$, and $+5$. The bonds formed by antimony are more covalent than those of bismuth because the valence electrons are closer to the nucleus of an antimony atom and are more tightly bound. The existence of simple Sb^{+++} ions, though commonly assumed, is not supported by any convincing evidence. Antimony(III) probably exists only in molecules or complexes: $Sb(OH)_2^+$, $Sb(OH)_4^-$ (antimonite ion), SbS_2^- or SbS_3^{---} (thioantimonite ion), $SbCl_4^-$, $SbCl_5^{--}$, $SbCl_3OH^-$, $SbS(OH)_2^-$. Antimony(V) certainly exists only in molecular or complex form:

$SbCl_5$, $Sb(OH)_6^-$ (antimonate ion), SbS_4^{---} (thioantimonate ion), $SbCl_6^-$, $SbCl_5OH^-$, $SbCl_4^+$. Some basic salts contain the antimonyl radical SbO^+, but this is not a simple ion in crystals; a hydrated form $Sb(OH)_2^+$ may exist in solution.

b. Comparison with Bismuth. It is to be expected that antimony, which lies above bismuth in Periodic Group VB, should be less metallic than its congener, and this is displayed in various ways. Unlike bismuth, antimony exists in several allotropic forms, one of which, unstable yellow antimony, is nonmetallic and similar to white phosphorus in structure and instability. Antimony compounds of the -3 or $+5$ oxidation states, e.g., SbH_3, Sb_2O_5, and $SbCl_5$, in which the binding is predominantly covalent, are more stable than those of bismuth. The oxides of antimony are more acidic and less basic than those of bismuth and in this respect resemble those of tin. Basic salts or antimonyl salts are known but are less stable than the bismuthyl compounds.

c. Compounds and Reactions of Antimony.
(1) The hydride stibine SbH_3. This evil-smelling, very poisonous gas (bp of liquid $-18°$) can be prepared by reduction with zinc of antimony compounds dissolved in hydrochloric or sulfuric acid:

$$3Zn + Sb(OH)_2^+ + 5H^+ \rightarrow 3Zn^{++} + SbH_3 \uparrow + 2H_2O$$

It burns with a green flame which deposits a stain of metallic antimony on a cold dish. The gas decomposes in a heated tube:

$$2SbH_3 \rightarrow 2Sb \downarrow + 3H_2 \uparrow$$

to give a mirror of the metal that is insoluble in hypochlorite but soluble in tartrates. It is reduced by silver ion in the presence of moisture to black Ag_3Sb:

$$3Ag^+ + SbH_3 \rightarrow Ag_3Sb \downarrow + 3H^+$$

(2) The oxides Sb_2O_3 and Sb_2O_5. The molecular weight of antimony(III) oxide, obtained from its vapor density, is twice that expected for Sb_2O_3; thus the true formula is Sb_4O_6. The oxides are precipitated in white, gelatinous hydrated form by adding strong bases or carbonates to acid solutions of antimony compounds. The action of concentrated nitric acid on metallic antimony gives a relatively insoluble hydrated form of Sb_2O_5 similar to metastannic acid:

$$xH_2O + 2Sb + 10H^+ + 10NO_3^- \rightarrow Sb_2O_5 \cdot xH_2O \downarrow + 10NO_2 \uparrow + 5H_2O$$

Antimony(III) oxide is slightly soluble in dilute acids, more soluble in strong bases:

$$Sb_2O_3 \downarrow + H_2O + 2H^+ \rightleftharpoons 2Sb(OH)_2^+ \qquad \frac{[Sb(OH)_2^+]}{[H^+]} = 0.00077$$

$$Sb_2O_3 \downarrow + 3H_2O + 2OH^- \rightleftharpoons 2Sb(OH)_4^- \qquad \frac{[Sb(OH)_4^-]}{[OH^-]} = 0.0088$$

The small values of the concentration ratios show that these reactions occur to only a small extent when the reagents are dilute. Both oxides of antimony dissolve readily in acids that form complexes, e.g., concentrated hydrochloric acid, tartaric acid, and oxalic acid:

$$Sb_2O_5 \downarrow \; + 10H^+ + 12Cl^- \; \rightleftharpoons 2SbCl_6^- + 5H_2O$$

$$Sb_2O_3 \downarrow \; + 6H_2C_2O_4 \qquad \rightleftharpoons 2Sb(C_2O_4)_3^{---} + 3H_2O + 6H^+$$

Antimony(V) oxide dissolves in strong bases to give antimonates:

$$Sb_2O_5 \downarrow \; + 2OH^- + 5H_2O \rightleftharpoons 2Sb(OH)_6^-$$

Potassium hydroxide is the best reagent for this because the sodium salt is only slightly soluble. The octahedral structure of the antimonate ion has been established by x-ray measurements on crystals of $NaSb(OH)_6$. There is no SbO_4^{---} ion analogous with the arsenate or phosphate ion; the large size of an antimony atom makes it possible for it to coordinate with six atoms rather than four. Despite the existence of the antimonite and antimonate ions, the free antimonous acid [$HSb(OH)_4$ or, in less hydrated form, $HSbO_2$ or H_3SbO_3] and antimonic acid [$HSb(OH)_6$] are unknown. In this respect antimony(V) again resembles tin(IV).

(3) The sulfides Sb_2S_3 and Sb_2S_5. These are obtained as deep orange precipitates by the action of hydrogen sulfide or thioacetamide on dilute hydrochloric acid solutions of antimony compounds or by acidification of solutions of the thioanions. The trisulfide precipitated by thioacetamide from solutions containing the antimony oxalate complex is often more red than orange; the massive form found in nature as stibnite is gray. These differences in color are caused by differences in particle size. The pentasulfide tends to lose sulfur and form the trisulfide, particularly in the presence of HCl.

Both sulfides are very soluble in HCl if the concentration is greater than 6 M: at 60° the solubility is about 6 mg of Sb_2S_5/ml in 3 M acid and 330 mg/ml in 6.35 M acid. Solution takes place because of the formation of hydrogen sulfide and chlorocomplexes, e.g.,

$$Sb_2S_3 \downarrow \; + 6H^+ + 8Cl^- \rightarrow 2SbCl_4^- + 3H_2S \uparrow$$

The trisulfide is soluble in K_2S, $(NH_4)_2S$, and KOH; the pentasulfide is also somewhat soluble in NH_3 solution. Thio- and oxyanions are formed in these reactions:

$$Sb_2S_5 \downarrow \; + 3S^{--} \; \rightleftharpoons 2SbS_4^{---}$$

$$Sb_2S_3 \downarrow \; + 6OH^- \rightleftharpoons SbS_3^{---} + SbO_3^{---} + 3H_2O$$

The existence of tetrahedral SbS_4^{---} ions has been established in crystals of $Na_3SbS_4 \cdot 9H_2O$ by x-ray diffraction. Mixed oxythioanions such as $SbS(OH)_2^-$ may also form. In their reactions with these basic reagents, the sulfides of antimony behave as acids and thus resemble SnS_2 more closely than Bi_2S_3, which is only very weakly acidic.

(4) Other compounds of antimony(III). The anhydrous sulfate $Sb_2(SO_4)_3$ and various halides such as $SbCl_3$ and $SbCl_5$ are known. The antimony-halogen bonds are largely covalent and the halides are relatively volatile substances. All these compounds hydrolyze when added to water, and basic salts precipitate unless an excess of acid is present:

$$SbCl_3 + H_2O \rightleftharpoons SbOCl \downarrow + 2H^+ + 2Cl^-$$

Besides the antimonyl chloride other basic chlorides are known, such as $Sb_4O_5Cl_2$ ("powder of algaroth").

d. Redox Reactions. Some antimony couples are given in Table 18-7. The ability of zinc and aluminum to reduce antimony to the hydride is apparent from the positions of these couples in the table. The free metal, rather than the hydride, is formed when iron is used as the reducing agent. Some antimony is formed by reduction with zinc or aluminum in acid solutions and this is the only product in alkaline media. Tin(II) chloride will not reduce antimony(III) to antimony(0). Antimony(V) is a fairly good oxidizing agent. Nitric acid is sufficiently active to oxidize antimony to Sb_2O_5.

TABLE 18-7.

Some Redox Couples of Antimony and Other Substances

Change in oxidation number of Sb	Reduced form (reducing agent)	Oxidized form (oxidizing agent)	$\mathcal{E}^0$ at 25° in volts
	$Al \rightleftharpoons Al^{+++} + 3e^-$		1.66
	$Zn \rightleftharpoons Zn^{++} + 2e^-$		0.76
$-3 \rightleftharpoons 0$	$SbH_3 \rightleftharpoons Sb + 3H^+ + 3e^-$		.51
	$Fe \rightleftharpoons Fe^{++} + 2e^-$		.44
	$H_2 \rightleftharpoons 2H^+ + 2e^-$		.00
$0 \rightleftharpoons +3$	$Sb + 2H_2O \rightleftharpoons Sb(OH)_2^+ + 2H^+ + 3e$		$-.21$
$+3 \rightleftharpoons +5$	$2Sb(OH)_2^+ + H_2O \rightleftharpoons Sb_2O_5 \downarrow + 6H^+ + 4e^-$		$-.58$
	$NO + 2H_2O \rightleftharpoons NO_3^- + 4H^+ + 3e^-$		$-.96$

18-9. The Ions of Arsenic.

a. Electronic Structure and Oxidation States.   Arsenic atoms, like those of bismuth and antimony, have two s and three p valence electrons. They have no tendency to lose these to form positive ions such as As^{+++} and As^{+5} but share electrons with other atoms to achieve oxidation states of -3, $+3$, and $+5$. The only positive ions that As forms are complex: $As(OH)_2^+$ and $AsCl_4^+$. It usually forms molecules such as $AsCl_3$, $As(OH)Cl_2$, $As(OH)_2Cl$, $As(OH)_3$, and H_3AsO_4. The anions most commonly found are those of its acids, e.g., AsO_4^{---}, $H_2AsO_4^-$, or $H_2AsO_3^-$, or the thioanions, AsS_2^-, AsS_3^{---}, and AsS_4^{---}. Halogen complexes are unusually rare, e.g., AsF_6^-, AsF_5OH^-, and possibly $AsCl_4^-$.

b. Comparison of Arsenic with Antimony, Bismuth, and Phosphorus. Arsenic lies between phosphorus and antimony in Periodic Group VB and, as we might expect from this position, is the most nonmetallic of the elements encountered in the cation analysis. It is considered with the cations only because it forms an insoluble sulfide. Like antimony it has a semimetallic allotrope, gray in color and with an electrical conductivity about 4% of that of silver at 0°. It also has a reactive yellow allotrope, similar to yellow antimony and white phosphorus, which is nonmetallic and composed of simple As_4 molecules. Its hydride AsH_3 lies between PH_3 and SbH_3 in stability. Its halides are molecular substances that hydrolyze to give an acid of arsenic and not a basic salt as do the halides of antimony and bismuth. Its oxides and hydroxides are acidic.

c. Compounds and Reactions of Arsenic.

(1) The hydride arsine AsH_3. The behavior of this compound is similar to that of stibine. It is a very poisonous, evil-smelling gas formed by reduction of arsenic compounds with zinc or aluminum in dilute hydrochloric or sulfuric acid, e.g.,

$$6H^+ + H_3AsO_3 + 3Zn \rightarrow AsH_3 \uparrow + 3Zn^{++} + 3H_2O$$

In the *Marsh test* the arsine is burned, and a cold dish held in the flame acquires a deposit of arsenic. Alternatively, the arsine is decomposed in a heated tube to give a black mirror of arsenic:

$$2AsH_3 \rightarrow 2As \downarrow + 3H_2 \uparrow$$

Unlike the similar deposit of antimony obtained from stibine, this mirror is soluble in sodium hypochlorite:

$$6OH^- + 5ClO^- + 2As \downarrow \rightarrow 2AsO_4^{---} + 5Cl^- + 3H_2O$$

In the *Gutzeit test* the arsine reduces silver nitrate to yellow $Ag_3As \cdot AgNO_3$ or black Ag. The yellow product is obtained with solid silver nitrate, the black with a dilute solution. Mercury(II) chloride gives a yellow or brown stain. Arsine cannot be distinguished from stibine in these tests. If the arsenic is in the +3 state, it can be reduced with aluminum and potassium hydroxide to arsine:

$$H_2AsO_3^- + 4H_2O + OH^- + 2Al \rightarrow AsH_3 \uparrow + 2Al(OH)_4^-$$

Antimony is not reduced to stibine under these conditions.

(2) The oxides As_2O_5 and As_2O_3 and acids H_3AsO_4 and H_3AsO_3. The molecular weight of the trioxide indicates that its true formula is As_4O_6. It dissolves to some extent in water to give a solution of arsenious acid, H_3AsO_3 or $As(OH)_3$. Like other acids of the general type $X(OH)_n$, it is very weak; for the loss of one proton the ionization constant is only about 10^{-10}. For

this reason the formula H_3AsO_3 is preferred to $HAsO_2$, a less hydrated or *meta* form, which would be a stronger acid. This indirect reasoning must be used because the free acid has never been isolated. The trioxide dissolves readily in strong bases to give solutions of arsenites:

$$H_2O + As_2O_3 \downarrow + 2OH^- \rightarrow 2H_2AsO_3^-$$

It dissolves in concentrated hydrochloric acid to give arsenic(III) chloride:

$$As_2O_3 \downarrow + 6H^+ + 6Cl^- \rightarrow 3H_2O + 2AsCl_3$$

Its solution in 6 M HCl contains $AsCl_3$, $As(OH)Cl_2$, $As(OH)_2Cl$, $As(OH)_3$, and $As(OH)_2^+$.

The pentoxide is a white deliquescent solid that dissolves in water to give orthoarsenic acid:

$$As_2O_5 \downarrow + 3H_2O \rightarrow 2H_3AsO_4$$

Arsenic acid, like phosphoric acid, is a moderately strong acid with a first ionization constant of about 10^{-2}, a second of 10^{-7}, and a third of about 10^{-11}. It differs from phosphoric acid in being a moderately good oxidizing agent in acid solutions.

(3) The sulfides As_2S_3, As_2S_5, and As_4S_4. The true formula of arsenic(III) sulfide is As_4S_6. These sulfides are all molecular substances. The relation between their structures and that of yellow arsenic (As_4) is shown in Fig. 18-1.

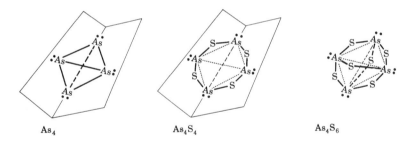

As_4 $\qquad$ As_4S_4 $\qquad$ As_4S_6

FIG. 18-1. The molecular structures of yellow arsenic, realgar, and orpiment.

Arsenic(III) sulfide is obtained as a strong yellow precipitate by the action of thioacetamide or hydrogen sulfide on acid solutions of arsenic(III). Arsenic(V) sulfide is difficult to precipitate with hydrogen sulfide, unless the reaction is carried out in cold 12 M hydrochloric acid. Thioacetamide reduces arsenic(V) and precipitates As_2S_3 rapidly even in 0.1 to 0.3 M HCl. The tetrasulfide As_4S_4 is the red mineral realgar, which is of no analytical importance.

The yellow sulfides differ from the sulfides of tin and antimony in being virtually insoluble in 5-7 M HCl. The solubility increases in more concentrated acid but is still only about 25 mg of As_2S_5 per milliliter of 10 M

HCl at 60°. Nitric acid dissolves the sulfides by oxidation of sulfide to sulfur and arsenic(III) to arsenic acid:

$$10H^+ + 10NO_3^- + As_2S_3 \downarrow \rightarrow 2H_3AsO_4 + 10NO_2 + 3S^0 \downarrow + 2H_2O$$

The sulfides dissolve in NH_3, KOH, Na_2S, and $(NH_4)_2S$ with the formation of oxy- and thioanions:

$$As_2S_3 \downarrow + 6OH^- \rightleftharpoons AsS_3^{---} + AsO_3^{---} + 3H_2O$$
$$As_2S_5 \downarrow + 3S^{--} \rightleftharpoons 2AsS_4^{---}$$

The sulfides are reprecipitated by acidifying the solutions, e.g.,

$$2AsS_4^{---} + 6H^+ \rightarrow As_2S_5 \downarrow + 3H_2S \uparrow$$

(4) Other compounds of arsenic. The only pentahalide of arsenic is AsF_5. The trichloride $AsCl_3$ is a liquid which boils at 130°. It hydrolyzes to give arsenious acid:

$$AsCl_3 + 3H_2O \rightleftharpoons H_3AsO_3 + 3H^+ + 3Cl^-$$

Various molecular intermediates such as $As(OH)Cl_2$ are formed before the acid is obtained.

Sodium and potassium arsenites are soluble. Yellow silver arsenite and green copper(II) arsenite can be precipitated in neutral or alkaline solution:

$$3Ag^+ + H_3AsO_3 + 3OH^- \rightarrow Ag_3AsO_3 \downarrow + 3H_2O$$
$$Cu^{++} + H_3AsO_3 + 2OH^- \rightarrow CuHAsO_3 \downarrow + 2H_2O$$

Both precipitates dissolve in nitric acid because of the formation of weakly dissociated H_3AsO_3 and in ammonia because of the formation of the ammonia complex ions of the cations.

Arsenates resemble phosphates closely in solubility and crystal form; compare, for example, $MgNH_4AsO_4 \cdot 6H_2O$ with $MgNH_4PO_4 \cdot 6H_2O$. Occasionally there is a difference in color, e.g., yellow Ag_3PO_4 and reddish brown Ag_3AsO_4. Lead and calcium arsenates are important insecticides. All the arsenates are soluble in strong acids because of the removal of arsenate ions to give weakly dissociated $H_2AsO_4^-$ ions.

d. Redox Reactions. Various arsenic couples are given in Table 18-8. Their positions indicate why zinc and aluminum can be used to prepare arsine and why arsenates result from the action of nitric acid on arsenic(0) or arsenites. The oxidizing action of arsenic acid is illustrated by its action on iodides:

$$2I^- + 2H^+ + H_3AsO_4 \rightleftharpoons H_3AsO_3 + H_2O + I_2$$

In acid solutions the reaction goes from left to right; in neutral or weakly alkaline solutions the hydrogen ion concentration is so low that iodine oxidizes arsenious acid.

From the positions of the couples we can also predict that tin(II) chloride would reduce arsenic(III) and arsenic(V) to free arsenic. This is *Bettendorf's test.* It is carried out in hot, concentrated hydrochloric acid. Mercury gives a gray precipitate unlike the dark brown arsenic; antimony is not reduced.

TABLE 18-8.

Some Redox Couples of Arsenic and Other Substances

Change in oxidation number of As	Reduced form (reducing agent)		Oxidized form (oxidizing agent)	$\mathcal{E}^0$ at 25° in volts
	Al	$\rightleftharpoons$	$Al^{+++} \quad + 3e^-$	1.66
	Zn	$\rightleftharpoons$	$Zn^{++} \quad + 2e^-$	0.76
$-3 \rightleftharpoons 0$	AsH_3	$\rightleftharpoons$	$As + 3H^+ \quad + 3e^-$	0.60
	$6Cl^- + Sn^{++}$	$\rightleftharpoons$	$SnCl_6^{--} \quad + 2e^-$	-0.14
$0 \rightleftharpoons +3$	$3H_2O + As$	$\rightleftharpoons$	$H_3AsO_3 + 3H^+ \quad + 3e^-$	-0.25
	$2I^-$	$\rightleftharpoons$	$I_2 \quad + 2e^-$	-0.54
$+3 \rightleftharpoons +5$	$H_2O + H_3AsO_3$	$\rightleftharpoons$	$H_3AsO_4 + 2H^+ \quad + 2e^-$	-0.56
	$2H_2O + NO$	$\rightleftharpoons$	$NO_3^- + 4H^+ \quad + 3e^-$	-0.96

18-10. Discussion of the Analytical Procedure. The sulfides of this group have lower solubility products than sulfides of later groups and require a lower sulfide ion concentration for their precipitation. In a saturated solution of hydrogen sulfide (whether prepared from the gas or by hydrolysis of thioacetamide) the ion product

$$K_{ip} = [H^+]^2[S^{--}]$$

holds, and hence the sulfide ion concentration varies inversely with the square of the hydrogen ion concentration. When the latter is regulated between 0.1 and 0.3 M, the concentration of sulfide ion is held at a sufficiently low level so that zinc sulfide, the most insoluble of Cation Group 3, will not precipitate, and yet cadmium sulfide, the most soluble of Cation Group 2, will.

After precipitation the sulfides are subdivided according to their basic or acidic character into the Copper and Arsenic Sections. The sulfides of arsenic, antimony, and tin dissolve in 0.5 M KOH. The amount of mercury(II) that accompanies them is small, as long as this low a concentration of base is used. The tin must be in its $+4$ oxidation state, for SnS is not very soluble in KOH. Furthermore, SnS can reduce the thio- and oxyanions of arsenic and antimony to the free elements and cause them to be missed. Tin is therefore oxidized to tin(IV) with hydrogen peroxide before precipitation of the group.[3]

[3]The hydrogen peroxide also reduces dichromates and permanganates to simple Cr^{+++} and Mn^{++} ions. Both $Cr_2O_7^{--}$ and MnO_4^- are strong oxidizing agents and convert H_2S or thioacetamide to sulfur or even sulfate ion. At best this is a nuisance; at worst the sulfate may cause premature precipitation of Ba^{++} and Sr^{++} ions.

The analysis of the Copper Section starts with HgS, PbS, Bi_2S_3, CuS, and CdS, the sulfides insoluble in KOH. All but the very insoluble sulfide of mercury(II) dissolve in 3 M HNO_3. Aqua regia is used to dissolve HgS. Mercury is identified in this solution by reduction with tin(II) chloride to white Hg_2Cl_2 or a gray mixture of Hg_2Cl_2 and Hg. Nitrate and excess chloride interfere and are removed by evaporation before the test.

Lead is separated from the nitric acid solution of the sulfides by precipitation as lead sulfate. This precipitate is appreciably soluble in nitric acid because of the reactions

$$Pb^{++} + NO_3^- \rightleftharpoons PbNO_3^+ \qquad K = 14$$
$$H^+ + SO_4^{--} \rightleftharpoons HSO_4^- \qquad K = 98$$

In concentrated sulfuric acid solutions nitric acid is largely in the molecular form and is driven off by evaporation. After the nitric acid and most of the water are gone, the temperature rises on further heating to 340°, and then sulfuric acid decomposes and gives off dense white fumes of sulfur trioxide:

$$H_2SO_4 + NO_3^- \rightarrow HNO_3 \uparrow + HSO_4^-$$
$$H_2SO_4 \rightarrow SO_3 \uparrow + H_2O \uparrow$$

The appearance of these fumes is thus a signal that nitric acid has been removed. The lead sulfate that forms during this evaporation is often contaminated with small amounts of bismuth and copper sulfates. But lead sulfate, unlike these impurities, dissolves in hot 3 M ammonium acetate with the formation of a lead acetate complex ion. Lead is finally identified by precipitation as the chromate.

After the removal of lead, bismuth is separated from copper and cadmium by the addition of an excess of ammonia. Bismuth does not form an ammonia complex but precipitates as the hydroxide $Bi(OH)_3$. It is identified by reduction to black bismuth with stannite.

Copper(II) and cadmium combine with an excess of ammonia to give the weakly dissociated complex ions $Cu(NH_3)_4^{++}$ and $Cd(NH_3)_4^{++}$. The blue color of the former is usually sufficient indication of the presence of copper, but if this is indecisive, the reddish ferrocyanide can be precipitated from acetic acid solution. Cadmium ferrocyanide is white.

A test for cadmium in the presence of copper is more difficult. It is usually identified as the yellow sulfide, but the color of this is easily masked by black copper(II) sulfide. Many methods of separating copper from cadmium have been proposed. One of the best uses cyanide to reduce and complex the copper. The dissociation of $Cu(CN)_3^{--}$ is so low that Cu_2S will not precipitate, but CdS will still form. In our procedure copper(II) is reduced to metallic copper by sodium dithionite (also called sodium "hyposulfite" or "hydrosulfite"). This reagent also reduces lead, bismuth, antimony, mercury, and arsenic, so that if these are present in the solution because of careless separations, they too are removed and do not interfere with the cadmium test.

Analysis of the Arsenic Section starts with the alkaline solution containing the thio- and oxyanions of arsenic, antimony, and tin(IV). Small amounts of mercury(II) may accompany these elements. The sulfides are precipitated by acidifying the solution. The sulfides of antimony and tin are dissolved by 6-8 M hydrochloric acid, but that of arsenic is virtually insoluble in HCl. It is dissolved and converted to arsenate by a mixture of ammonia and hydrogen peroxide, a more rapid oxidizing agent than nitric acid, which is sometimes used. The arsenate is precipitated as magnesium ammonium arsenate by "magnesia mixture," an ammoniacal solution of magnesium nitrate that contains sufficient ammonium nitrate to prevent the precipitation of magnesium hydroxide. The conditions used for this precipitation are similar to those used in the separation of magnesium ammonium phosphate in Cation Group 5 (Sec. 21-6a). The precipitate is dissolved in acetic acid because of the formation of weakly dissociated dihydrogen arsenate ions. Arsenic is identified by precipitation of pale reddish brown silver arsenate. The Gutzeit test could also be used.

Antimony is identified by precipitation of the deep orange sulfide Sb_2S_3. Precipitation of tin(IV) sulfide is prevented by the use of oxalate which ties up the tin as a weakly dissociated oxalate complex.

Tin is identified by the reducing action of Sn^{++} ion on $HgCl_2$ also used to identify mercury. The hydrochloric acid solution of tin and antimony sulfides contains tin(IV) as $SnCl_6^{--}$ ion, and it must be reduced to Sn^{++} before the test can be made. Iron or aluminum is most commonly used for this purpose. Aluminum is sufficiently active to reduce some tin to the free metal, but this redissolves in hot hydrochloric acid after the aluminum has been consumed. Antimony is also reduced to the metal, but it is not soluble in hydrochloric acid.

Mercury will appear in the Arsenic Section only if the other members of this section are present, and even then its solubility is low if the concentration of KOH is only 0.5 M. In small amounts it dissolves in 12 M hydrochloric acid; any that remains with arsenic sulfide is unaffected by ammonia and hydrogen peroxide. Mercury(II) is reduced to the free metal by aluminum and does not interfere with the tin test. Its sulfide will precipitate with that of antimony but can be distinguished from it by its insolubility in 6 M HCl or ammonium sulfide.

18-11. Cross References.   Familiarity with Chapters 1-4 is assumed.
Sec. 5-5 (partially covalent or polarized bonds)
Sec. 6-2 (ligands, coordination number)
Sec. 6-5 (tetrahedral and octahedral complexes)
Secs. 6-9 to 11 (electrostatic theory of complexes)

Sec. 6-12 (s, p, d orbitals)
Sec. 6-14 (color)
Exercises 6-21, -22 (formulas of arsenate and antimonate)
Sec. 7-7 (hydrolysis of thioacetamide)
Sec. 7-12 (weakness of $X(OH)_n$ acids)
Sec. 7-13 (equilibrium constants and direction of reaction)
Sec. 7-19 (ion product of H_2S)
Sec. 8-2 (solubility product)
Sec. 8-8 (supersaturation and precipitation)
Secs. 8-10, -11 (coprecipitation)
Sec. 8-12 (precipitation of sulfides by H_2S)
Sec. 8-13 (precipitation of sulfides by thioacetamide)
Sec. 8-15 (dissolution of precipitates)
Sec. 8-16 (soln of sulfides in HCl, HNO_3, aqua regia; acidic sulfides)
Sec. 8-17 (amphoteric hydroxides)
Secs. 8-18 to 21 (colloidal sulfides)
Sec. 9-3 (equilibrium constant and direction of reaction)
Sec. 9-5 (effect of concentrations on direction of reaction)
Sec. 9-7 (direction of redox reactions)
Sec. 9-8 (standard oxidation potentials, $\mathcal{E}^0$)
Sec. 10-5 (ion product of H_2S, calculations)
Sec. 10-12 (formation and dissolution of sulfides, calculations)
Sec. 11-6 (hydrolysis of metal ions)
Sec. 12-2 (effect of H^+ on [S^{--}], calculations)
Sec. 12-9 (indicators)
Sec. 12-10 (measurement of pH)
Sec. 14-3, Example 4 (precipitation of CdS in presence of CN^-)
Secs. 15-12 to 15 (oxidation potentials)

18-12. The Successive Reactions of the Ions of Cation Group 2.

Mercury(II)

1. Precipitation of the group. Reagent: thioacetamide or hydrogen sulfide in 0.3 M hydrochloric acid

$$HgCl_2 + H_2S \rightarrow HgS \downarrow + 2H^+ + 2Cl^-$$

2. Separation of Copper and Arsenic Sections. Reagent: 0.5 M potassium hydroxide. Slight reaction with HgS if Arsenic Section is present.

$$HgS \downarrow + S^{--} \rightleftharpoons HgS_2^{--}$$

3. Separation from Pb, Bi, Cu, and Cd. Reagent: 3 M nitric acid. No reaction with HgS if chloride is absent.

4. Dissolution of HgS. Reagent: aqua regia
(a) $HgS \downarrow + Cl^- + NO_3^- \rightarrow HgCl_4^{--} + NO_2$ (This is only a skeleton

equation and should be balanced by the ion-electron or oxidation number method.)

(b) $HgCl_4^{--} \rightleftharpoons HgCl_2 + 2Cl^-$ (after evaporation of excess HCl)

5. Identification of Hg(II). Reagent: tin(II) chloride. See equations under mercury(I) in Sec. 17-8.

6. Reactions of Hg(II) in the Arsenic Section.

(a) With HCl: $HgS_2^{--} + 2H^+ \rightarrow HgS \downarrow + H_2S \uparrow$

(b) With concd HCl: $HgS + 2H^+ + 4Cl^- \rightarrow HgCl_4^{--} + H_2S \uparrow$

(c) On evaporation: $HgCl_4^{--} \rightleftharpoons HgCl_2 + 2Cl^-$

(d) With thioacetamide: $HgCl_2 + H_2S \rightarrow$? (Complete and balance.)

(e) With Al: $3HgCl_2 + 2Al \rightarrow 3Hg \downarrow + 2Al^{+++} + 6Cl^-$

Lead

1. Precipitation of the group. Reagent: thioacetamide or hydrogen sulfide in 0.3 M hydrochloric acid

$$Pb^{++} + H_2S \rightarrow PbS \downarrow + 2H^+$$

2. Separation from the Arsenic Section. Reagent: 0.5 M potassium hydroxide. No reaction with PbS.

3. Separation from HgS in the Copper Section. Reagent: 3 M nitric acid.

Skeleton equation: $PbS \downarrow + NO_3^- \rightarrow NO \uparrow + Pb^{++} + S^0 \downarrow$

(Balance by the ion-electron or oxidation number method.)

4. Separation from Bi, Cu, and Cd. Reagent: sulfuric acid in the absence of nitrates

$$Pb^{++} + SO_4^{--} \rightarrow PbSO_4 \downarrow$$

5. Dissolution of $PbSO_4$. Reagent: hot 3 M ammonium acetate

$$PbSO_4 \downarrow + 3C_2H_3O_2^- \rightarrow Pb(C_2H_3O_2)_3^- + SO_4^{--}$$

(Other complexes such as $PbC_2H_3O_2^+$ or $Pb(C_2H_3O_2)_2$ may also form.)

6. Identification of Pb. Reagent: potassium chromate

$$Pb(C_2H_3O_2)_3^- + CrO_4^{--} \rightarrow PbCrO_4 \downarrow + 3C_2H_3O_2^-$$

Bismuth

(To simplify the equations the formula Bi^{+++} is used.)

1. Adjustment of acidity before precipitation of the group. Reagents: water and ammonia

$$Bi^{+++} + Cl^- + H_2O \rightarrow BiOCl \downarrow + 2H^+$$

2. Precipitation of the group. Reagent: thioacetamide or hydrogen sulfide in 0.3 M hydrochloric acid

$$2Bi^{+++} + 3H_2S \rightarrow Bi_2S_3 \downarrow + 6H^+$$

$$2BiOCl \downarrow + 3H_2S \rightarrow Bi_2S_3 \downarrow + 2Cl^- + 2H^+ + 2H_2O$$

3. Separation from the Arsenic Section. Reagent: 0.5 M potassium hydroxide. No reaction with Bi_2S_3.

4. Separation from Hg in the Copper Section. Reagent: 3 M nitric acid. Skeleton equation:

$$Bi_2S_3 \downarrow + NO_3^- \rightarrow Bi^{+++} + S^0 \downarrow + NO \uparrow$$

(Balance by the ion-electron or oxidation number method.)

5. Separation from Pb. Reagent: sulfuric acid. Normally no reaction. Sometimes precipitation of bismuthyl sulfate

$$2Bi^{+++} + 2H_2O + SO_4^{--} \rightarrow (BiO)_2SO_4 \downarrow + 4H^+$$

6. Separation from Cu and Cd. Reagent: ammonia solution

$$Bi^{+++} + 3NH_3 + 3H_2O \rightarrow Bi(OH)_3 \downarrow + 3NH_4^+$$

7. Identification of Bi. Reagent: sodium stannite
Skeleton equation:

$$Bi(OH)_3 \downarrow + Sn(OH)_3^- \rightarrow Sn(OH)_6^{--} + Bi^0 \downarrow$$

(Why is this equation not balanced? Balance it by the ion-electron method or oxidation number method; note that the solution is alkaline.)

Copper(II)

1. Adjustment of the acidity before precipitation of the group. Reagent: excess ammonia solution

$$Cu^{++} + 4NH_3 \rightleftharpoons Cu(NH_3)_4^{++}$$

2. Precipitation of the group. Reagent: thioacetamide or hydrogen sulfide in 0.3 M hydrochloric acid

$$Cu^{++} + H_2S \rightarrow ?$$

(Supply the products and balance the equation.)

3. Separation from the Arsenic Section. Reagent: 0.5 M potassium hydroxide. No reaction with CuS.

4. Separation from HgS in the Copper Section. Reagent: 3 M nitric acid

$$CuS \downarrow + NO_3^- \rightarrow ?$$

(Supply the products and balance the equation.)

5. Separation from Pb. Reagent: sulfuric acid. No reaction.

6. Separation from Bi and identification. Reagent: ammonia solution. See Eq. 1.

7. Confirmation of Cu(II). Reagents: acetic acid and potassium ferrocyanide [potassium hexacyanoferrate(II)]

(a) $Cu(NH_3)_4^{++} + 4HC_2H_3O_2 \rightarrow Cu^{++} + 4NH_4^+ + 4C_2H_3O_2^-$

(b) $2Cu^{++} + Fe(CN)_6^{----} \rightarrow Cu_2Fe(CN)_6 \downarrow$

8. Separation from Cd. Reagent: sodium dithionite

$$S_2O_4^{--} + Cu(NH_3)_4^{++} + 2H_2O \rightarrow Cu \downarrow + 2SO_3^{--} + 4NH_4^+$$

Cadmium

These equations are left for the student to write. Follow the same pattern as that used for the other ions.

Arsenic

1. Precipitation of the group. Reagent: thioacetamide or hydrogen sulfide in 0.3 M hydrochloric acid

$$As(III): 2H_3AsO_3 + 3H_2S \rightarrow As_2S_3 \downarrow + 6H_2O$$
$$As(V): \ \ 2H_3AsO_4 + 5H_2S \rightarrow As_2S_5 \downarrow + 8H_2O$$

With thioacetamide two complex reactions occur: (1) direct reaction of As(V) with thioacetamide without the intervention of H_2S and (2) hydrolysis of thioacetamide to H_2S and reduction of As(V) to thio-oxyacids of the type H_3AsO_2S. The result of either reaction series is precipitation of As_2S_3 and formation of S^0.

2. Separation of the Arsenic and Copper Sections. Reagent: 0.5 M potassium hydroxide

$$As_2S_3 \downarrow + 6OH^- \rightarrow AsS_3^{---} + AsO_3^{---} + 3H_2O$$

3. Reprecipitation of the sulfides. Reagent: 2 M hydrochloric acid

$$AsO_3^{---} + AsS_3^{---} + 6H^+ \rightarrow As_2S_3 \downarrow + 3H_2O$$

4. Separation of As from Sb and Sn. Reagent: 12 M hydrochloric acid. No reaction with As_2S_3.

5. Dissolution of As_2S_3. Reagents: ammonia and hydrogen peroxide Skeleton equation:

$$H_2O_2 + As_2S_3 \downarrow \ \rightarrow S \downarrow + AsO_4^{---} + OH^-$$

(Balance by the ion-electron or oxidation number method. Note that the solution is alkaline.)

6. Precipitation of magnesium ammonium arsenate. Reagent: magnesia mixture (magnesium nitrate, ammonium nitrate, and ammonia)

$$Mg^{++} + NH_4^+ + AsO_4^{---} + 6H_2O \rightarrow MgNH_4AsO_4 \cdot 6H_2O \downarrow$$

7. Confirmation of As. Reagents: acetic acid and silver nitrate

(a) $2HC_2H_3O_2 + MgNH_4AsO_4 \cdot 6H_2O \downarrow \rightarrow$
$$Mg^{++} + NH_4^+ + H_2AsO_4^- + 2C_2H_3O_2^- + 6H_2O$$

(b) $H_2AsO_4^- + 3Ag^+ \rightarrow Ag_3AsO_4 \downarrow + 2H^+$

Antimony

1. Adjustment of the acidity before precipitation of Group 2. Reagents: water and ammonia

$$SbCl_4^- + H_2O \rightarrow SbOCl \downarrow + 2H^+ + 3Cl^-$$

2. Precipitation of the group. Reagents: thioacetamide or hydrogen sulfide in 0.3 M hydrochloric acid

$$SbCl_4^- + H_2S \rightarrow ?$$ (Complete and balance.)

$$SbOCl + H_2S \rightarrow ?$$ (Complete and balance.)

3. Separation of the Arsenic and Copper Sections. Reagent: 0.5 M potassium hydroxide

$$Sb_2S_3 \downarrow + OH^- \rightarrow ?$$ (Complete and balance.)

4. Reprecipitation of the sulfide. Reagent: 2 M hydrochloric acid

$$? \qquad \rightarrow Sb_2S_3 \downarrow + ?$$ (Complete and balance.)

5. Separation of Sb and Sn from As. Reagent: 12 M hydrochloric acid

$$Sb_2S_3 \downarrow + 6H^+ + 8Cl^- \rightarrow 2SbCl_4^- + 3H_2S \uparrow$$

6. Identification of Sb. Reagents: thioacetamide and oxalic acid

(a) $SbCl_4^- + 3H_2C_2O_4 \rightleftharpoons Sb(C_2O_4)_3^{---} + 4Cl^- + 6H^+$

(b) $2SbCl_4^- + 3H_2S \rightarrow Sb_2S_3 \downarrow + 6H^+ + 8Cl^-$

7. Separation from Sn. Reagent: aluminum metal

$$SbCl_4^- + Al^0 \rightarrow Sb^0 \downarrow + Al^{+++} + 4Cl^-$$

Tin

1. Oxidation of tin(II) to tin(IV) before precipitation of the group. Reagent: hydrogen peroxide in acid solution

$$Sn^{++} + Cl^- + H_2O_2 \rightarrow SnCl_6^{--} + H_2O$$

(Complete and balance this skeleton equation by the ion-electron or oxidation number method.)

2. Precipitation of the group. Reagent: thioacetamide or hydrogen sulfide in 0.3 M hydrochloric acid

$$SnCl_6^{--} + H_2S \rightarrow ?$$

3. Separation of the Copper and Arsenic Sections. Reagent: 0.5 M potassium hydroxide

$$SnS_2 \downarrow + OH^- \rightarrow ?$$

4. Reprecipitation of the sulfides. Reagent: 2 M hydrochloric acid

$$? \qquad \rightarrow SnS_2 \downarrow + ?$$

5. Separation from As. Reagent 12 M hydrochloric acid

$$SnS_2 \downarrow + 4H^+ + 6Cl^- \rightarrow SnCl_6^{--} + 2H_2S \uparrow$$

6. Separation from Sb. Reagents: oxalic acid and thioacetamide

$$SnCl_6^{--} + 3H_2C_2O_4 \rightarrow Sn(C_2O_4)_3^{--} + 6H^+ + 6Cl^-$$

No reaction with thioacetamide

7. Reduction of Sn(IV) to Sn(II). Reagent: aluminum metal

$$SnCl_6^{--} + Al \rightarrow Al^{+++} + Sn^{++} + Cl^- \qquad \text{(Balance.)}$$
$$Sn^{++} + Al \quad \rightarrow Al^{+++} + Sn^0 \downarrow \qquad \text{(Balance.)}$$
$$Sn^0 \downarrow + 2H^+ \rightarrow H_2 + Sn^{++}$$

8. Identification of Sn. Reagent: mercury(II) chloride

The equations are the same as those for the identification of mercury.

EXPERIMENTAL PART

18-13. Introductory Experiments.

1. The hydrolysis of thioacetamide and precipitation of sulfides from homogeneous media. (Secs. 7-7 and 8-13). A bath of vigorously boiling water is required; start heating it well before you need it. Test tubes must be scrupulously clean; rinse three tubes each three times with distilled water.

In each of the three test tubes mix 1 drop of the standard solution of Cd^{++} ion with about 1 ml (20 drops) of distilled water. To one tube add 1 drop of 2 M HCl, to another, 1 drop of 6 M NH_3, and to the third, add neither acid nor base. To each tube add one drop of thioacetamide solution and mix well. Heat all three tubes simultaneously in the vigorously boiling water. Note the times required to produce yellow cadmium sulfide. Account for the differences.

2. Conditions for precipitation of Cation Group 2. (Secs. 8-12 and 8-13). Prepare some 1 M HCl by diluting 5 drops of the 6 M acid with water. Mix thoroughly. Dilute some of this further to make 30 drops of 0.3 M HCl.

Divide the 1 M HCl equally between two test tubes. To one add a drop of the standard solution of Cd^{++}, to the other, a drop of the standard solution of Cu^{++}. Add a drop or two of thioacetamide solution and heat both tubes in the vigorously boiling water for several minutes. (A white turbidity may appear in one tube. It is colloidal sulfur. Wait for the appearance of a colored sulfide.)

Divide the 0.3 M HCl equally between two test tubes. To one add a drop of the standard solution of Cd^{++}, to the other a drop of the standard solution of Ni^{++}, and to each a drop or two of thioacetamide solution. Heat for several minutes.

Record your observations. Look up the solubility products of the three sulfides, and account for the difference in their behavior. Compare the two hydrochloric acid solutions with respect to (1) concentration of hydrogen ion, (2) concentration of sulfide ion after heating with thioacetamide, and (3) rate of hydrolysis of thioacetamide.

3. Colloidal copper(II) sulfide. Dilute 1 drop of the standard solution of Cu^{++} with 20 drops (1 ml) of water, add a drop of thioacetamide solution, and heat for several minutes. Repeat the experiment but include 2 drops of 6 M NH_4Cl in the mixture. Centrifuge both mixtures. Account for the effect of the ammonium chloride.

4. Colloidal arsenic(III) sulfide. Heat 10 drops of thioacetamide with one-fifth of a spatula-full of arsenic(III) oxide (side shelf) in boiling water for 5 minutes. Simultaneously, heat in another tube two or three drops of the standard solution of As(III) with a few drops of thioacetamide solution. Centrifuge both mixtures. Save the colloid (or sol) for the next part. Write equations for the reaction of H_2S with As_2O_3 and $AsCl_3$ (the form of arsenic in the standard solution). If electrolytes flocculate sols, which experiment would you expect to produce a colloid? Check with your observations.

Divide the arsenic sulfide sol between two tubes. To one add a drop of 0.02 M NaCl (side shelf), to the other a drop of 0.02 M $MgCl_2$. Warm and centrifuge. If no change is observed, add another drop of each solution. Why is one electrolyte more effective than the other?

5. Precipitation of acidic sulfides. Take 1 drop of the standard solution of Sb(III) in each of two test tubes. To one add sodium hydroxide until the precipitate that first appears redissolves. To the other add a drop of 6 M HCl. Add one drop of thioacetamide solution to each and heat in the boiling water. Acidify the alkaline solution with 2 M HCl. Write equations for all of the reactions that antimony undergoes in these experiments.

6. The sulfides of tin. Take 2 drops of the standard solution of Sn^{++} in a test tube, dilute with 10 drops of water, and add a few granules of tin or a strip of tin foil. Warm for several minutes to make sure that any Sn(IV) is reduced to Sn(II). Write an equation for the reaction. Withdraw the solution to another test tube; add a drop of thioacetamide solution.

Take 2 drops of the standard solution of Sn(IV) in a test tube, dilute with 10 drops of water, and add a drop of thioacetamide solution. Warm both this tube and the one containing Sn^{++} ion until two sulfides that differ in color are obtained. Centrifuge and discard the solutions even if they are not completely clear. Wash each precipitate once with 10-20 drops of water to remove excess acid. Discard the washings. Determine the number of drops of 0.5 M KOH required to dissolve each sulfide. Account for the difference.

7. Volatile hydrides and the Gutzeit test. Perform this test under the *ventilating duct or in the hood*; arsine is very poisonous. Dilute 1 drop of the standard solution of As(III) with 9 drops of water and mix well. To 1 drop of this solution in a test tube add 10 drops of water, 1 drop of 18 M H_2SO_4, and several granules of zinc. Put a loose wad of cotton in the upper part of the tube to remove acid spray. Rest on top of the tube a small piece of filter paper moistened with silver nitrate reagent.

If time permits, the test can be repeated with Sb(III) in place of As(III) or with $HgCl_2$ in place of $AgNO_3$.

8. Separation of lead sulfate. To 1 drop of the standard solution of Pb^{++} ion in a centrifuge tube add 2 drops of 16 *M* HNO_3 and 1 drop of 18 *M* H_2SO_4. Mix and centrifuge. Remove the solution to a test tube; save the precipitate of lead sulfate for Experiment 9 if that is to be done. Make the solution alkaline with 15 *M* NH_3 (check with litmus) and add potassium chromate. Save this mixture for comparison with the result of the next experiment.

Take the same combination of acids and Pb^{++} ion solution in a casserole. Evaporate over a microflame. The first white fumes are nitric acid and water vapor. Withdraw the casserole momentarily from the flame and note that these fumes soon disappear. Continue heating *under the ventilating duct or in the hood* until persistent, heavy white fumes with a choking odor are copiously evolved. Do not evaporate to dryness. *Cool* and then dilute with 10 drops of water (caution!). Stir the mixture and rub the inner walls of the casserole to loosen granules of the precipitate. Transfer quickly to a centrifuge tube. Rinse the casserole once with water and add the rinsing to the centrifuge tube. Centrifuge and test the solution as before with chromate for the presence of lead. Compare with the previous result. Why was nitric acid removed? Write equations for the reactions.

9. Some reactions of lead(II). Dissolve the precipitated lead sulfate reserved from Experiment 8 in a few drops of ammonium acetate solution. Add a drop of potassium chromate solution, then 6 *M* NaOH until the change is complete, and finally thioacetamide. Arrange the four compounds or ions containing lead in order of decreasing concentration of lead ion allowed at equilibrium.

10. Hydrolysis of mercury(II) salts. Add about 1 ml of water to a crystal of mercury(II) nitrate. Determine the approximate *p*H of the solution with wide-range indicator paper. Represent the reaction by an equation. Add a drop or two of 6 *M* HNO_3 and warm. Account for the result.

Put 1 drop of $HgCl_2$ reagent (from your kit) in each of two carefully cleaned test tubes and dilute each sample with about 10 drops of water. Add a drop of methyl orange indicator to each (see Table 12-2 for the *p*H range and colors of this indicator). To one tube add one-quarter of a spatula-full of solid sodium chloride, a neutral salt. Mix until it dissolves and compare colors. Account for its action. Why cannot sodium nitrate be used to repress the hydrolysis of mercury(II) nitrate?

11. The hydrolysis of bismuth(III) salts. Add a drop of Bi^{+++} solution (this is bismuth nitrate) to about 2 ml of water and mix. Then add a drop of 6 *M* NH_4Cl solution and allow to stand for about 2 minutes. Why is the hydrolysis of the bismuth ion more extensive in the presence of chloride? Divide the mixture between two tubes and verify that (1) the hydrolysis is reversible and (2) bismuth sulfide is less soluble than the oxychloride. Describe what you did, and write equations for the reactions.

12. The Bettendorf test. To one drop of the standard solution of As(III) add a drop of $SnCl_2$ reagent and 10 drops of 12 M HCl. Warm in the hot water bath for several minutes. Verify that antimony does not react.

13. The action of acids on metallic tin. Add a few drops of concentrated nitric acid to some granules of tin. Identify the products and derive a balanced equation for the reaction.

Treat a few granules of tin with several drops of 6 M HCl. Warm for a few minutes. An excess of tin should remain. Transfer the solution to another tube and allow it to cool. Then add a drop of $HgCl_2$ reagent. What is the precipitate? Derive equations for the reactions.

14. Preparation of copper(1) chloride. Dissolve about one-fourth of a spatula-full of solid copper(II) chloride in 10 drops of water and 2 drops of 12 M HCl. Add a small amount of copper powder; warm and stir until the solution turns colorless. Add more copper if necessary. Withdraw the solution and dilute it with 1-2 ml of water. Identify the copper compound or ion in (1) the original solution (it is not $CuCl_2$ or Cu^{++}), (2) the dark color that forms if insufficient copper is present, (3) the colorless solution, (4) the final precipitate. By reference to Table 18-6 explain why CuCl can be prepared by reduction of the Cu(II) salt but $CuNO_3$ and Cu_2SO_4 cannot.

15. A flame test for tin. Mix in a crucible 1 drop of a solution to be tested for tin with 10 drops of 12 M HCl. Add a few granules of zinc. Dip the end of a test tube filled with cold water in the mixture, and then bring it into the inner cone (reducing zone) of a gas flame. A blue luminescence on the outer walls of the tube indicates the presence of tin. None of the elements we study in this text interferes, but the test is not very sensitive. Try it on (1) $SnCl_2$ reagent from your kit, (2) the standard solution of Sn^{++}, and (3) the standard solution of Sn(IV).

16. Precipitation of lead chromate from homogeneous medium. To 1 drop of $Pb(C_2H_3O_2)_2$ solution add 2 drops of the standard solution of Cr^{+++} (side shelf) and a few drops of potassium bromate solution. Heat five or ten minutes in a hot water bath. Compare the precipitate so formed with one obtained by direct reaction of lead acetate with potassium chromate. Chromate is generated slowly within the solution by oxidation of Cr^{+++} ion. Complete and balance the skeleton equation

$$BrO_3^- + Cr^{+++} \rightarrow Br_2 + CrO_4^{--}$$

by the ion-electron or oxidation number method (assume acid solution).

Because of the gradual formation of chromate, the crystals of lead chromate grow to larger size than those formed by direct reaction. What connection between size of crystals and color is suggested by your results?

Further details of this method and photomicrographs that show the difference in particle size are given by W. Hoffmann and W. Brandt, *Anal. Chem.*, **28**, 1487 (1957).

18-14. Analysis of Known and Unknown Samples.

a. Use 5 drops of a *known* or *practice* solution that contains 2 mg each of Hg^{++}, Bi^{+++}, Cu^{++}, As(III), and Sb(III), 4 mg of Pb^{++}, and 8 mg each of Cd^{++} and Sn(IV) per milliliter. If this is not already prepared, mix the following quantities of the standard solutions of the ions and use the whole mixture for analysis: 1 drop each of Hg^{++}, Bi^{+++}, Cu^{++}, As(III), Sb(III), 2 drops of Pb^{++}, and 4 drops of Cd^{++} and Sn(IV). Omit the preliminary treatment with H_2O_2.

b. The unknown may be (1) a solution containing the ions of this and possibly other groups or (2) a solid mixture. If the solution is Solution 1-1 from Outline 1, use all of it. If the solution contains a precipitate, shake well and quickly withdraw a representative sample. The solution will probably be acid, but if it is not, acidify it with 6 M HCl. If the unknown is a solid, dissolve about 20 mg of a representative sample in 6 M HCl.

The analytical procedure consists of (1) Preliminary Preparations, (2) Outline 2, Precipitation and Subdivision of the Group, (3) Outline 3, Analysis of the Copper Section, and (4) Outline 4, Analysis of the Arsenic Section.

18-15. Suggestions for Further Work.

1. Analyze known or unknown solutions by paper or column chromatography. Consult Chapter 25 for details.

2. Investigate the use of ion exchange resins for separations of the ions of this group. See Chapter 25.

3. Molybdenum is a member of this group that is omitted in our introductory treatment. Look up its properties and adapt the scheme of analysis to include it. See, for example, L. Lehrman and P. Schneider, *J. Chem. Educ.*, **33**, 621 (1956).

4. Read and report on the discussion of A. Benedetti-Pichler and M. Cefola [*Ind. Eng. Chem., Anal. Ed.*, **15**, 227 (1943)] on the analysis of microgram quantities of the ions of this group.

5. Read and report on the recent controversy on the relative merits of LiOH and KOH in subdividing the group. See H. Holness and R. Trewick, *Analyst*, **75**, 276 (1950); C. James and P. Woodward, *ibid.*, **80**, 825 (1955); and A. Vogel, W. Cresswell, G. Jeffrey, and J. Leicester, *ibid.*, **81**, 244 (1956).

6. Prepare several grams of one or more of the following compounds.

For references see Sec. 17-11, Footnote 9. $SnCl_4$, $SbCl_3$ (from stibnite), cinnabar, mosaic gold (SnS_2), $Sb_2(SO_4)_3$ (from Sb), $Na_3SbS_4 \cdot 9H_2O$ (Schlippe's salt), $Hg(SCN)_2$, $CuSO_4 \cdot 5H_2O$ (from Cu), $(NH_4)_2Cu(SO_4)_2 \cdot 6H_2O$, $Cu(NH_3)_4SO_4 \cdot H_2O$ (large needles can be obtained by layering ammoniacal $CuSO_4$ under water which, in turn, is layered under ethyl alcohol).

THE SYSTEMATIC ANALYSIS OF CATION GROUP 2
THE ACID HYDROGEN SULFIDE GROUP

Preliminary Preparations

P-1. Calibration of a Test Tube.   Measure 2.5 ml of water into a dry test tube. Mark the position of the bottom of the meniscus with a strip of label or, more permanently, with a file scratch.

P-2. Oxidation of Sn(II).   Transfer the solution to be analyzed, which should be acid (Sec. 18-14), to a small casserole, add 2 drops of 3% H_2O_2, and boil down the solution to a volume of a few drops. Using a microflame (T-7a, b), swirl the solution constantly to prevent dehydration in any part of the dish, and withdraw the dish from the flame somewhat before the final volume is reached. The chlorides of As, Sb, Sn, and Hg are sufficiently volatile so that some of these elements can be lost if evaporation is carried too far.

Dilute the remaining solution with 3 to 5 drops of water, and transfer it to the calibrated test tube (P-1). Rinse out the casserole walls and bottom twice with 3 to 5 drops of water, and transfer both rinses to the test tube. Do not be concerned if the solution is turbid. This is usually caused by SbOCl or BiOCl, and these compounds are readily converted to the sulfides in a later step.

P-3. Adjustment of Acidity.   Add 6 M NH_3 to the solution until it is basic to litmus or wide-range indicator paper. If Cu^{++} ion is present, the formation of the deep blue ammonia complex ion also acts as an indicator, but the blue color may be obscured by colored precipitates or complex ions of Group 3. To the basic solution add 2 M HCl drop by drop until the pH is between 2 and 3 according to the wide-range indicator paper. If the solution is made too acid, bring it back with a fraction of a drop of 6 M NH_3 (T-4b). Then add exactly 0.35 ml (7 standard drops or the number of drops from your calibrated dropper equivalent to this volume) of 2 M HCl. Add 4 drops of 13% thioacetamide solution (hereafter abbreviated TA) and enough water to make a total volume of 2.5 ml. Mix well (T-5b, c). Check the acidity against short-range indicator paper. It should have a pH of 0.5 corresponding to a hydrogen ion concentration of 0.3 M. This will correspond to a bright yellow color with Alkacid paper or orange with modified methyl violet. Treat the solution further by Outline 2.

OUTLINE 2. Precipitation and Subdivision of Cation Group 2

Precipitation of the group: Warm the soln contg TA at pH 0.5 from P-3 in a bath of vigorously boiling water for 5 minutes.[1] Centrifuge and withdraw soln to another test tube. Check the acidity with short range indicator paper.[2] Add 2 drops TA and heat for several minutes in the boiling water. Centrifuge if more ppt appears. Continue heating with TA as long as ppt is obtained. Then dilute several drops of the clear soln with twice its vol of water, add 1 drop TA, and heat again. If a ppt appears, treat the whole soln in the same way; divide it between several test tubes if necessary.[3]

Combine ppts if several portions have been obtained (T-11). Wash the pptd sulfides twice with about 20 drops hot water[4] contg 1 drop 6 M NH$_4$Cl (T-10).[5] Add the first washing to Soln 2-1 in a general analysis for all groups.

Precipitate 2-1. HgS, PbS, Bi$_2$S$_3$, CuS, CdS, As$_2$S$_3$, Sb$_2$S$_3$, SnS$_2$, S^0. Add 10 drops 0.5 M KOH and heat briefly in the water bath. Centrifuge and transfer soln to a centrifuge tube. Repeat the extn with a second portion of KOH soln. Combine solns.

Solution 2-1. Ions of later groups, HCl, NH$_4$Cl, H$_2$S, TA. If H$_2$S gas is used, examine for arsenate.[6]

If original sample contained ions of Group 2 only, discard this soln.

If soln is to be analyzed for later groups, add 1 ml 12 M HCl. Transfer to a casserole and evap almost to dryness.[7] Add several drops water and 1 drop 6 M HCl and reserve in a stoppered tube for **Group 3.**

Precipitate 2-2. HgS, PbS, Bi$_2$S$_3$, CuS, CdS, S^0. Wash twice with hot water to which either 1 drop 0.2 M NH$_4$NO$_3$ or a crystal of the solid salt has been added.

Analyze according to **Outline 3.**[8]

Solution 2-2. AsS$_3$$^{---}$, AsO$_3$$^{---}$, SbS$_3$$^{---}$, SbO$_3$$^{---}$, SnS$_3$$^{--}$, SnS$_2OH^-$, (HgS$_2$$^{--}$), KOH. Recentrifuge to remove the last traces of Ppt. 2-2.[9] Transfer the clear, yellow soln to a test tube.

Analyze according to **Outline 4.**[10]

Notes on Outline 2

1. Allow sufficient time for the hydrolysis of TA. Heating also helps to coagulate the sulfides so that they are easier to settle by centrifugation. If hydrogen sulfide gas is used as a source of H_2S, saturate the solution with the gas whenever the directions call for the use of TA.

2. Hydrogen ions are liberated in the precipitation of the sulfides, e.g., $Cu^{++} + H_2S \rightarrow CuS \downarrow + 2H^+$. If the solution becomes too acid, ammonia must be added to bring the pH back to 0.5.

3. The diluted solution will have a hydrogen ion concentration of 0.1 M (pH 1). The dilution may be necessary to obtain complete precipitation of CdS. If a bright yellow precipitate forms that is soluble in 6 M HCl but insoluble in KOH, it is CdS, and no further test for Cd^{++} need be made. If the concentration of chloride ion is unusually high, black PbS may also precipitate.

4. Use water from a test tube in the hot water bath or add cold water and heat in the water bath for a few minutes. Washing is necessary to remove excess H_2S, which increases the solubility of HgS in KOH, together with ions of later groups, if present.

5. Ammonium chloride prevents peptization of the sulfides (Sec. 8-21).

6. Hydrogen sulfide, unlike thioacetamide, acts very slowly on arsenate. If H_2S gas was used to precipitate the group, evaporate Solution 2-1 in a casserole to a volume of about 1 ml. Add 1 ml (20 drops) of 12 M HCl and saturate the solution with H_2S. Centrifuge. Wash the precipitate of As_2S_5 with 2 M HCl and add the washing to the solution. Combine the precipitate with Precipitate 2-1. Save the solution for Group 3; remove H_2S as directed in Outline 2.

7. This evaporation is necessary to remove H_2S and TA which are slowly oxidized by atmospheric oxygen to sulfur and even sulfate. The latter will precipitate Ba^{++} and Sr^{++} ions and cause them to be lost.

8. If analysis of the Copper Section cannot be done at once, cover the sulfides with water and a drop of TA, and stopper the tube with a cork or medicine dropper bulb. It is better, if possible, to carry the analysis as far as the separation of Precipitate 3-1 and Solution 3-1 in Outline 3.

9. Complete separation of solution and precipitate is difficult in a test tube. Hence a second centrifugation and separation are made in a centrifuge tube. If a dark brown colloid persists, add a few crystals of NH_4NO_3 (or a drop of a 0.2 M solution) and warm to coagulate it.

10. If this solution cannot be analyzed at once, add a drop of TA and preserve it in a tightly stoppered tube. A precipitate sometimes appears after the solution has stood for a day or so. If it is colored, it is a sulfide. Its formation does no harm; keep it with the solution.

OUTLINE 3. The Systematic Analysis of the Copper Section of Cation Group 2.

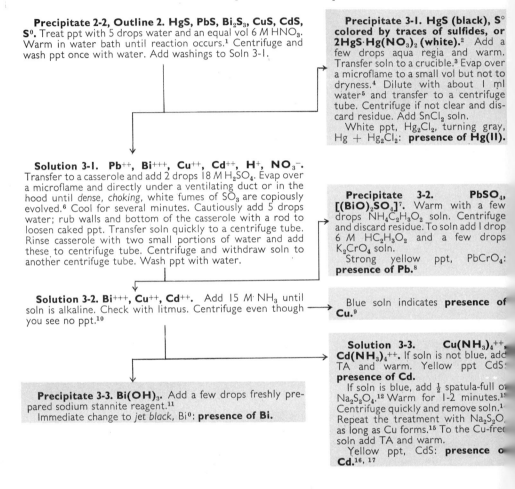

Precipitate 2-2, Outline 2. HgS, PbS, Bi$_2$S$_3$, CuS, CdS, S^0. Treat ppt with 5 drops water and an equal vol 6 M HNO$_3$. Warm in water bath until reaction occurs.[1] Centrifuge and wash ppt once with water. Add washings to Soln 3-1.

Precipitate 3-1. HgS (black), S^0 colored by traces of sulfides, or 2HgS·Hg(NO$_3$)$_2$ (white).[2] Add a few drops aqua regia and warm. Transfer soln to a crucible.[3] Evap over a microflame to a small vol but not to dryness.[4] Dilute with about 1 ml water[5] and transfer to a centrifuge tube. Centrifuge if not clear and discard residue. Add SnCl$_2$ soln.

White ppt, Hg$_2$Cl$_2$, turning gray, Hg + Hg$_2$Cl$_2$: **presence of Hg(II).**

Solution 3-1. Pb^{++}, Bi^{+++}, Cu^{++}, Cd^{++}, H$^+$, NO$_3$$^-$. Transfer to a casserole and add 2 drops 18 M H$_2$SO$_4$. Evap over a microflame and directly under a ventilating duct or in the hood until *dense*, *choking*, white fumes of SO$_3$ are copiously evolved.[6] Cool for several minutes. Cautiously add 5 drops water; rub walls and bottom of the casserole with a rod to loosen caked ppt. Transfer soln quickly to a centrifuge tube. Rinse casserole with two small portions of water and add these to centrifuge tube. Centrifuge and withdraw soln to another centrifuge tube. Wash ppt with water.

Precipitate 3-2. PbSO$_4$, [(BiO)$_2$SO$_4$].[7] Warm with a few drops NH$_4$C$_2$H$_3$O$_2$ soln. Centrifuge and discard residue. To soln add 1 drop 6 M HC$_2$H$_3$O$_2$ and a few drops K$_2$CrO$_4$ soln.

Strong yellow ppt, PbCrO$_4$: **presence of Pb.**[8]

Solution 3-2. Bi^{+++}, Cu^{++}, Cd^{++}. Add 15 M NH$_3$ until soln is alkaline. Check with litmus. Centrifuge even though you see no ppt.[10]

Blue soln indicates **presence of Cu.**[9]

Solution 3-3. Cu(NH$_3$)$_4$$^{++}$, Cd(NH$_3$)$_4$$^{++}$. If soln is not blue, add TA and warm. Yellow ppt CdS: **presence of Cd.**
If soln is blue, add ½ spatula-full of Na$_2$S$_2$O$_4$.[12] Warm for 1-2 minutes.[13] Centrifuge quickly and remove soln.[14] Repeat the treatment with Na$_2$S$_2$O$_4$ as long as Cu forms.[15] To the Cu-free soln add TA and warm.
Yellow ppt, CdS: **presence of Cd.**[16, 17]

Precipitate 3-3. Bi(OH)$_3$. Add a few drops freshly prepared sodium stannite reagent.[11]
Immediate change to *jet black*, Bi^0: **presence of Bi.**

Notes on Outline 3

1. There is an induction period during which no apparent change occurs. Then bubbling starts and the bubbles often carry sulfur and sulfides to the surface.

2. As these formulas and colors imply, a black precipitate at this stage is not necessarily an indication of the presence of mercury, nor is the formation of a white or yellow precipitate proof of its absence. Therefore, the precipitate must always be dissolved and the mercury must be sought in the solution.

3. In drawing off the solution leave behind any yellow particles of sulfur.

4. Mercury(II) chloride is somewhat volatile and should not be heated too strongly.

5. Evaporation destroys nitrate and removes excess HCl. The concentration of acid is further decreased by dilution, because the reaction between $HgCl_2$ and Sn^{++} ion is slow if the concentration of HCl is too high.

6. The formation of SO_3 is a signal that nitrate has been removed as molecular HNO_3. Once seen, fumes of SO_3 are easy to recognize thereafter. They are heavier and more irritating than the fumes of nitric acid that come off at first. Failure to evaporate until copious fumes are evolved may cause enough lead to stay in solution to spoil subsequent tests. Yet evaporation should not be carried to dryness because the anhydrous sulfates come back into solution slowly. If this should happen, add 2 drops of 6 M H_2SO_4 and 3 drops of water, and warm the casserole on the water bath for several minutes. Stir to disperse the residue in the solution.

7. Formation of a precipitate at this point is not a certain indication of the presence of Pb. Occasionally other sulfates, e.g., $(BiO)_2SO_4$, precipitate here. The bismuth compound is less soluble in $NH_4C_2H_3O_2$ and $(BiO)_2CrO_4$ is more soluble in $HC_2H_3O_2$ and is insoluble in NaOH.

8. If a large quantity of bismuth is found, check the solubility of this precipitate in NaOH.

9. If the blue color is faint and further confirmation is required, acidify a drop of the solution with $HC_2H_3O_2$ and add a drop of $K_4Fe(CN)_6$ solution. Copper(II) forms a red ferrocyanide whereas that of cadmium is white.

10. Beginners find small, gelatinous precipitates of $Bi(OH)_3$ hard to see, particularly when suspended in a blue solution.

11. To 1 drop of $SnCl_2$ reagent add 6 M NaOH drop by drop with careful mixing until the precipitate of $Sn(OH)_2$ redissolves. This will take at least 2 drops of NaOH solution. The $SnCl_2$ solution is gradually oxidized by air. If there is any doubt as to its effectiveness, prepare some stannite from it and test its action on $Bi(OH)_3$ made from the standard solution of Bi^{+++} ion.

12. Sodium dithionite is a powerful reducing agent and is unstable. Keep it dry and away from heat. Use a dry spatula in measuring the solid. One-half of a spatula-full or about 50 mg should reduce 12.5 mg of Cu^{++} ion. The blue color of the copper ammonia complex ion should permanently disappear upon addition of the dithionite.

13. Precipitated copper is red. Black or brown residues frequently obtained here are colored by other metals. This does no harm; in fact, it is an advantage to remove traces of the other metals before the cadmium test.

14. If the solution stands in contact with the copper too long, some copper can redissolve.

15. After prolonged treatment with dithionite a yellow coloration may appear. This is cadmium sulfide. Add TA at once and warm. The sulfide

apparently comes from decomposition of the dithionite after removal of the copper.

16. Occasionally a buff, green, or black precipitate is obtained at this point. This is a result of careless separations in previous steps. If the precipitate is large, remove the solution and discard it. Dissolve the precipitate as far as possible in 1 drop of 6 M HCl. Centrifuge and transfer the clear solution to a test tube. Dilute with 1 ml of water, add TA, and warm to reprecipitate the sulfide.

17. Cadmium may also be identified during precipitation of the group. See Note 3 to Outline 2.

OUTLINE 4. The Systematic Analysis of the Arsenic Section of Cation Group 2

Solution 2-2, Outline 2. AsS$_3$$^{---}$, AsO$_3$$^{---}$, SbS$_3$$^{---}$, SbO$_3$$^{---}$, SnS$_3$$^{--}$, SnS$_2OH^-$, (HgS$_2$$^{--}$), KOH. Add 1 drop TA.[1] Then very carefully add 2 M HCl until soln is just acid to litmus.[2] Note the color and character of the ppt.[3] Transfer mixture to a centrifuge tube and centrifuge.[4] Draw off supernatant liquid as completely as possible and discard it.[5]

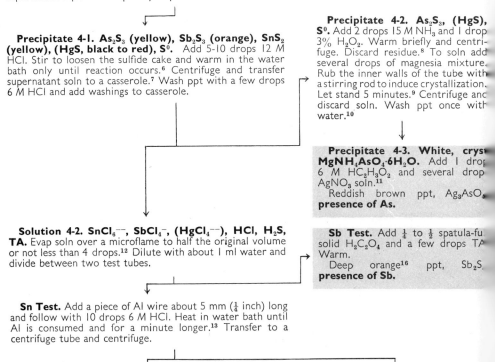

Precipitate 4-1. As$_2$S$_3$ (yellow), Sb$_2$S$_3$ (orange), SnS$_2$ (yellow), (HgS, black to red), S^0. Add 5-10 drops 12 M HCl. Stir to loosen the sulfide cake and warm in the water bath only until reaction occurs.[6] Centrifuge and transfer supernatant soln to a casserole.[7] Wash ppt with a few drops 6 M HCl and add washings to casserole.

Precipitate 4-2. As$_2$S$_3$, (HgS), S^0. Add 2 drops 15 M NH$_3$ and 1 drop 3% H$_2$O$_2$. Warm briefly and centrifuge. Discard residue.[8] To soln add several drops of magnesia mixture. Rub the inner walls of the tube with a stirring rod to induce crystallization. Let stand 5 minutes.[9] Centrifuge and discard soln. Wash ppt once with water.[10]

Precipitate 4-3. White, cryst MgNH$_4$AsO$_4$·6H$_2$O. Add 1 drop 6 M HC$_2$H$_3$O$_2$ and several drop AgNO$_3$ soln.[11]
Reddish brown ppt, Ag$_3$AsO$_4$ **presence of As.**

Solution 4-2. SnCl$_6$$^{--}$, SbCl$_4$$^-$, (HgCl$_4$$^{--}$), HCl, H$_2$S, TA. Evap soln over a microflame to half the original volume or not less than 4 drops.[12] Dilute with about 1 ml water and divide between two test tubes.

Sb Test. Add $\frac{1}{4}$ to $\frac{1}{2}$ spatula-fu solid H$_2$C$_2$O$_4$ and a few drops TA Warm.
Deep orange[16] ppt, Sb$_2$S **presence of Sb.**

Sn Test. Add a piece of Al wire about 5 mm ($\frac{1}{4}$ inch) long and follow with 10 drops 6 M HCl. Heat in water bath until Al is consumed and for a minute longer.[13] Transfer to a centrifuge tube and centrifuge.

Solution 4-4. Sn^{++}, Al^{+++}, HCl. Dilute with equal vol of water. Without delay[15] add 1-2 drops HgCl$_2$ soln.
White to gray ppt, Hg$_2$Cl$_2$ and Hg^0: **presence of Sn.**

Precipitate 4-4. Black flecks Sb^0.[14]

Notes on Outline 4

1. Thioacetamide is required to supply H_2S that is lost by volatilization.

2. If the solution is made too acid, some SnS_2 may be lost. Hence 2 M rather than 6 M HCl is used. Mix thoroughly after each addition.

3. The sulfides of this section are all highly colored. A white, hazy turbidity that does not settle readily upon centrifugation is sulfur in colloidal form. When only this is obtained, the arsenic section is absent.

4. The sulfides are precipitated in a test tube to allow careful neutralization and thorough mixing. Since they do not pack down well, separation of precipitate and solution is improved if a centrifuge tube is used.

5. The extraction with 12 M HCl in the next step will fail if the acid becomes diluted with excess water on the precipitate.

6. Note any change in character of the precipitate during this treatment. A bright yellow residue is usually As_2S_3; a black precipitate may contain HgS. A colorless solution and a white turbidity of S^0 indicate the absence of As. Do not prolong the heating of the mixture, for some As_2S_3 may dissolve slowly.

7. Draw off the supernatant solution through a wisp of cotton wrapped around the tip of the pipet. If the pipet or casserole contains water, this may decrease the concentration of HCl to such an extent that Sb_2S_3 reprecipitates. This does no harm.

8. A black residue is probably HgS. It can be identified by the procedure given under Precipitate 3-1, Outline 3. Ammonia readily dissolves As_2S_3 but not HgS; the H_2O_2 oxidizes As(III) to As(V).

9. This precipitate sometimes supersaturates badly. Give it time to form before reporting a negative result.

10. A washing here removes traces of chloride that would precipitate with silver nitrate in the next step.

11. If a white precipitate of AgCl forms, add more $AgNO_3$.

12. If evaporation is carried too far, some $SnCl_4$ may be lost.

13. Aluminum can reduce Sn(IV) and Sn(II) to gray Sn^0. It will dissolve in HCl after the Al has been consumed; Sb will not dissolve.

14. If the regular Sb test was indecisive, a confirmatory test can be made on this residue. Wash it with water and dissolve in a drop of 6 M HNO_3. Dilute with water, add TA, and warm to precipitate Sb_2S_3.

15. Since Sn^{++} is oxidized by oxygen of the air, the addition of $HgCl_2$ should not be delayed.

16. The precipitate is frequently orange at first and then it darkens by post-precipitation of impurities. If it is yellow, it may be As_2S_3 because the treatment of Precipitate 4-1 with HCl was too prolonged. Test its solubility in 12 M HCl and in $NH_3 + H_2O_2$. If the precipitate in the Sb test is very dark, it may be contaminated with HgS. Remove the solution. Add 6 M HCl

to the precipitate and warm for a minute or so. Centrifuge and discard the residue. Dilute the solution, add TA, and warm to reprecipitate Sb_2S_3.

EXERCISES

18-1. Name the elements of this analytical group and tell why they occur in the group.

18-2. For each element of Group 2 give its position in the Periodic Table and its principal oxidation states.

18-3. Give the number of s, p, and d electrons in the outer shells of Sn^{++}, Cd^{++}, Bi^{+++}, and Cu^{++}.

18-4. (a) Write electron dot formulas for the following molecules or complex ions; (b) Calculate the effective atomic number of the central atom in each.

$HgCl_2$, $SbBr_3$, AsO_4^{---}, SbH_3, $Cu(NH_3)_4^{++}$, $Pb(OH)_4^{--}$, AsF_5, $PbCl_4$, $Sn(OH)_3^-$, $CdCl_4^{--}$, $SnCl_6^{--}$, $Cu(OH)_4^{--}$.

18-5. What is meant by "lanthanide contraction"? What is the effect of this on the properties of some of the elements in the third long period?

18-6. Identify by formula: metastannic acid, thioacetamide, cinnabar, yellow arsenic, stibine, bismuthyl ion, aqua regia, sodium dithionite, thioarsenite ion, tetrammine copper(II) ion, arsine, antimonate ion, sodium stannite, hexachloro-stannate(IV) ion, and azurite.

18-7. Give the colors of: HgO, $CdCl_2$, $CuSO_4$, $BiOCl$, As_2S_3, PbO_2, $Cu_2Fe(CN)_6$, SnS_2, Sb_4, CuO, Sb_2S_3, $CuSO_4 \cdot 5H_2O$, $Cd(NH_3)_4^{++}$, $PbSO_4$, $2HgS \cdot Hg(NO_3)_2$, H_3AsO_3, $MgNH_4AsO_4 \cdot 6H_2O$, PbS, CdO, HgI_2, CuS, $SnCl_4$.

18-8. Name the substances in Exercise 18-7.

18-9. Write formulas for the principal form (ion, molecule, or precipitate) of the elements of this group in (a) 0.3 M HCl, (b) 12 M HCl, (c) 6 M NaOH.

18-10. An "unknown" solution is alkaline. Which of the elements of Group 2 cannot be present? Give the formulas of the ions that could be in the solution.

18-11. If an "unknown" was a clear solution and contained Sn^{++} and Cl^-, what ion or ions must be absent? If it contained $Sn(OH)_3^-$ and was a clear solution with a white precipitate at the bottom of the tube, what ions must be absent?

18-12. Arrange the following in order of increasing concentration of Cu^{++} ion: a saturated solution of $CuSO_4$, a mixture of $CuSO_4$ and an excess of 15 M NH_3, a saturated solution of $Cu(OH)_2$, and a saturated solution of CuS.

18-13. Arrange the following in order of increasing concentration of Hg^{++} ion: a saturated solution of HgS, 0.1 M $HgCl_2$, 0.1 M K_2HgI_4, and 0.1 M $Hg(NO_3)_2$.

18-14. Predict the direction of these reactions if the ions are all present at approximately the same concentration.

(a) $4I^- + H_2O + HgO \downarrow \rightleftharpoons HgI_4^{--} + 2OH^-$
(b) $CdCO_3 \downarrow + 3Cl^- \rightleftharpoons CdCl_3^- + CO_3^{--}$
(c) $Cd^0 \downarrow + Zn^{++} \rightleftharpoons Cd^{++} + Zn^0 \downarrow$
(d) $CuCrO_4 \downarrow + 4NH_3 \rightleftharpoons Cu(NH_3)_4^{++} + CrO_4^{--}$
(e) $2Cu^{++} + 4Cl^- \rightleftharpoons 2CuCl \downarrow + Cl_2 \uparrow$
(f) $Cd^0 \downarrow + Cu(NH_3)_4^{++} \rightleftharpoons Cd(NH_3)_4^{++} + Cu^0 \downarrow$

18-15. Cite evidence to support these assertions: (a) lead is more metallic than tin; (b) antimony is more metallic than arsenic; (c) antimony(V) in some respects resembles tin(IV); (d) the formula of the stannate ion is $Sn(OH)_6^{--}$.

18-16. Compare the hydrides of arsenic, antimony, and bismuth with respect to thermal stability and account for the difference.

18-17. The boiling points of the hydrides of Group IVB are: CH_4, $-184°$; SiH_4, $-112°$; GeH_4, $-90°$; and SnH_4, $-52°$. Predict the approximate boiling point of the very unstable PbH_4. Why do the boiling points increase with increase in molecular weight?

18-18. The dipole moments of NH_3, PH_3, and AsH_3 are, respectively, 1.3, 0.55, and 0.16 debyes. Account for the difference.

18-19. The vapor density of arsenic(III) oxide at $518°$ C and 1 atm pressure is 6.22 g/l. The freezing point of a solution of 1 g of the crystalline oxide in 50 g of nitrobenzene is $0.4°$ below that of the pure solvent. The molal freezing point depression of nitrobenzene is $8.1°$. Show that both experiments lead to the formula As_4O_6.

18-20. Arrange the following in order of increasing acidic character: $Cd(OH)_2$, Sb_2O_3, $Bi(OH)_3$, Sb_2O_5, $Cu(OH)_2$, and $Pb(OH)_2$.

18-21. Arrange the following in order of increasing acidic character: Bi_2S_3, CdS, SnS_2, HgS.

18-22. Describe the structures of SnO_2, As_4S_6, PbS, $CuCl_2$.

18-23. The dipole moments of the arsenic halides are: AsF_3, 2.65; $AsCl_3$, 2.06; $AsBr_3$, 1.60; and AsI_3, 0.96 debyes. Account for this order.

18-24. The dipole moments of $SnCl_4$ and $HgCl_2$ are zero. Why?

18-25. Silver chloride is only incompletely precipitated from a mixture of silver nitrate and mercury(II) nitrate by hydrochloric acid. Mercury(II) arsenate is sparingly soluble in water but readily soluble in KCl solution. Hot concentrated sulfuric acid does *not* displace the more volatile HCl from $HgCl_2$. Although HCN is a much weaker acid than HCl, it can displace the latter from $HgCl_2$. What information about the nature of $HgCl_2$ and $Hg(CN)_2$ is given by these observations?

18-26. Robert Boyle described tin(IV) chloride as "a spiritous liquor, which as soon as the free air come to touch it, will, before very long, send up abundance of white exhalations in the form of thick white smoak." Suggest an explanation for his observation.

18-27. At room temperature $SnCl_4$ is a liquid but $SnCl_4 \cdot 5H_2O$ is a solid. Suggest an explanation.

18-28. The equivalent conductances of some chlorides at their melting points are: $CdCl_2$, 51.4; $HgCl_2$, 0.0025; $SnCl_4$, 0; $SnCl_2$, 21.9. These data are often cited in support of the molecular or ionic character of the salt. Explain.

18-29. Represent by equations the reactions responsible for the acidic reaction of solutions of $HgCl_2$, $Cu(NO_3)_2$, $Bi(NO_3)_3$, $AsCl_3$, HgF_2, $CdSO_4$, and $SnCl_2$.

18-30. Which salt in each pair is more highly hydrolyzed? Explain. (a) $HgCl_2$ — $Hg(ClO_4)_2$, (b) $SnCl_2$ — $SnCl_4$, (c) $BiCl_3$ — $Bi(NO_3)_3$.

18-31. Write an equation for the hydrolysis of thioacetamide in acid solution. What is the role of H^+ in this reaction? Why is the formation of H_2S not suppressed by an excess of HCl?

18-32. By reference to appropriate equilibrium constants explain how it is possible to separate Cd^{++} from Zn^{++} with hydrogen sulfide in 0.1 to 0.3 M HCl.

18-33. Cite examples from the analytical procedure of separations based on (a) formation of an ammonia complex ion, (b) the acidic nature of some sulfides, (c) selective reduction of one ion, (d) differing solubility products of the sulfides.

18-34. Of the three acids HCl, HNO_3, and aqua regia, which would you choose to dissolve HgS? CuS? SnS? Justify each choice.

18-35. Write equations for the successive reactions of the ions of this group (see Sec. 18-12).

18-36. If silver were not precipitated in Group 1 but came down as the sulfide in Group 2, where would it appear in the course of the analysis?

18-37. What reagent or combination of reagents would you use to separate these pairs in one step? (a) $Ag^+ - Cu^{++}$, (b) $Bi(OH)_3 - Cu(OH)_2$, (c) $Hg^{++} - Ni^{++}$, (d) $SnS_2 - CuS$, (e) $Bi_2S_3 - HgS$, (f) $Pb(NO_3)_2 - Cu(NO_3)_2$, (g) $Cu^{++} - Cd^{++}$, (h) $HgS - As_2S_3$, (i) $As_2S_3 - SnS_2$, (j) $BaSO_4 - PbSO_4$, (k) $Zn^{++} - Sb^{+++}$, (l) $SnCl_6^{--} - SbCl_4^-$.

18-38. What errors in technique might be responsible for (a) failure to obtain CdS from Solution 3-3, (b) formation of a yellow precipitate in the Sb test, (c) formation of a brown precipitate in the Cd test, (d) complete dissolution of Precipitate 2-2 by 3 M HNO_3 even though HgS was present, (e) failure to obtain Bi^0 from $Bi(OH)_3$, (f) failure to obtain Precipitate 4-3 even though arsenate was present.

18-39. Give a reason for each: (a) the use of freshly prepared sodium stannite; (b) the use of ammonium salts in the wash water when washing sulfides; (c) dilution of the solution after removal of the first group precipitate; (d) the quick separation of copper from the solution after the dithionite treatment; (e) the use of acetic acid in the lead test; (f) the use of oxalic acid in the antimony test; (g) the use of a dilute solution for the reaction between tin(II) and mercury(II); (h) why chloride solutions of the ions of this group are never evaporated to dryness.

18-40. A solid "unknown" may contain one or more of these substances: CdS, BiOCl, $Pb(NO_3)_2$, HgO, $CuSO_4 \cdot 5H_2O$, Na_2SO_4. The unknown is white and partially soluble in water. It is completely dissolved by sodium hydroxide in excess. Which substances are probably present, which are absent, and for which is the evidence inconclusive?

CHAPTER NINETEEN

Cation Group 3

The Basic Hydrogen Sulfide Group

Al^{+++}, Cr^{+++}, Fe^{+++}, Fe^{++}, Mn^{++}, Co^{++}, Ni^{++}, Zn^{++}

19-1. Introduction. The eight ions of this group are precipitated as sulfides or hydroxides by a combination of hydrogen sulfide or thioacetamide with an ammonia-ammonium chloride buffer. None of these ions form chlorides, sulfides, or hydroxides sufficiently insoluble to precipitate from a solution that is 0.1 to 0.3 *M* in hydrochloric acid.

IA	IIA	IIIA	IVA	VA	VIA	VIIA	VIII	VIII	VIII	IB	IIB	IIIB
	4 Be											
												13 **Al** (III)
		21 Sc	22 Ti	23 (V)	24 **Cr** (III)	25 **Mn** (II)	26 **Fe** (II)	27 **Co** (II)	28 **Ni** (II)		30 **Zn** (II)	31 Ga
		39 Y	40 Zr	41 Nb	42 Mo							49 In
		57 La*	72 Hf	73 Ta	74 (W)							81 Tl
		89 Ac†										

* The lanthanides, atomic numbers 58-71.
† The actinides, atomic numbers 90-103.

The positions in the Periodic Table of the seven elements that we study and of the less common members of Cation Group 3 are shown above. Heavy lines enclose the elements that are usually precipitated as sulfides; the rest are brought down as hydroxides or hydrated oxides. Vanadium and tungsten are, at best, only incompletely precipitated and are shown in parentheses.

Six of the seven common members of Cation Group 3 belong to the transition series of the first long period. These elements often resemble their neighbors on either side more closely than the congeners below; e.g., iron resembles manganese and cobalt more closely than it does ruthenium and osmium. Aluminum and beryllium, although not in the long periods, fall in this analytical group because of the insolubility of their hydroxides. Their resemblance to each other is an illustration of a diagonal relation between the two short periods. Boron, which lies above aluminum in Group IIIB, resembles silicon, which lies diagonally to its right, rather than aluminum.

19-2. The Oxidation States of These Elements.   All but zinc give compounds in more than one oxidation state, but the most common states are $+2$ and $+3$. In the following summary the very rare oxidation states, i.e., those found in only a few complexes, are given in parentheses, and the very common ones are in bold face.

Element	Oxidation states
Al	(1), (2), **3**
Cr	**2**, **3**, (4), (5), **6**
Mn	(1), **2**, **3**, **4**, (5), 6, 7
Fe	**2**, **3**, (6)
Co	(1), **2**, 3, (4)
Ni	(0), (1), **2**, (3), 4
Zn	**2**

The resemblance between the elements when they are in the same oxidation state is so strong that it will be convenient to discuss first the properties of the bivalent ions, then those of the trivalent ions, and finally those of higher oxidation states.

19-3. The Electronic Structures of the Atoms and Ions.   The aluminum atom has a simple structure that sets it apart from atoms of the other elements in this group. There are three electrons in its outer shell: two of the s type and one of the p type. It normally loses all three to form Al^{+++} ion, thereby exposing the electronic configuration $2s^2 2p^6$ found in the inert gas neon. The loss of three electrons requires the investment of a large amount of energy, viz., 1227 kcal/g-atom, which must be repaid by a release in energy if Al^{+++} ions are to be stable. This requirement is fulfilled by hydrating the ion, which releases about 1113 kcal/g-atom, or by forming stable crystals such as Al_2O_3, which releases 1805 kcal/g-atom of Al. At very high temperatures, where hydration or lattice energies are less effective stabilizers, compounds of Al(I) and Al(II) are formed, e.g., AlCl and AlO. The energy required to remove a fourth electron and form an Al^{++++} ion is more than twice that required to remove the first three electrons, and compounds of Al(IV) are unknown.

The remaining elements of this group are in the first long period and their atoms and ions differ in the number of $3d$ electrons as shown in Table 19-1. The anomalous structures of chromium and copper atoms can be rationalized by attributing extra stability to a half-filled or completely filled $3d$ subshell. Because of this the configuration of Cr^0 is $3d^54s^1$ and not $3d^44s^2$ and that of Cu^0 is $3d^{10}4s^1$ and not $3d^94s^2$. The unusual stability of Mn^{++} ions can also be attributed to the $3d^5$ configuration.

TABLE 19-1.

The Electronic Structures of Atoms and Ions of Elements 20 to 30

Element	Atomic number	Electronic configurations		
		Atom, Me⁰	Me⁺⁺ ion	Me⁺⁺⁺ ion
Ca	20	Ar core* + $4s^2$	Ar core	
Sc	21	Ar core + $3d^14s^2$		Ar core
Ti	22	Ar core + $3d^24s^2$	Ar core + $3d^2$	Ar core + $3d^1$
V	23	Ar core + $3d^34s^2$	Ar core + $3d^3$	Ar core + $3d^2$
Cr	24	Ar core + $3d^54s^1$	Ar core + $3d^4$	Ar core + $3d^3$
Mn	25	Ar core + $3d^54s^2$	Ar core + $3d^5$	Ar core + $3d^4$
Fe	26	Ar core + $3d^64s^2$	Ar core + $3d^6$	Ar core + $3d^5$
Co	27	Ar core + $3d^74s^2$	Ar core + $3d^7$	Ar core + $3d^6$
Ni	28	Ar core + $3d^84s^2$	Ar core + $3d^8$	
Cu	29	Ar core + $3d^{10}4s^1$	Ar core + $3d^9$	
Zn	30	Ar core + $3d^{10}4s^2$	Ar core + $3d^{10}$	

*Ar core stands for the inert gas configuration of argon atoms: $1s^22s^22p^63s^23p^6$

The $4s$ electrons are always lost first in ionization. The loss of another electron is frequently possible because the energies of the $3d$ and $4s$ electrons are not greatly different.

The presence of $3d$ electrons in these atoms and ions has an important influence on their properties. Those that contain unpaired $3d$ electrons are paramagnetic and form colored compounds. The ions of the transition elements have higher nuclear charges than calcium; and the higher charge is not very effectively screened off by the $3d$ electrons, for they do not penetrate as closely to the nucleus as do those of the s and p types but are more diffusely spread. Thus transition metal ions exert a strong polarizing action on other ions and molecules, and complex formation is a characteristic property of all of these ions.

THE PROPERTIES OF THE BIVALENT IONS

19-4. Some Characteristics of the $+2$ Oxidation State.   The compounds of this oxidation state are predominantly ionic in character. We shall consider the Mn^{++}, Fe^{++}, Co^{++}, Ni^{++}, and Zn^{++} ions and shall add, for comparison, the Cu^{++} ion but shall exclude the unstable Cr^{++} ion. The properties of these ions are summarized in Table 19-2. All have the same charge and about the same radius. Some consequences of this are:

1. All form soluble chlorides, bromides, iodides, acetates, nitrates, sulfates, perchlorates, and thiocyanates.

2. All form insoluble hydroxides, sulfides, carbonates, oxalates, cyanides, and phosphates.

3. There are several series of similar compounds:
    (a) the schönites or Tutton's salts, $X_2Y(SO_4)_2 \cdot 6H_2O$, e.g., $(NH_4)_2Fe(SO_4)_2 \cdot 6H_2O$ (Mohr's salt), $(NH_4)_2Mn(SO_4)_2 \cdot 6H_2O$, and $(NH_4)_2Ni(SO_4)_2 \cdot 6H_2O$.
    (b) the vitriols,[1] e.g., red $CoSO_4 \cdot 7H_2O$, pink $MnSO_4 \cdot 5H_2O$, green $FeSO_4 \cdot 7H_2O$, emerald green $NiSO_4 \cdot 7H_2O$, and blue $CuSO_4 \cdot 5H_2O$.
    (c) the ammonium phosphates and arsenates, e.g., $ZnNH_4PO_4 \cdot 6H_2O$, $CoNH_4PO_4 \cdot 6H_2O$, and $MnNH_4PO_4 \cdot H_2O$.

4. All the bivalent ions hydrolyze slightly to give weakly acidic solutions:

$$Me^{++} + H_2O \rightleftharpoons MeOH^+ + H^+ \qquad K = 10^{-8} \text{ to } 10^{-10}$$

These ions differ in the solubility products of their hydroxides and sulfides and in the dissociation constants of their complex ions. The negative logarithms of these constants are recorded in Table 19-2. The values increase steadily from Mn to Cu and then drop again for Zn. Since the largest negative logarithm corresponds to the smallest constant, the data show that Cu^{++} ion forms the least soluble hydroxide and sulfide and the most weakly dissociated complexes. Because of the insolubility of its sulfide, copper comes down with Cation Group 2. Irving and Williams[2] first called attention to the order of stability of the complexes. They noted that it ran parallel to the ionic radii and to the energy required to remove two electrons from isolated

---

[1] The name "vitriol" is from the Latin *vitrium*, glass, an allusion to the glassy surface of the crystals. Blue and green vitriol were known in Roman times. Concentrated sulfuric acid is called "oil of vitriol" because it can be made from the sulfur trioxide and water that are driven off some of these salts by heat.

[2] H. Irving and R. Williams, *J. Chem. Soc.*, 3192 (1953).

atoms of the elements. This ionization energy is an indication of the attraction of the ions for electrons and is greatest for copper. Thus copper(II) ions would be expected to attract the electron pairs of ligands most strongly. The standard oxidation potentials given at the end of Table 19-2 show an analogous trend: copper is the least active metal, manganese the most active.

In the following sections the properties of the bivalent oxides, hydroxides, and sulfides are discussed, and then the special features of the chemistry of each bivalent ion are presented.

TABLE 19-2.

Some Properties of the Bivalent Ions

Ion	Mn^{++}	Fe^{++}	Co^{++}	Ni^{++}	Cu^{++}	Zn^{++}
Atomic number	25	26	27	28	29	30
Radius, A	0.80	0.75	0.72	0.69	0.70	0.74
$-\log K_{sp}$ of MeS $\rightleftharpoons Me^{++} + S^{--}$*	12.6	17.2	24.7	25.7	35.2	24.1
$-\log K_{sp}$ of Me(OH)$_2$ $\rightleftharpoons Me^{++} + 2OH^-$*	12.8	15.1	15.7	17.2	19.7	16.9
$-\log K$ of Me(NH$_3$)$_4^{++}$ $\rightleftharpoons Me^{++} + 4NH_3$	?	3.7	5.0	7.5	12.0	8.7
$-\log K$ of Me(gl)$_2$ $\rightleftharpoons Me^{++} + 2gl^-$†	6.0	7.8	8.9	11.0	15.4	9.3
$-\log K$ of Me(EDTA)$^{--}$ $\rightleftharpoons Me^{++} + EDTA^{-4}$‡	13.6	14.3	16.2	18.6	18.8	16.3
Ionization energy, kcal/g-atom	532	555	574	594	646	631
$\mathcal{E}^0$ for Me $\rightarrow Me^{++} + 2e^-$, volts	1.18	0.44	0.28	0.25	−0.34	0.76

*The solubility products are those of the most insoluble forms of the sulfides and hydroxides.
†The abbreviation gl$^-$ is used for the glycinate ion, $C_2H_4O_2N^-$.
‡The abbreviation EDTA^{-4} is used for the ethylenediaminetetraacetate ion.

19-5. The Oxides MeO and Hydroxides Me(OH)$_2$.   The oxides of Cr, Fe, Co, and Ni have the sodium chloride structure with 6 oxide ions about each Me^{++} ion. In crystalline zinc oxide the coordination number of each ion is four. The hydroxides of these ions are known and have layer structures like that of CdI$_2$ or Mg(OH)$_2$ (Fig. 2-9a). Only zinc hydroxide is appreciably amphoteric. Manganese(II) and cobalt(II) hydroxides are slightly soluble in concentrated alkalies. Compounds such as Na$_2$Co(OH)$_4$, Ba$_2$Co(OH)$_6$, and Na$_2$Mn(OH)$_4$ have been isolated but they are decomposed by water.

When solutions of soluble salts of the divalent cations are treated with bases, the initial precipitate is usually a basic salt, e.g., Ni(OH)Cl or

$CoCl(OH)\cdot 4Co(OH)_2\cdot 4H_2O$. This gradually changes to the hydroxide as it stays in contact with excess alkali, and the solubility of the precipitate decreases as this change takes place. The products obtained with various basic reagents are summarized in Table 19-3. The pH at which precipitation begins when strong base is added to a dilute solution of a salt is also given; it is only an approximate value and varies with the concentration of salt, the nature of the anion, and the temperature. Table 19-3 also includes the solubility products of the freshly precipitated and aged hydroxides. The combination of ammonia and ammonium chloride gives no precipitate with any of the bivalent ions. For Fe^{++} and Mn^{++} ions this is a result of the low concentration of hydroxide ion allowed by the combination of the weak base and its salt. The other three hydroxides do not precipitate because of the removal of metal ions to give weakly dissociated complex ions.

TABLE 19-3.

Properties of the Hydroxides $Me(OH)_2$

Ion	Mn^{++}	Fe^{++}	Co^{++}	Ni^{++}	Zn^{++}
Color of hydroxide	white	white	blue or pink	light green	white
Product with excess NaOH	$Mn(OH)_2$*	$Fe(OH)_2$*	$Co(OH)_2$*	$Ni(OH)_2$	$Zn(OH)_4^{--}$
Product with excess NH_3	$Mn(OH)_2$*	$Fe(OH)_2$*	$\left\{\begin{array}{c}Co(OH)_2\\Co(NH_3)_6^{++}\end{array}\right\}$	$Ni(NH_3)_6^{++}$	$Zn(NH_3)_4^{++}$
Product with NH_3 + NH_4Cl	No ppt†	No ppt	$Co(NH_3)_6^{++}$†	$Ni(NH_3)_6^{++}$	$Zn(NH_3)_4^{++}$
Approx pH of initial pptn	8.5 to 8.8	5.5	6.8	6.7	7.0
Solubility product	2×10^{-13}	8×10^{-16}	2×10^{-16} aged, pink 6×10^{-15} blue	6×10^{-18} aged 3×10^{-15} active	7×10^{-18} aged 1×10^{-16} fresh

*Slowly oxidized by oxygen of air: $Mn(OH)_2$ turns brown; $Fe(OH)_2$, a dirty green, then black; $Co(OH)_2$, brown.

†Solutions darken on standing: Mn^{++} is oxidized to $MnO(OH)$ which precipitates; $Co(NH_3)_6^{++}$ is oxidized to brown complexes of Co(III).

19-6. The Sulfides MeS. Several curious features of the crystalline sulfides are worth noting. Some of them are polymorphic, i.e., exist in more than one form. Zinc sulfide, for example, crystallizes in the "zinc blende" and "wurtzite" structures. In both of these each zinc is surrounded by four sulfides and each sulfide by four zincs. The zinc blende structure is like that of diamond but with alternate zinc and sulfur atoms replacing those of carbon (Fig. 19-1). In wurtzite this pattern is distorted to give a more layered structure. Manganese sulfide can exist in three forms: one like sodium chloride, another like zinc blende, and a third like wurtzite. The structures of FeS, CoS, and NiS are intermediate between ionic and metallic. Each metal ion is surrounded by six sulfide ions, but two other metal ions are very close; e.g., in FeS the Fe-S distance is 2.45 A and the Fe-Fe distance is 2.89, only a little larger. These sulfides are also peculiar in having somewhat variable composition. Thus FeS is always deficient in iron as if its formula were $Fe_{1-x}S$ where x is sometimes as large as 0.11. In the crystal the pattern made by the sulfide ions remains intact, but some of the iron atoms are missing. Such compounds which do not conform to the law of definite composition are called *nondaltonide* or berthollide compounds.[3] Other nondaltonide compounds include FeO and MnO_2.

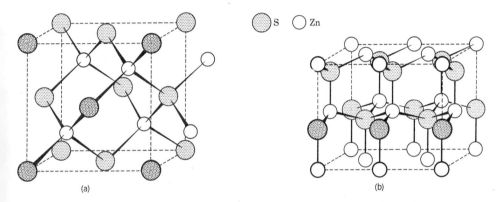

(a)   (b)

FIG. 19-1. The crystal structures of (a) zinc blende and (b) wurtzite. [Adapted by permission from *Structural Inorganic Chemistry* by A. F. Wells, 2nd ed. Copyright, 1950, by the Clarendon Press, Oxford.]

Another sulfide of Fe(II) that has some metallic character and is found extensively in nature is FeS_2, pyrite or fool's gold. The sulfur is present as a disulfide ion and the Fe^{++} and S_2^{--} ions are arranged in a cubic pattern like that of sodium chloride.

All of these sulfides have larger solubility products than do the sulfides of Group 2 and will not precipitate in 0.1 to 0.3 M HCl solutions. Their precipitation under other conditions is summarized in Table 8-2. They precipitate first in an amorphous, often nondaltonide form that becomes crystalline and less soluble on standing. Cobalt and nickel sulfides, in particular, exist in several forms with different solubilities. The *alpha* forms, obtained by precipitation from basic solutions in the absence of air, are

[3] These names recall the old controversy over the fixity of composition of chemical compounds. The advocates of constant composition, Lavoisier, Proust, Richter, and John Dalton (1766–1844) eventually overcame the opposition of Claude Louis, Comte Berthollet (1748–1822).

amorphous and soluble in acetic acid. The *beta* forms, precipitated from weakly acid solutions, are crystalline and only slightly soluble in 1 M hydrochloric acid.

19-7. Other Properties of the Mn^{++} Ion.

a. Anhydrous compounds of Mn(II) are white, whereas the hydrated salts and concentrated aqueous solutions are pink. The pink color of dilute aqueous solutions is usually too faint to be noticeable.

b. The least soluble compound of Mn(II) is MnS, yet even this is the most soluble of the sulfides of this group. It is precipitated only from alkaline solution as a pinkish white or pale orange pink form, readily soluble in dilute acids. There is also a somewhat less soluble green form. The white hydroxide $Mn(OH)_2$ and greenish white ferrocyanide $Mn_2Fe(CN)_6$ are almost as insoluble as the sulfide. The carbonate, oxalate, and ammonium phosphate are moderately insoluble.

c. There are no complex ions of Mn(II) of any importance in cation analysis. Anion complexes, possibly $MnCl_4^{--}$, exist in 12 M hydrochloric acid solutions and are used in anion analysis to test for the presence of oxidizing agents.

d. Manganese metal is the most active of the transition metals in this group (Table 19-2). It displaces hydrogen from water and dilute acids:

$$Mn + 2H^+ \rightarrow Mn^{++} + H_2 \uparrow$$

In acid solution the Mn^{++} ion is comparatively stable; it is oxidized only by strong oxidizing agents, usually in the presence of 16 M nitric acid. Its oxidation to brown, insoluble manganese dioxide MnO_2 by chlorate is used to separate manganese from the other elements of this group. Manganese is identified by oxidation to deep purple permanganate ion MnO_4^- with "sodium bismuthate" (impure Bi_2O_5). Oxidation of Mn(II) is easier in basic solution. Precipitated $Mn(OH)_2$ gradually turns brown as oxygen of the air slowly oxidizes it to MnO(OH) (or $Mn_2O_3 \cdot H_2O$). As the charge on the manganese ions increases from $+2$ to $+3$, there is a compensating displacement of OH^- ions by O^{--} ions. These changes occur gradually, ion by ion, and not in a single step as might be inferred from the over-all equation

$$O_2 + 4Mn(OH)_2 \downarrow \rightarrow 4MnO(OH) \downarrow + 2H_2O$$

19-8. Other Properties of the Fe^{++} Ion.

a. Anhydrous salts of Fe(II) are usually yellow, but the hydrated salts and aqueous solutions are green.

b. The black sulfide is the most insoluble compound; it is precipitated completely in basic solution, very incompletely from a weakly acid mixture of acetic acid and sodium acetate. It dissolves readily in dilute hydrochloric acid. A white ferrocyanide $K_2Fe^{II}Fe^{II}(CN)_6$ and deep blue ferricyanide (Turnbull's blue) can be precipitated. The structure of the latter varies somewhat with the method of preparation; a comparatively soluble form of Turnbull's blue is represented by $KFe^{II}Fe^{III}(CN)_6$.

c. The most important complex of Fe(II) is that with cyanide. It is obtained as a yellow-green solution by addition of an excess of KCN to a solution of a iron(II) salt. The complex is inert and its solutions give no test for iron or cyanide. The greenish yellow potassium salt $K_4Fe(CN)_6 \cdot 3H_2O$ is a familiar laboratory reagent. There are no stable thiocyanate or fluoride complexes and the ammines are too unstable to be of any analytical importance. Chloroanions of Fe(II) exist in hydrochloric acid solutions if the concentration of acid is more than 4 M. A brown complex with nitric oxide, $FeNO^{++}$, is formed in the brown ring test for nitrate ion.

d. Iron is a moderately active metal which dissolves readily in dilute hydrochloric and sulfuric acids with the formation of Fe^{++} ions. Oxidation of Fe^{++} to Fe^{+++} ions is more difficult:

$$Fe^{++} \rightarrow Fe^{+++} + e^- \qquad \mathcal{E}^0 = -0.77 \text{ v}$$

but can be accomplished by the use of active oxidizing agents such as chlorine, bromine, permanganate, dichromate, hydrogen peroxide, and oxygen. The action of the last of these is slow but solutions of Fe(II) salts almost invariably contain some Fe(III) as a result of it. In basic solution the reaction is more rapid. Pure white $Fe(OH)_2$ is hardly ever seen. The usual precipitate is dirty green $Fe(OH)_2$ contaminated with small amounts of Fe(III). As this precipitate stands, the color deepens to black and lightens to rust color only after all the Fe(II) has been oxidized to Fe(III). This gradual change is similar to that in the oxidation of $Mn(OH)_2$. The black intermediate may be the magnetic iron(II,III) oxide, Fe_3O_4.

19-9. Other Properties of the Co^{++} Ion.

a. The common hydrated cobalt(II) salts are light red to dark reddish orange; the aqueous solutions are red. Cobalt(II) chloride becomes blue when treated with $CaCl_2$, $AlCl_3$, and certain organic solvents or when partially dehydrated. It has been postulated that the red colored complex is $Co(H_2O)_6^{++}$ or $CoCl_2X_4$ where X is a solvent molecule and that the blue complex is $CoCl_4^{--}$, $CoCl_3X^-$, or $CoCl_2X_2$.

b. The least soluble compound is the sulfide. The black form obtained in basic solution becomes less soluble in HCl as it ages but can be dissolved easily by HNO_3 or aqua regia. It is easily peptized to give a sol and must always be washed with water containing an electrolyte. Blue $Co(OH)_2$ is the first precipitate obtained by addition of strong base to a solution of a Co(II) salt; it changes to the less soluble pink form on standing (Table 19-3).

Cobalt(II) forms a red ferricyanide $Co_3[Fe(CN)_6]_2$ and a gray-green ferrocyanide $Co_2Fe(CN)_6 \cdot 7H_2O$. Alkali metal carbonates precipitate blue basic carbonates; the red normal carbonate is obtained only if the solution is saturated with carbon dioxide.

c. There are a number of important complex ions of cobalt(II): pink $Co(NH_3)_6^{++}$, blue $Co(SCN)_4^{--}$, blue $CoCl_4^{--}$, brown $Co(C_4H_7N_2O_2)_3^{-}$, and violet $Co(CN)_5^{---}$. The blue thiocyanate complex can be extracted by a mixture of amyl alcohol and ether and the color is used to identify cobalt. The blue chloride complex is often observed during evaporation of cobalt salt solutions with hydrochloric acid. The reaction between dimethylglyoxime and cobalt(II) in basic solution gives the brown complex but no precipitate; this reaction distinguishes cobalt from nickel.

d. Cobalt is a less active metal than iron but more active than tin or lead. It dissolves slowly in dilute hydrochloric or sulfuric acids but readily in dilute nitric acid; the product in all of these reactions is Co^{++} ion. Oxidation of Co^{++} to Co^{+++} is exceedingly difficult in acid solutions. The hydroxide, like those of manganese(II) and iron(II), is slowly oxidized by oxygen of air and more rapidly by H_2O_2, OCl^-, Cl_2, or Br_2. The product is black Co_2O_3 hydrate or approximately $Co(OH)_3$.

19-10. Other Properties of the Ni^{++} Ion.

a. Anhydrous nickel(II) salts are usually yellow ($NiSO_4$ and NiF_2), but the color becomes deeper as the anion becomes more polarizable: $NiCl_2$, yellow-brown; $NiBr_2$, dark brown; NiI_2 and NiS, black. The hydrated salts and aqueous solutions are green.

b. Nickel resembles cobalt very closely in its reactions. The solubility of the black sulfide NiS, like that of CoS, depends on the method of preparation and aging. It dissolves readily in nitric acid or aqua regia. It is easily peptized. Nickel ferrocyanide is a greenish-white precipitate. The reaction of $Ni(II)$ with carbonates is similar to that of cobalt(II).

c. The complexes of nickel(II) include the blue ammine, $Ni(NH_3)_6^{++}$; green thiocyanate, $Ni(SCN)_4^{--}$ (less stable than that of $Co(II)$ and insoluble in amyl alcohol-ether); and yellow $Ni(CN)_4^{--}$. These are all labile, the most weakly dissociated being the cyanide complex. Nickel(II) forms an insoluble, deep red inner complex salt with dimethylglyoxime in basic solution, $Ni(C_4H_7N_2O_2)_2$, whereas cobalt gives a soluble complex ion.

d. Nickel metal is only slightly less active than cobalt (Table 19-2). Oxidation of nickel(II) to higher oxidation states is very difficult and of no importance in qualitative analysis.

19-11. Other Properties of the Zn^{++} Ion.

a. Zinc compounds are usually colorless because the zinc ion contains no unpaired electrons.

b. Zinc sulfide is the only white sulfide that we encounter (rare Ga_2S_3 is also white). It can be precipitated from solutions as acid as 0.01 M and is frequently coprecipitated with the sulfides of Group 2. Unlike white colloidal sulfur, with which it otherwise might be confused, it is readily soluble in dilute (6 M) acids. The white ferrocyanide is complex: $Zn\{Zn_3[Fe(CN)_6]_2\}$. The white hydroxide is amphoteric; i.e., it dissolves in strong acids and strong bases:

$$Zn(OH)_2 \downarrow + 2H^+ \rightarrow Zn^{++} + 2H_2O$$
$$Zn(OH)_2 \downarrow + 2OH^- \rightarrow Zn(OH)_4^{--}$$

It is also soluble in ammonia because of the formation of the weakly dissociated tetrammine complex $Zn(NH_3)_4^{++}$. There are many basic zinc salts, e.g., $Zn(OH)Cl$ and $Zn_5(OH)_6(CO_3)_2$. The latter is obtained when solutions of zinc salts are treated with alkali carbonate.

c. Zinc forms many complex ions, all of them colorless. Some of the more important ones, in order of increasing stability, are: $ZnCl_4^{--}$, $Zn(C_2O_4)_2^{--}$, $Zn(NH_3)_4^{++}$, $Zn(OH)_4^{--}$, and $Zn(CN)_4^{--}$. All of these are decomposed by sulfide. Zinc forms a purple-red chelate with dithizone, $Zn(C_{13}H_{11}N_4S)_2$.

d. Zinc metal is an active reducing agent (Table 19-2) and reacts vigorously with acids to give solutions containing Zn^{++} ions. Zinc also dissolves in alkali hydroxides and ammonia with liberation of hydrogen and formation of complex ions.

THE PROPERTIES OF THE TRIVALENT IONS

19-12. Some Characteristics of the +3 Oxidation State. The compounds in this state are less ionic than those of the bivalent ions. The anhydrous chlorides of iron(III) and aluminum(III) are good illustrations. Aluminum chloride crystallizes in a layer lattice. It melts at a comparatively low temperature (194°) and is very soluble in water and organic solvents such as ether, chloroform, and carbon tetrachloride. Its vapor and solutions in nonpolar solvents contain Al_2Cl_6 molecules in which each aluminum atom is coordinated to four chlorides:

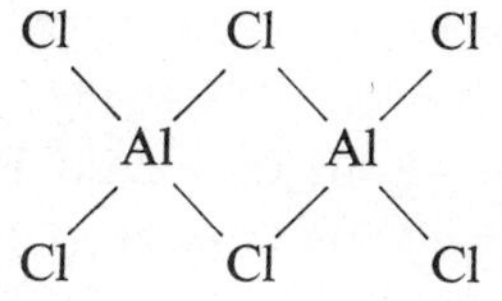

The trivalent ions form many complexes. Indeed, Cr^{+++} and Co^{+++}, together with platinum, form more complexes than any other elements. The tendency toward covalent binding and complex formation is a consequence of the high charges and small radii of these ions (Table 19-4). If aluminum falls behind the others in formation of complex ions, this is to be expected of an ion with inert gas structure.

TABLE 19-4.

Some Properties of the Trivalent Ions

Ion	Cr^{+++}	Mn^{+++}	Fe^{+++}	Co^{+++}	Al^{+++}
Atomic number	24	25	26	27	13
Ionic radius, A	0.64	0.70	0.67	0.64	0.50
K_a of $Me(H_2O)_6^{+++}$	1.6×10^{-4}	?	6.7×10^{-3}	?	1.1×10^{-5}
K_{sp} of $Me(OH)_3$	10^{-30}	?	10^{-37}	10^{-43}	10^{-32}

Some further generalizations can be made.

1. All these ions form soluble acetates, nitrates, perchlorates, chlorides, bromides, iodides, thiocyanates, and sulfates.

2. All form insoluble phosphates and hydroxides.

3. There are several series of similar compounds:
(a) the alums $XY(SO_4)_2 \cdot 12H_2O$ such as $KAl(SO_4)_2 \cdot 12H_2O$ (ordinary alum), $NH_4Fe(SO_4)_2 \cdot 12H_2O$ (ferric alum), and $KCr(SO_4)_2 \cdot 12H_2O$ (chrome alum).
(b) the spinels, XY_2O_4 such as $FeCr_2O_4$ (chromite ore), $MgAl_2O_4$ (spinel), $CoAl_2O_4$ (Thenard's blue), Fe_3O_4 (magnetite), Co_3O_4, and Mn_3O_4. None of these contains YO_2^- ions; each Y atom is surrounded by six oxygen atoms.

4. All of the trivalent ions hydrolyze:

$$Me^{+++} + H_2O \rightleftharpoons MeOH^{++} + H^+$$

These can also be regarded as ionization reactions of the hydrated cations as acids. Their acidity constants are much larger than those of the bivalent ions (Tables 19-4 and 19-2). Because of the strongly acid nature of these ions their salts with weak acids are usually decomposed by water. None of the trivalent sulfides or carbonates can be prepared by precipitation. The sulfides of aluminum and chromium(III) are made by direct union of the elements. It is doubtful if Fe_2S_3 exists, although it is frequently stated that it precipitates in basic solution. It should be unstable with respect to decomposition into FeS_2 and FeS. The following are typical equations for the reactions of the trivalent ions with strongly basic anions:

$$2Al^{+++} + 3S^{--} \quad + 6H_2O \rightarrow 2Al(OH)_3 \downarrow + 3H_2S \uparrow$$
$$2Fe^{+++} + 3CO_3^{--} + 3H_2O \rightarrow 2Fe(OH)_3 \downarrow + 3CO_2 \uparrow$$

19-13. Other Properties of the Al^{+++} Ion.

a. Compounds of aluminum(III) are colorless because the ion has the electronic structure of an inert gas.

b. Several oxides and hydroxides are known. Aluminum oxide occurs in two forms, *alpha* and *gamma*, which represent different ways of packing together aluminum and oxygen atoms. The *alpha* form occurs in nature as corundum or emery (a refractory and an abrasive), ruby (colored by a trace of Cr), and sapphire (colored by a trace of Co). It is insoluble in water and acids. The other form is hygroscopic and soluble in acids. The crystalline hydrated forms are: $Al(OH)_3$, gibbsite and bayerite, and $AlO(OH)$, böhmite. They have complicated layer structures with six hydroxide ions about each metal ion (Fig. 2-9b).

When ammonia is first added to a solution of an aluminum salt, an amorphous gel begins to form when the pH has risen to about 4. The precipitate gradually changes to böhmite or gamma-$AlO(OH)$. If precipitation is carried out in hot solutions, this is formed immediately.

Many ions are coprecipitated by aluminum hydroxide. This can be largely avoided by precipitating the basic succinate from homogeneous medium:

$$Al^{+++} + OH^- + C_4H_4O_4^{--} \rightarrow AlOHC_4H_4O_4 \downarrow$$

The hydrolysis of urea can be used as a means of gradually raising the pH of the solution.

Aluminum hydroxide is amphoteric:

$$Al(OH)_3 \downarrow + 3H^+ \rightarrow Al^{+++} + 3H_2O$$

$$Al(OH)_3 \downarrow + OH^- \rightleftharpoons Al(OH)_4^- \qquad K = \text{about } 16$$

The presence of the hydroxide complex is inferred from the existence of crystalline compounds such as $NaAl(OH)_4 \cdot 2H_2O$ and $Ca_3[Al(OH)_6]_2$. The solution in strong base is stable when heated, but the hydroxide can be reprecipitated by addition of a limited amount of acid or of an ammonium salt:

$$Al(OH)_4^- + NH_4^+ \rightarrow Al(OH)_3 \downarrow + NH_3 + H_2O$$

c. Aluminum ion forms complexes with fluoride and with oxyanions: AlF_6^{---} and $Al(C_2O_4)_3^{---}$, but not with ammonia or chloride. Hydroxide complexes such as $AlOH^{++}$ and $Al_2(OH)_2^{+4}$ are present in all but strongly acid solutions. All of the complexes are labile.

d. Aluminum is a very active metal in either acidic or basic solution:

$$Al \rightarrow Al^{+++} + 3e^- \qquad \mathcal{E}^0 = 1.66 \text{ v}$$

$$4OH^- + Al \rightarrow Al(OH)_4^- + 3e^- \qquad \mathcal{E}^0 = 2.35 \text{ v}$$

Although it should displace hydrogen from water, it does only in basic solution. In nitric acid solution the metal is protected by a thin oxide film. This film is dissolved by HCl or NaOH, and the metal readily dissolves in these reagents. It is *passive* towards concentrated nitric acid. Chromium and iron also show passivity towards this acid. Aluminum is used in qualitative analysis to reduce tin(IV) to tin(II) and nitrate ion to ammonia.

19-14. Properties of the Cr^{+++} Ion.

a. The hydrated ion is violet but chloride complexes such as $CrCl_2(H_2O)_4{}^+$ have a strong green color. The hydrated oxide $Cr(OH)_3$ is gray-green and the chromite ion $Cr(OH)_4{}^-$ is also green.

b. The oxide Cr_2O_3 has the same crystal form as corundum. No definite hydrate corresponding to the formula $Cr(OH)_3$ is known, but we shall continue to use this formula for convenience. Precipitation of the hydrated oxide begins at about pH 5. Ammonia, strong bases, carbonates, and sulfides can be used to precipitate it. In an excess of strong base it dissolves to give the chromite ion $Cr(OH)_4{}^-$. This is less stable than the aluminate ion and decomposes to the hydroxide if the solution is boiled.

c. Although Cr^{+++} ion forms many complexes, e.g., $Cr(NH_3)_6{}^{+++}$, $Cr(H_2O)_3Cl_3$, $Cr(CN)_6{}^{---}$, $Cr(C_2O_4)_3{}^{---}$, $Cr(H_2O)_6{}^{+++}$, and $Cr(SCN)_6{}^{---}$, most of these are inert. They are difficult to form and difficult to decompose and thus are seldom used in qualitative analysis.

d. Chromium metal is potentially more active than zinc and dissolves readily in hydrochloric acid:

$$Cr + 2H^+ \rightarrow Cr^{++} + H_2 \uparrow$$

The chromium(II) ion so formed is unstable and can reduce water or H^+ ions:

$$2Cr^{++} + 2H^+ \rightarrow 2Cr^{+++} + H_2 \uparrow$$

It also reacts quantitatively with dissolved oxygen:

$$4Cr^{++} + 4H^+ + O_2 \rightarrow 4Cr^{+++} + 2H_2O$$

and can be used to remove oxygen from gas mixtures. Reduction of Cr^{+++} to Cr^{++} in acid solution requires a very active reducing agent such as zinc metal:

$$Zn + 2Cr^{+++} \rightarrow 2Cr^{++} + Zn^{++}$$

Oxidation of $Cr(III)$ to $Cr(VI)$ is difficult in acid solution and requires a strong oxidizing agent such as potassium chlorate in nitric acid solution. Oxidation is easier in basic solution:

$$2Cr^{+++} + 7H_2O \rightarrow Cr_2O_7{}^{--} + 14H^+ + 6e^- \qquad \mathscr{E}^0 = -1.33 \text{ v}$$
$$Cr(OH)_4{}^- + 4OH^- \rightarrow CrO_4{}^{--} + 4H_2O + 3e^- \qquad \mathscr{E}^0 = -0.02 \text{ v}$$

A peroxide or hypochlorite is generally used to oxidize chromite to chromate.

19-15. Properties of the Fe^{+++} Ion.

a. The hydrated ion is pale violet in crystals of ferric alum and iron(III) nitrate. In solution the characteristic color is yellow or brown owing to the formation of complexes.

b. Crystalline alpha-Fe_2O_3 is the important mineral hematite and is isomorphous with corundum. A crystalline hydroxide FeO(OH), limonite, is also known. The addition of a base to a solution of an iron(III) salt produces a gelatinous, red-brown hydrated form of Fe_2O_3 which is usually represented by the formula $Fe(OH)_3$ for convenience, although no definite hydroxide has been isolated. Precipitation begins at a pH as low as 2, a fairly acid solution. This is testimony to the insolubility of the hydrated oxide. Like the hydrated forms of Al_2O_3 and Cr_2O_3, it can be precipitated almost completely by the mixture of ammonium chloride and ammonia that fails to precipitate any of the bivalent hydroxides $Me(OH)_2$.

Iron(III) can be separated as a basic formate which is denser and less adsorptive than the hydrated oxide.

The freshly precipitated hydrated oxide is easily dissolved by acids and is somewhat soluble in concentrated alkalies to give a solution of a ferrite, FeO_2^-, or possibly $Fe(OH)_8{}^{-5}$. The ferrites are much less stable than aluminates and chromites.

c. The only important insoluble compounds of iron(III) in addition to the oxide or hydroxide are the phosphate and ferrocyanide. The phosphate can be precipitated from acetic acid solution:

$$HPO_4{}^{--} + Fe^{+++} \rightleftharpoons FePO_4 \downarrow + H^+$$

This reaction can be used to remove phosphate before the precipitation of Group 3, for the phosphates of Group 4, which are insoluble in neutral or alkaline solution, would otherwise precipitate with the earlier group.

The ferrocyanide of iron(III), Prussian blue, is indistinguishable from Turnbull's blue (Sec. 19-8). In their more soluble forms Prussian and Turnbull's blues are, respectively, $KFe^{III}Fe^{II}(CN)_6$ and $KFe^{II}Fe^{III}(CN)_6$. The deep colors are attributed to the exchange of electrons between the two kinds of iron atoms. The crystal structures of these two compounds and of white $K_2Fe^{II}Fe^{II}(CN)_6$ and brownish $Fe^{III}Fe^{III}(CN)_6$ are shown in Fig. 19-2. Each iron ion is surrounded by six cyanide ions; the former occupy the corners and the latter the edges of a cubic pattern. In Prussian blue a K^+ ion is required for every pair of Fe^{+++} and $Fe(CN)_6{}^{----}$ ions to balance the charge. In the crystal these K^+ ions occupy the centers of alternate cubes. In white $K_2FeFe(CN)_6$ there are K^+ ions at the centers of all the cubes. These compounds are all giant complexes.

d. The complexes of iron(III) include inert reddish brown $Fe(CN)_6{}^{---}$ and labile red $FeSCN^{++}$, colorless $FeF_6{}^{---}$, yellow $FeCl^{++}$ and $FeCl_4{}^-$, and green $Fe(C_2O_4)_3{}^{---}$.

e. The oxidation of Fe(0) and Fe(II) has been discussed in Sec. 19-8. The Fe^{+++} ion is a moderately good oxidizing agent, being reduced to Fe^{++} ion by Fe^0, I^-, H_2SO_3, and H_2S, e.g.,

$$2Fe^{+++} + Fe \rightarrow 3Fe^{++}$$
$$2Fe^{+++} + H_2S \rightarrow 2Fe^{++} + S^0 \downarrow + 2H^+$$

The first of these reactions is used to preserve solutions of Fe^{++} against oxidation by oxygen of the air. Because of the second reaction, any iron(III) originally present will have been converted to iron(II) during the precipitation of Group 2. Tests for the oxidation state of iron must be made on the original sample before treatment with hydrogen sulfide.

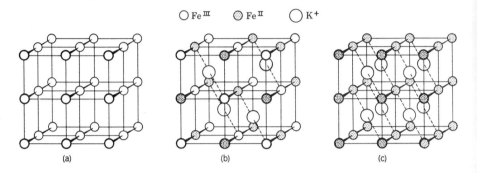

FIG. 19-2. The crystal structures of the complex cyanides of iron.
(a) $Fe^{III}Fe^{III}(CN)_6$.   (b) $KFe^{II}Fe^{III}(CN)_6$ or $KFe^{III}Fe^{II}(CN)_6$.
(c) $K_2Fe^{II}Fe^{II}(CN)_6$. [Adapted by permission from *Structural Inorganic Chemistry* by A. F. Wells, 2nd ed. Copyright, 1950, by the Clarendon Press, Oxford.]

COMPOUNDS OF THE ELEMENTS IN HIGHER OXIDATION STATES

19-16. The Oxides and Acids.   These include red chromium(VI) oxide, CrO_3; blue chromium(VI) peroxide, CrO_5; brown or black manganese(IV) oxide, MnO_2; and olive green manganese(VII) oxide, Mn_2O_7. The oxides CrO_3 and Mn_2O_7 are covalently bound and dissolve in water to give solutions of acids:

$$2CrO_3 + 2H_2O \rightarrow 2H_2CrO_4 \quad \rightarrow \quad H_2Cr_2O_7 + H_2O$$
chromic acid   dichromic acid

$$Mn_2O_7 + H_2O \rightarrow 2HMnO_4$$
permanganic acid

Chromium and manganese in these high oxidation states are behaving as nonmetals. Both oxides are produced by the action of concentrated sulfuric acid on their salts. Manganese(VII) oxide is an unstable, oily liquid that often decomposes with explosive violence. Manganese(IV) oxide is a nondaltonide compound, the correct formula being closer to $MnO_{1.95}$ than to MnO_2. It is less acidic than the higher oxide. The brown hydrated form that results from the oxidation of Mn(II) salts in alkaline solution reacts to some extent with both strong acids and strong bases. Chromium peroxide is formed by addition of hydrogen peroxide to cold solutions of dichromates or chromates in nitric or sulfuric acid.

19-17. The Salts. The chromates, dichromates, and permanganates are familiar laboratory reagents, e.g., $PbCrO_4$, $Na_2Cr_2O_7$, and $KMnO_4$, colored, respectively, yellow, orange, and purple. Chromates can be converted to dichromates by addition of acid, and addition of base reverses the reaction. The acid chromate ion, $HCrO_4^-$, is an intermediate. The equilibria can be expressed by

$$HCrO_4^- \rightleftharpoons H^+ + CrO_4^{--} \qquad K_a = 3.2 \times 10^{-7}$$

$$2HCrO_4^- \rightleftharpoons Cr_2O_7^{--} + H_2O \qquad K = 34$$

$$2CrO_4^{--} + 2H^+ \rightleftharpoons Cr_2O_7^{--} + H_2O \qquad K = \frac{[Cr_2O_7^{--}]}{[H^+]^2[CrO_4^{--}]^2} = 3.3 \times 10^{14}$$

Thus the ratio $[Cr_2O_7^{--}]/[CrO_4^{--}]^2$ at pH 7 is 3.3; at pH 3 it is 3.3×10^8, and at pH 9 it is 3.3×10^{-4}.

Chromium(VI) salts that contain more than 2 chromium atoms per anion are known, e.g., $Cr_3O_{10}^{--}$ and $Cr_4O_{13}^{--}$. Vanadium, which comes just before chromium in the first long Period, and molybdenum and tungsten, which lie below it in Group VIA, have a phenomenal tendency to form such polyanions.

Other salts such as the green manganates, e.g., K_2MnO_4, and ferrates, e.g., Na_2FeO_4, contain Mn and Fe in the +6 oxidation state. They are stable only in alkaline media. The manganate disproportionates in acid solution:

$$4H^+ + 3MnO_4^{--} \rightarrow 2MnO_4^- + MnO_2 \downarrow + 2H_2O$$

19-18. Redox Reactions. All these compounds are active oxidizing agents, particularly in acid solution. They are most commonly obtained by oxidation of lower forms in basic media. The reactions of chromium and manganese compounds are summarized in the charts of Figs. 19-3 and 19-4. The important compounds and ions are shown in rectangles.

19-19. Discussion of the Analytical Procedure. Certain tests can be made on the original sample if the test is specific for the particular ion and interfering ions are removed or masked. Several different methods of avoiding interferences are used in the preliminary tests:

1. Precipitation, e.g., in the Ni and Mn tests. Insoluble hydroxides are precipitated and removed before addition of dimethylglyoxime lest they obscure a small scarlet precipitate of nickel dimethylglyoxime. Chlorides are removed by precipitation as silver chloride; they reduce bismuthate and permanganate and interfere with the test for Mn.

2. Masking or complexing, e.g., in the test for Co. Iron(III) forms a deep red complex with thiocyanate that can obscure the blue color of cobalt thiocyanate. The addition of fluoride converts iron(III) to the more stable and colorless fluoride complex.

3. Redox, e.g., in the test for Co. Copper(II) and iron(III) are reduced by tin(II) chloride to copper(I) and iron(II), which give colorless compounds with thiocyanate.

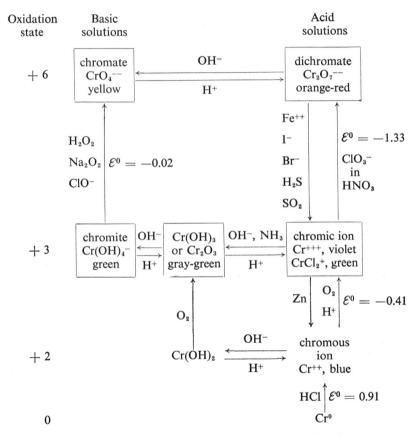

FIG. 19-3. The redox behavior of chromium compounds.

4. Extraction, e.g., in the test for Co. Blue cobalt(II) thiocyanate complexes are soluble in a mixture of amyl alcohol and ether. Extraction into this solvent mixture serves to intensify the color and separate the complex from other colored ions such as complexes of nickel.

5. Differential diffusion and adsorption on spot paper, e.g., in the test for Zn. Ions differ in the extent to which they are adsorbed by paper and in

their rates of diffusion through the solvent in the pores of the paper. In the zinc test an alkaline solution of the sample is spotted on paper impregnated with dithizone. Hydroxide ions diffuse most rapidly and give an outer orange ring. Zincate ions are the next most active and give a purple-red ring. The other ions diffuse so slowly or are adsorbed so tightly that they do not move at all and they give a central spot.

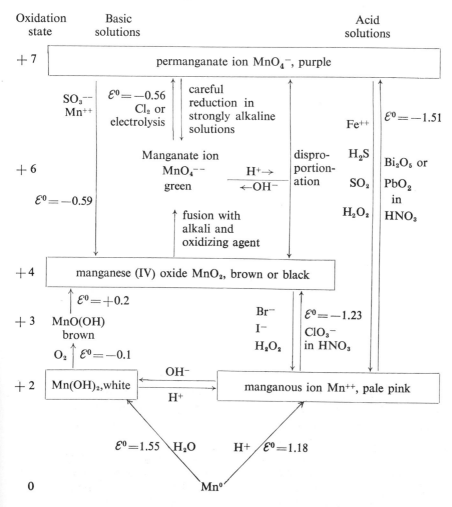

FIG. 19-4. The redox behavior of manganese compounds.

Another problem in the analysis of this group is that of distinguishing between trace amounts and bona fide tests. Nickel is a common impurity in cobalt salts because of the difficulty of separating these two metals. A small test for nickel is thus often obtained from cobalt salts. Iron is a very common contaminant of even so-called C.P. (chemically pure) reagents. The test for iron(III) with thiocyanate is sufficiently sensitive to give a color reaction with such traces. If there is any doubt as to the validity of a test, a comparison should be made with a known solution containing 0.1 mg of ion per milliliter.

A combination of ammonia, ammonium chloride, and thioacetamide or hydrogen sulfide is used to precipitate the group. The sulfides of Mn^{++}, Fe^{++}, Co^{++}, Ni^{++}, and Zn^{++} have higher solubility products than the sulfides of Cation Group 2 and therefore require a higher concentration of sulfide ion for their precipitation. In alkaline solution the concentration of hydrogen ion is low, and hence, according to the ion product of hydrogen sulfide

$$K_{ip} = [H^+]^2[S^{--}]$$

the concentration of sulfide ion must be comparatively large. The trivalent ions of aluminum and chromium precipitate as hydroxides or hydrated oxides. Although the concentration of hydroxide ion is low in a mixture of the weak base ammonia with its salt, ammonium chloride, the solubility products of aluminum and chromium(III) hydroxides are so small that they are almost completely precipitated. Magnesium hydroxide has a much higher solubility product and is not precipitated. The situation can be represented schematically by

$$K_b = \frac{[OH^-][NH_4^+]}{[NH_3]} \qquad K_{sp} < [Al^{+++}][OH^-]^3 \qquad K_{sp} > [Mg^{++}][OH^-]^2$$

If the sample being analyzed for Group 3 has been treated previously with thioacetamide or hydrogen sulfide, iron will be in the form of Fe^{++} ions and will precipitate as the sulfide.

The group precipitate is dissolved in nitric acid. The reagent acts as an acid on the basic hydroxides of aluminum and chromium and dissolves the sulfides by oxidizing the sulfide ion to sulfur. Although the sulfides of zinc, manganese(II), and iron(II) are readily soluble in hydrochloric acid, the aged sulfides of cobalt and nickel are not. Furthermore, the presence of chloride is undesirable in the subsequent separation of manganese. Hence, nitric acid is the best solvent for the group precipitate.

Manganese must be removed at an early stage in the analysis of the group or it will cause trouble in later separations. It is separated by oxidation to MnO_2 with chlorate in 16 M nitric acid solution. Chloride must be absent, for it reduces MnO_2. It is removed by repeated evaporations with concentrated nitric acid:

$$4H^+ + 3Cl^- + NO_3^- \rightarrow NOCl\uparrow + Cl_2\uparrow + 2H_2O$$

Chromium(III) is also oxidized by chlorate to dichromate, and this is advantageous in later steps.

After separation of the manganese dioxide, it is dissolved in acidified hydrogen peroxide. Manganese is identified by oxidation to the purple permanganate ion with a powerful oxidizing agent such as sodium bismuthate. Chloride must be absent. The chart in Fig. 19-4 should be used as a guide through this maze of redox reactions.

The group is subdivided after the removal of manganese by separating the acidic or amphoteric hydroxides from the basic ones. The former are soluble in excess base:

$$OH^- + Al(OH)_3 \downarrow \; \rightarrow Al(OH)_4^-$$

$$2OH^- + Zn(OH)_2 \downarrow \; \rightarrow Zn(OH)_4^{--}$$

$$2OH^- + H_2CrO_4 \quad \rightarrow CrO_4^{--} + 2H_2O$$

The hydroxides of iron(III) and nickel are not appreciably soluble in excess base but that of cobalt(II) is. Hydrogen peroxide is thus used in conjunction with the base to convert $Co(OH)_2$ to the less soluble $Co(OH)_3$ (or hydrated Co_2O_3) and improve the separation. Were chromium(III) present here, it would in principle pass into solution as $Cr(OH)_4^-$ ion. This is unsatisfactory in practice because zinc and chromium coprecipitate with the hydroxides when they occur together. If manganese were present here, it too would coprecipitate with zinc. Manganese was thus removed as the dioxide and chromium was oxidized to chromate in an earlier step.

The basic hydroxides of iron, cobalt, and nickel are dissolved in hydrochloric acid. Iron is identified as the deep red thiocyanate complex, cobalt as the blue thiocyanate complex, and nickel as the deep red, insoluble chelate with dimethylglyoxime. Cobalt forms a brown complex in solution with dimethylglyoxime, and sufficient reagent must be added to sequester the cobalt before the nickel compound will precipitate.

The presence of chromate is generally indicated by a yellow color in the alkaline solution after removal of the hydroxides of iron, cobalt, and nickel. Further confirmation is obtained by the precipitation of bright yellow lead chromate from weakly acid solution and formation of blue, unstable CrO_5 in more strongly acid solution. The ratio of concentrations $[Cr_2O_7^{--}]/[CrO_4^{--}]^2$ varies markedly with changes in pH (Sec. 19-17). In weakly acid solutions the concentration of chromate, although low, is still large enough to precipitate lead chromate. In strongly acid solutions the concentration of chromate is so reduced that lead chromate dissolves.

Aluminum is separated from zinc and chromium by precipitation of the hydroxide from an ammonia-ammonium chloride buffer. Zinc ions are sequestered in the weakly dissociated $Zn(NH_3)_4^{++}$ complex so that zinc hydroxide cannot precipitate. The aluminum hydroxide is redissolved in acid and aluminum is reprecipitated in the presence of aluminon reagent (a salt of aurintricarboxylic acid) to give a red chelate, $Al(C_{22}H_{13}O_9)_3$. The pH must be regulated between 5 and 7.2. In more acid solutions no reaction occurs; in more basic solutions the reagent itself gives a red color. The solution is therefore buffered with acetic acid and ammonium acetate. Iron(III) and chromium(III) interfere by giving colored reactions, but they should be absent if the preceding separations were carefully done. The principal purpose of the test is to distinguish between aluminum hydroxide and silica (hydrated SiO_2), both of which are gelatinous white precipitates. Silica is frequently introduced unwittingly by the use of alkaline reagents which become contaminated with it when stored in glass bottles. It does not give a red color or lake with aluminon.

Zinc is identified first by precipitation of white zinc sulfide and then by the dithizone spot test. Chromate must be removed by precipitation of barium chromate before precipitation of the sulfide or it will oxidize thioacetamide or hydrogen sulfide to white colloidal sulfur which might be confused with zinc sulfide. The precipitated zinc sulfide, unlike sulfur, is soluble in acids. Nitric acid is used to dissolve it in preference to hydrochloric acid in order to destroy the sulfide. Zinc must be converted to $Zn(OH)_4^{--}$ for the dithizone test, and if sulfide or hydrogen sulfide were present, ZnS would be reprecipitated upon addition of base and the dithizone test would fail.

19-20. Cross References.   Familiarity with Chapters 1 to 4 is assumed.
Sec. 5-5 (partially covalent or polarized bonds)
Sec. 6-2 (ligands, coordination number)
Sec. 6-6 (inert and labile complexes)
Sec. 6-8 (chelates)
Secs. 6-9 to -11 (electrostatic theory of complexes)
Sec. 6-12 (s, p, d orbitals)
Sec. 6-13 (magnetic moments)
Sec. 6-14 (colors)
Sec. 7-7 (hydrolysis of thioacetamide)
Sec. 7-17 (extraction)
Sec. 7-19 (K_{ip} (H_2S))
Sec. 8-2 (solubility product)
Secs. 8-10, -11 (coprecipitation)
Secs. 8-12, -13 (precipitation of sulfides)
Sec. 8-14 (precipitation of hydroxides)
Sec. 8-16 (dissolution of sulfides)
Sec. 8-17 (dissolution of hydroxides, amphoterism)
Sec. 8-21 (peptization)
Sec. 9-8 (standard oxidation potentials)
Sec. 10-3 (pH)
Sec. 10-5 (K_{ip} (H_2S), calculations)
Sec. 10-12 (precipitation of hydroxides and dissolution of sulfides, calculations)

Sec. 11-6 (metal ions as cation acids, hydrolysis)

Sec. 12-6 (buffer solutions)

Sec. 12-8 (buffers and the precipitation of hydroxides and sulfides)

Sec. 13-5 ($(NH_4)_2S$ calculations)

Sec. 13-6 (salts of metal hydroxides and weak acids, calculations)

Sec. 14-3, Example 3 ($Zn(OH)_4^{--}$ and $Zn(NH_3)_4^{++}$)

Sec. 14-4 (the dissociation constants of zinc hydroxide complexes)

Secs. 15-12 to -15 (oxidation potentials)

19-21. The Successive Reactions of the Ions of Cation Group 3.

Iron

1. Preliminary tests.

P-1a. Test for Fe++.   Reagent: potassium ferricyanide

$$K^+ + Fe^{++} + Fe(CN)_6^{---} \rightarrow KFeFe(CN)_6 \downarrow$$

P-1b. Test for Fe+++.   Reagent: ammonium thiocyanate

$$Fe^{+++} + SCN^- \rightarrow FeSCN^{++}$$

P-2 Test for Ni.   Reagent: ammonia solution

$$Fe^{+++} + 3NH_3 + 3H_2O \rightarrow Fe(OH)_3 \downarrow + 3NH_4^+$$

P-4. Test for Co. Reagents: ammonium thiocyanate and sodium fluoride

$$Fe^{+++} + SCN^- \rightarrow FeSCN^{++}$$
$$FeSCN^{++} + 6F^- \rightarrow FeF_6^{---} + SCN^-$$

P-5. Test for Zn.   Reagent: sodium hydroxide

$$Fe^{+++} + 3OH^- \rightarrow Fe(OH)_3 \downarrow$$

2. Precipitation of Group 2. Reagent: thioacetamide or hydrogen sulfide in 0.3 *M* hydrochloric acid

$$Fe^{+++} + H_2S \rightarrow H^+ + S^0 \downarrow + Fe^{++} \qquad \text{(Balance.)}$$

3. Precipitation of Group 3. Reagents: thioacetamide or hydrogen sulfide in an ammonia-ammonium chloride buffer

$$Fe^{++} + S^{--} \rightarrow FeS \downarrow$$

4. Dissolution of the group precipitate

(*Skeleton equation.*) $FeS \downarrow + NO_3^- \rightarrow Fe^{+++} + S^0 \downarrow + NO_2 \uparrow$

(Complete and balance by the ion-electron or oxidation number method.)

5. Separation of Mn. Reagents: nitric acid and potassium chlorate. No reaction with Fe+++.

6. Separation from Al, Cr, and Zn. Reagents: sodium hydroxide and hydrogen peroxide

$$Fe^{+++} + 3OH^- \rightarrow Fe(OH)_3 \downarrow$$

7. Dissolution of the hydroxide. Reagent: hydrochloric acid

$$Fe(OH)_3 \downarrow + H^+ \rightarrow ?$$

8. Iron, cobalt, and nickel tests. See under Step 1. Preliminary tests.

Chromium

1. Preliminary to precipitation of Group 2 (P-2, Outline 2). Reagent: hydrogen peroxide in acid solution

(*Skeleton equation.*) $Cr_2O_7^{--} + H_2O_2 \rightarrow O_2 \uparrow + Cr^{+++}$

(Complete and balance by the ion-electron or oxidation number method.)

2. Precipitation of Group 3. Reagents: thioacetamide or hydrogen sulfide in an ammonium chloride-ammonia buffer

$$Cr^{+++} + NH_3 + H_2O \rightarrow ?$$

3. Dissolution of the group precipitate. Reagent: nitric acid

$$Cr(OH)_3 \downarrow + H^+ \rightarrow ?$$

4. Separation from Mn. Reagents: concentrated nitric acid and potassium chlorate

(*Skeleton equation.*) $Cr^{+++} + ClO_3^- \rightarrow ClO_2 \uparrow + Cr_2O_7^{--}$

(Complete and balance by the ion-electron or oxidation number method.)

5. Separation from Fe, Co, and Ni. Reagents: sodium hydroxide and hydrogen peroxide

$$Cr_2O_7^{--} + 2OH^- \rightarrow 2CrO_4^{--} + H_2O$$

6. Identification. Reagents: acetic acid and lead acetate

$$Pb(C_2H_3O_2)_2 + CrO_4^{--} \rightarrow PbCrO_4 \downarrow + 2C_2H_3O_2^-$$

7. Confirmation. Reagents: nitric acid and hydrogen peroxide

(a) Dissolution of the precipitate

$$2PbCrO_4 \downarrow + 2H^+ \rightarrow 2Pb^{++} + Cr_2O_7^{--} + H_2O$$

(b) Formation of blue color

$$Cr_2O_7^{--} + 4H_2O_2 + 2H^+ \rightarrow 2CrO_5 + 5H_2O$$

8. Separation from Al and Zn. Reagent: barium chloride

$$Ba^{++} + CrO_4^{--} \rightarrow BaCrO_4 \downarrow$$

Aluminum

1. Precipitation of Group 3. Reagents: thioacetamide or hydrogen sulfide in an ammonium chloride-ammonia buffer

$$Al^{+++} + NH_3 + H_2O \rightarrow ?$$

2. Dissolution of the group precipitate. Reagent: nitric acid

$$Al(OH)_3 \downarrow + H^+ \rightarrow ?$$

3. Separation of Mn. Reagents: nitric acid and potassium chlorate. No reaction with Al^{+++}.

4. Separation from Fe, Co, and Ni. Reagents: excess sodium hydroxide and hydrogen peroxide

$$Al^{+++} + 4OH^- \rightarrow Al(OH)_4^-$$

5. Separation of Al from Zn and Cr.

(a) Acidification with hydrochloric acid

$$Al(OH)_4^- + 4H^+ \rightarrow Al^{+++} + 4H_2O$$

(b) Precipitation with ammonia and ammonium chloride

$$Al^{+++} + NH_3 + H_2O \rightarrow \ ?$$

6. Identification.

(a) Dissolution in hydrochloric acid. See Step 2.

(b) Formation of chelate. Reagents: aluminon, acetic acid, and ammonium acetate

$$Al^{+++} + 3C_{22}H_{13}O_9^- \rightarrow Al(C_{22}H_{13}O_9)_3 \downarrow$$

Manganese

1. Preliminary to precipitation of Group 2 (P-2, Outline 2). Reagent: hydrogen peroxide in acid solution.

(*Skeleton equation.*) $\qquad MnO_4^- + H_2O_2 \rightarrow \ ?$

(Complete and balance by the ion-electron or oxidation number method.)

2. Preliminary tests to Group 3. P-3. Test for Mn. Reagents: nitric acid and sodium bismuthate

(*Skeleton equation.*) $\quad Mn^{++} + Bi_2O_5 \rightarrow Bi^{+++} + MnO_4^-$

(Complete and balance by the ion-electron or oxidation number method.)

3. Precipitation of Group 3. Reagents: thioacetamide or hydrogen sulfide in an ammonium chloride-ammonia buffer

$$Mn^{++} + S^{--} \rightarrow MnS \downarrow$$

4. Dissolution of the group precipitate. Reagent: concentrated nitric acid

(*Skeleton equation.*) $\quad MnS \downarrow + NO_3^- \rightarrow NO_2 \uparrow + Mn^{++}$

(Complete and balance by the ion-electron or oxidation number method.)

5. Separation of Mn. Reagents: nitric acid and potassium chlorate

(*Skeleton equation.*) $\quad Mn^{++} + ClO_3^- \rightarrow MnO_2 \downarrow + ClO_2 \uparrow$

(Complete and balance by the ion-electron or oxidation number method.)

6. Dissolution of MnO_2. Reagents: nitric acid and hydrogen peroxide

(*Skeleton equation.*)　　　　　$MnO_2 \downarrow + H_2O_2 \rightarrow$?

(Complete and balance by the ion-electron or oxidation number method.)

7. Identification of Mn. See Step 2.

Cobalt

1. Preliminary tests.

(a) Test for Co (P-4). Reagent: ammonium thiocyanate in a mixture of amyl alcohol and ether

$$Co^{++} + 4SCN^- \rightarrow Co(SCN)_4^{--}$$

(b) Test for Ni (P-2). Reagents: ammonia and dimethylglyoxime

$$Co^{++} + 6NH_3 \rightarrow Co(NH_3)_6^{++}$$

$$Co(NH_3)_6^{++} + 3C_4H_7O_2N_2^- \rightarrow 6NH_3 + Co(C_4H_7O_2N_2)_3^-$$

(c) Test for Zn (P-5). Reagent: sodium hydroxide

$$Co^{++} + 2OH^- \rightarrow Co(OH)_2 \downarrow$$

2. Precipitation of Group 3. Reagents: thioacetamide or hydrogen sulfide in an ammonium chloride-ammonia buffer

$$Co^{++} + 6NH_3 \rightarrow Co(NH_3)_6^{++}$$

$$Co(NH_3)_6^{++} + S^{--} \rightarrow CoS \downarrow + 6NH_3$$

3. Dissolution of the group precipitate. Reagent: nitric acid

$$CoS \downarrow + NO_3^- \rightarrow ?$$

(Complete and balance the equation by the ion-electron or oxidation number method.)

4. Separation of Mn. Reagents: nitric acid and potassium chlorate. No reaction with Co^{++}.

5. Separation from Cr, Al, and Zn. Reagents: sodium hydroxide and hydrogen peroxide.

(a) $Co^{++} + 2OH^- \rightarrow Co(OH)_2 \downarrow$

(b) (*Skeleton equation.*)　$Co(OH)_2 \downarrow + H_2O_2 \rightarrow Co(OH)_3 \downarrow$　　(Balance.)

6. Dissolution of $Co(OH)_3$. Reagent: hydrochloric acid

(*Skeleton equation.*)　$Co(OH)_3 \downarrow + Cl^- \rightarrow Cl_2 \uparrow + Co^{++}$

(Complete and balance by the ion-electron or oxidation number method.)

7. Identification of Co. See Step 1a.

8. Identification of Ni. See Step 1b.

Nickel

These equations are left for the student to write. Follow the same pattern as that used for the other ions.

Zinc

1. Preliminary test (P-5). Reagents: excess sodium hydroxide and dithizone.

(a) $Zn^{++} + 4OH^- \rightarrow Zn(OH)_4^{--}$

(b) $Zn(OH)_4^{--} + 2C_{13}H_{11}N_4S^- \rightarrow Zn(C_{13}H_{11}N_4S)_2 + 4OH^-$

2. Precipitation of Group 3. Reagents: thioacetamide or hydrogen sulfide in an ammonium chloride-ammonia buffer

$$Zn^{++} + 4NH_3 \rightarrow Zn(NH_3)_4^{++}$$
$$Zn(NH_3)_4^{++} + S^{--} \rightarrow ZnS \downarrow + 4NH_3$$

3. Dissolution of the group precipitate. Reagent: nitric acid

$$ZnS \downarrow + NO_3^- \rightarrow ?   \text{(Complete and balance.)}$$

4. Separation from Mn. Reagents: nitric acid and potassium chlorate. No reaction with Zn^{++}.

5. Separation from Fe, Co, and Ni. Reagents: excess sodium hydroxide and hydrogen peroxide

$$Zn^{++} + 4OH^- \rightarrow Zn(OH)_4^{--}$$

6. Acidification. Reagent: hydrochloric acid

$$Zn(OH)_4^{--} + H^+ \rightarrow ?$$

7. Separation from Al. Reagents: ammonia and ammonium chloride

$$Zn^{++} + NH_3 \rightarrow ?$$

8. Separation and identification of Zn.

(a) Reagent: thioacetamide or hydrogen sulfide. See Step 2.

(b) Reagent: concentrated nitric acid. See Step 3.

(c) Reagent: excess sodium hydroxide. See Step 5.

(d) Reagent: dithizone. See Step 1b.

EXPERIMENTAL PART

19-22. Introductory Experiments.

1. The test for Fe^{++} ion.   Carry out the test as described in P-1a preceding Outline 5 on a solution prepared by dissolving a crystal of iron(II) sulfate in 10 drops of water. Try the action of the $K_3Fe(CN)_6$ reagent on single drops of the standard solutions of Fe^{+++}, Co^{++}, and Ni^{++}.

2. The test for Fe^{+++} ion.   Prepare by successive dilutions three solutions having 1, 0.1, and 0.01 mg of Fe^{+++} ion per milliliter. To each add a drop of KSCN solution or a few crystals of solid NH_4SCN, mix, and compare colors. A valid test for Fe^{+++} ion must have a color as deep as or deeper than that of the second tube. See remarks under P-1b to Outline 5.

3. Sensitivity of the test for Zn^{++} ion.   Prepare from the standard solution of Zn^{++} solutions that have 1 and 0.1 mg Zn/ml. Carry out the test for zinc as described in P-5 to Outline 5. Also do a "blank" test; i.e., carry out the test on 10 drops of distilled water to which the same amount of 6 M NaOH was added as that used for the zinc solutions. The purple-red color of the dithizone-zinc chelate should be distinguishable for both zinc samples. It is often observed only at the instant of adding the drop to the spot paper or by treating the paper with a drop of water and observing the under side of the paper. Comparison with the blank test is also helpful.

4. Test for Ni^{++} ion in the presence of Co^{++} ion.   Mix 1 drop each of the standard solutions of these two ions with 3 drops of 6 M NH_4Cl and 1 drop of 15 M NH_3. If the mixture is not alkaline, add more NH_3. Now add dimethylglyoxime solution drop by drop, mixing after each addition, until a voluminous red precipitate forms. Record the number of drops of reagent that was added. Why must an excess be used? To observe the scarlet color of the precipitate to better advantage, remove and discard the supernatant liquid, and add about 1 ml of water to the precipitate.

5. The aluminon test.   Take single drops of the standard solutions of Fe^{+++}, Cr^{+++}, and Al^{+++} in separate test tubes and add to each a drop of 15 M NH_3 to precipitate the hydroxide. Centrifuge and discard the solutions. Dissolve the precipitates in single-drop portions of 6 M hydrochloric acid. In a fourth tube dilute a drop of 6 M HCl with several drops of water; this will be the "blank". To each tube add 2 drops of aluminon reagent and about 5 drops of 3 M $NH_4C_2H_3O_2$. Check the pH with wide-range indicator paper; it should be between 5 and 7. Note the appearance of the tubes. What conclusions do you draw?

6. Precipitation of hydroxides by ammonia-ammonium chloride buffers.   In separate test tubes take 2 drops each of the standard solutions of Al^{+++} and Mn^{++} ions. Dilute each sample with 1 ml of water, add 3 drops of 6 M NH_4Cl, and make the solution alkaline with 15 M NH_3. Centrifuge to observe the character and bulk of the precipitate. Save the tube containing the precipitate for Experiment 7. Account for the difference in behavior of the Al^{+++} and Mn^{++} ions. Your discussion should include the values of the solubility products of their hydroxides and the equilibrium for the ionization of ammonia.

In Experiment 4 why did the hydroxides of Co^{++} and Ni^{++} fail to precipitate?

Examine the tube containing the Mn^{++} ion after it has stood for several minutes. Account for the change.

7. Coprecipitation. Take 2 drops each of the standard solutions of Al^{+++} and Co^{++} ions in the same test tube and precipitate $Al(OH)_3$ in the same way as in Experiment 6. Centrifuge and compare the precipitate with that obtained in the previous experiment. Withdraw and discard the supernatant solution. Wash the precipitate twice with approximately 1 ml portions of water. What evidence is there that the precipitate contains cobalt? Is it removed by washing? Confirm by dissolving the precipitate in 1 drop of 6 M HCl and doing the confirmatory test given in P-4.

8. Precipitation from homogeneous medium. (See Sec. 8-11). To another mixture of Al^{+++} and Co^{++} solutions add about a milliliter of water, several drops of succinic acid solution, and one spatula-full of urea. Heat in a boiling water bath for 5 minutes or until precipitation appears to be complete. Centrifuge and treat the precipitate as in Experiment 7. Compare the amount of cobalt that is coprecipitated and account for the difference.

9. Some reactions of chromium. Start with 1 drop of K_2CrO_4 reagent, and convert it successively to dichromate, chromic ion, chromic hydroxide, chromite ion, and chromate. Record your observations and the reagents you used. Write equations for all reactions.

19-23. Analysis of Known and Unknown Samples. You are to assume, unless instructed otherwise, that phosphate, oxalate, tartrate, and other interfering anions are not present. The organic anions are destroyed in the preparation of the sample. Phosphate can be removed by an ion-exchange separation. These procedures are given in Chapters 24 and 25.

a. Use 5 drops of a *known* or *practice solution* that contains 2 mg/ml each of Al^{+++}, Cr^{+++}, Ni^{++}, Co^{++}, and Mn^{++} and 4 mg/ml of Zn^{++}. If a solution is not already prepared, mix 1 drop of each of the standard solutions of the first five ions with 2 drops of the solution of Zn^{++}. *Note that the practice solution contains no iron.* Carry out the tests for iron and note the faint colorations that may appear owing to impurities. Then add 1 drop of Fe^{+++} solution to the test and observe the appearance of a bona fide test.

b. If the *unknown* is Solution 2-1 from Outline 2, use all of it in the systematic analysis of Outline 5. If it is an unknown solution containing only the ions of this group, use 5 drops for the systematic analysis. More must be available for the preliminary tests. If the unknown is a solid, take a representative sample and dissolve about 50 mg in water or 6 M HCl. Use about a fifth or a third of this solution for the systematic analysis.

Always note the color of the known or unknown samples. Compare with the test solution of the ions. Some of the most common ions and colors are: Cr^{+++}, violet; $Ni(NH_3)_6^{++}$, blue; $CoCl_2$ and $CoCl_4^{--}$, blue; Ni^{++}, green; Fe^{++}, pale green; $CrCl_2^+$ and $Cr(OH)_4^-$, deep green; $FeCl^{++}$, yellow; $Fe(III)$—OH complexes, yellow to red; Co^{++}, red; Mn^{++}, very pale pink, almost colorless;

Al^{+++} and Zn^{++}, colorless. In the solid state combination of colors must be considered: green nickel and red cobalt salts give a gray mixture.

It is possible to make specific tests for some of the ions of this group on the original sample even when it contains ions of other groups. These preliminary tests are given in P-1 to P-5. It is wise to confirm them by the systematic analysis according to Outline 5.

19-24. Suggestions for Further Work.

1. Investigate other tests for these ions, e.g., the morin test for Al, dimethylglyoxime test for Fe; chromotropic acid test for Cr; ammonium tetrathiocyanatomercurate(II) test for Zn and Co; 1-nitroso-2-naphthol test for Co; rubeanic acid test for Ni; and the persulfate-silver nitrate test for Mn.

2. Look up the properties and analytical behavior of one of the members of this group that we have not considered, e.g., uranium or titanium. Adapt the scheme of analysis so that this element can be detected.

3. Investigate separations by paper chromatography or ion-exchange. Consult Chapter 25.

4. Prepare several grams of one or more of the following (see Sec. 17-11, footnote 9): $K_2Cr_2O_7$ from chromite; $Na_3Co(NO_2)_6$; chrome or ferric alum; Mohr's salt; $K_3Fe(C_2O_4)_3$; $[Co(NH_3)_6]Cl_3$; $Ni(NH_3)_6Br_2$; $[Co(NH_3)_5Cl]Cl_2$; $[Co(NH_3)_5CO_3]NO_3$; $[Co(NH_3)_5NO_2](NO_3)_2$.

THE ANALYSIS OF CATION GROUP 3
THE BASIC HYDROGEN SULFIDE GROUP

Preliminary Tests

P-1. Tests for Fe.   In a general analysis all Fe^{+++} ions are reduced to Fe^{++} by H_2S or TA. Tests for the oxidation state of iron must be made on the original sample.

a. Test for Fe^{++}. Dissolve one crystal of $K_3Fe(CN)_6$ in about 20 drops (1 ml) of water. Add a drop of this solution to a drop of the solution under test. A blue color or blue precipitate of $KFeFe(CN)_6$ indicates the presence of Fe^{++}. If the test is green, the yellow color of the ferricyanide reagent may be too strong. Dilute it and try the test again. Other ions give colored precipitates with the reagent, but only Fe^{++} ion gives a blue one.

b. Test for Fe^{+++}. Dissolve a few crystals of NH_4SCN in a little water and add a few drops of the reagent to the solution under test. A dense red color, not a precipitate, of FeSCN^{++} indicates the presence of Fe^{+++} ion. Light pink or red colorations are caused by traces of iron, a common impurity in reagents. All aged solutions of Fe^{++} will give a test for Fe^{+++}, for the iron(II) is slowly oxidized by oxygen of air. Do not report traces. If you are in doubt as to whether the color is deep enough, try the test on a few drops of a solution that contains 0.1 mg of Fe^{+++} per milliliter (dilute one drop of the standard Fe^{+++} solution with 5 ml of water and mix well). Indications of the presence of iron are also obtained in the test for Co (P-4).

P-2. Test for Ni. To one drop of the solution under test add a few drops of water and 15 M NH_3 until the solution is strongly alkaline. Centrifuge and draw off the clear solution to another tube. To it add several drops of dimethylglyoxime solution. A deep red precipitate of nickel dimethylglyoxime indicates the presence of Ni. If a brown coloration caused by Co forms, add more reagent. This test will fail when only a small amount of nickel is present because of coprecipitation with a large precipitate of the gelatinous hydroxides.

P-3. Test for Mn. Test a drop of the solution for chloride by acidifying the solution with nitric acid, if necessary, and adding $AgNO_3$ solution.

a. If chloride is absent, add a drop of 16 M HNO_3 and one-quarter of a spatula-full of sodium bismuthate. A purple color of MnO_4^- indicates the presence of Mn. Centrifuge to see the color.

b. If chloride is present, add $AgNO_3$ solution until no more precipitate forms. Then test with HNO_3 and sodium bismuthate as before.

P-4. Test for Co (and Fe). To a drop of the (acid) solution add a few drops of water and several crystals of NH_4SCN. If a red color ($FeSCN^{++}$) appears, add solid NaF a little at a time until the color goes away. Then add 5 to 10 drops of a solution of NH_4SCN in alcohol-ether. A blue upper layer containing $Co(SCN)_4^{--}$ indicates the presence of Co. A green upper layer indicates the presence of a low concentration of either Co^{++} or SCN^-. If the color is indistinct or fades on shaking, add a spatula-full of solid NH_4SCN. If the color is red, add more NaF. If the color is a dark muddy green (due to Cu), add a drop of $SnCl_2$ to reduce Cu(II) to CuSCN or $Cu(SCN)_2^-$.

P-5. Test for Zn. To one drop of the solution under test add 6 M NaOH until the solution is basic, and then add 1 or 2 drops in excess. Touch a pipet to this mixture without squeezing the bulb. Some of the solution will rise in the tip by capillary action. Bring the tip down vertically on the center of a square of dithizone paper. A purple-red spot indicates the presence of Zn. An orange ring is caused by NaOH alone. Mercury(I or II) and lead(II) give purple-blue spots and Sn(II) gives a pink one. Touch the pipet to some water, and bring the tip down on the center of the spot. The zinc spot will spread as the water flows out; the other spots will not. The dithizone paper should be a purplish gray; if its deterioration is suspected, test it with a known zinc solution.

Precipitation of the Group: Dilute sample with water until total vol is about 2 ml. Add 6 drops 6 M NH$_4$Cl and make soln alk with 15 M NH$_3$ (check with litmus) and add 1 drop NH$_3$ in xs.[1] Note the occurrence and color of any ppt.[2] Then add 4 drops TA and heat in vigorously boiling water for at least 5 minutes. Centrifuge and wash ppt with hot water containing a crystal of NH$_4$NO$_3$ or a drop of a soln of the salt.[3] Combine the washing with Soln. 5-1.

Solution 5-1. Ions of later groups, NH$_3$, TA, NH$_4$Cl, H$_2$S. If Ppt 5-1 is large, check with litmus and, if necessary, add more NH$_3$ and TA. Reheat.

In general analyses add 1 ml 12 M HCl and evap almost to dryness to remove H$_2$S and TA. Dilute with water, stopper, and save for **Group 4, Outline 6.**

Precipitate 5-1. Al(OH)$_3$, Cr(OH)$_3$, FeS, NiS, CoS, MnS, ZnS. Add 10 drops 16 M HNO$_3$ and warm until ppt dissolves.[4] Centrifuge and transfer soln to a casserole. Discard the residue of S^0.

Solution 5-2. Fe^{+++}, Al^{+++}, Cr^{+++}, Ni^{++}, Co^{++}, Mn^{++}, Zn^{++}, HNO$_3$, (Cl$^-$). Evap almost to dryness over a microflame. Add 10-15 drops 16 M HNO$_3$ and manipulate the casserole so that it wets all of the inner walls. Evap almost to dryness again. Add more 16 M HNO$_3$ and evap a third time.[5] Add 10-15 drops 16 M HNO$_3$.

Heat remaining soln to a boil and add to it a few crystals of KClO$_3$ at a time. Boil after each addn and add 16 M HNO$_3$ to replace that lost by evapn.[7] Continue the addn of KClO$_3$ until a brown-black ppt forms[8] or until one-half spatula-full of KClO$_3$ (50-75 mg) has been added. Transfer to a centrifuge tube and rinse casserole with a few drops of water, adding these rinsings to the tube. Centrifuge and wash ppt with water.

A side test for Mn can be made on this soln if desired. Dilute 1 drop with several drops of water in a centrifuge tube. Add a definite xs of sodium bismuthate. Centrifuge. Deep purple soln,[6] MnO$_4^-$: **presence of Mn.**

Precipitate 5-3. MnO$_2$. If previous test was doubtful, add a few drops 6 M HNO$_3$ and 1 drop 3% H$_2$O$_2$. Then add an xs of sodium bismuthate.[9] Centrifuge. Purple soln, MnO$_4^-$: **presence of Mn.**

Solution 5-3. Fe^{+++}, Al^{+++}, Cr$_2$O$_7^{--}$, Ni^{++}, Co^{++}, Zn^{++}, HNO$_3$. Neutralize the acid with 6 M NaOH and add 5-10 drops in xs. Follow with 1 drop 3% H$_2$O$_2$. Warm for a few minutes.[10] Centrifuge and wash ppt with about 10 drops H$_2$O containing 1-2 drops NaOH. Combine washings and soln in a centrifuge tube and centrifuge again to remove last traces of Ppt. 5-4.

Co and Fe tests. Cool.[12] Add a few crystals of NH$_4$SCN. Deep red color, FeSCN^{++}: **presence of Fe.**[13] Discharge color with NaF. Add 10 drops of soln of NH$_4$SCN in alcohol ether. Blue upper layer, Co(SCN)$_4^=$: **presence of Co.**[14]

Solution 5-4. CrO$_4^{--}$, Al(OH)$_4^-$, Zn(OH)$_4^=$, xs NaOH. If soln is yellow, CrO$_4^{--}$ is probably present. Divide into 2 parts; use $\frac{1}{4}$ for Cr test, the rest for tests for Al and Zn. If the soln is not yellow, use all for Al and Zn tests.

Precipitate 5-4. Fe(OH)$_3$, Ni(OH)$_2$, Co(OH)$_3$, (Zn). Add a few drops 12 M HCl and warm. Dilute with 10 drops water. Divide soln, which contains Fe^{+++}, Ni^{++}, and Co^{++}, between 2 test tubes.

Ni test. Add NH$_3$ until alk. Centrifuge and discard ppt. To soln add dimethylglyoxime soln in xs.[15] Deep red ppt, nickel dimethyl glyoxime: **presence of Ni.**[16]

Cr test. Acidify with HC$_2$H$_3$O$_2$ and add a few drops Pb(C$_2$H$_3$O$_2$) soln. A bright yellow ppt, PbCrO$_4$: **presence of Cr.** To confirm, centrifuge and discard soln. Dissolve ppt in 1 drop 6 M HNO$_3$. Dilute with several drops water and transfer to a spot plate. Add 1 drop 3% H$_2$O$_2$. Fleeting blue color, CrO$_5$: **presence of Cr.**[17]

Al and Zn Tests. Acidify with 6 M HCl. Add 5 drops 6 M NH$_4$Cl and NH$_3$ until basic. Centrifuge and wash ppt with water.

Solution 5-5. CrO$_4^{--}$, Zn(NH$_3$)$_4^{++}$, NH$_3$, NH$_4$Cl. If CrO$_4^{--}$ is present, add 2-3 drops BaCl$_2$ soln. Centrifuge and discard ppt (BaCO$_3$, BaCrO$_4$, BaSO$_4$). If CrO$_4^{--}$ is not present, omit this step. Add TA and heat. A white ppt may be ZnS. Centrifuge and discard soln. Dissolve ppt in 1 drop 16 M HNO$_3$. Warm for a few minutes to oxidize sulfide. Add xs 6 M NaOH and apply to dithizone paper. Purple-red spot: **presence of Zn.**

Precipitate 5-5. Al(OH)$_3$, white, gelatinous.[18] Dissolve in 1 drop 6 M HCl. Add 2 drops aluminon reagent and 5 drops NH$_4$C$_2$H$_3$O$_2$ soln. Check pH.[19] Red color: **presence of Al.** Make barely alk with NH$_3$ and centrifuge to settle the red lake.

Notes on Outline 5

1. The solution must be definitely basic, yet if it is too basic, small amounts of Al and Cr may be lost.

2. The precipitate may be white $Al(OH)_3$, gray-green $Cr(OH)_3$, or reddish-brown $Fe(OH)_3$ (this will not form if the iron has been reduced by TA or H_2S in acid solution). Absence of these precipitates indicates probable absence of these ions, but the precipitates are sometimes hard to see when suspended in a colored solution.

3. Ammonium nitrate prevents peptization of the sulfides.

4. A black, floating globule of sulfur colored by occluded sulfides often forms. If difficulty is experienced in dissolving the sulfides, add a drop of 12 M HCl; but avoid this if possible, for chloride must be removed in the next step.

5. Repeated evaporation is necessary to remove chloride, which interferes with the separation of MnO_2.

6. If the purple color appears and then fades rapidly, chloride is present. Add more bismuthate.

7. The oxidation of Mn(II) to MnO_2 by chlorate requires vigorous boiling, the presence of 16 M nitric acid, and the absence of chloride. Avoid adding too much $KClO_3$ at a time or evolution of ClO_2 may be too violent.

8. If the side test shows the absence of Mn, no precipitate will be obtained. Even so, the potassium chlorate treatment is made to oxidize Cr(III) to $Cr_2O_7{}^{--}$.

9. The first bismuthate that is added will oxidize H_2O_2 to O_2. An excess is present when the layer of brown or black solid on the bottom is several millimeters thick and no bubbles are evolved.

10. The hydrogen peroxide oxidizes $Co(OH)_2$ to $Co(OH)_3$ and a better separation of Co from Al and Zn results. Warming serves to accelerate the reaction and to decompose excess H_2O_2.

11. A double centrifugation is advisable to ensure complete separation of Fe, Co, and Ni from Cr, Al, and Zn.

12. The thiocyanate reagent contains ether and amyl alcohol which are volatile solvents. If the solution is warm when the reagent is added, most of the solvents will evaporate.

13. The preliminary test P-1 is a more reliable indication of iron than a red color at this stage. A certain amount of iron is frequently picked up during the analysis from impurities in the reagents or through careless technique. Thus even when no iron is detected in P-1, a pink color is sometimes obtained here.

14. If the blue color fades after mixing, add a spatula-full of solid NH_4SCN. A large water layer extracts so much thiocyanate from the upper layer that the sensitivity of the test is reduced.

15. A large, false nickel test may be found here if at any earlier stage the solution was stirred with a nickel spatula. Use glass rods for stirring.

16. If cobalt is present, it combines with dimethylglyoxime to give a brown *solution* before any dimethylglyoxime will react with nickel. If a brown color forms, be sure to add a sufficient excess of reagent.

17. The blue color will not appear if the solution is too warm or contains too much acid or hydrogen peroxide. Even at best it lasts only a few seconds. The color may be stabilized somewhat by extracting it into ether.

18. If the aluminum hydroxide is brownish, it may contain iron. Dissolve in a drop or two of 6 M NaOH and centrifuge to remove the brown $Fe(OH)_3$. Neutralize the solution with 6 M HCl and add NH_4Cl and NH_3 to reprecipitate $Al(OH)_3$.

19. The best lake is formed if the pH of the acid solution containing the aluminon is raised to between 5 and 7.2 by addition of the ammonium acetate. A precipitate may form in this weakly acid solution if large amounts of Al are present. Otherwise, it will not appear until the solution is made weakly basic. An excess of NH_3 is harmful. Silica does not give a red lake but Fe, Cr, Pb, and other metals do; they will not be present here if the earlier separations were carefully done.

EXERCISES

19-1. Name the metals of this group and locate them in the Periodic Table. Why do they occur together in this analytical group?

19-2. For each element in Group 3 give the principal oxidation states and the electronic structures of the simple ions.

19-3. Account for the existence of compounds of Al(III) but the nonexistence of those of Al(IV) and the instability of those of Al(I).

19-4. Explain why Al^{+++} ion forms more complexes than Mg^{++} ion does but fewer than Cr^{+++} does.

19-5. Tell what is meant by each term and give an example: labile complex, nondaltonide compound, disproportionation, passivity.

19-6. Name Cr_2O_3, $Fe(CN)_6^{---}$, $Zn(OH)_4^{--}$, $Mn(OH)_2$, $Cr_2O_7^{--}$, Mn_3O_4, NiO_2, MnO_4^-, $Cr(OH)_4^-$, K_2MnO_4, $CoCl_2$, $Al(OH)_4^-$, $Co(NH_3)_6^{++}$, $NH_4Al(SO_4)_2 \cdot 12H_2O$.

19-7. Give the colors of

(a) the hydrated forms of Cr^{+++}, Mn^{++}, Fe^{++}, Fe^{+++}, Co^{++}, Ni^{++}, Zn^{++}, and Al^{+++}
(b) $Cr(OH)_4^-$, $Zn(OH)_4^{--}$, $Al(OH)_4^-$, $FeOH^{++}$
(c) MnO_4^{--}, MnO_4^-, CrO_4^{--}, $Cr_2O_7^{--}$
(d) $FeCl^{++}$, $CrCl_2^+$, $CoCl_4^{--}$
(e) $Co(NH_3)_6^{++}$, $Ni(NH_3)_6^{++}$, $Zn(NH_3)_4^{++}$
(f) $Fe(OH)_3$, $Zn(OH)_2$, $Cr(OH)_3$, $Al(OH)_3$, $Co(OH)_2$, $Mn(OH)_2$, $Ni(OH)_2$
(g) MnS, FeS, NiS, CoS, ZnS

19-8. The acidity constants of the hydrated forms of Zn^{++}, Al^{+++}, and Cr^{+++} range from very small to moderately large. Account for this.

19-9. Explain why the combination of ammonia and ammonium chloride does not precipitate $Mg(OH)_2$, $Mn(OH)_2$, and $Ni(OH)_2$. Reference should be made to the appropriate equilibria.

19-10. Arrange in order of increasing acid character: (a) ZnO, FeO, CoO, (b) CrO, CrO_3, Cr_2O_3.

19-11. Discuss the effect on the sulfide ion concentration in a solution of hydrolyzed thioacetamide or hydrogen sulfide of variations in the concentration of hydroxide ion. Relate to the precipitation of Group 3.

19-12. Describe the crystal structures of CoO, FeS, pyrite, zinc blende, Prussian blue, $Ni(OH)_2$.

19-13. Account for the existence of various series of similar compounds such as the schönites or alums.

19-14. Account for the fact that aluminum hydroxide can be precipitated from a solution that is acid, although the precipitate contains hydroxide ions.

19-15. Why is Cr_2S_3 decomposed by water? Why does $Cr_2(SO_3)_3$ not precipitate when sodium sulfite is added to a solution of a chromium(III) salt?

19-16. In a series of oxides or hydroxides of the same element, how is acidity or basicity generally related to the oxidation number of the element? Illustrate by reference to manganese compounds.

19-17. Identify the lettered compounds in this series of reactions. A bright yellow solid A is insoluble in water and acetic acid. When A is treated with sulfuric acid it turns white (B) and an orange solution C forms. Hydrogen sulfide blackens B. When more concentrated sulfuric acid is added to C a red solid D separates. A pungent gas E is evolved when sodium chloride is added to the solution above the red solid, and the solution turns deep green (F). When F is diluted and allowed to stand for several months, it turns to violet G.

19-18. Account for the observation that a pink color with thiocyanate is not obtained from a freshly prepared solution of iron(II) sulfate but is found after the solution has stood for several days.

19-19. By reference to standard oxidation potentials, account for the fact that iron(II), not iron(III), is produced by the action of hydrochloric acid on iron.

19-20. Explain why aluminum will liberate hydrogen from water in a basic solution but not in a neutral solution.

19-21. Explain why Co(II) is oxidized to Co(III) in basic solution rather than in acid solution.

19-22. Identify the lettered compounds. A green solid A decomposes upon treatment with acid to give a dark solid B and a solution C. Acidified hydrogen peroxide dissolves B to give a virtually colorless solution D and a gas E. Addition of sodium sulfate to solution C results in the formation of a white precipitate F insoluble in ammonium acetate or dilute hydrochloric acid. The solution above the white precipitate is withdrawn, and made alkaline with sodium hydroxide, and sodium sulfite is added little by little. First a green color G appears and then a precipitate forms which is identical with B.

19-23. Prepare a table with columns headed: H_2S in 0.01 M HCl; H_2S in $HC_2H_3O_2 - NaC_2H_3O_2$ buffer; H_2S in $NH_3 - NH_4Cl$ buffer; excess NaOH, excess NH_3, and $NH_3 + NH_4Cl$. Make a row for each ion of this group. Fill in the spaces of the table with the formulas of compounds or ions.

19-24. What reagent or combination of reagents would you use to separate each of the following pairs in one step? (a) $Fe^{+++} - Cr^{+++}$, (b) $Al^{+++} - Mg^{++}$, (c) $Bi^{+++} - Cr^{+++}$, (d) $Fe^{+++} - Al^{+++}$, (e) $Mn^{++} - Co^{++}$, (f) $Zn(OH)_2 - Mn(OH)_2$, (g) $Al^{+++} - Zn^{++}$, (h) $Ca^{++} - Co^{++}$.

19-25. Suggest an error or errors that could lead to the following observations: (a) In the manganese test the purple color fades quickly. (b) In the nickel test only a dark brown solution was obtained although nickel was present. (c) A red-brown lake is obtained in the aluminon test although no aluminum is present. (d) A pale green upper layer is obtained in the cobalt test although cobalt is present.

19-26. Give a reason for each operation: (a) precipitation of the group from a large volume of solution; (b) evaporation with nitric acid before separation of Mn; (c) the use of hydrogen peroxide with sodium hydroxide in subdividing the group; (d) removal of chromate before the test for Zn; (e) separation of Mn before subdividing the group; (f) the use of dimethyglyoxime in excess when a brown coloration appears; (g) the use of ammonium chloride in precipitating the group; (h) the addition of sodium fluoride in the Co test.

19-27. Cite examples from the analysis of the group of separations based on: (a) control of the concentration of hydroxide ion, (b) formation of ammonia complex ions, (c) amphoterism, (d) differences in rates of diffusion, (e) extraction, (f) selective oxidation.

19-28. Write equations for the successive reactions of the ions of this group (Sec. 19-21).

19-29. An "unknown" may contain one or more of these substances

$$KCl, \ MnSO_4, \ Al_2(SO_4)_3, \ ZnSO_4, \ NaOH, \ Pb(NO_3)_2, \ NiCl_2$$

The unknown is completely soluble in water. When hydrogen sulfide is passed through the solution a gelatinous white precipitate gradually forms. Which substances are probably present, which are probably absent, and for which is the evidence insufficient to allow any definite conclusions?

CHAPTER TWENTY

Cation Group 4

The Ammonium Carbonate Group

Ca^{++}, Sr^{++}, Ba^{++}

20-1. Introduction. The three ions of this group form carbonates that are precipitated by ammonium carbonate in the presence of an ammonium chloride-ammonia buffer. Their chlorides, sulfides, and hydroxides are much too soluble to precipitate with preceding groups.

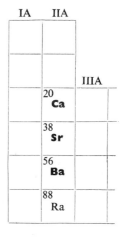

Calcium, strontium, and barium are the alkaline earth metals of Periodic Group IIA. Radium, the last member of this group, resembles barium in its chemical behavior but is not considered here because of its scarcity and radioactivity. Beryllium, the first member, resembles aluminum more closely than it does the other members of Group IIA and accompanies aluminum in the analytical separations of qualitative analysis. Magnesium, too, stands apart from the alkaline earth metals, although it resembles calcium more closely than it does beryllium. By proper choice of conditions, little if any magnesium carbonate is precipitated with Cation Group 4.

20-2. Electronic Structures and Oxidation States. Atoms of these elements have two valence electrons. When these are lost, the Me^{++} ions that are formed have outer shells of eight electrons, the inert gas octet. It is more difficult to remove the first electron from atoms of Ca, Sr, and Ba than it is from atoms of the neighboring alkali metals, K, Rb, and Cs. This is a consequence of the higher nuclear charges in atoms of the alkaline earth metals. The first ionization potential of calcium, for example, is 140.8 kcal/g-atom as compared with 100.1 for potassium. Removal of the second electron is easier for the alkaline earth metal, e.g., 273.6 to change Ca^+ to Ca^{++} but 733 to change K^+ to K^{++} and destroy the inert gas octet. Although considerable energy is required to form Ca^{++} ions, this investment is repaid by release of energy in forming stable crystals (lattice energy) or hydrated ions (hydration energy). Calcium, strontium, and barium always occur in solid compounds and in solution as bivalent ions.

20-3. Some Properties of the Atoms and Ions. Some of the pertinent characteristics of atoms and ions of the alkaline earth metals are given in Table 20-1. Those of beryllium and magnesium are also given for comparison. As was noted in the introduction, beryllium and magnesium stand apart from the other members of the family in their properties. The implications of the data in the table will be examined first by comparing these elements with the alkali metals and then by comparing them with each other.

TABLE 20-1.

Some Properties of the Atoms and Ions of Periodic Group IIA

Property	Be	Mg	Ca	Sr	Ba
Number of electron shells in ion	1	2	3	4	5
Atomic radius, A	0.90	1.36	1.74	1.92	1.98
Ionic radius, A	.31	0.65	0.99	1.14	1.35
Charge/radius	6.4	3.1	2.0	1.8	1.5
Ionization potential, Me → Me⁺, kcal/g-atom	215	176	141	131	120
Ionization potential, Me⁺ → Me⁺⁺, kcal/g-atom	410	347	274	254	230
Ionization potential, Me⁺⁺ → Me⁺⁺⁺, kcal/g-atom	3547	1840	1180	1000	850
Heat of hydration of gaseous Me⁺⁺, kcal/g-atom	−594	−459	−380	−345	−311
Lattice energy of $MeCl_2$, kcal/mole	−713	−595	−537	−506	−488
Lattice energy of MeF_2, kcal/mole		−698	−629	−597	−564
Lattice energy of MeO, kcal/mole	−1053	−913	−823	−781	−741

20-4. Comparison with the Alkali Metals. Since atoms of the alkaline earth metals have twice as many valence electrons about an inert gas kernel as the alkali metal atoms do, the sharing of electrons in the metals is more effective. Their crystals are thus harder, denser, and more difficult to break apart than those of the alkali metals. Compare, for example, cesium, atomic number 55, density 1.87 g/cc, melting point 28.45°, boiling point 708° with barium, atomic number 56, density 3.74, melting point 710°, and boiling point 1696°. Although more energy is required to ionize atoms of barium, strontium, and calcium, than atoms of the alkali metals, more energy is also released in hydrating the ions. As a result, barium, strontium, and calcium are almost as powerful reducing agents as the alkali metals. Their reaction with water is less vigorous because the surface of the metal is protected by a film of oxide or hydroxide. Because of their double charges, Ca^{++}, Sr^{++}, and Ba^{++} ions form stable lattices with small or highly charged anions such as F^-, O^{--}, or SO_4^{--}.[1] Such compounds are much less soluble than those of the alkali metal ions, which are larger and have lower charges. The high charge and small size of the alkaline earth metal ions (or large ratio of charge to radius) makes it possible for them to attract other ions or molecules and form more complexes than the alkali metal ions do.

20-5. Relations Between Calcium, Strontium, and Barium. The properties recorded in Table 20-1 vary regularly from calcium to barium; i.e., those of strontium are almost halfway between the properties of the other two. Similar gradations are found in stabilities and solubilities. The thermal decomposition of the solid peroxides, carbonates, and hexammine chlorides is represented by

$$2MeO_2 \rightleftharpoons 2MeO + O_2 \uparrow$$

$$MeCO_3 \rightleftharpoons MeO + CO_2 \uparrow$$

$$Me(NH_3)_6Cl_2 \rightleftharpoons MeCl_2 + 6NH_3 \uparrow$$

The stability of these compounds is indicated by the temperature required to produce a specified equilibrium pressure of gas; a high temperature corresponds to a compound that is stable, i.e., hard to decompose. These equilibrium temperatures show a regular variation, e.g., 840° for BaO_2, 357° for SrO_2, CaO_2 nonexistent (for $P_{O_2} = 1$ atm); 1360° for $BaCO_3$, 1289° for $SrCO_3$, and 900° for $CaCO_3$ (for $P_{CO_2} = 1$ atm); 12.5° for $Ba(NH_3)_6Cl_2$, 71.9° for $Sr(NH_3)_6Cl_2$, and 105.4° for $Ca(NH_3)_6Cl_2$ (for $P_{NH_3} = 1$ mm).

The solubilities frequently show similar gradations. The calcium compounds are generally most soluble; this is true of the chlorides, bromides, iodides, chlorates, bromates, iodates, nitrites, nitrates, sulfites, sulfates, and chromates. The reverse order, i.e., with the barium salt most soluble, is exhibited by the hydroxides, fluorides, and oxalates. The carbonates, acetates, and perchlorates behave irregularly. The molar solubilities of the more

---

[1] A large amount of energy is released when a stable lattice is formed. The negative sign of this lattice energy indicates that the energy is given off in forming the crystal from the gaseous ions (Sec. 5-3).

important compounds are given in Table 20-2. The relation of solubility to lattice and hydration energies is discussed in Sec. 5-7.

TABLE 20-2.

The Solubilities* of Compounds of the Alkaline Earth Metals at 25°

Calcium compounds		Strontium compounds		Barium compounds	
Compound	Solubility	Compound	Solubility	Compound	Solubility
$CaCrO_4 \cdot 2H_2O$	1.0	$Sr(OH)_2 \cdot 8H_2O$	0.084	$Ba(OH)_2 \cdot 8H_2O$	0.27
$Ca(OH)_2$	0.020	$SrCrO_4$	.0047	BaF_2	.0069
$CaSO_4 \cdot 2H_2O$	.015	SrF_2	.0031	$BaC_2O_4 \cdot 2H_2O$	.00048
CaF_2	.0002	$SrSO_4$	.00082	$BaCO_3$	.000091
$CaCO_3$	.00013	$SrC_2O_4 \cdot H_2O$	.00026	$BaCrO_4$	.0000115
$CaC_2O_4 \cdot H_2O$	.000049	$SrCO_3$	.000055	$BaSO_4$	.0000104

*All solubilities are expressed as moles of compound per liter of solution.

20-6. Compounds of Calcium, Strontium, and Barium. All compounds of the alkaline earth metals are colorless unless they contain a colored anion such as the yellow chromate ion. Their lack of color is characteristic of ions with inert gas structure.

Many of the salts are hydrated, particularly those of calcium, e.g., $CaCl_2 \cdot 6H_2O$, $CaC_2O_4 \cdot H_2O$, $Ca(NO_3)_2 \cdot 4H_2O$, $CaSO_4 \cdot 2H_2O$ (gypsum), and $CaSO_4 \cdot \frac{1}{2}H_2O$ (plaster of Paris). Because the barium ion is larger and attracts water molecules less strongly, its salts are less hydrated or even anhydrous, e.g., $BaCl_2 \cdot 2H_2O$, $BaSO_4$, $Ba(NO_3)_2$, and $BaCrO_4$.

The salts with univalent anions, e.g., the nitrates, chlorides, and acetates, are usually soluble in water. The principal exceptions are the fluorides and iodates. Calcium chloride and calcium nitrate are remarkably soluble in pure ethyl alcohol; strontium chloride is also somewhat soluble, but neither strontium nor barium nitrate dissolves in alcohol. A separation of calcium from strontium and barium is based on this difference in solubilities. On the other hand, calcium nitrate is fairly soluble in 79-81% nitric acid and strontium and barium nitrates are only very slightly soluble, even when the acid concentration is as low as 70-72% as in ordinary concentrated nitric acid. There is no simple explanation of the insolubility of strontium and barium nitrates, but it is not unusual for nitrates and sometimes chlorides to be insoluble in the concentrated acid, e.g., $Pb(NO_3)_2$ in HNO_3 and $NaCl$ in HCl. The common ion effect is not responsible for the decrease in solubility. Concentrated nitric acid is not highly ionized and the concentration of nitrate ion in the 70% acid is about the same as that in the highly ionized $2 M$ acid, yet strontium nitrate is much less soluble in the former.

The hydroxides of these metals are only moderately soluble (Table 20-2). They are not precipitated when NH_3, NaOH, or KOH is added to dilute solutions of the salts such as we encounter in qualitative analysis, but they can be precipitated by using more concentrated solutions of salt and a strong base. The basic reagents absorb carbon dioxide from the air, and the turbidity that often develops when they are added to dilute solutions of the alkaline earth ions is caused by precipitation of the carbonates. All three hydroxides are moderately strong bases although some ion-pair formation occurs:

$$Ca^{++} + OH^- \rightleftharpoons CaOH^+$$

Solutions of barium hydroxide ("baryta water") are standardized and used to titrate acids. In qualitative analysis they are used to test for carbonate:

$$Ba^{++} + 2OH^- + CO_2 \rightarrow BaCO_3 \downarrow + H_2O$$

The sulfides of all these elements are prepared by reducing the solid sulfates with carbon at high temperature:

$$BaSO_4 + 4C \overset{\Delta}{\rightarrow} BaS + 4CO \uparrow$$

The sulfides are decomposed by water and cannot be prepared by precipitation:

$$BaS \downarrow + H_2O \rightarrow Ba^{++} + HS^- + OH^-$$

Salts of bivalent and trivalent ions are generally almost insoluble in water and can be prepared by precipitation:

$$Sr^{++} + SO_3^{--} \rightarrow SrSO_3 \downarrow$$
$$Ca^{++} + HPO_4^{--} \rightarrow CaHPO_4 \downarrow$$
$$3Ca^{++} + 2HPO_4^{--} + 2NH_3 \rightarrow Ca_3(PO_4)_2 \downarrow + 2NH_4^+$$

The last two equations demonstrate that the monohydrogen phosphate is precipitated in neutral or weakly basic solutions whereas in strongly basic solutions the normal phosphate is obtained. The salts of weak acids can be dissolved by stronger acids, e.g.,

$$SrSO_3 \downarrow + 2H^+ + 2Cl^- \rightarrow Sr^{++} + 2Cl^- + H_2SO_3$$
$$CaHPO_4 \downarrow + H^+ + NO_3^- \rightarrow Ca^{++} + NO_3^- + H_2PO_4^-$$

20-7. Complexes of Calcium, Strontium, and Barium. Although these ions form more complexes than do those of the alkali metals, none of these complexes is very stable. As compared with other bivalent ions such as Fe^{++}, Co^{++}, or Cd^{++}, the ions of calcium, strontium, and barium are large and have inert gas structures; these features are not favorable to formation of complexes. The ions coordinate best with oxygen and to a much lower extent with nitrogen. Oxygen complexes are illustrated by the hydrated metal ions and complexes with sugars and alcohols. A number of chelates are formed, e.g., the calcium-triethanolamine complex in which calcium is bonded to both oxygen and nitrogen. Calcium ion is the smallest of the three metal ions and forms the most stable complexes.

20-8. The Properties of the Alkaline Earth Metal Carbonates.   These salts are precipitated by addition of ammonium, sodium, or potassium carbonates to solutions of the alkaline earth metal ions. They dissolve readily in strong acids and in acids as weak as $HC_2H_3O_2$ and H_2CO_3:

$$CaCO_3 \downarrow \; + \; 2HC_2H_3O_2 \rightarrow Ca^{++} + 2C_2H_3O_2^- + H_2O + CO_2$$
$$BaCO_3 \downarrow \; + \; H_2CO_3 \rightarrow Ba^{++} + 2HCO_3^-$$

They are slightly soluble in solutions of ammonium salts because carbonate ion is removed to some extent by the proton transfer reaction

$$NH_4^+ + CO_3^{--} \rightleftharpoons NH_3 + HCO_3^-$$

All three carbonates are close together in solubility in water (Table 20-2), and it is not possible to separate one from the others. Magnesium carbonate, however, is about 100 times as soluble and can be separated from the carbonates of Group 4 by regulation of the concentration of carbonate ion. In solutions of ammonium carbonate alone the concentration of carbonate is sufficiently high to precipitate magnesium carbonate to some extent unless the reagent is dilute. If ammonium chloride is mixed with the ammonium carbonate, the excess of ammonium ions causes a more rapid removal of carbonate and at a new equilibrium the carbonate ion concentration is lower than before the addition of the ammonium chloride. Now if too much ammonium salt is present, the decrease in concentration of carbonate ion concentration may go too far so that precipitation of the carbonates of Group 4 would be incomplete. This is avoided in two ways. First, the large amounts of ammonium salts left in solution after the analysis of Groups 2 and 3 are removed, and a controlled amount is added. Second, some ammonia is added to partially counteract the effect of ammonium ions. If we put strong players on both teams (i.e., both sides of the equation) neither can go too far.

20-9. The Properties of the Alkaline Earth Metal Sulfates.   The sulfates of barium and strontium are readily precipitated from solutions of their soluble salts when dilute sulfuric acid or soluble sulfates are added. Calcium sulfate is much more soluble and precipitates only from fairly concentrated solutions. The concentration of sulfate ion in its saturated solution is sufficiently high to precipitate barium or strontium sulfates. Calcium sulfate also differs from the other two in its crystal form; distinctive needles frequently are clustered together in beautiful bundles, in contrast with the tiny, nondescript grains of barium and strontium sulfates.

The sulfate ion is the anion of a moderately strong acid $[K_a (HSO_4^-) = 0.01]$, so the reaction of a sulfate with strong acids such as HCl or HNO_3

$$MeSO_4 \downarrow + H^+ \rightleftharpoons Me^{++} + HSO_4^-$$

occurs to an appreciable extent only if the sulfate is fairly soluble in water. Thus only calcium sulfate dissolves to any large extent in acids; strontium sulfate is slightly more soluble in acids than in water and barium sulfate dissolves in acids to only a very slight extent. The last is dissolved by concentrated sulfuric acid:

$$BaSO_4 \downarrow + H_2SO_4 \rightleftharpoons Ba^{++} + 2HSO_4^-$$

but little is gained thereby because barium sulfate reprecipitates when the solution is diluted. In dilute solutions the extent of ionization of HSO_4^- ion is too large to make it possible to regulate the concentration of sulfate ion very closely. Thus, although strontium and barium sulfate differ considerably in solubility (Table 20-2), it is not possible to adjust the concentration of sulfate ion from a soluble sulfate so that only one precipitates and not the other. The concentration can be regulated by a kinetic, instead of an equilibrium, method. Sulfamic acid at 100° hydrolyzes slowly to give sulfate ions. The concentration of sulfate builds up so slowly within the solution that only barium sulfate can precipitate.

When it is necessary to separate the alkaline earth metal ions from sulfate, a transposition with carbonate is generally used:

$$MeSO_4 \downarrow + CO_3^{--} \rightleftharpoons MeCO_3 \downarrow + SO_4^{--}$$

Inspection of Table 20-2 reveals that the carbonates of calcium and strontium are less soluble than the sulfates, so that the transposition should readily occur. It is more difficult for barium sulfate, which is less soluble than the carbonate. This is revealed also by the ratio of concentrations of sulfate to carbonate at equilibrium which is 0.06 for Ba, 1000 for Sr, and 5000 for Ca. A large excess of carbonate must be used to drive the transposition of barium sulfate to the right, or, better still, the solid sulfate can be fused with carbonate. When the carbonate has been washed free of sulfate, it can be dissolved in an acid to give a solution of the alkaline earth metal ion. This indirect method is the best method of converting the sulfates to soluble compounds.

20-10. Properties of the Alkaline Earth Metal Chromates. These are more soluble compounds than the sulfates, and only that of barium is readily precipitated. Strontium chromate precipitates only from concentrated solutions or when alcohol is added to decrease the dielectric constant and increase the force between strontium and chromate ions.

Chromates, unlike sulfates, are readily soluble in strong acids. The equilibria represented by

$$2CrO_4^{--} + 2H^+ \rightleftharpoons 2HCrO_4^- \rightleftharpoons Cr_2O_7^{--} + H_2O$$

show that if the concentration of hydrogen ion is made high, that of chromate is decreased. The ratio of concentrations of chromate ion to hydrogen chromate ion at equilibrium is about 3 in a neutral solution, 0.03 in an ammonium acetate-acetic acid mixture, and 0.0000003 in 0.1 M hydrochloric acid. The concentration of chromate ion required to precipitate barium chromate is sufficiently low so that it can form from the second mixture, but it will dissolve in hydrochloric acid. Strontium chromate is much more soluble and will not precipitate from an acidic solution. Although both barium sulfate and barium chromate are much less soluble than the strontium compounds, it is much easier to separate the chromates than the sulfates because of the ease with which the concentration of chromate ion can be regulated. The mixture of ammonium acetate and acetic acid not only sets the concentration of hydrogen ion, and hence that of chromate, at the proper level, but it also maintains this low level despite production of hydrogen ions during precipitation. These are taken care of by the excess of acetate ion present:

$$HCrO_4^- + Ba^{++} \rightarrow BaCrO_4 \downarrow + H^+$$

$$H^+ + C_2H_3O_2^- \rightarrow HC_2H_3O_2$$

Were this not done, it is possible that precipitation of barium chromate would not be complete.

20-11. Properties of the Alkaline Earth Metal Oxalates. The calcium compound is the least soluble, but strontium and barium oxalates are also readily precipitated by soluble oxalates from neutral or alkaline solutions. All three are soluble in strong acids because of formation of weakly dissociated hydrogen oxalate ions:

$$MeC_2O_4 \downarrow + H^+ \rightleftharpoons HC_2O_4^- + Me^{++}$$

Calcium oxalate is sufficiently less soluble than the other two to be unaffected by acetic acid; the others are somewhat soluble in this weak acid. Because all three oxalates are fairly insoluble in alkaline solutions it is necessary to separate barium and strontium carefully before calcium is identified by precipitation as the oxalate.

20-12. Discussion of the Analytical Procedure. The elements of Cation Group 4 are so closely related, and their chemistry is so undistinguished that separations are difficult. The compounds do not differ greatly in solubility, the complex ions are few and unstable, and there are no redox reactions of use in analysis.

The group is precipitated as the carbonates with a mixture of ammonium carbonate, ammonium chloride, and ammonia. This combination of reagents controls the concentration of carbonate ion so that the more soluble carbonate of magnesium cannot precipitate (Sec. 20-8). The excess of ammonium ion, by repressing the ionization of ammonia

$$NH_3 + H_2O \rightleftharpoons NH_4^+ + OH^-$$

keeps the concentration of hydroxide ion low enough so that precipitation of magnesium hydroxide is prevented. An important advantage of precipitating the group as carbonates instead of oxalates or sulfates is the ease with which the anion can be destroyed after it has served its purpose. Acetic acid is sufficiently strong to liberate carbon dioxide and bring the carbonates into solution. Stronger acids could be used but they would have to be neutralized before the separation of barium chromate.

Barium is easiest to separate first because its chromate is much less soluble than those of strontium and calcium. The efficiency of the separation is increased by controlling the concentration of chromate ion with a mixture of ammonium acetate and acetic acid (Sec. 20-10). The formation of yellow $BaCrO_4$ is usually sufficient indication of the presence of barium, but confirmation can be obtained by dissolving the precipitate in strong acid and precipitating $BaSO_4$. If the slow hydrolysis of sulfamic acid

$$HNH_2SO_3 + H_2O \rightarrow NH_4^+ + HSO_4^- \qquad \text{(slow)}$$
$$HSO_4^- \rightleftharpoons H^+ + SO_4^{--} \qquad \text{(fast)}$$

is used as a source of sulfate, strontium sulfate will not precipitate.

There are various ways of separating strontium from calcium. Strontium chromate, for example, can be precipitated by addition of ethyl alcohol to the solution after precipitation of barium chromate. Other methods require the prior removal of chromate ion. Sodium carbonate is used to precipitate the carbonates of strontium and calcium. Magnesium is not present here, so control of the concentration of carbonate ion is not required. Thus sodium carbonate, which supplies carbonate at high concentration, is preferred to ammonium carbonate as the reagent. After the carbonates of strontium and calcium have been dissolved in acid, the two cations can be separated by (1) precipitating $SrSO_4$ in the presence of triethanolamine, (2) extracting $Ca(NO_3)_2$ with alcohol from the dry residue left after evaporation of the water, or (3) precipitating $Sr(NO_3)_2$ with concentrated nitric acid. The last method is used in this text. The acid must be at least 70% HNO_3, so dilution of the mixture with water must be avoided. The nitrate supersaturates easily; this is counteracted by cooling, stirring, and waiting.

Strontium is identified by precipitation as the sulfate. In case any calcium was accidentally carried along with the strontium, precipitation is done in the presence of triethanolamine which sequesters the calcium as a complex so that its sulfate cannot precipitate.

Calcium is identified by precipitation as the oxalate from a weakly alkaline solution. Precipitation is done in a hot solution to increase the particle size of the precipitate, an advantage when the precipitate is small, and its bulk is to be determined.

It is critically important to obtain sharp separations in the analysis of this group. If barium is not completely removed as the chromate, it will precipitate as the nitrate; if strontium is not removed as the nitrate, it will precipitate as the oxalate.

Characteristic flame colors are given by all three elements of this group: orange-red for calcium, carmine for strontium, and yellowish green for barium. The best results are obtained with the chlorides, which are more volatile than the nitrates, oxalates, sulfates, or carbonates. No flame color is satisfactory by itself for identification of the ion. Other elements give flame colors that can obscure or be confused with those of the alkaline earth metals; the flame colors of copper and sodium compounds, for example, can be confused with that of barium. Furthermore, the flame color of any one of the Group 4 elements is obscured by those of the other two when the latter are present in large excess. Thus in the hands of inexperienced workers these flame tests are not as reliable as the precipitation reactions used in Outline 6. If they are used to supplement the precipitation tests, it is wise to compare the flame color of the unknown with flame colors from known solutions of the ions.

When observed through a spectroscope, the flame colors of calcium, barium, and strontium are resolved into bands of color. These are groups of very closely spaced lines and are given by molecules, in this case the oxides of these metals which form by oxidation of the salts in the flame. The alkali metals give single sharp lines obtained by excitation of their atoms. The line or atomic spectra of the alkaline earth metals are obtained only at the high temperatures that occur in an electric arc.

20-13. Cross References.   Familiarity with Chapters 1 to 4 is assumed.
Sec. 5-2 (ionization potentials)
Sec. 5-3 (lattice energy)
Sec. 5-6 (hydration of ions)
Sec. 5-7 (solubility as determined by lattice and hydration energies)
Sec. 6-8 (chelates)
Sec. 6-9 (complex formation)
Sec. 6-10 (size and charge of cation and stability of complexes)
Secs. 7-5, -6 (hydrolysis of sulfamic acid)
Sec. 7-8 (acidity constants)
Sec. 8-2 (solubility product)
Sec. 8-3 (solubility and K_{sp})
Sec. 8-8 (formation of precipitates)

Secs. 8-10, -11 (coprecipitation)

Sec. 8-15 (dissolution of precipitates)

Sec. 10-11 (fractional precipitation of sulfates and chromates)

Sec. 10-12 (transposition of sulfates to carbonates)

Secs. 12-6, -8 (regulation of H^+ ion concentration by mixtures of weak acids and their salts, buffers)

Sec. 13-5 (calculation of the concentrations of ions in $(NH_4)_2CO_3$ solutions)

20-14. The Successive Reactions of the Ions of Cation Group 4.

Barium

1. Precipitation of the group. Reagents: ammonium carbonate, ammonium chloride, and ammonia

$$Ba^{++} + CO_3^{--} \rightarrow BaCO_3 \downarrow$$

2. Dissolution of the precipitate. Reagent: acetic acid

$$BaCO_3 \downarrow + 2HC_2H_3O_2 \rightarrow Ba^{++} + 2C_2H_3O_2^- + H_2O + CO_2 \uparrow$$

3. Separation of Ba from Sr and Ca. Reagents: potassium chromate, ammonium acetate, and acetic acid

$$Ba^{++} + CrO_4^{--} \rightarrow BaCrO_4 \downarrow$$

4. Dissolution of the precipitate. Reagent: hydrochloric acid

$$2BaCrO_4 \downarrow + 2H^+ \rightarrow 2Ba^{++} + Cr_2O_7^{--} + H_2O$$

5. Identification of Ba. Reagent: sulfamic acid in hot solution

$$Ba^{++} + SO_4^{--} \rightarrow BaSO_4 \downarrow$$

Strontium

1. Precipitation of the group. Reagents: ammonium carbonate, ammonium chloride, and ammonia

$$Sr^{++} + CO_3^{--} \rightarrow SrCO_3 \downarrow$$

2. Dissolution of the group precipitate. Reagent: acetic acid

$$SrCO_3 \downarrow + HC_2H_3O_2 \rightarrow ?$$

(Complete and balance.)

3. Separation from Ba. Reagents: potassium chromate, ammonium acetate, and acetic acid. No reaction with Sr^{++}.

4. Separation from excess chromate. Reagent: sodium carbonate

$$Sr^{++} + CO_3^{--} \rightarrow SrCO_3 \downarrow$$

5. Dissolution of the carbonate. Reagent: nitric acid

$$SrCO_3 \downarrow + H^+ \rightarrow ?$$

(Complete and balance.)

6. Separation from Ca. Reagent: concentrated nitric acid

$$Sr^{++} + 2NO_3^- \rightarrow Sr(NO_3)_2 \downarrow$$

7. Dissolution of the nitrate. Reagent: water

$$Sr(NO_3)_2 \downarrow \rightarrow Sr^{++} + 2NO_3^-$$

8. Identification of Sr. Reagents: ammonium sulfate, ammonia, and triethanolamine

$$Sr^{++} + SO_4^{--} \rightarrow SrSO_4 \downarrow$$

Calcium

These equations are to be worked out by the student. Follow the same pattern. The complex with triethanolamine is probably $Ca[N(C_2H_4OH)_3]_2^{++}$.

EXPERIMENTAL PART

20-15. Introductory Experiments.

1. Precipitation of Carbonates.   Calculate the number of drops (20 drops per milliliter) of the standard solutions of the ions (10 mg of ion per milliliter) that must be taken to give (a) 1 mg of ion and (b) 0.5 mg of ion. Then prepare mixtures in six test tubes as indicated in the table

	Tube					
	A	*B*	*C*	*X*	*Y*	*Z*
mg of Mg^{++}	1	1	1	—	—	—
mg of Ca^{++}	—	—	—	0.5	0.5	0.5
drops of H_2O	5	5	4	10	9	0
drops of 6 M NH_4Cl	1	0	1	0	1	10
drops of 2 M $(NH_4)_2CO_3$	0	1	1	1	1	1

Mix the contents of each tube before recording your observations. Then to each tube add 1 drop of 15 M NH_3 and mix again. Note any changes.

Write equations for the ionization of ammonia and the proton transfer reaction between ammonium and carbonate ions. On the basis of these equilibria account for (a) the formation of precipitates in some tubes without the addition of NH_3, (b) the formation of precipitates in other tubes after addition of NH_3, and (c) the formation of no precipitate in still other tubes. What are the implications of these experiments with reference to the precipitation of Group 4?

2. Precipitation of chromates.   Take sufficient standard solution of Ba^{++} to give 3 mg of that ion. Add a drop of potassium chromate solution and centrifuge. Is precipitation complete? How can you tell? If it is not, add another drop of reagent. Centrifuge again, and withdraw the solution to another test tube and save it. Add a few drops of water to the precipitate, and divide it between three test tubes (Technique 11, Sec. 16-3). Test the solubility of the precipitate in 6 M NaOH, $HC_2H_3O_2$, and HCl. Between 1 and 3 drops of reagent should suffice to show whether any reaction occurs. Write equations for such reactions.

To the solution from which $BaCrO_4$ was precipitated add 1 drop of $(NH_4)_2SO_4$ reagent.

To about 3 mg of Sr^{++} add potassium chromate as before, and again try the effect of ammonium sulfate.

Compare your results with predictions based on Table 20-2. Both barium and strontium are finally identified by precipitation as the sulfates. Why is barium first precipitated as the chromate?

3. Precipitation of sulfates from homogeneous medium. In separate test tubes take sufficient volumes of the standard solutions of barium, strontium, and calcium ions to contain 2 mg of each ion. Dilute each sample with about 1 ml of water and to each add about one-quarter of a spatula-full (about 0.03 g) of solid sulfamic acid (HNH_2SO_3) (Technique 3). Stir to dissolve the acid. Warm all three tubes in a bath of boiling water, and note the approximate time in minutes required to form the first precipitate. Rub the inner walls of the other two tubes with a rod (why?) and continue heating for 10 minutes longer.

Represent the hydrolysis of sulfamic acid by a chemical equation. Account for your results.

4. Precipitation of oxalates. Take 1 drop each of the standard solutions of Ca^{++}, Sr^{++}, and Ba^{++} ions in separate test tubes, and dilute each sample with 1 ml (20 drops) of water. Heat for a minute or two in a bath of boiling water, and then add a drop of ammonium oxalate reagent to each. Record your results.

To new portions of the ion solutions add 15 drops of water and 5 drops of 6 M acetic acid. Heat and add ammonium oxalate as before. Is there any difference?

Can these ions be separated by fractional precipitation of their oxalates? In the analytical procedure calcium is the last ion to be identified. Account for this.

5. Flame tests. Obtain 1 or 2 drops of each of the standard solutions of the ions of this group in separate test tubes, and to each add 2 drops of 12 M HCl. Clean a platinum (or Nichrome) wire by heating it for some time in the flame; if necessary, dip the hot wire in 12 M HCl to dissolve residual salts. Then test the flame color of each ion. Clean the wire between tests. Note the color and persistence of each flame.

Ask a neighbor to prepare a mixture of two of the three ions. See whether you can determine which two are present in this "unknown" by a flame test.

6. A problem. This is designed to test your powers of observation and deduction. Ask your instructor for a sample of a mixture that may contain some, but not all, of the following solids:

$$Ba(NO_3)_2, \ MgCl_2, \ K_2CO_3, \ KCl, \ Na_2CrO_4, \ NH_4HSO_4$$

(a) Take a representative sample of about 20-30 mg in a test tube. Add about 1 ml of water and mix. Warm on a water bath for a few minutes. Not all of the sample may dissolve. Centrifuge to observe the character of the precipitate.

Record your observations on the original sample and on the sample after addition of water. Do not neglect to note colors and odors (smell cautiously). Though not always conclusive in themselves, such clues are too useful to neglect.

(b) To the mixture from (a) add 6 M acetic acid until it is acid to litmus. Mix well after each addition. Record observations.

(c) If precipitate remains, remove it by centrifugation. To the clear solution in another tube add 6 M sodium hydroxide until the solution is alkaline (verify with litmus). Centrifuge. Record observations.

On the basis of your observations in steps (a), (b), and (c), and these alone, decide which of the six substances are (1) probably present, (2) probably absent, (3) indeterminate for lack of evidence. Do not fail to note that these substances may react with each other to give new substances when water is added. In your report, which may be oral or written at the discretion of the instructor, consider the substances one at a time, and give a definite reason for your decision.

20-16. The Analysis of Known and Unknown Samples.

1. A *known* or *practice solution* for this group should contain 3 mg/ml of Ba^{++}, Sr^{++}, Ca^{++}, and Mg^{++} ions and about 30 mg/ml of NH_4^+ ion. Use 10 drops for the analysis. If such a mixture is not already prepared, take 3 drops of each of the standard solutions of the metal ions and add 7 drops of 6 M NH_4Cl. Remove the ammonium salts and analyze the group according to Outline 6. As a check on your technique, add ammonium sulfate and ammonium oxalate to Solution 6-1 as directed in Sec. 21-12b(3). There should be not more than a trace of precipitate even after warming. Add Na_2HPO_4 to this solution to precipitate $MgNH_4PO_4 \cdot 6H_2O$ and verify that magnesium was not precipitated with Group 4.

2. The *unknown* may contain ions of Group 4 alone or of Groups 4 and 5 together. If it is a solution, use 10 drops for the analysis according to Outline 6. If it is a solid, take a representative sample and dissolve 20-30 mg in

water or 6 *M* HCl and use this solution for the analysis. Remove ammonium salts only if a positive test for the ammonium ion is obtained (Preliminary Test, Outline 7).

If the unknown is Solution 5-1 from Cation Group 3, it should have been evaporated with hydrochloric acid to remove thioacetamide and hydrogen sulfide before any nitric acid is added, for the latter can oxidize sulfide to sulfate and cause premature precipitation of barium and strontium.

20-17. Suggestions for Further Work.

1. Examine the flame colors with a spectroscope (see Chapter 25).

2. Investigate the use of a microscope in the identification of calcium as the sulfate, strontium as the nitrate, and barium as the chromate (see Chapter 25).

3. Investigate the rhodizonate test for barium and strontium (see Chapter 25).

4. Investigate the separation and identification of these ions by paper chromatography (see Chapter 25).

5. Look up and report on the qualitative detection of radium by chemical and physical methods.

OUTLINE 6. The Systematic Analysis of Cation Group 4

Removal of excess ammonium salts. To soln under test (Sec. 20-16) in a casserole add 5 drops 16 M HNO_3 and evap to dryness (T-7b) over a microflame. Bake walls and bottom of the dish in the flame until dense white clouds of ammonium salts are no longer evolved.[1] Keep temperature below red heat.[2] Cool. Add several drops 6 M HCl[3] and with a rod rub the acid against walls and bottom of the casserole to help bring residue into soln.[4] Dilute with about 10 drops water and transfer soln to a centrifuge tube. Rinse casserole with another 5-10 drops water and add the rinsing to the first soln. If soln is not clear, centrifuge and discard the residue.[5]

$\downarrow$

Precipitation of the group. To the soln in the centrifuge tube add 1 drop 6 M NH_4Cl. Then make it alk with 15 M NH_3 (T-12).[6] Add 5 drops $(NH_4)_2CO_3$ soln and stir. Set the tube in a bath of *warm*, not hot, water only long enough to coagulate the ppt (less than 1 minute).[7] Centrifuge and separate Soln 6-1. Wash the pptd carbonates with a little water.[8]

Solution 6-1. Mg^{++}, K$^+$, Na$^+$, NH$_4$ salts, NH$_3$. Make sure that soln is alk. Then add 1 drop $(NH_4)_2CO_3$. If more ppt forms, combine it with ppt 6-1. If pptn is complete, acidify soln with HCl and set it aside for the analysis of **Group 5.**

Precipitate 6-1. BaCO$_3$, SrCO$_3$, CaCO$_3$.[9] Dissolve in a min of 6 M $HC_2H_3O_2$. Any residue insol in the acid can be removed and discarded. To the soln (Ba^{++}, Sr^{++}, Ca^{++}) add several drops 3 M $NH_4C_2H_3O_2$ and dil with 10 drops water. Add a few drops K_2CrO_4 soln. Centrifuge. Wash ppt with water.

Precipitate 6-2. Yellow BaCrO$_4$, (SrCrO$_4$). Dissolve in 1-2 drops 6 M HCl. Dilute with about 1 ml water Add $\frac{1}{4}$ spatula-full HNH_2SO_3 and stir to dissolve. Heat in a bath of vigorously boiling water for 10 minutes.
White cryst ppt, BaSO$_4$: **presence of Ba.**

Solution 6-2. Sr^{++}, Ca^{++}, CrO$_4$$^{--}$. If soln is not bright yellow, add more K_2CrO_4. Make soln alk with 6 M NaOH and add 5 drops freshly prepd Na_2CO_3 soln.[10] Warm to coagulate ppt. (If no ppt forms, Sr and Ca are absent.) Centrifuge and withdraw soln to a centrifuge tube and add more Na_2CO_3 soln. If no ppt forms on warming, discard soln. Wash the pptd carbonates twice with water to remove CrO$_4$$^{--}$.

$\downarrow$

Precipitate 6-3. SrCO$_3$, CaCO$_3$. Dissolve in a few drops HNO_3 and transfer to a casserole. Rinse tube with water and add rinsings to casserole. Evap soln over a microflame almost to dryness; withdraw from flame and let heat of dish complete the evapn. Cool. Add 5 drops 16 M HNO_3. Rub inside of casserole with a *dry* stirring rod to loosen ppt and pour mixture quickly[11] into a *dry* centrifuge tube.[12] Rinse the casserole with 5 more drops 16 M HNO_3 and pour into the tube. Insert a *dry* rod and stir and rub walls. Let stand for at least 5 minutes in cold water with occasional stirring.[13] Centrifuge and wash ppt with 16 M HNO_3.

Precipitate 6-4. Sr(NO$_3$)$_2$, [Ca(NO$_3$)$_2$]. Dissolve in 5-10 drops water. Make alk with NH_3 and add several drops of triethanolamine and a few drops $(NH_4)_2SO_4$. Rub the inner walls with a rod and warm.[14]
White, crystn ppt, SrSO$_4$: **presence of Sr.** Confirm by a flame test.[15]

Solution 6-4. Ca^{++}, HNO$_3$. Dilute with about 1 ml water. Make slightly alk with 15 M NH$_3$.[16] Add a few drops $(NH_4)_2C_2O_4$.
Smoky white ppt, CaC$_2O_4$: **presence of Ca.**

Notes on Outline 6

1. Use a somewhat higher flame in the baking than in the evaporation and play it over the walls as well as the bottom of the casserole. Otherwise, ammonium salts after being vaporized may re-form on the cooler upper walls.

2. If too high a temperature is reached, alkali halides may become fused into the glaze of the dish and lost.

3. Magnesium chloride may lose HCl at high temperatures during removal of water. The basic chloride that is formed is not soluble in water but dissolves in HCl [Sec. 21-5f(4)].

4. The baked residue goes into solution slowly and adheres to the casserole.

5. In a general analysis Solution 5-1 will contain organic matter from the hydrolysis of thioacetamide. Some of this is destroyed by the nitric acid; the rest is charred during the baking. This accounts for a black residue of carbon often obtained at this point.

6. Recall that mixing is difficult in a centrifuge tube because of the tapered bottom. Work the glass rod up and down to prevent layering of the NH_3 solution on top of the solution under test (T-5).

7. Ammonium carbonate decomposes completely into NH_3, CO_2, and H_2O if heating is prolonged and precipitation of the group would be incomplete.

8. In washing these dense precipitates be careful to disperse them completely in the wash water.

9. The precipitates of this group are more densely packed than the sulfides and hydroxides of preceding groups, yet small though they appear, it is possible to obtain satisfactory tests from them.

10. Dissolve a heaping spatula-full (about 0.15 g) of solid Na_2CO_3 in 10 drops of water. When such solutions are stored in glass bottles, they etch the glass and dissolve some silica. This would precipitate with the carbonates of strontium and calcium and make it difficult to judge the quantity of these substances. It is best to use a fresh solution of the reagent.

11. The solid nitrate settles rapidly. Unless the mixture is poured quickly, only the supernatant solution is decanted; the precipitate is left behind in the casserole. Examine the casserole if no precipitate is obtained to see if any crystals are adhering to the walls.

12. For a satisfactory separation of $Sr(NO_3)_2$ the concentration of HNO_3 must not be below 70% (16 M); ideally, it should be close to 80%. Thus the introduction of water must be avoided by (1) using a dry tube, (2) pouring instead of pipetting, and (3) using a dry rod. Dry the tube with a *clean* towel or in an oven. Alternatively, the tube can be rinsed with three separate portions of 16 M HNO_3. Use about 5 drops each time, make sure that it wets all the inner wall of the tube, and remove each portion with a pipet *as completely as possible.*

CAUTION: 16 M HNO_3 is very corrosive. It will produce a yellow stain on skin that takes about a week to wear (or peel) off. Flood with water all spills of nitric acid, whether on the skin or on the desk.

13. Strontium nitrate tends to supersaturate. Stirring, rubbing, and standing are the usual techniques of coping with supersaturation. Cooling also helps, not because the solubility is appreciably decreased, but because the supersaturated solution becomes more unstable.

14. Strontium sulfate also tends to supersaturate. Allow at least 5 minutes for it to form.

15. The sulfate must be transposed to the carbonate and then dissolved in hydrochloric acid. Remove the solution above the precipitate, and treat the latter with $(NH_4)_2CO_3$ solution. Stir up the cake and warm briefly. Centrifuge and wash the precipitate several times to remove sulfate. Dissolve it in a few drops of 12 M HCl and do the flame test (Introductory Experiment 5).

16. Since 10 drops of 16 M HNO_3 were used in the separation of $Sr(NO_3)_2$, it will take about this much 15 M NH_3 for the neutralization. The nitric acid was diluted with water to make the reaction less violent.

EXERCISES

20-1. Name the ions of this group, tell why they occur together, and place them in the Periodic Table.

20-2. Arrange the hydroxides of Periodic Group IIA in order of decreasing solubility. Why does beryllium hydroxide precipitate with Cation Group 3? Why is magnesium a member of Group 5?

20-3. It takes almost as much energy to remove one electron from a beryllium atom as to remove two from a barium atom. Yet both elements occur as Me^{++} ions. Explain.

20-4. What are some consequences of the smaller size and higher charge of Ca^{++} as compared with K^+?

20-5. In what respects does Ca resemble K more closely than it does Cr, Fe, or Zn?

20-6. Cite evidence to support the assertion that calcium ions exert a stronger attraction for molecules or anions than barium ions do.

20-7. Predict the direction of the following reactions if all ions are at approximately equal concentrations.

(a) $Sr(OH)_2 \cdot 8H_2O \downarrow + 2F^- \rightleftharpoons SrF_2 \downarrow + 2OH^- + 8H_2O$
(b) $BaSO_4 \downarrow + 2F^- \rightleftharpoons BaF_2 \downarrow + SO_4^{--}$
(c) $CaCO_3 \downarrow + SO_4^{--} + 2H_2O \rightleftharpoons CaSO_4 \cdot 2H_2O \downarrow + CO_3^{--}$
(d) $CaCrO_4 \cdot 2H_2O \downarrow + Ba^{++} \rightleftharpoons BaCrO_4 \downarrow + Ca^{++} + 2H_2O$

20-8. Arrange the following compounds in order of decreasing concentration of Sr^{++} in their saturated solutions

$$SrSO_4, \; Sr(NO_3)_2, \; SrCrO_4, \; SrCO_3, \; SrC_2O_4 \cdot H_2O$$

20-9. Account for the fact that the ions of this group form soluble chlorides but insoluble fluorides, soluble nitrates but insoluble carbonates.

20-10. Which of these pairs will react in dilute solutions? Write equations for those that do: (a) sodium hydroxide and barium chloride, (b) strontium nitrate and disodium hydrogen phosphate, (c) barium sulfate and hydrochloric acid, (d) normal calcium phosphate and nitric acid, (e) calcium hydroxide and sulfur dioxide.

20-11. The ammine $Ca(NH_3)_6Cl_2$ can be made by reaction between dry calcium chloride and ammonia gas. If calcium forms stronger bonds to oxygen than to nitrogen, what would you expect to happen when the solid ammine is dissolved in water?

20-12. Account for the fact that calcium carbonate will dissolve in nitric acid and carbonic acid but not in hydrocyanic acid.

20-13. Write an equation for the proton transfer reaction between ammonium and carbonate ions. What is the effect on this equilibrium of (a) addition of ammonium nitrate, (b) addition of ammonia, (c) heat?

20-14. Explain why a combination of ammonium chloride and ammonia is used along with ammonium carbonate to precipitate Group 4.

20-15. Explain why barium is separated as the chromate rather than as the sulfate although the latter is more insoluble.

20-16. Write equations for the following transformations. More than one step may be required. (a) $SrSO_4 \rightarrow SrS$, (b) $SrSO_4 \rightarrow SrCl_2$, (c) $SrSO_4 \rightarrow SrCO_3$.

20-17. Explain how the concentration of chromate ion can be controlled by a mixture of ammonium acetate and acetic acid.

20-18. In the precipitation of barium chromate what harm would result if acetic acid were replaced by (a) hydrochloric acid, (b) ammonia?

20-19. Write equations for the successive reactions of the ions of this group (Sec. 20-14).

20-20. What reagent or combination of reagents would you use to separate in one step the members of each pair? (a) $Ba^{++} - Ca^{++}$, (b) $Sr^{++} - Mg^{++}$, (c) $Sr(NO_3)_2 - Ca(NO_3)_2$, (d) $Sr^{++} - Ba^{++}$, (e) $Ag^+ - Ba^{++}$, (f) $Sr^{++} - Ca^{++}$, (g) $BaCrO_4 - CaCrO_4$, (h) $Cu^{++} - Ca^{++}$, (i) $Zn^{++} - Sr^{++}$.

20-21. Explain why each of the following is done in the systematic analysis: (a) Triethanolamine is present during precipitation of $SrSO_4$. (b) Ammonium salts are removed before precipitation of the group. (c) The group is precipitated with ammonium carbonate, but sodium carbonate is used to precipitate $SrCO_3$ and $CaCO_3$ after removal of barium. (d) During precipitation of the group the mixture is warmed very briefly. (e) Dry equipment is used in precipitating $Sr(NO_3)_2$. (f) Barium sulfate is precipitated with sulfamic acid, but strontium sulfate is precipitated with ammonium sulfate. (g) ammonium carbonate, rather than sodium carbonate, is used to transpose the $SrSO_4$ before the flame test for Sr. (h) A freshly prepared solution of sodium carbonate is used to precipitate the carbonates of Sr and Ca. (i) The solution is heated when $BaSO_4$ is precipitated.

20-22. What difficulties would result if (a) the group precipitate were dissolved in HCl; (b) ammonium salts were not removed before precipitation of the group; (c) sodium carbonate were used to precipitate the group; (d) ammonia were not added in precipitation of the group?

CHAPTER TWENTY-ONE

Cation Group 5
The Soluble Group
Na^+, K^+, Mg^{++}, NH_4^+

IA	IIA		
3 Li			
11 **Na**	12 **Mg**		
19 **K**			
37 Rb			
55 Cs			
87 Fr			

21-1. Introduction.[1] The ions of this analytical group are left in solution after separation of all the other cations (see block diagram in Sec. 16-1). The position in the Periodic Table of the three metals and of the less common members of the Soluble Group are shown at the right.

THE PROPERTIES OF THE METALS AND IONS

21-2. The Alkali Metals and Their Ions. Although sodium and potassium are the only members of this family included in the analytical scheme, it is instructive to consider their behavior in relation to that of the whole family.

a. Electronic Structures and Oxidation States. Atoms of these elements have a single valence electron and readily lose this to expose a kernel with the electronic structure of an inert gas: 2 electrons in Li^+ as in He; 8 outer electrons in the rest of the ions. The energy required to remove the valence electron of isolated sodium atoms, the *first ionization potential*, is 118.4 kcal/g-atom, whereas removal of the second electron to give Na^{++} ions requires about nine times as much energy. Because of this, compounds of sodium are restricted to those containing Na^+ ions. The other alkali metals are likewise univalent. The first ionization potential is largest for lithium (124.3 kcal/g-atom) and smallest for cesium (89.8); that for francium is not

[1]See Sec. 16-6 for a description of the general plan of this chapter.

known. The latter has atoms with the highest nuclear charge, but it has the most inner shells of electrons to screen off this charge from the valence electrons.

b. The Metals.   Atoms of the metals are bonded together in crystals by partial sharing of valence electrons. Because each atom has only one and holds it loosely, the bonds between atoms in the crystals are weak. These metals have unusually low melting points and high conductivities. The hardest, lithium, is as soft as talc; the others are as soft as wax. The metals are active reducing agents because they lose their valence electrons easily, e.g.,

$$2Na \rightarrow 2Na^+ + 2e^-$$

$$2e^- + 2H_2O \rightarrow H_2 + 2OH^-$$

$$\overline{}$$

$$2Na + 2H_2O \rightarrow H_2 + 2Na^+ + 2OH^-$$

The reaction with water is vigorous. They form salt-like hydrides such as Na^+H^- and many other typically ionic compounds. They burn in air to give several types of oxides: normal (Li_2O), peroxide (Na_2O_2), and superoxide (KO_2, RbO_2, and CsO_2).

c. The Ions.   These are smaller than the atoms, for loss of the valence electron permits the nucleus to act more effectively on those that remain.

	Element					
	Li	Na	K	Rb	Cs	Fr
Atomic radius, A	1.23	1.57	2.03	2.16	2.35	
Ionic radius, A	0.68	0.98	1.33	1.48	1.67	(1.75)

Each cation is the largest in its period. Their comparatively large size, low charge, and inert gas structure allow them to exert only weak attraction on other ions or molecules. Complexes containing these ions are therefore very rare. In aqueous solution they attract the oxygen end of water molecules and become hydrated. The lithium ion, which is the smallest, is the most highly hydrated.

d. The Compounds.   The solids are ionic crystals. Lithium and, to a lesser extent, sodium salts are frequently hydrated, e.g., $LiClO_4 \cdot 3H_2O$, $NaI \cdot 2H_2O$, $Na_2SO_4 \cdot 10H_2O$. Addition of water to any of these ionic crystals causes a separation of the ions, their hydration, and their dispersal in the solvent. In solution the compounds are strong electrolytes. The halides are completely ionized at all concentrations. Although molecules do not exist in solution, loose ion-pairs may form between these cations and highly charged anions, e.g., $NaSO_4^-$ and $KFe(CN)_6^{---}$, in concentrated solutions. Sodium and potassium salts of strong acids give neutral solutions. Salts of polyprotic acids may give an acid solution if the anion can lose a proton:

$$Na^+ + HSO_4^- \rightleftharpoons Na^+ + H^+ + SO_4^{--}$$

$$K^+ + H_2PO_4^- \rightleftharpoons K^+ + H^+ + HPO_4^{--}$$

or a basic solution if the anion can remove a proton from a water molecule:

$$2K^+ + S^{--} + H_2O \rightleftharpoons 2K^+ + OH^- + HS^-$$

$$Na^+ + C_2H_3O_2^- + H_2O \rightleftharpoons Na^+ + OH^- + HC_2H_3O_2$$

These are proton transfer reactions.

The compounds of the alkali metals are colorless unless the anion is colored, e.g., Na_2CrO_4, yellow; $KMnO_4$, purple. Color is associated with absorption of light energy by ions. The energy is used principally to change their electronic motions. Visible light does not carry sufficient energy to disturb the stable electronic arrangements of the alkali metal ions and is not affected by them.

e. Solubilities.   Almost all of the compounds of the alkali metals are comparatively soluble. The attraction between these large, low-charged ions in the crystals is not sufficiently strong to resist disruption of the crystals by water. The solubilities of many of the salts, particularly those of weak acids, increase from the lithium compound to the cesium. This is attributable to a decrease in stability of the crystals as the size of the cation increases. Crystals containing bulky anions such as ClO_4^-, $PtCl_6^{--}$, and $Co(NO_2)_6^{---}$ are all comparatively weak; the sodium and lithium compounds are then the most soluble because hydration stabilizes these ions in solution. In several series of compounds the changes in solubility are irregular because of the interplay of crystal stability and hydration.

Most of the chemical reactions of the compounds of the alkali metals are attributable to the anions, e.g.,

$$2Na^+ + CO_3^{--} + 2H^+ + 2Cl^- \rightarrow 2Na^+ + 2Cl^- + H_2O + CO_2\uparrow$$

The cations form no molecules and do not usually give precipitates. Some of the rare precipitation reactions are used in analysis and are described in the next sections.

21-3. Detection of Sodium.   The principal slightly soluble compounds are the antimonate $NaSb(OH)_6$ and triple acetates of the type $NaMe(UO_2)_3(C_2H_3O_2)_9\cdot9H_2O$ where Me can be Mg, Zn, or Cu. The magnesium compound is used in the procedure given in this text. The precipitate is bulky, an advantage when only a small amount of sodium has to be detected; 100 mg of the precipitate is obtained from only 1.53 mg of sodium.

The precipitate is fairly soluble and careful control of conditions is required. Even at best precipitation will occur only when the concentration of sodium exceeds 0.7 mg/ml. The loss of sodium because of the solubility of the precipitate can be decreased by keeping low the volume of solution under test and adding an excess of reagent. The latter is a mixture of magnesium acetate, uranyl acetate, and acetic acid saturated with the sodium compound. The ions that interfere with this test are (1) H^+ from strong acid, for it consumes acetate ion to give molecular acetic acid. (2) K^+ if present at a concentration much larger than 50 mg/ml. The precipitate is paler than that with sodium. Li^+, Ag^+, Hg^{++}, and Sr^{++} also form precipitates. (3) Bi^{+++}, Sb^{+++}, and $Sn(IV)$, which hydrolyze to give precipitates in weakly acid solutions. (4) PO_4^{---}, AsO_4^{---}, OH^- from strong base, and other anions which form precipitates with uranium.

Sodium gives a characteristic, persistent yellow flame test caused by emission of light of wave lengths 5890 and 5896 A. This test is too sensitive to be used by itself. Even traces of sodium give a strong yellow coloration to the flame. If the test is used to corroborate the precipitation reaction, its validity must be checked by comparison with flame tests obtained from samples of known concentration. Sodium can be determined quantitatively in a flame photometer. A solution of the sample is sprayed into a flame of constant characteristics, and the intensity of the yellow light is measured photoelectrically and compared with that of solutions of known concentration.

21-4. Detection of Potassium. Slightly soluble potassium compounds include the perchlorate, $KClO_4$, the chloroplatinate, K_2PtCl_6, the cobaltinitrite [or hexanitrocobaltate(III)], $K_2NaCo(NO_2)_6 \cdot H_2O$, and the tetraphenylboron compound, $KB(C_6H_5)_4$. The last one is the least soluble, but the cobaltinitrite is more suitable for introductory work. Its saturated solution is about 0.001 M, and as little as 0.02 mg K/ml can be detected. The composition of the precipitate varies somewhat with temperature and concentration. There are a number of interfering ions. (1) NH_4^+ forms a similar precipitate. (2) H^+ from strong acid decomposes the reagent. Nitrite is converted to oxides of nitrogen $3NO_2^- + 2H^+ \rightarrow 2NO + NO_3^- + H_2O$; $2NO + O_2 \rightarrow 2NO_2$ and Co(III) is reduced to pink Co^{++}. (3) OH^- from strong base precipitates black $Co(OH)_3$. (4) Oxidizing and reducing agents destroy the reagent. (5) Readily hydrolyzable ions give precipitates in the weakly acid solution.

Potassium gives a brief violet flame color, easily masked by sodium, caused by emission of light of wave lengths 4045 A (violet) and 7665 and 7699 A (red). Cobalt glass can be used to block the yellow sodium light and permit the potassium flame color to be observed. The variation of transmittancy of cobalt glass with wave length of light is shown in Fig. 21-1. The glass transmits light only at the ends of the visible portion of the spectrum and these are the very regions in which the spectral lines of the potassium flame color lie.

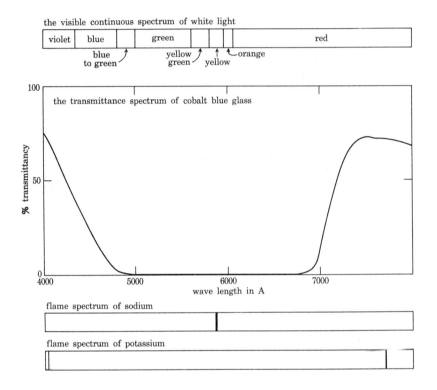

FIG. 21-1. The transmittance spectrum of cobalt blue glass. The glass is opaque to light with wave lengths between 5000 and 6700 A. At 4000 A two thicknesses of blue glass transmit 75% as much light as the same thickness of clear glass. The colors of the visible spectrum and the lines in the flame spectra of sodium and potassium are given on the same wave length scale. A similar curve is given by R. Hahn, *J. Chem. Educ.*, **27**, 597 (1950).

21-5. The Properties of Magnesium Metal and its Ion.

a. Relation of Magnesium to the Alkaline Earth Metals and Lithium. Magnesium is a member of Periodic Group IIA but stands apart in its behavior from both beryllium, the first member, and calcium, strontium, and barium. It differs from the latter in forming an insoluble hydroxide, moderately soluble oxalate and chromate, and very soluble sulfate. The resemblance between magnesium and lithium is noteworthy. Like lithium, but unlike the other alkali metals, magnesium metal has a comparatively high melting point. It forms the stable nitride Mg_3N_2 similar to Li_3N, whereas sodium gives only an amide $NaNH_2$. Its chloride, bromide, and iodide are very soluble; its fluoride is only slightly soluble. Its carbonate and phosphate are moderately insoluble, and its perchlorate, like lithium perchlorate, is remarkably soluble in organic solvents such as alcohols, ethers, acetone, and ethyl acetate. The first member of a main group in the Periodic Table often shows a strong resemblance to the second member of the next group: lithium with magnesium, beryllium with aluminum, and boron with silicon.

b. Electronic Structure of Magnesium. Magnesium atoms have two valence electrons in the third or M shell. The first ionization potential is 176.3 kcal/g-atom, the second 346.6, and the third (to give Mg^{+++}) 1803. The energy required to produce Mg^{+++} is so large that its compounds are unknown. The Mg^{++} and Na^+ ions have the same electronic structure, but because of its larger nuclear charge the Mg^{++} has about the same radius as the Li^+, namely 0.65 A. The similarity in ionic radii is partially responsible for the resemblance of lithium and magnesium. Because of the stability of the electronic arrangement in Mg^{++}, magnesium compounds give no flame test and are colorless unless the anion is colored.

c. Magnesium Metal. Magnesium is a more active metal than aluminum but less active than sodium. Although it is active enough to liberate hydrogen from water, it can be protected by surface films. The ion is reduced to the metal with difficulty, the usual methods being electrolytic reduction of the fused chloride and reduction of the oxide with silicon at high temperature.

d. Complexes of Magnesium. Because of its high charge and small size, Mg^{++} ion forms a number of complexes. Most of these have Mg—O bonds, but none are particularly stable or of use in qualitative analysis. Complex compounds with Mg—N bonds are still less common. The reaction of gaseous ammonia with solid magnesium chloride gives compounds of the type $MgCl_2 \cdot xNH_3$ where x can be 2, 4, or 6. The combination is loose and is broken by water. The chlorophylls are very stable and important compounds in which a Mg^{++} ion is bonded to four nitrogen atoms which are part of an organic molecule.

e. Compounds of Magnesium. All of the salts are highly ionized with the probable exception of magnesium oxalate. The ionization of $Mg(OH)_2$ to $MgOH^+$ and OH^- is complete, but that of $MgOH^+$ to Mg^{++} and OH^- is not. The double charge on Mg^{++} causes it to attract negative ions more strongly than Li^+ does. This is illustrated by the data in Table 21-1. The four ions Mg^{++}, Na^+, F^-, and O^{--} all have the same electronic structure but differ in nuclear charge. Lithium fluoride is included because of the close similarity in ionic radii of Li^+ and Mg^{++}. The strikingly different properties of MgO are consequences of the strong forces between doubly charged ions.

The magnesium ion also has a strong attraction for water, as shown by the fact that many soluble magnesium salts are highly hydrated, e.g.,

$MgCl_2 \cdot 6H_2O$, $MgSO_4 \cdot 7H_2O$ (epsom salt), and $Mg(NO_3)_2 \cdot 6H_2O$. The number of water molecules per formula usually varies with temperature; $MgSO_4 \cdot 7H_2O$, for example, is stable between 1.8 and 48.3° while other hydrates having 1, 6, and 12 H_2O are stable in other ranges of temperature. Hydration promotes solubility unless counteracted by strong bonds in the crystal. The chloride, bromide, iodide, sulfate, nitrate, and chromate are all soluble salts, whereas the fluoride in which magnesium ion is strongly bonded to small fluoride ions is moderately insoluble.

TABLE 21-1.

The Effect of Ionic Charge on Properties

Property	MgO	NaF	LiF
Melting point, °C	2800	992	870
Hardness, Moh's scale*	6.5	3.2	3.3
Density, g/cc	3.7	2.8	2.3
Solubility, g/100 g H_2O	0.002	4	0.13
Lattice energy, kcal/mole†	−940	−215	−240
Cation-anion distance, A	2.10	2.31	2.01

*An empirical scale in which talc has a hardness of 1 and diamond a hardness of 10.
†Energy released when a crystal is formed from the gaseous ions (Sec. 5-3). A large negative value corresponds to a stable crystal.

f. Reactions of Mg^{++} ion. The formation of precipitates is the most common type of reaction of this ion. The most common slightly soluble compounds are the hydroxide, the basic carbonate, and the phosphates.

(1) The white, gelatinous hydroxide is precipitated from solutions of magnesium salts by addition of a strong base or ammonia. The first precipitate forms when the concentration of hydroxide ion exceeds about 0.00003 M, which is larger than that required to precipitate most insoluble hydroxides. Like many gelatinous hydroxides, it is contaminated with other ions from the solution but becomes purer and less soluble as it ages. Magnesium hydroxide is not precipitated completely by ammonia and is not precipitated at all by a combination of ammonia and an ammonium salt. The ammonium ions repress the ionization of ammonia and drive the equilibrium

$$2NH_4^+ + Mg(OH)_2 \downarrow \rightleftharpoons Mg^{++} + 2NH_3 + 2H_2O$$

to the right.

(2) The normal carbonate $MgCO_3$ occurs as the mineral magnesite and in association with $CaCO_3$ as the mineral dolomite. It cannot be precipitated unless the solution contains considerable carbon dioxide. Sodium and potassium carbonates give strongly alkaline solutions because of the reaction

$$CO_3^{--} + H_2O \rightleftharpoons HCO_3^- + OH^-$$

and they precipitate a basic carbonate $Mg_5(OH)_2(CO_3)_4\cdot 5H_2O$, a gelatinous white precipitate like $Mg(OH)_2$ readily soluble in acids. The combination of ammonium carbonate and ammonium chloride furnishes too low a concentration of carbonate ion to precipitate $MgCO_3$ because the equilibrium $NH_4^+ + CO_3^{--} \rightleftharpoons NH_3 + HCO_3^-$ is shifted to the right by an excess of ammonium ion. When alcohol is added, the double carbonate $Mg(NH_4)_2(CO_3)_2\cdot 4H_2O$ can be precipitated.

(3) The acid phosphate $MgHPO_4$ is obtained by addition of Na_2HPO_4 to solutions of magnesium salts. The normal phosphate $Mg_3(PO_4)_2$ precipitates only in strongly alkaline solutions. In the presence of ammonia and ammonium salts, magnesium ammonium phosphate is formed:

$$Mg^{++} + NH_4^+ + PO_4^{---} + 6H_2O \rightarrow MgNH_4PO_4\cdot 6H_2O \downarrow$$

This is the best of the precipitation reactions for the separation of magnesium because the precipitate is crystalline, hence purer than the gelatinous compounds, and is the least soluble of the common compounds of magnesium. A saturated solution of this salt at $25°$ contains only 0.078 mg of salt per ml or the equivalent of 0.0136 mg Mg/ml. It readily dissolves in acids because of removal of phosphate ion to form weakly dissociated HPO_4^{--} and $H_2PO_4^-$ ions.

(4) Hydrolysis of magnesium salts

$$Mg^{++} + H_2O \rightleftharpoons MgOH^+ + H^+$$

is usually weak and unimportant, because $MgOH^+$ is highly, though not completely, dissociated. Under exceptional conditions it can be driven to completion. When magnesium sulfide prepared by direct union of the elements is added to water, complete hydrolysis occurs:

$$MgS + 2H_2O \rightarrow Mg(OH)_2 \downarrow + H_2S \uparrow$$

because of the removal of sulfide as gaseous hydrogen sulfide and of magnesium as the insoluble hydroxide. Magnesium sulfide cannot be precipitated from aqueous solution. Hydrolysis also becomes important when moist magnesium chloride is heated. Hydrogen chloride is driven off and a basic chloride is precipitated:

$$2Mg^{++} + 4Cl^- + 7H_2O \rightleftharpoons 3HCl \uparrow + Mg_2(OH)_3Cl\cdot 4H_2O \downarrow$$

The residue is only partially soluble in water, but addition of hydrochloric acid reverses the reaction and brings the basic salt into solution.

21-6. Separation and Detection of Magnesium.

a. Magnesium is almost always separated as magnesium ammonium phosphate. The conditions that must be established for a successful separation are

(1) Absence of other ions precipitated by OH^- or PO_4^{---}. These are usually removed in the precipitation of Groups 1 to 4 before separation of

magnesium. Traces of calcium, strontium, and barium that escape precipitation with Group 4 are removed by addition of ammonium oxalate and ammonium sulfate:

$$Ca^{++} + C_2O_4^{--} \rightarrow CaC_2O_4 \downarrow$$
$$Sr^{++} + SO_4^{--} \rightarrow SrSO_4 \downarrow$$
$$Ba^{++} + SO_4^{--} \rightarrow BaSO_4 \downarrow$$

(2) Presence of ammonia. This neutralizes the hydrogen phosphate ion:

$$NH_3 + HPO_4^{--} \rightleftharpoons NH_4^+ + PO_4^{---}$$

and ensures a high enough concentration of PO_4^{---} to give the precipitate.

(3) Presence of ammonium salts. The ammonium ion is not only required for the precipitate itself but also represses the ionization of ammonia

$$NH_3 + H_2O \rightleftharpoons NH_4^+ + OH^-$$

so that insufficient concentration of hydroxide ion is present to precipitate magnesium hydroxide.

(4) Precautions to overcome supersaturation. The precipitate is slow to form. Crystallization is induced by rubbing the inner walls of the vessel with a rod and by stirring.

b. The identification of magnesium is based on formation of a "lake," a precipitate of magnesium hydroxide colored by an adsorbed dye. The two dyes most commonly used are Titan Yellow, which gives a red lake, and S. and O. reagent [paranitrobenzeneazoresorcinol, $(HO)_2C_6H_3N = NC_6H_4NO_2$ (named after Suitzu and Okuma, who investigated its behavior)], which gives a blue lake. As little as 0.002 mg of magnesium can be detected by use of the latter. The conditions of the test are

(1) Absence of other elements that form insoluble hydroxides. This condition will be satisfied if magnesium is precipitated as $MgNH_4PO_4$ after the separation of Groups 1 to 4.

(2) Absence of a large amount of ammonium salts. Precipitation of magnesium hydroxide is suppressed by ammonium salts unless a large excess of sodium hydroxide is added.

21-7. Properties of the Ammonium Ion.

a. Structure of NH_4^+. The ammonium ion is formed by adding a proton to an ammonia molecule. Its structure is shown in Fig. 21-2. Since the ammonium ion contains 10 electrons and a total of 11 protons in the nuclei, the ion as a whole is positively charged. It is roughly spherical with a radius of 1.43 A, intermediate between those of potassium (1.33) and rubidium (1.48) ions. Its salts resemble those of potassium in solubility and must be removed before the detection of potassium.

b. Compounds of NH₄⁺. Crystals of the salts are built from ammonium ions and anions. A pronounced cooling effect is often noted when ammonium salts are dissolved in water; the heat is absorbed to break apart the crystal lattice. In solution the salts are completely dissociated but ion-pair formation can occur, e.g., $NH_4^+SO_4^{--}$ in ammonium sulfate solutions.

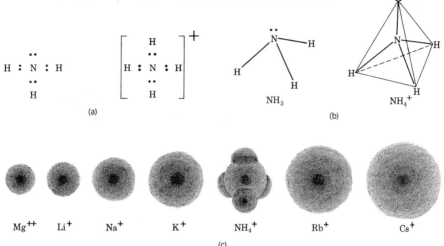

(a)

(b)

(c)

FIG. 21-2. The structure of ammonia and the ammonium ion. (a) Electron dot formulas. (b) Geometrical arrangement of the bonds. (c) The size of the ammonium ion compared with those of related ions.

c. Reactions of the Ammonium Ion.

(1) Precipitation is confined to formation of compounds such as the cobaltinitrite $(NH_4)_2NaCo(NO_2)_6$ and chloroplatinate $(NH_4)_2PtCl_6$. Most ammonium salts are very soluble.

(2) Proton transfer reactions can occur in which the ammonium ion is converted to molecular ammonia. Proton acceptors include, in order of increasing strength, water, acetate ion, carbonate ion, sulfide ion, and hydroxide ion:

$$NH_4^+ + H_2O \rightleftharpoons NH_3 + H_3O^+ \qquad 0.008\%$$
$$NH_4^+ + C_2H_3O_2^- \rightleftharpoons NH_3 + HC_2H_3O_2 \qquad 0.6\%$$
$$NH_4^+ + CO_3^{--} \rightleftharpoons NH_3 + HCO_3^- \qquad 47\%$$
$$NH_4^+ + S^{--} \rightleftharpoons NH_3 + HS^- \qquad 50\%$$
$$NH_4^+ + OH^- \rightleftharpoons NH_3 + H_2O \qquad 99\%$$

The percentages show the extent of conversion of ammonium ion to ammonia when the ions on the left are combined at 0.1 *M* concentration. The first four equations when read from left to right represent the hydrolysis reactions of the salts. When read from right to left they represent neutralization reactions that can be used to prepare solutions of the salts.

(3) Thermal decomposition of ammonium salts usually starts below $350°$. In one type of decomposition transfer of a proton occurs and ammonia gas is one product:

$$NH_4Cl(s) \quad \overset{\Delta}{\rightleftharpoons} NH_3\uparrow + HCl\uparrow$$

$$(NH_4)_2SO_4(s) \overset{\Delta}{\rightleftharpoons} 2NH_3\uparrow + SO_3\uparrow + H_2O\uparrow$$

$$(NH_4)_2CO_3(s) \overset{\Delta}{\rightleftharpoons} 2NH_3\uparrow + CO_2\uparrow + H_2O\uparrow$$

For salts such as ammonium carbonate or ammonium sulfide the decomposition can occur to a considerable extent in hot aqueous solution. The proton transfer is reversible in all of these; thus if the acidic and basic products come together at low temperature they can reunite. If the anion of the salt is an oxidizing agent, an irreversible decomposition can occur:

$$NH_4^+ + NO_2^- \rightarrow N_2\uparrow + 2H_2O \quad \text{(in solution)}$$

$$NH_4NO_3(s) \quad \rightarrow N_2O\uparrow + 2H_2O\uparrow$$

$$(NH_4)_2Cr_2O_7(s) \rightarrow N_2\uparrow + Cr_2O_3(s) + 4H_2O\uparrow$$

(4) Oxidation of ammonium ions generally produces nitrogen. Ammonium salts can be removed by evaporation with nitric acid:

$$4H^+ + 6NO_3^- + 2NH_4^+ \rightarrow N_2\uparrow + 6NO_2\uparrow + 6H_2O$$

21-8. Detection of Ammonium Ion.   The ammonium ion is converted to volatile ammonia by an excess of a strong base:

$$NH_4^+ + OH^- \rightarrow NH_3\uparrow + H_2O$$

The liberated ammonia can be detected in various ways. When it is absorbed by moist red litmus paper, the above reaction reverses to a sufficient extent to turn the litmus blue. The odor of ammonia can also be used for its detection, but this is not as sensitive a test as the litmus reaction. A yellow to brown coloration or precipitate is produced by ammonia with Nessler's reagent, a solution of mercury(II) iodide in excess potassium iodide and potassium hydroxide:

$$2HgI_4^{--} + 3OH^- + NH_3 \rightarrow 7I^- + 2H_2O + [OHg_2NH_2]I\downarrow$$

This is a very sensitive test.

The ammonium ion must be detected on the original sample because ammonia and ammonium salts are used as group reagents and the solution from which Groups 1 to 4 have been separated will inevitably contain large quantities of ammonium ion.

21-9. Cross References.   A number of sections in the theoretical part of the text deal with subjects more briefly mentioned in this chapter. These references are collected here for your convenience; it is not necessary that you read most or all of them at this time.

Sec. 2-6 (ionic crystals)
Sec. 2-7 (electronic structure of ions)
Sec. 2-8 (ionic radii)
Sec. 2-10 [layer lattices as in $Mg(OH)_2$]
Sec. 2-16 (equilibrium)
Sec. 2-18 (ion-pairs)
Sec. 2-19 (hydration of ions)
Sec. 2-22 (nature of bases in solution)
Sec. 2-23 (nature of salts in solution)
Sec. 3-3 (summary of solubilities)
Sec. 3-8 (proton transfer reactions)
Sec. 5-3 (lattice energy)
Sec. 5-5 (color and electronic structure)
Sec. 5-6 (hydration of ions)
Sec. 5-7 (solubility related to structure)
Sec. 6-8 (lakes and chelates)
Sec. 6-10 (relation of charge and radius to complex formation)
Sec. 11-6 (hydrolysis)
Sec. 12-8 [buffer action and precipitation of $Mg(OH)_2$]

21-10. The Successive Reactions of the Ions of Cation Group 5. Rules for writing formulas are given in Sec. 3-5.

Ammonium Ion

1. Identification. Reagents: sodium hydroxide and moist red litmus paper.

(a) In the crucible or beaker: $NH_4^+ + OH^- \rightarrow NH_3 \uparrow + H_2O$
(b) On the litmus paper: $NH_3 + H_2O \rightarrow NH_4^+ + OH^-$

2. Removal of ammonium salts before analysis of Groups 4 and 5. Reagent: nitric acid. Strong heating of solid residue.

$$4H^+ + 2NH_4^+ + 6NO_3^- \rightarrow N_2 \uparrow + 6NO_2 \uparrow + 6H_2O$$
$$NH_4Cl(s) \rightleftharpoons NH_3 \uparrow + HCl \uparrow$$
$$(NH_4)_2SO_4(s) \rightleftharpoons 2NH_3 \uparrow + SO_3 \uparrow + H_2O \uparrow$$
$$2NH_4^+ + CO_3^{--} \rightarrow 2NH_3 \uparrow + CO_2 \uparrow + H_2O$$
$$2NH_4^+ + S^{--} \rightarrow 2NH_3 \uparrow + H_2S \uparrow$$
$$(NH_4)_2C_2O_4(s) \rightarrow 2NH_3 \uparrow + CO \uparrow + CO_2 \uparrow + H_2O \uparrow$$

3. In the potassium test. Reagent: sodium cobaltinitrite.

$$NH_4^+ + NO_2^- \rightarrow N_2 \uparrow + 2H_2O$$
$$2NH_4^+ + Na^+ + Co(NO_2)_6^{---} \rightarrow (NH_4)_2NaCo(NO_2)_6 \downarrow$$

When heated, this decomposes; Co(III) is reduced to Co^{++} ion and NH_4^+ ions are oxidized to N_2.

Magnesium Ion

1. Separation. Reagents: ammonium chloride, ammonia, and disodium hydrogen phosphate.

$$Mg^{++} + NH_4^+ + PO_4^{---} + 6H_2O \rightarrow MgNH_4PO_4 \cdot 6H_2O \downarrow$$

2. Dissolution of the precipitate. Reagent: hydrochloric acid.

$$MgNH_4PO_4 \cdot 6H_2O \downarrow + 2H^+ \rightarrow Mg^{++} + NH_4^+ + H_2PO_4^- + 6H_2O$$

3. Identification. Reagents: sodium hydroxide and S. and O. reagent (p-nitrobenzeneazoresorcinol).

$$Mg^{++} + 2OH^- \rightarrow Mg(OH)_2 \downarrow$$

The dye is adsorbed on the precipitate to give a blue lake.

Potassium Ion

Identification. Reagent: sodium cobaltinitrite.

$$2K^+ + Na^+ + Co(NO_2)_6^{---} \rightarrow K_2NaCo(NO_2)_6 \downarrow$$

Sodium Ion

Identification. Reagent: uranyl magnesium acetate.

$$Na^+ + Mg^{++} + 3UO_2^{++} + 9C_2H_3O_2^- + 9H_2O$$
$$\rightarrow NaMg(UO_2)_3(C_2H_3O_2)_9 \cdot 9H_2O \downarrow$$

EXPERIMENTAL PART

21-11. Introductory Experiments. These experiments are designed to draw your attention to important reactions, techniques, and sources of difficulty in the analysis. Consult the earlier sections of the chapter for discussion and equations. See Sec. 16-5 concerning the record that should be kept of these experiments. The record should include a chemical equation for every reaction.

1. Sensitivity of the sodium test. Prepare from the standard solution[2] of Na^+ (side shelf) a solution that contains 1 mg of Na^+/ml. Start with 1 drop of standard solution, add the required number of drops of water,[3] and mix well (T-5, Sec. 16-3). With 1 drop of this solution prepare another containing 0.1 mg of Na^+/ml. In three separate test tubes take 1 drop each of the

[2]The standard solutions of the ions contain 10 mg of ion/ml.
[3]Always use distilled water in all analytical experiments.

standard solution and the two more dilute solutions and add to each 3 or 4 drops of magnesium uranyl acetate reagent. Stir and rub the inner walls of each tube with a glass rod; set the tubes aside for five minutes. How many mg of Na^+ were taken in each tube (assume 20 drops/ml)? What conclusion can you draw from these experiments regarding the sensitivity of the test?

2. Behavior of K^+ with the sodium reagent. Test the effect of the magnesium uranyl acetate reagent on 1 drop of standard solution of K^+. Half fill a depression of the spot plate with solid potassium chloride and stir it for a minute or two with a few drops of water. Withdraw a drop of the concentrated solution to a test tube and test the action of the reagent on it.

3. Stability of sodium cobaltinitrite reagent. Add 1 drop of the reagent to each of two depressions in the white spot plate. To one add a drop of 6 M HCl, to the other a drop of 6 M NaOH. Cautiously smell the acid mixture and note its color after it has stood for five minutes. Identify the compounds that are formed in each reaction. How should the potassium test be carried out to avoid these difficulties?

4. Properties of potassium and ammonium cobaltinitrites. Add 3 or 4 drops of the reagent to single drops of the standard solutions of potassium and ammonium ions in separate test tubes. Describe the results and write equations for the reactions. Warm each tube in a boiling water bath for five minutes. Cool and add more reagent. If both tubes still contain considerable precipitate, warm a second time. Account for the decrease in bulk of one of the precipitates.

5. Flame tests. Clean a platinum or Nichrome wire by dipping it in a little 12 M HCl in a test tube and holding it in a flame.[4] Repeat until the wire ceases to color the flame (the wire itself will be red-hot). Touch the wire while hot to some solid potassium chloride or carbonate and bring it again into the flame. Note the flame color first as viewed directly and then as seen through two thicknesses of cobalt blue glass. Mix a few crystals of sodium and potassium chlorides in a depression of the spot plate and carry out the flame test on this mixture. Try the effect of one and then two thicknesses of the cobalt glass. Compare the intensity and persistency of the two flame colors. Clean the wire thoroughly and try the flame test on a solution that contains potassium and sodium, each at a concentration of 0.1 mg/ml. Prepare this by mixing 1 drop each of the standard solutions with 1 ml of 6 M HCl and 4 ml of water in a small beaker. Look for the potassium color as soon as the wire is inserted in the flame. Clean the wire, draw it between your fingers after it cools, and observe the flame color. What conclusions do you draw from these experiments?

[4]The platinum wire should be sealed into a glass rod or tube which can be used as a handle. One end of the Nichrome wire can be thrust into a cork.

6. Magnesium hydroxide and magnesium ammonium phosphate.

(a) Prepare small portions of these precipitates. Start with about 1 drop of the standard solution of Mg^{++} (side shelf). Record in your notes the reagents you used; they are in the kit. Magnesium hydroxide is generally described as "gelatinous" and the other compound as "crystalline." How would you describe them? Centrifuge each mixture (T-8, Sec. 16-3). Draw off the supernatant solution with a capillary pipet (T-9) and discard it; save the precipitates for b and c.

(b) If a microscope is available, smear a thin layer of each precipitate on a slide with a rod and examine it under low magnification. You will see no crystals of $Mg(OH)_2$, for the precipitate is highly hydrated and amorphous. Describe or draw the crystals of $MgNH_4PO_4 \cdot 6H_2O$.

(c) Test the solubility of the remaining precipitates in 6 M NH_4Cl. Account for the difference.

7. The lake test for magnesium.

Take 1 drop of standard solution of Mg^{++} in each of two test tubes. To one add 3 drops of 6 M NH_4Cl, to the other 3 drops of water. To each add 1 drop of S. and O. reagent, a purple dye. Determine the number of drops of 6 M NaOH that must be added to each solution to produce the blue lake. Account for the difference.

8. Sensitivity of the test for ammonium ion.

Carry out the test as described in Preliminary Test of Outline 7 (Sec. 21-12) on three samples: (a) 2 drops of the standard solution of NH_4^+, (b) 2 drops of a solution prepared by diluting 1 drop of the standard solution with 9 drops of water (mix well; see T-5), and (c) 2 drops of distilled water. Note the time required for litmus to turn blue; wait five minutes at most with (c). Calculate the number of mg of NH_4^+ ion present in each experiment (assume 20 drops/ml). Give two errors in technique that could lead to an apparent positive result in (c).

9. Removal of ammonium salts.

(a) Heat a few crystals of solid ammonium chloride in a dry hard-glass test tube over a microflame (T-7a). What evidence is there that the change is reversible?

(b) Repeat the experiment with a few crystals of solid ammonium oxalate, $(NH_4)_2C_2O_4$ (side shelf). What collects on the upper walls of the tube?

(c) Evaporate 1 drop of ammonium carbonate solution in a small beaker (T-7e). Account for the result.

10. The Nessler reaction.

(a) Preparation of reagent. A number of important techniques are illustrated in this experiment. Dilute 1 drop of $HgCl_2$ solution in a test tube with about 20 drops of water. If the reagent was 0.1 M, how many drops of 0.1 M KI (side shelf) should be used to precipitate HgI_2? Carry out this precipitation. Centrifuge to settle the precipitate (T-8). Test for completeness of precipitation by adding another drop of KI solution. If more precipitate forms, stir and recentrifuge. Draw off the solution with a capillary pipet (T-9) and discard it. Wash the precipitate with 10 to 20 drops of water (T-10), centrifuge, and draw off and discard the wash water. Dissolve the precipitate by adding a few more drops of 0.1 M KI. Then make the solution strongly alkaline with 6 M NaOH; mix well and check with litmus or long-range indicator paper (T-12).

(b) Detection of ammonia. The test can be carried out in two ways. (1) Add several drops of Nessler's reagent to a drop of the standard solution of NH_4^+. (2) Carry out the test for the ammonium ion as described in Preliminary Test of Outline 7 but substitute for the moist litmus paper a small square of filter paper soaked in the Nessler reagent.

21-12. Analysis of Known and Unknown Samples.

a. Use 10 drops of a *known* or *practice* solution that contains about 2 mg of Mg^{++}, 2 mg of NH_4^+, 4 mg of K^+, and 4 mg of Na per milliliter. If this is not available, mix 2 drops each of the standard solutions of Mg^{++} and NH_4^+ with 4 drops each of the standard solutions of the other two ions.

b. The *unknown* may be (1) a solution containing only the ions of Group 5. Use 10 drops in testing for Mg^{++}, K^+, and Na^+ and a separate portion for the test for NH_4^+. (2) A solid mixture containing only the ions of Group 5. Take a representative sample (T-1) and use 20 mg (T-3b) for the tests for Mg^{++}, Na^+, and K^+. Dissolve in 8-10 drops of water. If the solution is acid, make it just alkaline with 6 M NH_3 (check with litmus; T-12). If the solution is alkaline, acidify with 6 M HCl and then make it just alkaline with 6 M NH_3. (3) Solution 6-1 (Outline 6, Cation Group 4, Chapter 20) obtained in a general analysis after removal of Groups 1 to 4. Use the entire solution for the tests for Mg^{++}, K^+, and Na^+. Add 1 drop each of $(NH_4)_2C_2O_4$ and $(NH_4)_2SO_4$ and 6 M NH_3, if necessary, until the solution is alkaline. Centrifuge (T-8) to settle the precipitate, which will contain traces of the ions of Group 4 that escaped precipitation. Withdraw the solution and use it for the analysis; discard the residue. The test for the ammonium ion must be done on a separate portion of the original unknown.

21-13. Suggestions for Further Work.

1. Examine the flame spectra of sodium and potassium (Chapter 25).
2. Consult some of the references given in Sec. 16-7 for the analytical behavior of lithium and devise an adaptation of Outline 7 that would include the identification of this element.
3. Sodium tetraphenylboron is a recently discovered reagent for

potassium. Find the conditions that are appropriate for its use and try it out on known and unknown samples. Read R. Muraca, H. Collier, J. Bonsack, and E. Jacobs, *Chemist Analyst*, **43**, 102 (1954).

4. The sensitivity of the sodium test can be increased by microscopic examination or by fluorescence. For the former consult E. Chamot and C. Mason, *Handbook of Chemical Microscopy*, 2nd ed., vol. II, Wiley, New York, 1939-46. Homemade apparatus for fluorescence observations is described by C. E. White, *J. Chem. Educ.*, **28**, 369 (1951).

OUTLINE 7. The Systematic Analysis of Cation Group 5

Preliminary test for the ammonium ion. This must be done on original sample, for ammonia and ammonium salts are added during the analysis for the other ions.

In a 5 ml beaker or a crucible put 2 drops soln or 10 mg solid sample. Add a small piece of red litmus paper. Cut another piece of red litmus paper smaller than the diameter of the beaker, moisten it, and attach it to the convex side of a watch glass. Add 6 M NaOH drop by drop to contents of beaker, stirring after each addition, until soln is alkaline; then add a few[1] drops in xs.[2] (If metal ions of Groups 1 through 3 are present, then add 1-2 drops Na_2S soln.[3]) Cover immediately with the watch glass so that litmus paper is centered over soln.[4] If the paper turns blue within 2 minutes, report **presence of NH_4^+.**[5] It is advisable to carry out the same test on a sample of distilled water to check your technique.

Analysis for Mg+, K++, and Na+. Start with a known or unknown soln described in Sec. 21-12. Divide into two parts: $\frac{1}{3}$ in a centrifuge tube for Mg test, $\frac{2}{3}$ in a casserole for K and Na tests.

Mg test. Pptn of $MgNH_4PO_4 \cdot 6H_2O$. Soln should be alk. Add 1 drop 6 M NH_4Cl if ammonium salts are not already present. Then add a few drops Na_2HPO_4 soln. Stir and rub the inner bottom wall of the tube with a rod. Set aside for at least 5 minutes. Centrifuge (T-8)[7] and draw off and discard the soln (T-9).

White cryst ppt $MgNH_4PO_4 \cdot 6H_2O$. Dissolve in a few[1] drops 6 M HCl. Add 1 drop (no more) S and O. reagent and make soln alk with 6 M NaOH (T-12). If soln and ppt are orange, add another drop NaOH. Centrifuge to settle ppt so that it can be observed more readily.[8]

Deep blue lake, $Mg(OH)_2$: **presence of Mg^{++}.**

K and Na tests. Removal of NH_4 salts. Evap to dryness (T-7b)[7] over a microflame (T-7a[9]). Cool. Add 10 drops 16 M HNO_3 and manipulate casserole so that acid wets walls as well as bottom. Again evap to dryness either under ventilating duct or in the hood. Bake residue until clouds of ammonium salts cease to come off. Heat walls as well as bottom of casserole, but do not heat to redness.[10] Cool almost to room temp. Then add 4 drops H_2O and rub inside of casserole with a rod to loosen caked residue. Transfer to a centrifuge tube and centrifuge if soln is turbid (T-8). Discard residue and divide soln equally between 2 centrifuge tubes. Avoid diluting it.[11]

Na test. Add 6 drops magnesium uranyl acetate. Stir and rub the inside wall of the tube. Let stand for 5 minutes.[15] with occasional stirring.

Pale, greenish yellow cryst ppt, $NaMg(UO_2)_3$ $(C_2H_3O_2)_9 \cdot 9H_2O$: **presence of Na+.**

K test. Add 1 drop 6 M $HC_2H_3O_2$ and a single crystal of $NaNO_2$. Warm to destroy traces of NH_4. Cool and add a few drops $Na_3Co(NO_2)_6$ reagent. If a ppt forms, warm for several minutes in the hot water bath.[13] Cool and add more reagent.

Yellow ppt, $K_2NaCo(NO_2)_6$: **presence of K+.**

Notes on Outline 7

1. The words "a few" generally mean 1 or 2, and "several" is taken to mean 2 to 4. The directions have purposely been left vague so that you will learn to judge for yourself how much reagent to add. This is better than slavishly adding a set number of drops regardless of the quantity of material under test. It is wise to be conservative in adding reagent, although inexperience may lead some to believe that if 1 drop is good, a liter is better.

2. Avoid a large excess of base, for this dilutes the solution so that not enough ammonia gas may be liberated to change the color of the litmus.

3. Certain cations such as Cu^{++}, Ag^+, and Zn^{++} form complex ions with ammonia and hinder its volatilization. The Na_2S removes these cations as insoluble sulfides.

4. If the litmus touches the sides of the beaker and these are wet with NaOH, a false test can be obtained.

5. The sensitivity of the test can be increased by (1) concentrating the solution before the test by evaporation and by (2) warming the solution before adding the NaOH. These precautions are not usually necessary. The paper may turn blue on prolonged exposure to laboratory air which frequently contains ammonia fumes.

6. The magnesium ammonium phosphate tends to form supersaturated solutions. Stirring and rubbing the walls helps induce crystallization. Since crystallization is slow, allow plenty of time for it.

7. This and similar references are to the techniques described in Sec. 16-3.

8. Note that the lake is a blue *precipitate*. The solution itself should be purple. If there is any doubt as to the color of the precipitate, remove the solution (T-9) and wash the precipitate once with 5-10 drops of water (T-10). Recentrifuge and observe the precipitate. Avoid an excess of S. and O. reagent, for this has a very strong color and may make the lake too dark.

9. If the solution starts to spatter, remove it from the flame for a few seconds. Keep the casserole well above the flame and swirl the contents steadily. Patience is required.

10. Failure to remove ammonium salts completely will lead to a false potassium test, but if too high a temperature is used, the alkali metal salts may fuse with the glaze of the dish and be lost.

11. These tests are based on the formation of fairly soluble precipitates and require concentrated solutions and excess of reagents. If you add too much water here, you may fail to get the tests.

12. The sodium cobaltinitrite reagent is unstable. It should have a deep reddish-amber color. Pale yellow or pink solutions should be discarded. Test the reagent with a standard solution of K^+ if its potency is doubted.

13. A voluminous precipitate at this point is often $(NH_4)_2NaCo(NO_2)_6$, which is indistinguishable from the potassium compound, if ammonium salts

were not completely removed. Warming will remove a small amount of the ammonium compound but not a large quantity.

14. Dissolve the precipitate in 1 drop of 6 M HCl. View the flame through two thicknesses of cobalt blue glass to cut out the sodium color. The potassium flame appears red.

15. Both the potassium and the sodium precipitates supersaturate easily. See note 6.

EXERCISES

Exercises 21-1 to 21-12 deal largely with the structure and chemical behavior of the ions while Exercises 21-13 to 21-22 cover the analytical procedure.

21-1. Name the ions of this analytical group. What positions do the elements occupy in the Periodic Table?

21-2. Give the number of electrons in all of the shells of Na^+, K^0, Mg^{++}, K^+, and Mg^{+++}. Why are compounds of the last ion not found?

21-3. Give a structural interpretation of each of the following; i.e., relate the observation to the structure of the atoms or ions: (a) the vigorous reducing action of the alkali metals, (b) the difference in radii of K^+ and K^0, (c) the lack of color of NaCl, KCl, and $MgCl_2$, (d) the relative solubilities of NaF and KF in water, (e) the resemblance of Li and Mg, (f) the relative ability of Na^+ and Mg^{++} to form complexes, (g) the frequency of hydration of sodium salts as compared with potassium salts, (h) the difference in first ionization potentials of Li and Na, (i) the difference in solubility of $MgSO_4$ and $BaSO_4$ in water.

21-4. Cite evidence to support the assertion that lithium and magnesium resemble each other.

21-5. Represent by equations the equilibria present in (a) ammonium sulfide solution, (b) magnesium nitrate solution, (c) sodium carbonate solution, (d) aqueous ammonia ("ammonium hydroxide").

21-6. Give the electronic structures of NH_3 and NH_4^+ ion. Explain why NH_3 is polar. Why does NH_3, but not NH_4^+, combine with metal ions?

21-7. In what respects do NH_4^+ and K^+ resemble each other? Account for the resemblance. Give three reactions of different type in which they behave *differently*.

21-8. Magnesium does not react appreciably with cold water, but if ammonium chloride is added bubbles of gas are seen to rise from the metal. Suggest an explanation.

21-9. Which of the following will react? Write an equation if reaction does occur: (a) potassium hydroxide and acetic acid in solution, (b) solid ammonium chloride and sodium carbonate heated, (c) magnesium hydroxide and ammonium sulfate solution, (d) potassium nitrate and sodium sulfate in solution, (e) aqueous ammonia and a solution of potassium hydrogen sulfate, (f) sodium dihydrogen phosphate and magnesium nitrate in solution.

21-10. A solution of magnesium chloride is evaporated to dryness. Moist blue litmus paper held in the escaping vapors turns pink. The residue is only partially soluble in water but completely soluble in dilute hydrochloric acid. Account for these observations. Give equations for the reactions.

21-11. Explain why magnesium sulfide cannot be precipitated.

21-12. Illustrate by equations different types of thermal decomposition of ammonium salts.

21-13. Why do these four ions occur in this analytical group?

21-14. Write equations for the reactions of these ions that are used in the analytical procedure.

21-15. Explain why magnesium carbonate is not precipitated with Cation Group 4 and why magnesium hydroxide is not precipitated with Cation Group 3. Consult the outline in Sec. 16-1 for the reagents used to precipitate these groups.

21-16. What reagent, combination of reagents, or operation would you use to separate in a single step the two substances in each pair? (a) Mg^{++} — Ca^{++} (b) NaCl — AgCl, (c) K^+ — Mg^{++}, (d) Na^+ — K^+, (e) NH_4Cl — KCl.

21-17. Give two reasons why an ammonium salt must be present when magnesium ammonium phosphate is precipitated.

21-18. Why must ammonium salts be removed before the potassium test? How does each of the following accomplish this? (a) heating the solid residue, (b) evaporating with nitric acid, (c) heating with sodium nitrite, (d) evaporating with sodium hydroxide.

21-19. What mistakes could lead to the following errors?

(a) A large yellow precipitate is obtained in the K^+ test, although no potassium is present.

(b) A white precipitate of magnesium ammonium phosphate forms but in the lake test an orange precipitate is obtained.

(c) Pale yellow needles form upon addition of magnesium uranyl acetate reagent, and yet the flame test is violet.

(d) A gelatinous white precipitate is obtained instead of magnesium ammonium phosphate.

(e) Sodium is present, and yet no precipitate is obtained.

(f) Potassium is present, but a pink solution is obtained and no precipitate.

(g) Ammonium ion is absent, and yet pink litmus over the alkaline solution turns blue immediately.

(h) Ammonium ion is absent, and yet a test for it is obtained on Solution 6-1.

21-20. Why are ammonium sulfate and ammonium oxalate added before separating magnesium? When may this step be omitted?

21-21. How would you distinguish between the two solids in each pair? (a) $(NH_4)_2SO_4$ — K_2SO_4, (b) $MgCl_2$ — KCl, (c) KNO_3 — $NaNO_3$, (d) $Mg(OH)_2$ — NaOH.

21-22. A solid unknown may contain some, but not necessarily all of the following: NH_4Cl, $NaNO_3$, MgO, $KMnO_4$. The sample is colorless. When water is added, it slowly dissolves with the evolution of a pungent gas.

On the basis of these observations, state which substances are probably present, which are probably absent, and those for which there is no evidence. Note that the substances may interact with each other.

The Properties of Anions

22-1. Introduction. Eighteen representative anions containing the twelve elements shown in a section of the Periodic Table at the right are considered in this text. They are F^-, Cl^-, Br^-, I^-, SCN^-, S^{--}, SO_3^{--}, SO_4^{--}, CrO_4^{--}, NO_2^-, NO_3^-, PO_4^{---}, AsO_3^{---}, AsO_4^{---}, CO_3^{--}, $C_2O_4^{--}$, $C_2H_3O_2^-$, and $B(OH)_4^-$. There are also twelve anions formed by adding protons to the bi- and trivalent ions, e.g., HCO_3^-, HPO_4^{--}, and $H_2AsO_4^-$. These are not considered separately.

IIIB	IVB	VB	VIB	VIIB	0
5 **B**	6 **C**	7 **N**	8 **O**	9 **F**	
		15 **P**	16 **S**	17 **Cl**	
		33 **As**		35 **Br**	
				53 **I**	

(Also Cr from Group VIA)

The properties of these anions are discussed in this chapter, while the procedure for their detection is given in the next. Three anions, viz., CrO_4^{--}, AsO_3^{---}, and AsO_4^{---}, contain elements ordinarily detected in the cation analysis, and they will not be dealt with here.[1] The properties of the anions that are considered are (a) electronic structure, (b) reaction with protons to give acids and the properties of these acids, (c) formation of insoluble salts, especially with Ag^+, Ca^{++}, and Ba^{++} ions, (d) formation of complexes, (e) redox reactions, and (f) miscellaneous reactions, if any. The ions are considered in the order in which they were listed in the first paragraph, a progression from Group VIIB back to Group IIIB in the Periodic Table.

22-2. Properties of Fluoride Ion, F^-.

a. Electronic Structure. The ion differs from a fluorine atom in having an extra electron, so its electronic configuration is the same as that of a neon

[1]See Sec. 18-9 for the ions of arsenic and Secs. 19-16 to -18 for chromate.

atom: two electrons in an inner shell and eight in an outer one. The electrons are tightly held and the structure is not readily distorted or polarized by cations. Thus fluoride ions form bonds predominantly ionic in character. Because of the stable electronic structure, fluorides are colorless unless the cation is colored.

b. Reaction with protons. *Hydrofluoric acid, HF.* The fluoride ion will react with strong acids to form molecular hydrofluoric acid ($K_a = 6.7 \times 10^{-4}$), somewhat stronger than formic acid. The boiling point of this acid is anomalously high (Table 22-1) because of hydrogen bonding (Sec. 1-10). The molecular acid can combine with anions to give the hydrogen fluoride ion

$$HF + F^- \rightleftharpoons HF_2^-$$

in which the hydrogen atom stands halfway between the two fluorides and is joined to them by hydrogen bonds. The ratio of the concentration of HF_2^- to that of HF increases with an increase in concentration of fluoride ion; when the latter is 0.1 M about $\frac{2}{7}$ of the acid is in the form of HF_2^-. Other anions such as $H_2F_3^-$ may also occur in concentrated solutions. Salts of hydrofluoric acid include normal ones such as CaF_2 and acid salts such as NH_4HF_2.

TABLE 22-1.

Some Properties of the Halogens, Halide Ions, and Hydrohalides

	F	Cl	Br	I
Atomic number	9	17	35	53
Melting point of X_2, °C	−223	−102	−7	+114
Boiling point of X_2, °C	−187	−35	+59	+183
Solubility of X_2 in H_2O at 25°, moles/l	decomp	0.092	0.212	0.00132
Number of electron shells in X^-	2	3	4	5
Ionic radius, A	1.33	1.81	1.96	2.19
Relative polarizability	1	3	4	6
$\mathcal{E}^0$ for $2X^- \rightarrow X_2 + 2e^-$ at 25°, volts	−2.87	−1.37	−1.09	−0.54
K for $X^- + X_2 \rightleftharpoons X_3^-$ at 25°		0.19	17	740
Boiling point of HX, °C	+19.54	−84.9	−66.8	−35.4
% HX in concd laboratory reagent	48–51	36.5–38	47–49	47–50
Approx molarity of HX in concd acid	30	12	9	5.5

c. Insoluble Salts. Most fluorides are insoluble with the exception of those of the alkali metals, ammonium, silver, aluminum, mercury(I and II), and tin(II and IV). Silver fluoride is the only very soluble silver halide (Sec. 5-7). Some of the more common insoluble fluorides in order of decreasing molar solubility (or of decreasing solubility product) are: BaF_2, MgF_2, PbF_2, SrF_2, and CaF_2. Barium fluoride is too soluble to precipitate from dilute solutions. Calcium fluoride is the least soluble in water and will not dissolve in acetic acid. All of the fluorides are dissolved by strong acids because of removal of fluoride ions to give molecular hydrogen fluoride.

d. Complex Ions.   Fluoride ion most commonly forms complexes with small, highly charged cations such as Be^{++}, Fe^{+++}, and Al^{+++} as in AlF_6^{---}.

e. Redox Reactions.   Oxidation of fluoride to fluorine is too difficult to accomplish by chemical oxidizing agents and is always done by electrolysis.

f. Miscellaneous Reactions.   In the presence of acid, fluorides etch glass, silicon dioxide, or silicates because of the liberation of gaseous silicon tetrafluoride and hexafluosilicic acid:

$$4HF + SiO_2 \rightleftharpoons SiF_4 \uparrow + 2H_2O$$
$$SiF_4 + 2HF \rightleftharpoons H_2SiF_6$$

Potassium fluosilicate K_2SiF_6 is only sparingly soluble.

22-3. Properties of Chloride Ion, Cl^-.

a. Electronic Structure.   The ion has the electronic configuration of argon atoms. It is more polarizable than fluoride and forms bonds with cations that have more covalent character. While most chloride salts are nevertheless predominantly ionic, the molecular character of $HgCl_2$ and the anhydrous chlorides of trivalent Fe, Al, and Cr is notable.

b. Reaction with Protons.   Hydrochloric acid, HCl.   Chloride ion is the anion of a strong acid and will accept protons only from exceptionally strong proton donors such as concentrated sulfuric or phosphoric acids:

$$H_2SO_4 + Cl^- \rightarrow HCl \uparrow + HSO_4^-$$

Mercury(II) chloride is too weakly ionized to give this reaction. The molecular hydrogen chloride is only slightly soluble in hot, concentrated sulfuric acid and is driven off as a colorless gas that fumes in moist air. It is very soluble in water (Table 22-1) and in all but very concentrated solutions is completely ionized (Sec. 2-21).

c. Insoluble Salts.   These include the familiar chlorides of silver, mercury(I) and lead(II), and the less familiar compounds of copper(I) and thallium(I). The barium and calcium salts are very soluble. Because of the low affinity of chloride ion for protons, the insoluble chlorides are not dissolved by nitric acid. They do dissolve in excess hydrochloric acid to form chlorocomplexes, e.g., $PbCl_4^{--}$. Silver chloride is readily dissolved by excess ammonia and is reprecipitated when the complex is destroyed by nitric acid:

$$AgCl \downarrow + 2NH_3 \rightarrow Ag(NH_3)_2^+ + Cl^-$$
$$Ag(NH_3)_2^+ + 2H^+ \rightarrow AgCl \downarrow + 2NH_4^+$$

The extent of dissociation of the complex

$$Ag(NH_3)_2{}^+ \rightleftharpoons Ag^+ + 2NH_3$$

is so high that a large excess of ammonia is required to depress it and thus dissolve silver chloride; this requirement is not satisfied by a mixture of $(NH_4)_2CO_3$ and $Ag(NH_3)_2NO_3$.

There are a number of sparingly soluble basic chlorides, such as $BiOCl$, which dissolve in acids.

d. Complex Ions. There are numerous chlorocomplexes of which the following are typical: $CdCl_3{}^-$, $AgCl_2{}^-$, $FeCl^{++}$, $SnCl_6{}^{--}$, $SbCl_4{}^-$, and $MnCl_4{}^{--}$.

e. Redox Reactions. Chloride ion is a weak reducing agent and usually requires a strong oxidizing agent in concentrated acid solution, e.g., MnO_2, $MnO_4{}^-$, PbO_2, or concentrated HNO_3 but not concentrated H_2SO_4. Oxidation by permanganate

$$10Cl^- + 16H^+ + 2MnO_4{}^- \rightarrow 2Mn^{++} + 5Cl_2\uparrow + 8H_2O$$

is too slow in dilute solutions to be of importance in qualitative analysis. Iron salts, if present, can catalyze the reaction.

f. Miscellaneous Reactions. Solid chlorides react with a mixture of potassium dichromate and concentrated sulfuric acid to form volatile, red chromyl chloride (bp 117°):

$$Cr_2O_7{}^{--} + 4Cl^- + 6H_2SO_4 \rightarrow 2CrO_2Cl_2\uparrow + 3H_2O + 6HSO_4{}^-$$

If bromides are present, red bromine will also vaporize. Chromyl chloride, unlike bromine, gives a yellow color when it dissolves in a solution of sodium hydroxide:

$$CrO_2Cl_2 + 4OH^- \rightarrow CrO_4{}^{--} + 2Cl^- + 2H_2O$$

22-4. Properties of Bromide Ion, Br⁻.

a. Electronic Structure. The ion has the electronic structure of atoms of the inert gas krypton. It is more polarizable than chloride ion and forms bonds with more covalent character.

b. Reaction with Protons. Hydrobromic acid, HBr. The bromide ion is the anion of a strong acid and will accept protons only from strong proton donors, such as concentrated sulfuric or phosphoric acids. The latter is preferable:

$$H_3PO_4 + Br^- \rightarrow HBr\uparrow + H_2PO_4{}^-$$

because concentrated sulfuric acid oxidizes some of the bromide to free bromine. Molecular hydrogen bromide is only slightly soluble in the hot concentrated acids and is driven off as a gas. It fumes in moist air, is very soluble in water (Table 22-1), and, like hydrochloric acid, is completely ionized. Only in less basic solvents does it prove to be a stronger acid than hydrochloric acid (Sec. 11-7).

c. Insoluble Salts.   These are similar to the chlorides but less soluble. They do not dissolve in nitric acid. Pale yellow silver bromide is less soluble than silver chloride in ammonia solution. It can be dissolved by the concentrated reagent but is insoluble in ammonium carbonate solution. Silver bromide is dissolved by an excess of bromide, thiosulfate, or cyanide to give weakly dissociated complex ions of silver. The bromide that it contains can be brought into solution by transposition with sulfide or by reduction of the silver ions with zinc:

$$2AgBr \downarrow + S^{--} \rightarrow Ag_2S \downarrow + 2Br^-$$

$$2AgBr \downarrow + Zn^0 \downarrow \rightarrow 2Ag^0 \downarrow + Zn^{++} + 2Br^-$$

The other silver halides undergo similar reactions.

d. Complex Ions.   These are very similar to chlorocomplexes.

e. Redox Reactions.   Bromide ion is a better reducing agent than chloride[2] and is oxidized to bromine by MnO_4^-, $Cr_2O_7^{--}$, Cl_2, BrO_3^-, hot concentrated sulfuric acid, $Fe(CN)_6^{---}$ in concentrated solutions, and H_2O_2 at 100°. The reaction with permanganate goes readily even in dilute acid solutions:

$$16H^+ + 2MnO_4^- + 10Br^- \rightarrow 5Br_2 \uparrow + 2Mn^{++} + 8H_2O$$

Some of the other reactions are represented by

$$Cl_2 + 2Br^- \rightarrow Br_2 \uparrow + 2Cl^-$$

$$6H^+ + BrO_3^- + 5Br^- \rightarrow 3Br_2 \uparrow + 3H_2O$$

$$H_2SO_4 + 2HBr \rightarrow Br_2 \uparrow + SO_2 \uparrow + 2H_2O$$

Free bromine produced by these reactions is recognized by its brownish-red color as a vapor or by the orange to brownish-red color of its solution in carbon tetrachloride or carbon disulfide. Bromine is about 25 times as soluble in carbon tetrachloride as in water, so it can largely be extracted from a water solution by the organic solvent. Extraction is hindered to some extent if excess bromide is present because of the formation of complexes such as Br_3^- or Br_5^- ion.

f. Miscellaneous Reactions.   Bromine obtained by the oxidation of bromide reacts with the organic compound fluorescein ($C_{20}H_{12}O_5$) to give

---

[2]This is indicated by its less negative standard oxidation potential ($\mathcal{E}^0$ in Table 22-1). The more complete table of oxidation potentials in the Appendix can be used to advantage to predict the direction of many of the redox reactions in this chapter (Secs. 9-7 and 9-8).

red eosin ($C_{20}H_8O_5Br_4$) and hydrogen bromide. A sensitive test for bromide is based on this reaction, but iodide and thiocyanate interfere.

22-5. Properties of Iodide Ion, I⁻.

a. Electronic Structure. The ion has the electronic configuration of atoms of the inert gas xenon. The outer electrons are further from the nucleus and are held more loosely than those of the other halide ions. Thus iodide ions are the most polarizable (Table 22-1), and their bonds with cations have the most covalent character. As a result solid iodides are often colored, e.g., yellow AgI and red HgI_2, and are often less soluble than the bromides and chlorides.

b. Reaction with Protons. *Hydriodic acid, HI.* Like the chloride and bromide ions, iodide is the anion of a strong acid and will accept protons only from powerful proton donors such as concentrated phosphoric acid in which hydrogen iodide is only slightly ionized and slightly soluble. Gaseous hydrogen iodide fumes in moist air and is very soluble in water (Table 22-1). It is completely ionized in aqueous solutions.

c. Insoluble Salts. The most notable of these is yellow silver iodide, insoluble in dilute nitric acid, ammonium carbonate, or concentrated ammonia solution. Unlike silver chloride and silver bromide, it is oxidized and dissolved by concentrated nitric acid:

$$4H^+ + 2NO_3^- + 2AgI \downarrow \rightarrow 2Ag^+ + I_2 + 2NO_2 + 2H_2O$$

It is slightly soluble in sodium thiosulfate and moderately soluble in potassium cyanide because of the formation of complex ions:

$$AgI \downarrow + 2CN^- \rightarrow Ag(CN)_2^- + I^-$$

Iodide ions can be brought into solution by transposition with sulfide or by reduction of the silver with zinc.

The other common insoluble iodides are red HgI_2, greenish yellow Hg_2I_2, and yellow PbI_2. Of these lead iodide is the most soluble, especially in hot water, though much less so than the chloride and bromide. The iodides of bismuth(III), antimony(III), and tin(IV) hydrolyze so extensively that excess acid must be present if they are to remain in solution.

d. Complex Ions. There are many of these, particularly with the elements of Groups IB to VB. Some of the more notable are CuI_2^-, AgI_3^{--}, HgI_4^{--}, CdI_4^{--}, PbI_4^{--}, and BiI_6^{---}. At a fixed concentration of free iodide ions, the most weakly dissociated is the complex of mercury(II).

Important complexes are also formed with molecular iodine, e.g., the brown tri-iodide ion:

$$I^- + I_2 \rightleftharpoons I_3^-$$

The comparable tribromide and trichloride ions are much less stable (Table

22-1). There are also penta- and heptaiodides, I_5^- and I_7^-. The central iodine atom in the tri-iodide ion has 10 electrons in its outer shell:[3]

$$:\overset{..}{\underset{..}{I}}:^- \; + \; :\overset{..}{\underset{..}{I}}:\overset{..}{\underset{..}{I}}: \; \rightleftharpoons \; :\overset{..}{\underset{..}{I}}:\overset{.\,.}{\underset{..}{I}}:\overset{..}{\underset{..}{I}}:^-$$

e. Redox Reactions.   Iodide ion in acid solution is a fairly good reducing agent (see footnote 2), because its extra electron is far from the nucleus and readily removed. It is oxidized by all oxidizing agents that attack chloride or bromide ions but under milder conditions, i.e., at lower temperatures and concentrations. In addition it is oxidized by a number of reagents that do not attack the other halide ions: HNO_2, Fe^{+++}, Cu^{++}, and Br_2:

$$2HNO_2 + 2H^+ + 2I^- \rightarrow I_2 + 2NO + 2H_2O$$

$$2Cu^{++} + 4I^- \rightarrow 2CuI \downarrow \; + I_2$$

Iodides and iodine are oxidized to iodate ion by excess of strong oxidizing agents such as concentrated nitric acid, chlorine, hypochlorous acid, chlorate ions, or bromate ions; e.g.,

$$I^- + 3HClO \rightarrow IO_3^- + 3Cl^- + 3H^+$$

Hot concentrated sulfuric acid oxidizes iodides to iodine and is reduced to SO_2, S, and H_2S:

$$8HI + H_2SO_4 \rightarrow 4I_2 \uparrow \; + H_2S \uparrow \; + 4H_2O$$

Solutions of iodides slowly turn yellow because of oxidation by oxygen of air:

$$4H^+ + 6I^- + O_2 \rightarrow 2I_3^- + 2H_2O$$

Free iodine that is liberated by these reactions can be detected by (1) the violet color of its vapor, (2) the violet color of its solutions in CCl_4 or CS_2, or (3) the blue color that it gives with starch (see f). Iodine is more than three times as soluble as bromine in carbon tetrachloride; the ratio at equilibrium of its concentration in CCl_4 to that in H_2O is 85 (Sec. 7-17). Because of this more favorable distribution and because of the stronger color of iodine, the extraction test for it is more sensitive than that for bromine. The iodine color is perceptible at concentrations as low as $2 \times 10^{-6} \; M$. The solubility in carbon tetrachloride is decreased by excess iodide because the equilibrium

$$I_2 + I^- \rightleftharpoons I_3^-$$

is forced to the right (only I_2 is soluble in CCl_4). Solutions of iodine in solvents such as alcohol are red-brown; there is an association of iodine with the solvent. The violet solutions and vapor contain simple I_2 molecules.

f. Miscellaneous Reactions.   Free iodine reacts with starch to give a blue complex. This is about as sensitive an indication of iodine as the color in

[3]The iodine atom can accept two more electrons than it requires to give the inert gas octet by making use of its $5d$ orbitals.

carbon tetrachloride, but it is favored, not hindered, by excess iodide. One constituent of starch, β-amylose, consists of long molecular chains wound into helices. Iodine molecules slide into the hollow center of a helix to give the intensely blue complex.

22-6. Properties of Thiocyanate Ion, SCN⁻.

a. Electronic Structure. The sequence of atoms in the ion is that indicated by SCN⁻ or NCS⁻ and not by CNS⁻ which is often given. The 16 valence electrons of the ion (6 from S, 4 from C, 5 from N, and 1 for the negative charge) can be shared in two ways

$$(:\ddot{\underset{..}{S}}\!-\!C\!\equiv\!N\!:)^{-} \quad\quad \text{or} \quad\quad (\ddot{\underset{..}{S}}\!=\!C\!=\!\ddot{\underset{..}{N}})^{-}$$

in which each atom acquires a share in an octet of electrons, the inert gas configuration. We would expect the S—C distance in the first to be larger than that in the second because multiple bonds draw atoms closer together. The observed distance of 1.61 A is in between those predicted for the single and double bonds, respectively 1.82 and 1.55 A. Hence the S—C bond is best described as having some of the character of both a single and a double bond, and, likewise, the C—N bond is intermediate between double and triple.[4]

b. Reaction with Protons. Thiocyanic acid, HNCS. The thiocyanate ion, like the chloride, bromide, and iodide ions, has a low affinity for protons. The acid is apparently strong. It is prepared by passing hydrogen sulfide over warm solid lead thiocyanate:

$$\text{Pb(SCN)}_2 \downarrow\ +\ H_2S \rightarrow PbS \downarrow\ +\ 2HNCS \uparrow$$

Although it decomposes unless kept cold or in dilute solution, its salts are fairly stable. They can be prepared by reactions of cyanides with sulfur.

c. Insoluble Salts. Thiocyanate resembles iodide in forming insoluble salts with silver, mercury(I and II), and copper(I). Lead thiocyanate is sparingly soluble. The silver salt is comparable with silver bromide in solubility and is, therefore, insoluble in dilute ammonia, ammonium carbonate, or dilute nitric acid but soluble in concentrated ammonia and sodium thiosulfate. It is reduced by zinc in acid solution to give not only silver metal but also hydrogen sulfide. Solid silver thiocyanate is decomposed by heat; this distinguishes it from the silver halides.

d. Complex Ions. Again thiocyanate resembles bromide and iodide ions in forming complexes with the cations of Groups IB to VB, e.g., $Cu(SCN)_4^{--}$, $Hg(SCN)_4^{--}$, and $Bi(SCN)_6^{---}$. The complex with mercury(II) is the most

---

[4] The actual structure of the ion is said to be a "resonance hybrid" of the two hypothetical structures represented by the formulas.

stable. It also forms complexes with cations of the first transition series, e.g., red $Cr(SCN)_6^{---}$, red $FeSCN^{++}$, and blue $Co(SCN)_4^{--}$. The thiocyanate ion is probably bonded to the metal ion through the nitrogen rather than the sulfur.

e. Redox Reactions. Bromine displaces the volatile, unstable dimer, thiocyanogen:

$$Br_2 + Pb(SCN)_2 \downarrow \rightarrow PbBr_2 \downarrow + (SCN)_2$$

Thiocyanogen, in turn, displaces iodine from an iodide and thus comes between bromine and iodine in oxidizing power. Resemblances between the thiocyanate and halide ions have already been noted. Because of these similarities, thiocyanogen is called a *pseudohalogen* (or halogenoid).

Nitrous acid, dilute nitric acid, or bromine in excess will oxidize thiocyanates to sulfate and hydrogen cyanide:

$$6HNO_2 + SCN^- \rightarrow HCN \uparrow + SO_4^{--} + 6NO \uparrow + H^+ + 2H_2O$$

This reaction is used to destroy thiocyanates. With more powerful oxidizing agents such as concentrated nitric acid, potassium permanganate, or hot concentrated sulfuric acid, a variety of products may be formed such as carbonyl sulfide (COS), carbon dioxide, sulfur, formic acid, and sulfur dioxide.

Thiocyanates can also be reduced. With zinc and acid, hydrogen sulfide and hydrogen cyanide are formed

$$Zn + SCN^- + 3H^+ \rightarrow H_2S \uparrow + HCN \uparrow + Zn^{++}$$

In alkaline solution thiocyanates are reduced by zinc or aluminum to ammonia.

22-7. Properties of Sulfide Ion, S^{--}.

a. Electronic Structure. The electronic configuration of the ion is the same as that of chloride ions or argon atoms. It is much more polarizable and polarizing because of its double charge and loosely held outer electrons. Many of its salts are, therefore, very slightly soluble and highly colored, e.g., yellow CdS, orange-red Sb_2S_3, red HgS, black CuS, and black FeS.

b. Reaction with Protons. **Hydrosulfuric acid, H_2S.** The sulfide ion is strongly basic, for HS^- ion is almost as weakly ionized as water ($K_a = 1.3 \times 10^{-13}$). Solutions of sulfides are strongly basic because of the hydrolysis reaction

$$S^{--} + H_2O \rightleftharpoons HS^- + OH^-$$

The pH of 0.1 M Na_2S, for example, is about 13. The hydrogen sulfide ion is also basic because H_2S is a weak acid ($K_a = 1 \times 10^{-7}$); the pH of 0.1 M NaHS is about 9.5.

Hydrogen sulfide is a very poisonous gas with a distinctive rotten egg odor. Its solubility in water is limited even at a pressure of one atmosphere, viz., 0.1 M at 25° and 0.036 M at 100°. Because of its low ionization and solubility, the gas is liberated from the more soluble sulfides by other acids. Thus even acetic acid will displace hydrogen sulfide from $(NH_4)_2S$, Na_2S, CaS, or MnS:

$$MnS \downarrow + 2HC_2H_3O_2 \rightarrow H_2S \uparrow + 2C_2H_3O_2^- + Mn^{++}$$

but hydrochloric or dilute sulfuric acid is required for the less soluble sulfides of zinc, iron(II), and cadmium. Hydrogen sulfide is liberated from still more insoluble sulfides by the combination of zinc and acid:

$$CuS \downarrow + Zn + 2H^+ \rightarrow Zn^{++} + Cu^0 \downarrow + H_2S \uparrow$$

The hydrogen sulfide can be detected by the formation of a brown or black precipitate or stain of PbS with lead acetate or alkaline plumbite:

$$Pb(C_2H_3O_2)_2 + H_2S \rightarrow PbS \downarrow + 2HC_2H_3O_2$$

c. Insoluble Salts. Most sulfides are insoluble but the solubilities cover a wide range from MnS to HgS. Black silver sulfide is the most insoluble compound of silver. It does not dissolve in ammonia, ammonium carbonate, or sodium thiosulfate, but it is dissolved by potassium cyanide and by dilute nitric acid:

$$3Ag_2S \downarrow + 8H^+ + 2NO_3^- \rightarrow 6Ag^+ + 3S^0 \downarrow + 2NO + 4H_2O$$

It is not transposed by sodium carbonate, but the sulfide can be liberated by treatment with zinc and dilute sulfuric acid.

The sulfides of sodium, potassium, and ammonium are soluble; those of calcium, strontium, and barium are moderately soluble. All of them hydrolyze to a considerable degree. The sulfides of magnesium, aluminum, and chromium(III) are completely decomposed by water with formation of the insoluble hydroxides and hydrogen sulfide.

d. Complex Ions. The sulfides of As, Sb, Sn(IV), and Hg(II) are dissolved by sodium or potassium sulfides with the formation of thioanions (Chapter 18): AsS_4^{---}, SbS_3^{---}, SnS_3^{--}, and HgS_2^{--}. These are decomposed by acid, and the insoluble sulfide is reprecipitated. With nitrosylpentacyano-ferrate(II) ion ["nitroprusside," $Fe(CN)_5NO^{---}$], even traces of sulfide in alkaline solution give a violet colored complex $[Fe(CN)_5NOS]^{-4}$.

e. Redox Reactions. Sulfide ion is generally oxidized to free sulfur. It is a better reducing agent than iodide ion:

$$H_2S + I_2 \rightarrow 2H^+ + 2I^- + S^0 \downarrow$$

and is oxidized by reagents such as HNO_2, MnO_4^-, $Cr_2O_7^{--}$, and Fe^{+++} which also oxidize iodide:

$$5H_2S + 2MnO_4^- + 6H^+ \rightarrow 5S^0 \downarrow + 2Mn^{++} + 8H_2O$$
$$H_2S + 2HNO_2 \rightarrow S^0 \downarrow + 2NO + 2H_2O$$
$$H_2S + 2Fe^{+++} \rightarrow S^0 \downarrow + 2Fe^{++} + 2H^+$$

In addition it reacts with ferricyanide and sulfurous acid, which do not oxidize iodide:

$$2H_2S + H_2SO_3 \rightarrow 3S^0 \downarrow + 3H_2O$$

In addition to sulfur, thiosulfate $S_2O_3^{--}$, pentathionate $S_5O_6^{--}$, and other complex sulfur anions are formed by this reaction.

Exceptionally active oxidizing agents such as hot concentrated nitric acid, chlorates, or bromine in acid solutions oxidize sulfide to sulfate:

$$H_2S + 4Br_2 + 4H_2O \rightarrow 8Br^- + SO_4^{--} + 10H^+$$

22-8. Properties of Sulfite Ion, SO_3^{--}.

a. Electronic Structure.   The 26 valence electrons (6 for S, 18 for three O, and 2 for the negative charge) can be so distributed as to give each atom a complete octet. The ion is pyramidal with the three oxygen atoms at the base and the lone pair of electrons of the sulfur atom at the apex. The following formulas show the relation of the structure of the sulfite ion to those of other sulfur oxyanions:

sulfite   sulfate   sulfamate

thiosulfate   dithionite   pyrosulfite

dithionate   pyrosulfate

The sulfur-oxygen bonds in these ions may have some double-bond character.

b. Reaction with Protons.   Sulfurous acid, H_2SO_3.   Sulfite ion is the anion of weakly ionized HSO_3^- ($K_a = 6.2 \times 10^{-8}$) and that in turn is the anion of sulfurous acid ($K_a = 1.7 \times 10^{-2}$). Solutions of sulfites are thus basic because of the proton transfer reaction with water,

$$SO_3^{--} + H_2O \rightleftharpoons HSO_3^- + OH^-$$

The pH of 0.1 M Na$_2$SO$_3$ is about 10. Solutions of hydrogen sulfites are acidic because the HSO$_3^-$ ion is a stronger acid than it is a base.

Free sulfurous acid is unstable and has not been isolated. The sulfur in its solutions is largely in the form of unhydrated sulfur dioxide, hydrogen sulfite ion, and pyrosulfite ion. Recent spectral measurements indicate that the concentration of H$_2$SO$_3$ must be not greater than 3% of the total, and it is probably much less than this.

Strong acids liberate sulfur dioxide from sulfites. A saturated solution of the oxide at 1 atm pressure is 1.2 M at 25° and 0.56 M at 50°. If the concentration of acid and sulfite are high enough, sulfur dioxide will escape as a gas. It can be detected by its sharp odor (not specific) and its decolorizing action on permanganate (see e). It reacts with barium hydroxide to precipitate barium sulfite, somewhat soluble in excess sulfur dioxide.

c. Insoluble Salts. Only the sodium, potassium, and ammonium salts are soluble. Silver sulfite is precipitated even by sulfurous acid. It is soluble in dilute strong acids to give sulfur dioxide and in excess sodium sulfite to give a complex. It is decomposed when a suspension of it is boiled:

$$2Ag_2SO_3 \downarrow \rightarrow Ag_2SO_4 \downarrow + SO_2 + 2Ag \downarrow \text{ (black)}$$

Silver sulfite dissolves in ammonia and ammonium carbonate with the formation of the silver ammine complex.

The other insoluble sulfites come down only in neutral or alkaline solutions and dissolve in sulfurous acid:

$$CaSO_3 \downarrow + H_2O + SO_2 \rightarrow Ca^{++} + 2HSO_3^-$$

Boiling reverses the reaction by driving off sulfur dioxide, and the salt reprecipitates. The barium salt is less soluble that that of calcium, and strontium sulfite falls in between.

d. Complex Ions. The only one of any consequence is that of silver: Ag(SO$_3$)$_2$$^{---}$. It is more highly dissociated than the complexes of silver with thiosulfate or cyanide but more stable than that with ammonia.

e. Redox Reactions. Sulfite contains sulfur in an oxidation state of $+4$ and accordingly it can function as a reducing or an oxidizing agent. Its activity is strongly dependent on the hydrogen ion concentration. If its solution is made basic, its power as an oxidizing agent decreases and that as a reducing agent increases.

The only important reactions as an oxidizing agent are those with sulfide (Sec. 22-7e) and with active metals such as zinc:

$$6H^+ + 3Zn + H_2SO_3 \rightarrow 3Zn^{++} + H_2S \uparrow + 3H_2O$$

Sulfurous acid and sulfites are common reducing agents and are generally oxidized to sulfate. Typical reactions are those with I_2, Fe^{+++}, MnO_4^-, $Cr_2O_7^{--}$, and NO_3^- in acid solution; e.g.,

$$H_2O + 2Fe^{+++} + H_2SO_3 \rightarrow SO_4^{--} + 2Fe^{++} + 4H^+$$

$$2MnO_4^- + 5H_2SO_3 \rightarrow 5SO_4^{--} + 2Mn^{++} + 3H_2O + 4H^+$$

$$2H^+ + Cr_2O_7^{--} + 3H_2SO_3 \rightarrow 3SO_4^{--} + 2Cr^{+++} + 4H_2O$$

In neutral or alkaline solution it is oxidized by oxygen of the air or hydrogen peroxide:

$$2SO_3^{--} + O_2 \rightarrow 2SO_4^{--}$$

$$SO_3^{--} + H_2O_2 \rightarrow SO_4^{--} + H_2O$$

Because of the first reaction, aged solutions of sulfites will always contain some sulfate.

22-9. Properties of Sulfate Ion, SO_4^{--}.

a. Electronic Structure. This was given in Sec. 22-8a. The ion is tetrahedral with an oxygen atom to each corner and the sulfur in the center. The oxidation state of sulfur in the ion is $+6$, its highest.

b. Reaction with Protons. Sulfuric acid, H_2SO_4. In dilute solutions the sulfate ions have little affinity for protons, because the hydrogen sulfate ion is a moderately strong acid ($K_a = 1.0 \times 10^{-2}$). The hydrolysis of sulfates is generally negligible. The acid sulfates such as $KHSO_4$ have no affinity for protons in dilute solutions, but their solutions are acidic because of the ionization of the anion; the pH of 0.1 M $NaHSO_4$ is about 1.4, so the solution is almost as acid as 0.1 M HCl.

Molecular H_2SO_4 is known in more concentrated solutions (Sec. 2-21). Pure hydrogen sulfate, though but little ionized, is a powerful proton donor, as has been noted in Secs. 22-3 and 22-4.

c. Insoluble Salts. Most sulfates are soluble with the exception of

$$Ag_2SO_4, \ CaSO_4 \cdot 2H_2O, \ Hg_2SO_4, \ SrSO_4, \ PbSO_4, \ BaSO_4$$

They are listed in order of decreasing solubility in water; in their saturated solutions the concentration of sulfate ion is highest for silver sulfate and lowest for barium sulfate. Silver sulfate will precipitate only from fairly concentrated solutions. Because the reaction $H^+ + SO_4^{--} \rightleftharpoons HSO_4^-$ is not very effective in removing sulfate ions, only the first few, more soluble, sulfates are appreciably dissolved by strong acids. The insolubility of barium sulfate in acids differentiates it from barium salts of weak acids such as $BaCO_3$, $BaSO_3$, and $Ba_3(PO_4)_2$.

There are a number of basic sulfates such as $(BiO)_2SO_4$. These are dissolved by acids.

d. Complex Ions. There are a number of unstable complexes such as that with Fe^{+++} ion.

e. Redox Reactions. In dilute solutions sulfate shows no tendency to act as an oxidizing agent. The concentrated acid oxidizes copper, bromides, iodides, thiocyanates, and sulfides. The usual reduction product is sulfur dioxide unless the reducing agent is an active one such as iodide (Sec. 22-5e). Solid sulfates fused with sodium carbonate are reduced by carbon to sulfides:

$$BaSO_4 + 4C \rightarrow BaS + 4CO$$

22-10. Properties of Nitrite Ion, NO_2^-.

a. Electronic Structure. The ion is triangular with the nitrogen atom between the oxygens and an angle of 114° between the two nitrogen-oxygen bonds. There are 18 valence electrons (5 from N, 12 from two O, and 1 for the charge). They can be arranged to give stable octets about each atom only if one of the nitrogen-oxygen bonds is double. The formation of double bonds is characteristic of the nonmetals oxygen, nitrogen, and carbon in the first short period. There are two possible structures for the nitrite ion:

$$\left[\ddot{\overset{..}{N}} \begin{matrix} \nearrow \\ :O \end{matrix} \begin{matrix} \searrow \\ :\ddot{O}: \end{matrix} \right]^- \quad \text{or} \quad \left[\ddot{\overset{..}{N}} \begin{matrix} \swarrow \\ :\ddot{O}: \end{matrix} \begin{matrix} \searrow \\ O: \end{matrix} \right]^-$$

The distance from the nitrogen nucleus to the oxygen nucleus is the same for both bonds, so it is better to describe them as being intermediate in character between double and single bonds. Neither picture by itself is an adequate description of the ion.

b. Reaction with Protons. Nitrous acid, HNO_2. The ion will combine with protons to form the acid ($K_a = 5.1 \times 10^{-4}$), stronger than formic acid and almost as strong as hydrofluoric. Nitrites thus hydrolyze only slightly:

$$NO_2^- + H_2O \rightleftharpoons HNO_2 + OH^-$$

The pH of 0.1 M $NaNO_2$ is about 8.

Blue solutions of nitrous acid can be prepared by mixing cold solutions of nitrites and strong acids. Decomposition occurs on warming, and the pure acid has never been isolated:

$$3HNO_2 \rightleftharpoons H^+ + NO_3^- + 2NO \uparrow + H_2O$$
$$2NO + O_2 \rightleftharpoons 2NO_2 \text{ (red-brown)}$$

The solution is colored yellow or brown by the nitrogen dioxide. The anhydride of nitrous acid, N_2O_3, is a combination of NO and NO_2. Hence fumes from the decomposition of nitrous acid are acidic and neutralize barium hydroxide:

$$N_2O_3 + 2OH^- \rightarrow 2NO_2^- + H_2O$$

c. Insoluble Salts. Nitrites are generally soluble but silver nitrite is only sparingly so (4.41 g/l at 25°, or 0.027 M). Silver nitrite dissolves readily in acids, ammonia, and ammonium carbonate. The nitrites of sodium and potassium are fairly stable to heat but other nitrites are decomposed:

$$Ba(NO_2)_2 \rightarrow BaO + NO \uparrow + NO_2 \uparrow$$

$$AgNO_2 \rightarrow Ag + NO_2 \uparrow$$

Ammonium nitrite decomposes even in dilute solutions (see e).

d. Complex Ions. The most notable complex is hexanitrocobaltate(III) or cobaltinitrite ion, $Co(NO_2)_6^{---}$. This forms potassium and ammonium salts of low solubility (Chapter 21). Rather unstable nitrite complexes are formed with silver, cadmium, mercury(II), and lead. The nitrite ion is generally coordinated to a cation through the lone pair of electrons of the nitrogen atom.

e. Redox Reactions. Since nitrite contains nitrogen in an oxidation state of $+3$, it can act as either a reducing agent or an oxidizing agent. It is a weak reducing agent and functions as such only with fairly active oxidizing agents; e.g.,

$$5HNO_2 + H^+ + 2MnO_4^- \rightarrow 2Mn^{++} + 5NO_3^- + 3H_2O \quad \text{(Acid solution.)}$$

$$NO_2^- + H_2O_2 \rightarrow NO_3^- + H_2O \qquad \text{(Basic solution.)}$$

As an oxidizing agent in acid solution it is usually reduced to nitrogen(II) oxide (nitric oxide), and it is sufficiently active to oxidize sulfide and iodide but not bromide or chloride. The reaction with iodide was given in Sec. 22-5e. Other typical reactions are represented by

$$2HNO_2 + H_2S \rightarrow S \downarrow + 2H_2O + 2NO \uparrow$$

$$2HNO_2 + H_2SO_3 \rightarrow SO_4^{--} + 2H^+ + 2NO \uparrow + H_2O$$

$$HNO_2 + H^+ + Fe^{++} \rightarrow Fe^{+++} + H_2O + NO \uparrow$$

The first two reactions indicate that nitrites are not compatible with sulfides or sulfites in acid solution. The third reaction produces a brown color caused by the combination of NO with excess Fe^{++} ion to give the complex $FeNO^{++}$. The color appears even in dilute acid solutions, whereas nitrate gives the same color only with concentrated sulfuric acid.

Nitrite ion is reduced to nitrogen gas by ammonium ions and sulfamic acid:

$$NH_4^+ + NO_2^- \rightarrow N_2 \uparrow + 2H_2O$$

$$HNH_2SO_3 + NO_2^- \rightarrow N_2 \uparrow + SO_4^{--} + H^+ + H_2O$$

The sequence of events in these reactions is complex. It is probable that reaction is preceded by an activation of HNO_2 to $H_2NO_2^+$ followed by a breakdown of this ion to water and the nitrosyl ion NO^+; the latter reacts directly with ammonium or sulfamate ions.

Nitrite ion is not a good oxidizing agent in alkaline solution. Very active reducing agents such as $Fe(OH)_2$, Zn, or Al reduce it to ammonia:

$$NO_2^- + 2Al + 5H_2O + OH^- \rightarrow NH_3 \uparrow + 2Al(OH)_4^-$$

f. Miscellaneous Reactions. Nitrous acid is an important reagent in organic technology for the formation of azo dyes. This is put to analytical use in the Griess reaction which is sensitive and specific for nitrite. Sulfanilic acid, α-naphthylamine, and nitrous acid combine to give the red dye

$$H_2N(C_{10}H_8)N = N(C_6H_4)SO_3H$$

22-11. Properties of Nitrate Ion, NO_3^-.

a. Electronic Structure. The oxygen atoms are arranged at the corners of an equilateral triangle with the nitrogen atom in the center. If the 24 valence electrons are distributed as shown,

each atom acquires an octet of electrons by sharing. The picture is incorrect insofar as it indicates that one oxygen-nitrogen bond is different from the others. The bonds are actually best described as intermediate between single and double; this description is supported by the observation that the N—O internuclear distance of 1.21 A lies between the values expected for a single and a double bond, namely 1.36 and 1.18 A.

b. Reaction with Protons. Nitric acid, HNO_3. Nitrate ions have a very low affinity for protons because nitric acid is a strong acid ($K_a = 23$). Alkali metal nitrates therefore give neutral solutions.

Nitric acid is prepared by the reaction of nitrogen(IV) oxide NO_2 with water or by heating nitrates with moderately concentrated sulfuric acid:

$$H_2SO_4 + NO_3^- \rightarrow HNO_3 \uparrow + HSO_4^-$$

The latter reaction takes place because hydrogen nitrate is weakly ionized and not very soluble in the sulfuric acid. Pure nitric acid decomposes slowly at room temperature when exposed to light or more rapidly when it is boiled. The reaction also occurs in the concentrated (16 M, 70%) acid:

$$4HNO_3 \rightarrow 4NO_2 + O_2 + 2H_2O$$

and the dissolved NO_2 colors the acid yellow. Red, fuming nitric acid contains an excess of dissolved NO_2. It is a powerful oxidizing agent. Anhydrous nitric acid undergoes self-ionization:

$$2HNO_3 \rightleftharpoons NO_2^+ + NO_3^- + H_2O$$

The nitronium ion NO_2^+ plays an important role in many reactions.

c. Insoluble Salts. There are no insoluble simple nitrate salts. Basic nitrates such as $Hg(OH)NO_3$ and $BiONO_3$ are soluble in nitric acid:

$$BiONO_3 \downarrow + 2H^+ \rightarrow Bi^{+++} + NO_3^- + H_2O$$

Barium nitrate is the least soluble of the familiar nitrates.

d. Complex Ions. There are a few, comparatively unstable ion-pairs, notably $PbNO_3^+$.

e. Redox Reactions. Nitrate ion contains nitrogen in its highest oxidation state, +5, and the acid is a familiar oxidizing agent. The possible reduction products include nitrogen(IV) oxide NO_2, nitrogen(II) oxide NO, hyponitrous acid $H_2N_2O_2$, nitrogen N_2, hydroxylamine NH_2OH, hydrazine N_2H_4, and the ammonium ion NH_4^+. Despite this bewildering variety, the common reactions give, if not a single product, at least a predominance of one. Thus reduction of dilute (3-6 M) acid gives largely NO, and reduction of the concentrated acid gives some NO but mostly NO_2 (or N_2O_4). With an active reducing agent such as zinc and very dilute acid, the principal product is the ammonium ion.

Nitric acid is potentially a very active oxidizing agent but is sometimes slow in its action. The reactions are frequently catalyzed by NO_2. Some typical reactions are represented by

$$4H^+ + NO_3^- + 3Cl^- \rightarrow NOCl \uparrow + Cl_2 \uparrow + 2H_2O$$

$$4H^+ + NO_3^- + Bi^0 \rightarrow NO \uparrow + Bi^{+++} + 2H_2O$$

$$4H^+ + NO_3^- + 3Fe^{++} \rightarrow NO \uparrow + 3Fe^{+++} + 2H_2O$$

The last reaction occurs readily only at high acidity such as that established by concentrated sulfuric acid and is the basis of famous "brown-ring" test. Some of the nitrogen(II) oxide combines with excess Fe^{++} ions to give the brown complex $FeNO^{++}$ at the interface between the concentrated acid and the solution under test. Nitrite ions give the same color even when the acid is dilute, and there are numerous other interferences.

Nitrate ion, like nitrite, is reduced to ammonia by zinc or aluminum in alkaline solution:

$$3NO_3^- + 8Al + 18H_2O + 5OH^- \rightarrow 8Al(OH)_4^- + 3NH_3 \uparrow$$

22-12. Properties of Phosphate Ion, PO_4^{---}.

a. Electronic Structure. The four oxygen atoms occupy the corners of a tetrahedron with the nonmetal in the center just as in the sulfate ion; the arrangement of the 32 valence electrons is also the same:

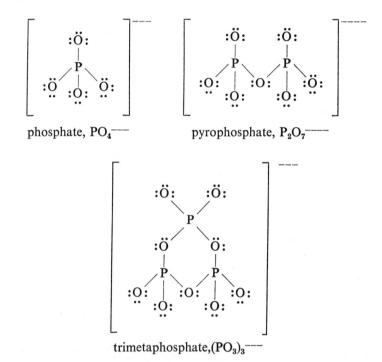

phosphate, PO_4^{---} pyrophosphate, $P_2O_7^{----}$

trimetaphosphate, $(PO_3)_3^{---}$

Two of the many condensed anions are also shown; in them phosphorus atoms are joined by oxygen bridges, but each phosphorus atom is still coordinated to four oxygen atoms. The condensed phosphates can be made by heating acid orthophosphates.

b. Reaction with Protons. Phosphoric acid, H_3PO_4. Phosphate ion is a strong base because of the low extent of ionization of the monohydrogen phosphate ion. The orthoacid dissociates in three steps:

$$H_3PO_4 \rightleftharpoons H^+ + H_2PO_4^- \qquad K_a = 7.1 \times 10^{-3}$$
$$H_2PO_4^- \rightleftharpoons H^+ + HPO_4^{--} \qquad K_a = 6.3 \times 10^{-8}$$
$$HPO_4^{--} \rightleftharpoons H^+ + PO_4^{---} \qquad K_a = 4.4 \times 10^{-13}$$

The normal phosphates, e.g., Na_3PO_4, give strongly basic solutions because of the proton transfer reaction

$$PO_4^{---} + H_2O \rightleftharpoons HPO_4^{--} + OH^-$$

The pH of 0.1 M trisodium phosphate is greater than 12. The monohydrogen phosphates give more weakly basic solutions because the HPO_4^{--} ion is both acidic and basic. The pH of 0.1 M Na_2HPO_4 is 9.2. The dihydrogen phosphates give acidic solutions; e.g., the pH of 0.1 M KH_2PO_4 is 4.5.

c. Insoluble Salts. Most normal phosphates, with the exception of those of sodium and potassium, are insoluble, and some of the monohydrogen phosphates, e.g., $CaHPO_4 \cdot 2H_2O$, can also be precipitated. Yellow silver phosphate is almost insoluble in neutral or basic solutions, but it dissolves in acids and in ammonia or ammonium carbonate:

$$Ag_3PO_4 \downarrow + 2H^+ \rightarrow 3Ag^+ + H_2PO_4^-$$

$$Ag_3PO_4 \downarrow + 6NH_3 \rightarrow 3Ag(NH_3)_2^+ + PO_4^{---}$$

Calcium phosphate, when freshly precipitated in alkaline solution,

$$3Ca^{++} + 2HPO_4^{--} + 2NH_3 \rightarrow Ca_3(PO_4)_2 \downarrow + 2NH_4^+$$

can easily be dissolved in acetic acid:

$$Ca_3(PO_4)_2 \downarrow + 4HC_2H_3O_2 \rightarrow 3Ca^{++} + 2H_2PO_4^- + 4C_2H_3O_2^-$$

The phosphates of iron(III), aluminum, and bismuth are sufficiently insoluble to precipitate from acetic acid solutions. Most of the phosphates are transposed to carbonates by boiling with sodium carbonate solution:

$$Ca_3(PO_4)_2 \downarrow + 3CO_3^{--} \rightarrow 3CaCO_3 \downarrow + 2PO_4^{---}$$

d. Complex Ions. Weak complexes are formed between Fe^{+++} (possibly also Al^{+++} ion) and HPO_4^{--} ion.

e. Redox Reactions. Although phosphoric acid contains phosphorus in its highest oxidation state, viz., $+5$, it is a very poor oxidizing agent. This is a contrast with the behavior of nitric and arsenic acids, which are the acids of the elements on either side of phosphorus in Group VB. Concentrated phosphoric acid (85% H_3PO_4) can be used in place of sulfuric acid when oxidation is to be avoided as in the displacement of HI from an iodide.

f. Miscellaneous Reactions. Bright yellow ammonium molybdophosphate precipitates when an excess of ammonium molybdate is added to a solution of a phosphate that also contains nitric acid. The composition of the precipitate is approximately $(NH_4)_3[PMo_{12}O_{40}] \cdot 6H_2O$. The radical in brackets is the anion of a *heteropolyacid: hetero-* because it contains two kinds of atoms other than oxygen and hydrogen ($H_6Mo_7O_{24}$ and $H_4P_2O_7$ are *iso*polyacids); *poly-* because it contains more than one molybdenum atom. There are a large number of such compounds: the central atom may be B, Si, P, Te, or I;

the other element may be Mo or W. Various cagelike structures have been proposed for the anion.

22-13. Properties of Carbonate Ion, CO$_3$$^{--}$.

a. Electronic Structure. The carbonate ion has a triangular structure similar to that of nitrate but with a higher net charge. The carbon-oxygen bonds are intermediate in character between double and single bonds.

b. Reaction with Protons. *Carbonic acid, H_2CO_3.* Carbonate ion has a strong affinity for protons, and solutions of carbonates are basic because of the proton transfer reaction

$$CO_3^{--} + H_2O \rightleftharpoons HCO_3^- + OH^-$$

The pH of 0.1 M Na$_2$CO$_3$, for example, is 11.5. The hydrogen carbonate ion is more basic than acidic, and its solutions are weakly alkaline; thus 0.1 M NaHCO$_3$ has a pH of 8.3. Addition of acids, even acetic acid, to carbonates liberates carbon dioxide. Because of its limited solubility (0.034 M at 25° and 1 atm), CO$_2$ comes off as a gas and can be detected by its reaction with barium hydroxide:

$$Ba^{++} + 2OH^- + CO_2 \rightarrow BaCO_3\downarrow + H_2O$$

Carbonic acid has never been isolated. Recent measurements show that only one out of every 400 molecules of CO$_2$ hydrates to H$_2$CO$_3$. The usual ionization constant (4.4×10^{-7}) counts CO$_2$ and H$_2$CO$_3$ together, but H$_2$CO$_3$ is intrinsically a stronger acid than this indicates. When allowance is made for the very low concentration of H$_2$CO$_3$ actually present, its ionization constant is 1.74×10^{-4} or about the same as that of formic acid. The hydrogen carbonate ion is a very weak acid ($K_a = 4.7 \times 10^{-11}$).

c. Insoluble Salts. Only the carbonates of sodium, potassium, and ammonium are very soluble. In order of decreasing solubility some of the more important carbonates are

$$MgCO_3,\ Ag_2CO_3,\ CaCO_3,\ BaCO_3,\ SrCO_3,\ CdCO_3,\ PbCO_3$$

Thus PbCO$_3$ allows the lowest concentration of carbonate ion in its saturated solution and MgCO$_3$ the highest. Sodium carbonate solutions are very alkaline and will precipitate basic carbonates of some metals, e.g., Mg, Zn, Cu, Pb, and Bi. If the carbonate is sufficiently insoluble, this can be avoided by using sodium bicarbonate:

$$Pb^{++} + 2HCO_3^- \rightarrow PbCO_3\downarrow + 2H^+$$

Sodium bicarbonate does not furnish a high enough concentration of carbonate ion to precipitate the more soluble carbonates. The carbonates of Al^{+++}, Fe^{+++}, Cr^{+++}, and other highly acidic cations cannot be prepared. The addition of a carbonate to a solution of the metal ions causes precipitation of the hydroxide and liberation of CO_2.

All carbonates dissolve in acids with the evolution of CO_2. Carbonates of the alkaline earth metals are dissolved by carbonic acid:

$$CO_2 + H_2O + BaCO_3 \downarrow \rightarrow Ba^{++} + 2HCO_3^-$$

d. Complex Ions.   Unstable complexes are formed by Ag^+ and Cu^{++} ions. The carbonate complex of uranium(VI) is important.

e. Redox Reactions.   There are none of any consequence.

22-14. Properties of Oxalate Ion, $C_2O_4^{--}$.

a. Electronic Structure.   The two carbon atoms are joined by a covalent bond:

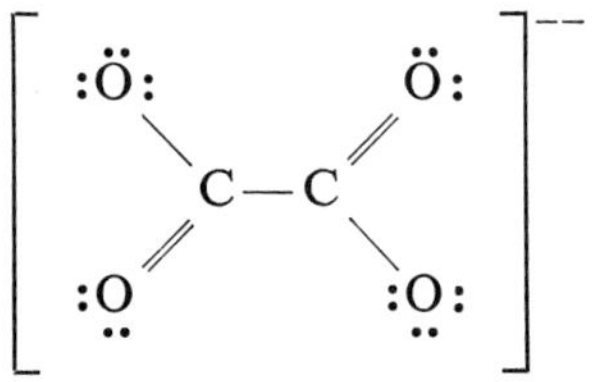

As in the carbonate ion, each carbon atom is bonded to three other atoms and the bonds to oxygen are intermediate between single and double.

b. Reaction with Protons.   Oxalic acid, $H_2C_2O_4$.   Oxalate ions have a weak attraction for protons, and solutions of oxalates are slightly basic:

$$C_2O_4^{--} + H_2O \rightleftharpoons HC_2O_4^- + OH^-$$

The pH of 0.1 M sodium oxalate is 8.5.

Oxalic acid is usually supplied as a white, crystalline hydrate $H_2C_2O_4 \cdot 2H_2O$. It is a moderately strong acid with respect to loss of the first proton:

$$H_2C_2O_4 \rightleftharpoons H^+ + HC_2O_4^- \qquad K_a = 5.4 \times 10^{-2}$$

$$HC_2O_4^- \rightleftharpoons H^+ + C_2O_4^{--} \qquad K_a = 5.4 \times 10^{-5}$$

c. Insoluble Salts.   All oxalates are insoluble except those of the alkali metals, ammonium, and iron(III). The last one probably dissolves because of formation of the complex $Fe[Fe(C_2O_4)_3]$. The oxalates of the bivalent metals do not differ greatly in molar solubility. The most soluble is MgC_2O_4 and the least soluble are CaC_2O_4 and PbC_2O_4. Magnesium oxalate and perhaps several of the others are extensively associated in solution. All are soluble in strong acids, and silver oxalate dissolves in ammonia or ammonium carbonate solution because of the formation of weakly dissociated $Ag(NH_3)_2^+$ ions. The least soluble common oxalates, those of calcium and lead, dissolve only slightly in acetic acid. The oxalates of the rare earth metals are insoluble in dilute acids.

d. Complex Ions. A number of complexes are formed of which those of the trivalent metals are most stable, e.g., $Zn(C_2O_4)_2^{--}$, $Al(C_2O_4)_3^{---}$, $Fe(C_2O_4)_3^{---}$, and $Mn(C_2O_4)_3^{---}$.

e. Redox Reactions. Although oxalic acid is potentially an active reducing agent, the rate of its reaction is slow in the absence of a catalyst. The only reaction of analytical importance is that with permanganate in acid solution:

$$5H_2C_2O_4 + 2MnO_4^- + 6H^+ \rightarrow 10CO_2 \uparrow + 2Mn^{++} + 8H_2O$$

The reaction is catalyzed by Mn^{++} ions, one of the products, and is extraordinarily complex. Apparently oxalate complexes of manganese are involved in certain steps of the reaction.

22-15. Properties of Acetate Ion, $C_2H_3O_2^-$.

a. Electronic Structure. The acetate ion contains a methyl group ($-CH_3$) joined to a carboxylate ion ($-COO^-$):

$$\left[\begin{array}{c} H \\ \backslash \\ H-C-C \\ / \\ H \end{array} \begin{array}{c} \ddot{O}: \\ \diagup \\ \diagdown \\ \ddot{O}: \\ \cdot\cdot \end{array} \right]^-$$

In oxalate ion, it may be noted, two carboxylate ions were joined together. There are many other organic acid anions which contain this charged group but differ in the other group attached to it.

b. Reaction with Protons. Acetic acid, $HC_2H_3O_2$. Since acetic acid is a moderately weak acid ($K_a = 1.8 \times 10^{-5}$), acetate ions accept protons:

$$C_2H_3O_2^- + H_2O \rightleftharpoons HC_2H_3O_2 + OH^-$$

$$2C_2H_3O_2^- + 2H^+ + SO_4^{--} \rightleftharpoons 2HC_2H_3O_2 + SO_4^{--}$$

Because of the reaction with water, solutions of acetates are often weakly basic; the pH of 0.1 M sodium acetate, for example, is 8.9. The second reaction shows the displacement of acetic acid by a strong acid. When the weak acid vaporizes, it can sometimes be recognized by its sharp, vinegar-like odor but this is not very distinctive.

The pure acid is a liquid which freezes at 16.6° to a icy solid, hence the name "glacial" acetic acid. It is extensively associated in the vapor, as a pure liquid, and in solutions:

$$
\begin{array}{ccc}
 & \text{O----H—O} & \\
 & \diagup\kern-0.3em\diagup \qquad\quad \diagdown & \\
\text{H}_3\text{C—C} & & \text{C—CH}_3 \\
 & \diagdown \qquad\quad \diagup\kern-0.3em\diagup & \\
 & \text{O—H----O} &
\end{array}
$$

(The dashed lines represent hydrogen bonds.)

c. Insoluble Salts.   All normal acetates are soluble although those of Ag, Hg(I), and Cr(II) are only sparingly so. Basic acetates such as those of Fe(III) and Al sometimes precipitate. They dissolve in strong acids. Solid acetates are decomposed by heat with the evolution of volatile substances such as acetone $(CH_3)_2CO$ as well as with charring.

d. Complex Ions.   Acetate ion forms unstable complexes with a number of cations. Those with Fe^{+++} and Pb^{++} ions are the only ones of much significance in qualitative analysis. The extent of dissociation of the lead acetate complexes is sufficiently low to make lead sulfate soluble in hot 3 M ammonium acetate (Chapter 18). Indium(III) and the uranyl ion UO_2^{++} are less common cations that form comparatively stable complexes with acetate.

e. Redox Reactions.   There are none of any consequence.

f. Miscellaneous Reactions.   With alcohols, acetic acid and many other acids (see Sec. 22-16f) form esters; these are fragrant, volatile liquids used as solvents. Esterification is a slow process, but it is catalyzed by acids, particularly concentrated sulfuric acid. The reaction between acetic acid and ethyl alcohol can be represented by

$$
\text{H}-\underset{\underset{\text{H}}{|}}{\overset{\overset{\text{H}}{|}}{\text{C}}}-\text{C}\!\!\overset{\diagup\!\!\diagup\;\text{O}}{\underset{\diagdown\;\text{OH}}{}} \;+\; \text{HO}-\underset{\underset{\text{H}}{|}}{\overset{\overset{\text{H}}{|}}{\text{C}}}-\underset{\underset{\text{H}}{|}}{\overset{\overset{\text{H}}{|}}{\text{C}}}-\text{H} \;\rightleftharpoons\; \text{H}_2\text{O} \;+\; \text{H}-\underset{\underset{\text{H}}{|}}{\overset{\overset{\text{H}}{|}}{\text{C}}}-\text{C}\!\!\overset{\diagup\!\!\diagup\;\text{O}}{\underset{\diagdown\;\text{O}}{}}\!\!\overset{\text{H}}{\underset{|}{}}\text{C}-\text{C}-\text{H}
$$

or

$$
\text{HC}_2\text{H}_3\text{O}_2 \;+\; \text{C}_2\text{H}_5\text{OH} \;\rightleftharpoons\; \text{H}_2\text{O} \;+\; \text{C}_2\text{H}_3\text{O}_2\text{C}_2\text{H}_5
$$

Other alcohols can be used in place of ethyl alcohol, and some of the esters have distinctive odors, e.g., isoamyl acetate with a banana-like odor.

22-16. Properties of Borate Ion, $B(OH)_4{}^-$.

a. Electronic Structure.   The structure of the simple borate ion is still uncertain. In solid boric acid (Fig. 2-4) each boron atom is bonded to three hydroxide groups, and the formula $B(OH)_3$ (or H_3BO_3) is well established. The most common solid salts are borax $Na_2B_4O_7 \cdot 10H_2O$ and metaborates such as $AgBO_2$, $Ba(BO_2)_2$, or $Ca(BO_2)_2$, but those do not contain simple $B_4O_7^{--}$ or BO_2^- ions. The structure of the metaborate ion in calcium metaborate is that of a long chain in which each boron atom is bonded to three oxygen atoms:

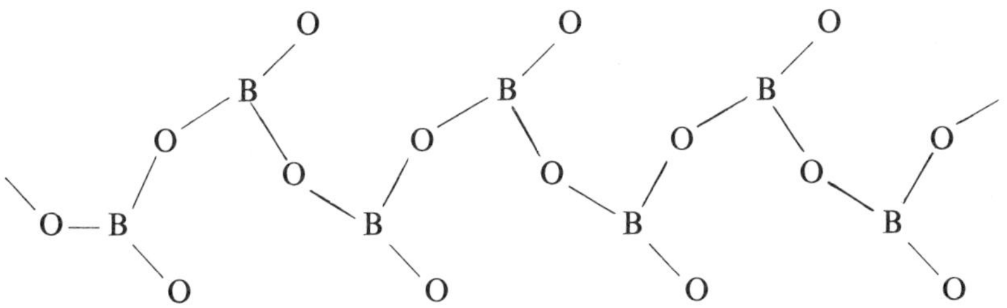

Since two oxygen atoms are shared with other boron atoms, the ratio of boron to oxygen is $1:2$ as required by the simplest formula $Ca(BO_2)_2$.

Boron has three valence electrons, and when it forms three bonds it does not acquire the electronic configuration of an inert gas. This it can do only by bonding to four groups, and there are a number of crystals that contain such ions as BF_4^- and $B(OH)_4^-$ or more complex anions such as $B_3O_3(OH)_5^{--}$ in which some of the boron atoms are coordinated to four and others to three oxygen atoms.

Solutions of borates undoubtedly contain several ions. Recent spectral measurements on concentrated solutions of potassium borate indicate the presence of tetrahedral $B(OH)_4^-$ ions. This, at least, is preferable to the unlikely formula BO_2^-.

b. Reaction with Protons. *Boric acid, H_3BO_3.* Since boric acid is a very weak acid ($K_a = 5.8 \times 10^{-10}$), borate ions have a strong affinity for protons. Solutions of borates are alkaline and contain free boric acid:

$$B(OH)_4^- \rightleftharpoons H_3BO_3 + OH^-$$

Borax solutions are, in effect, buffer mixtures of sodium borate and boric acid; dissolution of the salt in water is represented by

$$Na_2B_4O_7 \cdot 10H_2O \downarrow \rightarrow 2Na^+ + 2B(OH)_4^- + 2H_3BO_3 + 3H_2O$$

The pH of 0.1 M borax is 9.2.

Boric acid is a waxy solid, slightly soluble in water (5.5 g/100 g of solution at 25°, 28.7 g/100 g at 100°), less soluble in the presence of strong acids. It is appreciably volatilized from boiling solutions. The low ionization constant of boric acid is characteristic of acids which have no nonhydroxide oxygen atoms (Sec. 7-12). Whether it can lose more than one proton is as yet open to question; values of the second and third ionization constants have been reported (5×10^{-13} and 4×10^{-14}), but they cannot be accepted without reservation in view of their small magnitude (close to K_w of water) and of the unknown condition of boric acid in solution.

c. Insoluble Salts.   No borates can be precipitated from solutions that are even weakly acid. Alkali metal borates and borax precipitate the metaborates of weakly acidic cations, e.g., $AgBO_2$, $Ba(BO_2)_2$, and $Ca(BO_2)_2$. Precipitation is prevented by high concentrations of ammonium salts, doubtless because of a shift of the equilibrium

$$NH_4^+ + B(OH)_4^- \rightleftharpoons NH_3 + H_3BO_3 + H_2O$$

to the right. Borates do not cause serious difficulties in cation analysis. All borates are soluble in acids, even acetic acid, and silver borate dissolves in ammonia or ammonium carbonate solution.

d. Complex Ions.   There is little evidence for the formation of borate complexes with cations. Important complexes with fluoride and peroxide are known: BF_4^- and $B(OH)_3(O_2H)^-$. Boric acid reacts with organic compounds, such as glycerol and mannitol, that contain several hydroxide groups to give complexes that are more acidic than boric acid itself. This is the basis for a qualitative test for borate; when carefully neutralized solutions of borate and mannitol are mixed, the solution becomes acidic.

e. Redox Reactions.   There are none.

f. Miscellaneous Reactions.   (1) Boric acid forms volatile esters such as trimethyl borate:

$$\overset{H_2SO_4}{B(OH)_3 + 3CH_3OH \rightleftharpoons B(OCH_3)_3 + 3H_2O}$$

These burn with a green flame:

$$2B(OCH_3)_3 + 9O_2 \rightarrow B_2O_3 + 6CO_2 + 9H_2O$$

(2) Boric acid in slightly acid solutions gives a red color with turmeric which turns dark green or blue upon addition of sodium hydroxide. Turmeric is a yellow coloring matter, obtained from the East Indian plant *Curcuma longa*, used as a condiment in curries and pickles. The action of boric acid is obscure. The red product (rosocyanine) is simply a different form or isomer of turmeric ($C_{21}H_{20}O_6$).

EXERCISES

22-1. Write structural formulas for CO_3^{--}, H_3PO_4, HF_2^-, and I_5^-.

22-2. Boron, carbon, nitrogen, and sulfur form ions of general formula XO_3 but with different charges. Which ion or ions (a) has no double bonds, (b) has no complete octet about X, (c) is not planar?

22-3. Suggest an explanation for the fact that the formula of nitric acid is HNO_3 and not H_3NO_4 like H_3PO_4 (Hint: See Sec. 6-11).

22-4. Cite evidence to support the classification of thiocyanogen as a pseudo-halogen.

22-5. Cite evidence to support the assertion that the nitrogen-oxygen bonds in the nitrite ion are not simple single or double bonds.

22-6. A number of ions contain X—O—X bridges. Cite examples for $X = S, P$, and B.

22-7. Show how hydrogen bonding is involved in the structures of HF_2^-, crystalline H_3BO_3, and $(HC_2H_3O_2)_2$.

22-8. Discuss the problem of the constitution of borate ions.

22-9. Arrange the following anions in order of increasing affinity for protons:
$$S^{--}, NO_3^-, SO_3^{--}, C_2H_3O_2^-, NO_2^-$$

22-10. Write equations for the hydrolysis reactions in solutions of Na_3PO_4, K_2CO_3, and KF.

22-11. Arrange the following acids in order of increasing strength:
$$HF, HNO_2, HSO_3^-, H_3BO_3, HNCS$$

22-12. Concentrated orthophosphoric acid is 85% H_3PO_4 and has a density of 1.7 g/ml. Calculate the molarity of the acid.

22-13. Write equations for (a) the reaction of HF with $CaSiO_3$, (b) the reaction of concentrated H_3PO_4 with solid KI, (c) the reaction of HCl with borax, (d) the reaction of H_2S with $Pb(OH)_3^-$ ions.

22-14. Which of these silver salts
$$AgSCN, AgNO_2, Ag_3PO_4, AgCl, Ag_2CO_3$$
are soluble in (a) dilute nitric acid, (b) ammonium carbonate solution?

22-15. Write equations for the reaction of (a) zinc and acid with silver chloride, (b) silver iodide with sodium sulfide, (c) silver sulfite and hydrochloric acid, (d) silver phosphate and sodium chloride, (e) silver sulfate and barium nitrate.

22-16. Arrange in order of decreasing solubility in water:
$$BaSO_4, BaC_2O_4, BaI_2, Ba(NO_3)_2$$

22-17. How can you distinguish between (a) $BaSO_4$ and $BaSO_3$, (b) CaC_2O_4 and $CaCO_3$, (c) $BaSO_4$ and BaS, (d) CaF_2 and $CaCl_2$, (e) $BaSO_4$ and BaC_2O_4?

22-18. Write equations for the reactions that occur when (a) carbon dioxide is bubbled through a suspension of $CaCO_3$, (b) hydrochloric acid is added to calcium metaborate, (c) solid calcium nitrite is heated, (d) calcium chloride is heated with concentrated sulfuric acid, (e) calcium sulfate solution is added to lead nitrate solution.

22-19. Why is the fluoride complex of Al^{+++} ion more stable than that of Hg^{++} ion while the reverse is true of the iodide complexes?

22-20. Arrange the following reducing agents in order of increasing reducing power: $S^{--}, F^-, Br^-, I^-, SCN^-$.

22-21. Cite evidence to support the assertion that I^- ion falls between Fe^{++} and H_2SO_3 in reducing power.

22-22. Predict the products of the redox reactions between these pairs. Assume acid solution. (a) bromate ion and free iodine, (b) potassium dichromate and hydrogen sulfide, (c) bromine and calcium iodide, (d) zinc and bismuth sulfide, (e) hot concentrated sulfuric acid and sulfur, (f) bromine and potassium thiocyanate.

22-23. Complete and balance by the ion-electron or oxidation number method. Assume acid solution unless otherwise indicated.

(a) $MnO_4^- + Cl^- \rightarrow Cl_2 + Mn^{++}$

(b) $HNO_2 + I^- \rightarrow NO + I_2$

(c) $O_2 + I^- \rightarrow H_2O + I_3^-$

(d) $HNO_2 + SCN^- \rightarrow HCN + SO_4^{--} + NO$

(e) $HNO_2 + H_2S \rightarrow S + NO$

(f) $H_2SO_3 + H_2S \rightarrow S$

(g) $Br_2 + H_2S \rightarrow Br^- + SO_4^{--}$

(h) $Cr_2O_7^{--} + H_2SO_3 \rightarrow Cr^{+++} + SO_4^{--}$

(i) $O_2 + SO_3^{--} \rightarrow SO_4^{--}$ (Basic solution.)

(j) $HNO_2 + HNO_2 \rightarrow NO + NO_3^-$

(k) $SO_3^{--} + H_2O_2 \rightarrow SO_4^{--} + H_2O$ (Basic solution.)

(l) $H_2SO_3 + HNO_2 \rightarrow SO_4^{--} + NO$

(m) $NO_3^- + Al \rightarrow Al(OH)_4^- + NH_3$ (Basic solution.)

(n) $NO_3^- + Cl^- \rightarrow NOCl + Cl_2$

(o) $H_2C_2O_4 + MnO_4^- \rightarrow Mn^{++} + CO_2$

22-24. Predict the products and write a balanced equation for these redox reactions. Assume an acid solution unless otherwise indicated. (a) iron(III) nitrate and potassium iodide, (b) 16 M nitric acid and potassium iodide, (c) iodine and sulfurous acid, (d) potassium ferricyanide and hydrogen sulfide, (e) hot concentrated nitric acid and hydrogen sulfide, (f) iron(II) hydroxide and sodium nitrite (basic solution), (g) dilute nitric acid and sulfurous acid, (h) zinc and sodium nitrate (basic solution).

22-25. What is meant by "heteropolyacid"?

22-26. Represent by an equation the formation of ethyl nitrite, an ester, from nitrous acid and ethyl alcohol.

22-27. When ethyl acetate is hydrolyzed by H_2O^{18}, the heavy oxygen ends up in the acid and not in the alcohol. When acetic acid is esterified, does it lose a hydrogen atom or a hydroxide group?

CHAPTER TWENTY-THREE

The Identification
of Anions

23-1. Introduction. The eighteen anions that can be detected by the procedures given in this chapter are listed below together with the sections in which their detection is described:

F^- (23-12)	SO_3^{--} (23-20)	AsO_3^{---} (23-7)
Cl^- (23-13, -16, -17)	SO_4^{--} (23-21)	AsO_4^{---} (23-24)
Br^- (23-14, -16, -17)	CrO_4^{--} (23-9)	CO_3^{--} (23-25)
I^- (23-15, -16, -17)	NO_2^- (23-22)	$C_2O_4^{--}$ (23-26)
SCN^- (23-18)	NO_3^- (23-23)	$C_2H_3O_2^-$ (23-27)
S^{--} (23-19)	PO_4^{---} (23-24)	$B(OH)_4^-$ (23-28)

Three of these ions, CrO_4^{--}, AsO_3^{---}, and AsO_4^{---}, contain elements ordinarily detected in the cation analysis. Because they interfere with the tests for some of the other anions, provision must be made for their separation.

The analysis for anions can be carried out according to a systematic series of separations analogous to the usual method of analysis for cations, or tests can be made on separate portions of the sample if interfering ions are removed. In this text most of the anions are tested for individually, but it is convenient to use a systematic procedure for sulfide, arsenite, iodide, thiocyanate, bromide, and chloride ions. The test for any ion of this group will fail unless the ions that come before it in the sequence are removed.[1] The other anions can be detected in any convenient order if interfering ions are removed first.

A feature of anion analysis is the use of general elimination tests to indicate the absence of groups of ions. If, for example, no gas is evolved when a sample is treated with dilute sulfuric acid, the absence of carbonate, sulfite, nitrite, and sulfide is generally indicated. With the evidence from the elimination tests at hand it is seldom necessary to test for all 18 anions.

---

[1] The scheme used in this text is an adaptation of that given by R. Belcher and H. Weisz (*Mikrochim. Acta*, **1956**, 1847; **1958**, 571), and can readily be expanded to include 17 or more other anions.

The incompatibility of certain ions is a much greater problem in anion analysis than in cation analysis. Incompatible pairs of ions are usually a combination of an oxidizing agent and a reducing agent, e.g., Hg^{++} and Sn^{++}, SO_3^{--} and S^{--}, or CrO_4^{--} and I^-. Such combinations of anions are frequently stable in neutral or alkaline solutions, but reaction occurs when the solution is acidified. Provision must be made in the analysis for the separation of the pair before the ions destroy each other.

23-2. Preparation of the Sample for Analysis.

a. Principles. There is no problem if the anions are present as sodium, potassium, or ammonium salts, for these are all water soluble. Other cations may tie up the anions in salts that are insoluble. Furthermore, some of the "heavy" metals such as iron or tin may interfere with certain tests. It thus is necessary to precipitate the heavy metal ions and bring the anions associated with them into solution. This is accomplished by transposition with sodium carbonate: carbonates and hydroxides of the heavy metals precipitate and the solution contains the soluble sodium salts of the anions. Since the solution also contains an excess of carbonate ion, a test for that anion must be made on the original sample.

Transposition is generally carried out either by fusing the sample with sodium carbonate or boiling it with a solution of the reagent. The former is more effective but less convenient, and some anions are decomposed by heat. The success of transposition with the solution depends on the relative solubility products of the heavy metal salt and its carbonate and on the concentration of carbonate ion (Sec. 10-13). Consider, for example, the transposition of manganese(II) and lead sulfides as represented by

$$MnS + CO_3^{--} \rightarrow MnCO_3 + S^{--} \qquad K = K_{sp}(MnS)/K_{sp}(MnCO_3) = 0.11$$

$$PbS + CO_3^{--} \rightarrow PbCO_3 + S^{--} \qquad K = K_{sp}(PbS)/K_{sp}(PbCO_3)$$
$$= 5 \times 10^{-15}$$

The very small value of the second constant shows that this conversion will be much more difficult to bring about than the first. Certain materials found in nature are more recalcitrant than the freshly prepared compounds, and provision is made for the detection of the simpler of these. No attempt is made to give a procedure that can be used on all conceivable materials.

b. Procedure.

(1) Test the solubility of a pinch (about 20 mg) of sample in 1 ml of water. Warm if necessary in a hot water bath. If the sample dissolves completely, proceed to (2); otherwise, to (3).

(2) Test the water solution from (1) for heavy metals by adding a drop of sodium carbonate solution (dissolve a little of the solid reagent in a few drops of water). If *no* precipitate forms, dissolve 0.10 g of the original solid

sample in 5 ml of water, and use this solution for subsequent tests. If there is a precipitate of heavy metal carbonates, proceed to (3).

(3) If the sample is not completely soluble in water and contains heavy metals, weigh 0.10 g into a small (about 25 ml) Erlenmeyer flask of borosilicate glass (e.g., Pyrex or Kimax). Add 5 ml of water, 0.50 g of anhydrous sodium carbonate, and a carborundum chip to prevent bumping and promote smooth boiling. Note the level of the liquid in the flask. Boil the mixture for at least 10 minutes. Add water now and then to keep the volume approximately constant. Hold moist red litmus paper in the escaping vapors. If it turns blue, ammonia is being driven off. Ammonia is formed by reaction of ammonium salts with carbonate:

$$2NH_4{}^+ + CO_3{}^{--} \xrightarrow{\Delta} 2NH_3 \uparrow + CO_2 \uparrow + H_2O \uparrow$$

Boiling must be continued until no more ammonia is evolved.

Transfer the mixture to two centrifuge tubes and settle the precipitate by centrifugation. Combine the solutions. Wash the precipitates once with water and add the wash water to the solution. Reserve the solution, hereafter called the *Prepared Solution*, for the anion tests. If it is yellow, chromate is probably present (see also Elimination Test 4, Sec. 23-6, and Elimination Test 6, Sec. 23-8).

Combine the residues from the sodium carbonate treatment (Technique 11, Sec. 16-3). Add 6 M $HC_2H_3O_2$ to the residue until no more gas is evolved; put in a few drops at a time and mix well after each addition. Acetic acid dissolves all carbonates. If a residue remains, it may contain one or more of the following: F^-, $PO_4{}^{---}$, $AsO_4{}^{---}$, S^{--}, $SO_4{}^{--}$ (as $BaSO_4$), or $AgCl$, $AgBr$, and AgI. Save this residue and if tests for any of these ions with the Prepared Solution are negative or indecisive, test for them on the residue according to the directions that are given under each ion in the later sections of this chapter.

ELIMINATION TESTS

23-3. ET-1. Test for Strongly Acidic or Basic Anions. If and only if the sample is a solution or if it was a solid completely soluble in water and lacking any heavy metal ions, determine its pH with long-range indicator paper. A strongly acid reaction (pH less than 2) may be given by $HSO_4{}^-$ ion or free acids. A strongly alkaline reaction (pH of 10 or more) is given by S^{--}, $SO_3{}^{--}$, $PO_4{}^{---}$, $AsO_3{}^{---}$, $AsO_4{}^{---}$, $CO_3{}^{--}$, and $B(OH)_4{}^-$. Only a *strongly* basic solution is significant. In more weakly basic solutions these ions can still be present at low concentration or in the form of hydrogen anions such as HS^- or $HCO_3{}^-$, but so many ions give weakly alkaline reactions that no help is derived from such an observation. The Prepared Solution will obviously be strongly alkaline because of the excess sodium carbonate that it contains, and this test is pointless for it.

23-4. ET-2. Test for Volatile or Unstable Acids. Put sufficient solid sample in a *dry* test tube to make a layer at the bottom about 1 mm deep. Add 1 drop of 6 M H_2SO_4 and mix by flicking the bottom of the tube with your forefinger. Watch for the evolution of gas. Note the odor by wafting cautiously some of the gas toward your nose. Warm in a water bath if no distinct reaction occurs at room temperature. The following ions are detected: (1) CO_3^{--}: gives colorless, odorless CO_2. It is sometimes liberated slowly from minerals by H_2SO_4, more rapidly by HCl. (2) SO_3^{--}: gives colorless SO_2 with sharp odor. The test may fail in the presence of oxidizing agents such as chromate or reducing agents such as sulfide. (3) S^{--}: gives colorless H_2S with vile odor. The gas turns moist lead acetate paper black. The more insoluble sulfides are not decomposed by H_2SO_4 or HCl (Sec. 23-19). (4) NO_2^-: gives colorless NO which turns to red-brown NO_2 in air. The odor is sharp. Positive results must be confirmed by subsequent tests. A negative result indicates the absence of these four ions, unless the material is not readily attacked by the acid as noted under (1) and (3).

Certain other reactions may also occur: (a) formation of acetic acid vapor, colorless with vinegar-like odor, (b) liberation of free iodine, brown solution, violet vapor, and (c) change in color of mixture from yellow of CrO_4^{--} to orange of $Cr_2O_7^{--}$. The odor of acetic acid is easily obscured by those of SO_2, NO_2, or H_2S and will be observed only when these are absent and when the sample contains a high concentration of acetate. Iodine will form only if an oxidizing agent is present and reducing agents are absent. These changes are notable only when observed; their absence is not significant.

23-5. ET-3. Test for Strong Reducing Substances

a. Principle. The test depends upon the formation of Prussian blue by reduction of some $Fe(CN)_6^{---}$ to $Fe(CN)_6^{----}$ in the presence of Fe^{+++}:

$$Fe(CN)_6^{---} + e^- \text{ (from reducing agent)} \rightarrow Fe(CN)_6^{----}$$

$$K^+ + Fe^{+++} + Fe(CN)_6^{----} \rightarrow KFeFe(CN)_6 \text{ (Prussian blue)}$$

If reducing agents are absent, a brownish coloration is obtained

$$Fe(CN)_6^{---} + Fe^{+++} \rightarrow FeFe(CN)_6 \text{ (brown)}$$

b. Procedure. Prepare a fresh saturated solution of potassium ferricyanide [$K_3Fe(CN)_6$] by stirring some crystals of the salt with a few drops of water in a depression of the spot plate. A freshly prepared solution is required because old solutions may contain $Fe(CN)_6^{----}$ ions by decomposition and a false test would result.

Acidify a few drops of Prepared Solution [or solution from Sec. 23-2b(2)] with 6 M HCl. Add one drop of $FeCl_3$ solution and one of the fresh $K_3Fe(CN)_6$ solution. Let the mixture stand for 5 minutes. The following ions are detected by formation of a green-to-blue coloration or precipitate: I^-, S^{--}, SO_3^{--}, NO_2^-, and AsO_3^{---}. Thiocyanate forms a deep red complex ion $FeSCN^{++}$. Other reducing anions such as Br^- or $C_2O_4^{--}$ are unaffected by this test.

23-6. ET-4. Test for Strong Oxidizing Agents.

a. Principle. Certain ions can oxidize Mn(II) to a dark-colored chloro-complex of Mn(III) in strong hydrochloric acid solution. The formula of the complex has not been established.

b. Procedure. To 2 drops of Prepared Solution [or solution from Sec. 23-2b(2)] in a dry test tube add 6 drops of a saturated solution of $MnCl_2$ in 12 M HCl. Warm in the water bath for about a minute. A brown or black color indicates the presence of CrO_4^{--} or NO_3^-. Nitrite ion give a less distinctive brown or yellow color. If strong reducing agents were found in ET-3, this test may fail because of combination of the oxidizing and reducing agents in acid solution. A positive result is therefore more significant than a negative one.

23-7. ET-5. Test for Anions That Form Insoluble Silver Salts

a. Principle. Although a large number of anions form silver salts that are insoluble in neutral solutions, most of these salts are dissolved by a strong acid or by ammonia. In order of increasing molar solubility in ammonia solutions of a fixed concentration the silver salts are: Ag_2S (least soluble), AgI, AgBr, AgSCN, AgCl, Ag_3AsO_3 (?), Ag_3AsO_4, Ag_2SO_3, Ag_3PO_4, Ag_2CO_3, $Ag_2C_2O_4$, $AgNO_2$, $AgC_2H_3O_2$, $AgBO_2$ (?), Ag_2SO_4, and $AgNO_3$ and AgF (very soluble). If the concentration of ammonia is kept low, the extent of dissociation of the complex as represented by

$$Ag(NH_3)_2^+ \rightleftharpoons Ag^+ + 2NH_3 \qquad K = 6.3 \times 10^{-8}$$

will be large. Then the least soluble salts will not be dissolved. In the procedure below a mixture of silver nitrate, ammonia, and ammonium carbonate is used to precipitate the first six salts in the series. The carbonate ion is used to control the concentration of ammonia. If the latter is allowed to go too high, silver arsenite and silver chloride will not precipitate completely. The control of ammonia is based on the equilibrium:

$$NH_4^+ + CO_3^{--} \rightleftharpoons NH_3 + HCO_3^-$$

If by chance too much ammonia is present, some will be removed by combination with hydrogen carbonate ion. As ammonia is withdrawn to form the silver ammonia complex, more ammonia is generated by combination of carbonate and ammonium ions. Thus this equilibrium can be used to regulate the concentration of ammonia and through it the concentration of silver ion so only the six least soluble silver salts are precipitated. In practice the separation is not clear cut, and some silver arsenite often remains unprecipitated. The separation is still satisfactory for qualitative analyses.

b. Procedure. The scheme is given in condensed form in Outline 8.

(1) Preparation of ammoniacal silver nitrate-ammonium carbonate reagent. To 2 drops of 3.3 M AgNO$_3$ (Solution A) add ammoniacal ammonium carbonate solution (Solution B) drop by drop until the precipitate which forms at first just dissolves. Avoid an excess; about 7 drops of Solution B should be required.[2]

(2) Precipitation of the silver salts. To the reagent that you have just prepared add 20 drops (1 ml) of Prepared Solution. Mix well and allow to stand for a minute. *If no precipitate forms*, the absence of Cl$^-$, Br$^-$, I$^-$, SCN$^-$, S^{--}, and AsO$_3$$^{---}$ ions in the Prepared Solution is indicated. These ions may still be present in the original sample in the form of heavy metal salts that are not transposed by sodium carbonate.

Separate the precipitate and solution by centrifugation and wash the precipitate once with water. Treat the precipitate by step (3) which follows. Save the solution for ET-6. If it has a hazy appearance owing to the presence of colloidal silver salts, add a few crystals of ammonium nitrate (or a few drops of a solution of the salt), stir, and allow to stand for a minute or so before recentrifuging.

(3) Treatment of the precipitate from step (2): white AgCl and AgSCN, very pale yellow AgBr, yellow AgI and Ag$_3$AsO$_3$, and black Ag$_2$S.

(a) Identification of sulfide. A black precipitate indicates the presence of sulfide in the Prepared Solution, but it may be difficult to see in a large precipitate of the other silver salts. Transfer a little of the precipitate to a small square of filter or spot paper with a pipet. Add a few drops of 0.5 M Na$_2$S$_2$O$_3$ solution. The presence of sulfide is indicated by a residual brown or black stain (Sec. 22-7c). The white paper makes a convenient background for observing a dark residue. If sulfides were not transposed by sodium carbonate during preparation of the sample, no test for sulfide will be obtained here; see Sec. 23-19.

(b) Identification of arsenite. Add several drops of 6M HNO$_3$ to the precipitated silver salts and warm briefly. Centrifuge and transfer the solution to a test tube. Wash the precipitate with water and save for step (c) which follows. Make the solution basic with 15 M NH$_3$, add 3 drops of 3% H$_2$O$_2$, and warm for a few minutes in the water bath. Then make the solution just acid with acetic acid, and add several drops of AgNO$_3$ solution. The *presence of arsenite* is indicated by the formation of a red-brown precipitate of Ag$_3$AsO$_4$.

[2] A freshly prepared solution is used because old solutions may contain dangerous silver fulminate.

OUTLINE 8. Schematic summary of ET-5, -6, -7 and the systematic analysis for the halide ions (Secs. 23-7, -8, -9, -16)

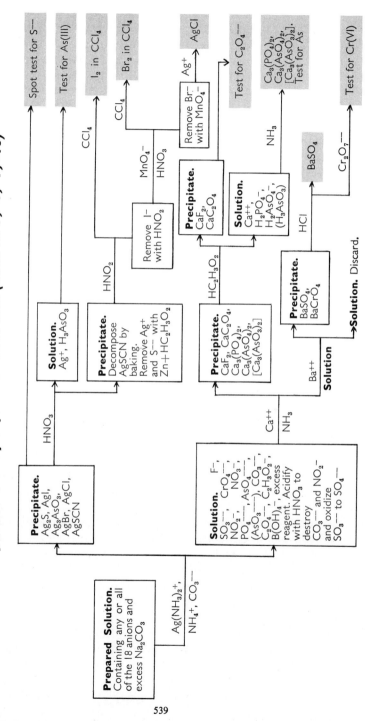

Silver arsenite is dissolved by nitric acid because of the formation of weakly ionized arsenious acid. Silver sulfide is also dissolved to some extent because of oxidation of the sulfide to sulfur (Sec. 22-7c). The arsenite ion is oxidized to arsenate by hydrogen peroxide in basic solution:

$$AsO_3^{---} + H_2O_2 \rightarrow AsO_4^{---} + H_2O$$

Silver arsenate will precipitate only in neutral or weakly acid solutions. If the solution is too acid, the concentration of arsenate ion allowed by the ionization of $HAsO_4^{--}$ is too low to permit the precipitation of the silver salt.

(c) Decomposition of silver thiocyanate. Cautiously heat in a micro-flame the test tube containing the silver salts from (b) until water is driven off. Then heat more strongly for a minute to decompose silver thiocyanate. Decomposition is accompanied by charring. Cool the tube before carrying out step (d).

(d) Removal of silver. To the residue from step (c) add 20 drops of 6 M $HC_2H_3O_2$ and half a spatula-full of zinc metal. Heat the tube in the water bath for 15 minutes. Break apart the clumps of precipitate with a rod now and then to bring fresh surfaces into contact with the reagents. Add more zinc, if necessary, to ensure a continuous reaction. While the reaction proceeds, carry out the remaining elimination tests and prepare the elimination chart (Sec. 23-10).

At the end of 15 minutes, dilute the mixture with 5-10 drops of $HC_2H_3O_2$ and transfer it to a centrifuge tube. Centrifuge to separate the solution from the last of the residue; transfer the solution to a test tube and save it for the systematic analysis of Sec. 23-16. It may contain I^-, Br^-, or Cl^- ions.

23-8. ET-6. Precipitation of Insoluble Calcium Salts.

Transfer the solution from ET-5, step (2), the precipitation of the silver salts, to a casserole. Cautiously acidify it with 16 M HNO_3. Other silver salts may precipitate as the ammonia is neutralized; they will redissolve in acid. Stir and warm until gas bubbles cease to come off. The acidification removes carbonate and nitrite, and sulfite is oxidized by the nitric acid to sulfate. Evaporate the solution until the volume is about half that after the acidification. Then make it basic with 15 M NH_3 and add a drop or two in excess. Transfer to a centrifuge tube. If there is a precipitate, remove it by centrifugation. To the clear solution add several drops of $Ca(NO_3)_2$ solution and allow the mixture to stand for 5 minutes before centrifugation. Save the solution for ET-7. Wash the precipitate twice with hot water to remove unwanted ions.

Further clues as to the ions present in the precipitate can be obtained by treating it with 5 drops of 6 M $HC_2H_3O_2$. Warm, stir, and centrifuge. A residue may be CaF_2 or CaC_2O_4. Wash with hot water to remove reducing anions and examine for oxalate (Sec. 23-26). The acetic acid solution may contain PO_4^{---}, AsO_4^{---}, and sometimes AsO_3^{---} if the separation of ET-5 was not clear cut. Neutralize the acid with 15 M NH_3. If these ions are present, their calcium salts will reprecipitate. Dissolve the precipitate in 6 M HCl, add a drop of 13% thioacetamide solution, and warm. A bright yellow precipitate of As_2S_3 indicates the presence of the ions of arsenic.

23-9. ET-7. Precipitation of Insoluble Barium Salts. To the solution from ET-6 add several drops of $Ba(NO_3)_2$ solution. The precipitate may be yellow $BaCrO_4$ (in which case the Prepared Solution was yellow) or white $BaSO_4$. Centrifuge and discard the solution. Treat the residue with 6 M HNO_3. A white precipitate of barium sulfate, insoluble in nitric acid, indicates the presence in the Prepared Solution of sulfite or sulfate. Confirm according to the procedure in Sec. 23-20. If desired, the acid solution of the barium precipitate can be treated with hydrogen peroxide; a fleeting blue color indicates the presence of chromium (See Outline 5, Cation Group 3).

23-10. Preparation of the Elimination Chart. It is convenient to summarize the results of the elimination tests in a chart. From this chart you can decide which anions need not be tested for because their absence is definitely established and which require further testing. A sample chart is given in Table 23-1. The sample was water soluble and contained no heavy metals.

TABLE 23-1.

A Sample Elimination Chart

Ion	ET-1	ET-2	ET-3	ET-4	ET-5	ET-6	ET-7	Summary	
F^-	—	—	—	—	—	A	—	A	
Cl^-	—	—	—	—	?	—	—		?
Br^-	—	—	—	—	?	—	—		?
I^-	—	—	A	—	(A)	—	—	A	
SCN^-	—	—	A	—	(A)	—	—	A	
S^{--}	?	A	A	—	A	—	—	A	
SO_3^{--}	?	?	A	—	—	—	(A)	A	
SO_4^{--}	—	—	—	—	—	—	P	P	
CrO_4^{--}	—	P	—	P	—	—	P	P	
NO_2^-	—	A	A	(A)	—	—	—	A	
NO_3^-	—	—	—	?	—	—	—		?
PO_4^{---}	?	—	—	—	—	?	—		?
AsO_3^{---}	?	—	—	—	A	(A)	—	A	
AsO_4^{---}	?	—	—	—	—	P	—		P
CO_3^{--}	?	P	—	—	—	—	—		P
$C_2O_4^{--}$	—	—	—	—	—	A	—	A	
$C_2H_3O_2^-$	—	—	—	—	—	—	—		?
$B(OH)_4^-$	?	—	—	—	—	—	—		?

In the chart the letter A stands for absent, P for present, (A) for absent when this was indicated by earlier tests, and ? when the test gives insufficient information to permit a distinction between several possible ions. A dash is used when the test gives no indication. The most significant entry is A; no further test is required. Although an ion appears to be present, it is advisable to confirm this by further tests.

TESTS FOR THE INDIVIDUAL ANIONS

23-11. The Plan.   The anions are listed according to the position of the element in the Periodic Table starting with the halide ions of Group VIIB and working back to the borate ion of Group IIIB. The tests may be performed in any order so long as the presence of interfering ions is checked beforehand. Sulfide ion, for example, must be removed before making the tests for chloride, bromide, and iodide ions. If its presence or absence is not clearly indicated by Elimination Tests ET-2, ET-3, or ET-5, a specific test should be made for it before carrying out the tests for the halide ions.

For each anion the information is organized under four headings:

a. Preliminary Indications.   Information given by the elimination tests.

b. Principle.   A brief summary of the basis for the test with reference to Chapter 22 for further details and equations.

c. Interferences.   Ions that interfere with the test and other difficult features.

d. Procedure.   Frequently a simplified procedure is given first for use in identifying single salts or in the absence of interferences. A more elaborate procedure is then given in which interfering ions are removed.

23-12. The Identification of Fluoride Ion, F^-.

a. Preliminary Indication.   ET-6, white precipitate insoluble in $HC_2H_3O_2$ may be CaF_2 or CaC_2O_4.

b. Principle.   Hydrogen fluoride and fluorides in the presence of acid attack glass (Sec. 22-2f). The surface of the freshly etched glass sheds water as if it were greasy. The glass is cleaned with a mixture of potassium dichromate, an oxidizing agent, and concentrated sulfuric acid, a strong acid, dehydrating agent, and oxidizing agent.

c. Interferences.   (1) Some natural fluorides are dissolved very slowly by the cleaning mixture. (2) The test is not sensitive to small amounts of fluoride if large amounts of ions such as Al^{+++} that form stable complexes with fluoride are present. (3) Chlorates and permanganates form dangerously unstable ClO_2 and Mn_2O_7 with concentrated sulfuric acid. Substances containing these anions must be excluded from consideration if the procedures in this chapter are to be used.

d. Procedure. In a clean, dry test tube place a few crystals of potassium dichromate and tap the tube to bring them to the bottom. Add 1 ml (20 drops) of 18 M H_2SO_4. Stir the mixture with a glass rod while it warms in the water bath. The cleaning mixture should become dark red. Withdraw the rod from the solution now and then and examine it. When it is clean, solution will drain from it evenly in a continuous film.

Now add to the cleaning mixture a pinch (about 20 mg) of the solid sample. Stir it into the solution and warm in the water bath. Again withdraw the rod at frequent intervals and examine it. If the solution collects in drops along that part of the rod that was immersed in the cleaning mixture, *fluoride is present.* Continue heating and examining the rod for 5 minutes before reporting the absence of fluoride.

Cool the mixture. Empty it into a sink near the drain while a copious stream of water flows through the sink (CAUTION).

23-13. The Identification of Chloride Ion, Cl⁻.

a. Preliminary Indication. ET-5, white AgCl, insoluble in ammoniacal silver nitrate-ammonium carbonate reagent.

b. Principle. If interfering ions are absent, chloride can be identified by precipitating silver chloride in acid solution. The presence of acid prevents the formation of silver salts of weak acids, e.g., Ag_3PO_4 or Ag_2CO_3, by keeping the concentrations of these anions too low. Silver chloride is soluble in excess ammonia and is reprecipitated when the ammoniacal solution is acidified (Sec. 22-3c).

c. Interferences.

(1) Sulfide, thiocyanate, bromide, and iodide ions form silver salts that are insoluble in dilute nitric acid. Silver thiocyanate and silver bromide are also partially soluble in ammonia solution and do not differ sufficiently in appearance from AgCl to permit a ready distinction.

(2) Insoluble chlorides such as AgCl may be only incompletely transposed by sodium carbonate.

(3) Traces of chloride are often present as impurities or are introduced accidentally and must be distinguished from the much larger amounts present in the samples under analysis.

d. Procedure.

(1) In the absence of interfering ions, acidify a few drops of the Prepared Solution with 6 M nitric acid. Add a drop of $AgNO_3$ solution. Centrifuge and discard the solution. Add a few drops of 6 M NH_3 to the precipitate. If

it dissolves, acidify the solution with 6 M HNO$_3$ (mix carefully and check with litmus—Sec. 16-3, T-12). The *presence of chloride* is indicated by the formation of white, curdy AgCl, soluble in 6 M NH$_3$, insoluble in HNO$_3$. A hazy opalescence which does not centrifuge down is caused by a trace of chloride and should not be reported.

(2) When interfering ions are present the procedure in Sec. 23-16 should be used. If the residue from the sodium carbonate treatment [Sec. 23-2b(3)] is not completely soluble in acetic acid, it should be examined for the presence of AgCl by the procedure in Sec. 23-17.

23-14. The Identification of Bromide Ion, Br⁻.

a. Preliminary Indication.   ET-5, pale yellow, almost white AgBr, insoluble in ammoniacal silver nitrate-ammonium carbonate reagent.

b. Principle.   Bromide ion is oxidized to free bromine by a strong oxidizing agent such as potassium permanganate in nitric acid solution (Sec. 22-4e). Free bromine is more soluble in carbon tetrachloride than in water and gives an orange to brownish red color in that solvent.

c. Interferences.

(1) Sulfide and thiocyanate ions are also oxidized by permanganate, so an inconvenient excess of the reagent may have to be added before bromide is oxidized.

(2) Iodide is oxidized by permanganate and the violet color in CCl$_4$ easily obscures the weaker orange of bromine.

(3) Insoluble bromides may be only incompletely transposed by sodium carbonate.

d. Procedure.

(1) In the absence of interfering ions acidify a few drops of the Prepared Solution with 6 M HNO$_3$ and add about 4 drops of acid in excess. Add 2 drops of CCl$_4$; avoid adding too much, for the color is more intense in a smaller volume. Now add 0.02 M KMnO$_4$ drop by drop, shaking after each addition, until an orange bead is obtained or the water layer remains pink for at least a minute. The *presence of bromide* is indicated by an orange lower layer.

(2) When interfering ions are present the procedure in Sec. 23-16 should be used. If the residue from the sodium carbonate treatment [Sec. 23-2b(3)] is not completely soluble in acetic acid, it should be examined for the presence of AgBr by the procedure in Sec. 23-17.

23-15. The Identification of Iodide Ion, I⁻.

a. Preliminary Indications.

(1) ET-3, formation of Prussian blue and

(2) ET-5, yellow silver iodide, insoluble in ammoniacal silver nitrate-ammonium carbonate reagent.

b. Principles. Iodide ion is an active reducing agent, easily oxidized to iodine or the triiodide ion by nitrous acid, a reagent which does not affect bromide or chloride. Molecular I_2 is much more soluble in CCl_4 than in water and gives a violet solution in the nonpolar solvent (Sec. 22-5e).

c. Interferences.

(1) Sulfide ion is also oxidized by nitrous acid, so that an inconvenient excess of the reagent may be required if it is present. Sulfide can be removed by evaporation with acetic acid. Thiocyanate ion also reacts with nitrous acid but this is less serious than the reaction with sulfide.

(2) Chromates in acid solution (or dichromates) will oxidize iodide. The two ions must be separated from each other in neutral or basic solution before carrying out the test for iodide.

(3) Insoluble iodides such as AgI may not be transposed by sodium carbonate.

d. Procedure.

(1) In the absence of interfering ions acidify a few drops of the Prepared Solution with 6 *M* sulfuric acid. Add a few crystals of $NaNO_2$ and several drops of CCl_4. Shake vigorously to extract the iodine. The *presence of iodide* is indicated by a violet lower layer.

(2) When interfering ions are present the procedure in Sec. 23-16 should be used. If the residue from the sodium carbonate treatment [Sec. 23-2b(3)] is not completely soluble in acetic acid, it should be examined for the presence of AgI by the procedure in Sec. 23-17.

23-16. The Analysis for the Halide Ions in the Presence of Interfering Ions.

a. Principles. The precipitation of the silver salts by ammoniacal silver nitrate-ammonium carbonate reagent in ET-5 separates these ions from chromate. Thiocyanate is removed by baking the dry silver salts. Reduction of the silver precipitate with zinc removes most of the sulfide as H_2S (Secs. 22-4c, -6e, -7b). Iodide is oxidized by nitrous acid and identified by the violet color of I_2 in CCl_4. By repeated evaporations with nitrous acid iodine is volatilized. Any excess nitrite must subsequently be destroyed with sulfamic acid, for otherwise the nitrous acid would consume too much permanganate. Bromide is identified by oxidizing it to bromine with permanganate and forming an orange solution in CCl_4. After its identification bromine is driven off by boiling. Chloride can then be identified by precipitation of silver chloride.

b. Procedure. Start with the acetic acid solution obtained in ET-5, step 3c.

(1) Add several crystals of sodium nitrite and extract the iodine with CCl_4 as in Sec. 23-15.

(2) Transfer the water layer to a casserole and add about one-half of a spatula-full of sodium nitrite and evaporate the solution to dryness under the ventilating duct or in the hood. Add 10 drops of 6 M $HC_2H_3O_2$ and more sodium nitrite and evaporate to dryness again.

After the last evaporation dissolve the residue in 10 drops of water and add 2 drops of 6 M HNO_3. Transfer the solution to a test tube and add a few crystals of sulfamic acid to destroy excess nitrite. Continue to add sulfamic acid until evolution of nitrogen ceases.

(3) Add 5 drops of 6 M HNO_3 to the solution which has been freed of iodide, thiocyanate, and nitrite. Carry out the test for bromide as described in Sec. 23-14.

(4) If bromide was present, again transfer the solution to a casserole. Add 5 more drops of 6 M HNO_3 and sufficient 0.02 M $KMnO_4$ to give a purple color that persists for about 1 minute. Evaporate the solution to half its initial volume to drive off bromine. Then dissolve MnO_2 and reduce excess $KMnO_4$ with a drop of 3 % H_2O_2. Transfer the clear solution to a test tube.

(5) Test the solution for chloride according to the procedure in Sec. 23-13. Before the silver chloride is dissolved in ammonia it should be washed once or twice with water to remove Mn^{++} ions.

23-17. The Detection of the Halides in the Insoluble Residue from the Prepared Solution. The residue from the treatment of the sample with sodium carbonate [Sec. 23-2b(3)] that is insoluble in acetic acid may contain AgCl, AgBr, or AgI. Treat it with 6 M $HC_2H_3O_2$ and Zn as in Sec. 23-7b(3c). Then test for the halides as described in Sec. 23-16.

23-18. The Identification of Thiocyanate Ion, SCN^-.

a. Preliminary Indications.

(1) ET-3, red complex $FeSCN^{++}$ with $FeCl_3$ and

(2) ET-5, white AgSCN, insoluble in ammoniacal silver nitrate-ammonium carbonate reagent.

b. Principle. Iron(III) and thiocyanate form a number of complexes of which the most prominent is the deep red $FeSCN^{++}$ ion (Sec. 22-6d).

c. Interferences.

(1) Iodide is oxidized by $FeCl_3$ to red-brown I_3^- which may obscure the red color of the complex or be confused with it.

(2) Iron(III) also oxidizes S^{--}, SO_3^{--}, and NO_2^- ions. At best this will make it necessary to add a large excess of $FeCl_3$.

(3) Iron(III) forms very stable complexes with F^-, PO_4^{---}, or $C_2O_4^{--}$

ions. Sufficient FeCl$_3$ must be added to combine with these ions before the thiocyanate complex will form.

d. Procedure.

(1) When interfering ions are absent, acidify a few drops of the Prepared Solution with 6 M HCl and add a drop of FeCl$_3$ reagent. The formation of a deep red color indicates the *presence of thiocyanate.*

(2) If interfering ions are present, warm the acidified solution to remove H$_2$S, SO$_2$, or NO. Add a few drops of Pb(NO$_3$)$_2$ solution to precipitate PbI$_2$ if iodide is present. Then add FeCl$_3$ solution until either the red FeSCN⁺⁺ color or the yellow of excess FeCl$_3$ is obtained.

23-19. The Identification of Sulfide Ion, S⁻⁻.

a. Preliminary Indications.

(1) ET-1, strongly basic solution if a soluble sulfide is present,

(2) ET-2, formation of H$_2$S with an odor of rotten eggs,

(3) ET-3, formation of Prussian blue, and

(4) ET-5, formation of black Ag$_2$S, insoluble in ammoniacal silver nitrate-ammonium carbonate reagent or sodium thiosulfate solution.

b. Principle. The more soluble sulfides are readily converted to very weakly ionized, gaseous hydrogen sulfide (Sec. 22-7b). The gas is detected by its effect on lead acetate paper. Less soluble sulfides are attacked by a combination of zinc and acid.

c. Interferences.

(1) Chromate and sulfite ions oxidize sulfide in acid solution and reduce the sensitivity of the test.

(2) The more insoluble sulfides are not transposed by sodium carbonate.

d. Procedure.

(1) In the absence of interferences acidify a few drops of the Prepared Solution with 6 M HCl and hold moist lead acetate paper in the escaping vapors. A dark brown or black stain of PbS indicates the *presence of sulfide.*

(2) When oxidizing agents are present add a drop of Pb(NO$_3$)$_2$ solution to a few drops of the strongly alkaline Prepared Solution. A brown or black color or precipitate of PbS, insoluble in NaOH, indicates the *presence of sulfide.* The procedure in Sec. 23-7 separates sulfide from oxidizing agents and provides for its identification.

(3) When the sodium carbonate treatment has left a residue insoluble in acetic acid [Sec. 23-2b(3)], examine it for insoluble sulfides. Treat a small portion with a few granules of zinc and several drops of 6 M H$_2$SO$_4$. Detect hydrogen sulfide gas with moist lead acetate paper. This test can also be done on the original unknown if sulfite and thiocyanate are known to be absent.

They too are reduced to hydrogen sulfide by zinc and acid (Secs. 22-6e and 22-8e).

23-20. The Identification of Sulfite Ion, SO_3^{--}.

a. Preliminary Indications.

(1) ET-2, evolution of colorless SO_2 with sharp odor,

(2) ET-3, formation of Prussian blue, and

(3) ET-7, formation of white $BaSO_4$ as a result of the oxidation of sulfite by nitric acid in ET-6.

b. Principle. Sulfite in acid solution is an active reducing agent and is oxidized to sulfate (Sec. 22-8e). It reduces permanganate to virtually colorless Mn^{++} ion. The formation of sulfate is detected by the insolubility of the barium salt in acid solution (Sec. 22-9c).

c. Interferences.

(1) Other reducing agents such as S^{--} or NO_2^- will also decolorize permanganate. Unlike sulfite, they do not form barium salts that are insoluble in neutral or alkaline solution, so that they can be removed by thorough washing of precipitated barium sulfite.

(2) Oxidizing agents such as CrO_4^{--}, NO_3^-, and NO_2^- will convert sulfite to sulfate in acid solution. Decolorization of permanganate will then not occur, but a precipitate of barium sulfate is still obtained. Chromate, unlike nitrate or nitrite, is not removed by washing the barium precipitate, for barium chromate is insoluble in neutral or alkaline solutions. You will not be issued unknowns that contain both sulfite and chromate.

d. Procedure. Treat several drops of the Prepared Solution with sufficient $BaCl_2$ solution to precipitate the insoluble barium salts. Centrifuge and discard the solution. Wash the precipitate three times with hot water: add about 10 drops of water each time, heat in the water bath for a minute, and centrifuge. Discard the washings. Add a few drops of 6 M HCl and dilute to a convenient volume with about 10 drops of water. The *presence of sulfate* is indicated by a white residue insoluble in HCl, but only a faint turbidity caused by a trace of sulfate often arises from the oxidation of sulfite. Centrifuge and withdraw the solution to a clean tube. Add 1 drop of 0.02 M $KMnO_4$. Decolorization of the permanganate and formation of white $BaSO_4$ are indications of the *presence of sulfite*. Slow decolorization of the permanganate will occur if the chloride concentration is high, but no barium sulfate will then form.

23-21. The Identification of Sulfate Ion, SO_4^{--}.

a. Preliminary Indications.

(1) ET-1, strongly acid solution if HSO_4^- is present, and

(2) ET-7, white BaSO$_4$, insoluble in 6 M HNO$_3$, but this may be from oxidation of sulfite.

b. Principle. Of all the anions that form insoluble barium salts, only sulfate is the anion of a moderately strong acid (HSO$_4^-$), and thus only BaSO$_4$ will precipitate in strongly acid solutions (Sec. 22-9c).

c. Interferences.

(1) Sulfate may be produced by oxidation of sulfite in acid solution by NO$_2^-$, NO$_3^-$, or CrO$_4^{--}$. The presence of these oxidizing agents will be indicated by ET-4. The effect of nitrite and nitrate can be eliminated by precipitating BaSO$_3$ in neutral or basic solution and washing the precipitate free of interfering ions before adding acid (Sec. 23-20d). Chromate cannot be eliminated in this way, and mixtures of chromate and sulfite will not be issued as unknowns.

(2) Even when the sample contains no oxidizing agent, slow oxidation of sulfite by air (Sec. 22-8e) will give rise to small amounts of sulfate.

d. Procedure.

(1) In the absence of oxidizing agents acidify a few drops of the Prepared Solution with 6 M HCl and add a drop or two of BaCl$_2$ solution. The formation of a white precipitate of BaSO$_4$ indicates the *presence of sulfate*. If the precipitate is very small, repeat the test on a sample containing 0.05 mg of SO$_4^{--}$ ion; i.e., dilute the standard solution of SO$_4^{--}$ (10 mg/ml) 1:10 with water and use 1 drop for the test. Report the presence of sulfate only if the precipitate from the Prepared Solution is larger than this control.

(2) If oxidizing agents are present, use the procedure in Sec. 23-20d.

23-22. The Identification of Nitrite Ion, NO$_2^-$.

a. Preliminary Indications.

(1) ET-2, evolution of NO$_2$, red-brown gas with sharp odor,

(2) ET-3, formation of Prussian blue, and

(3) ET-4, yellow or brown color, not very definite.

b. Principle. In acid solution nitrites react with sulfamic acid to give bubbles of nitrogen and sulfate ion (Sec. 22-10e). Sulfate is detected as insoluble BaSO$_4$; barium sulfamate is soluble. The test is sensitive to 0.07 mg of NO$_2^-$ per milliliter.

c. Interferences.

(1) Carbonate and sulfate interfere, the first by forming bubbles of CO$_2$ in acid solution, the second by precipitating with Ba^{++} ion. Both can be removed by precipitation with BaCl$_2$. Evolution of CO$_2$ is also retarded by the use of dilute solutions, for N$_2$ is less soluble and more rapidly evolved than CO$_2$. The detection of N$_2$ is 100 times as sensitive as that of CO$_2$.

(2) Sulfite and sulfide in acid solution are oxidized by nitrite, thereby reducing the sensitivity of the test. This is not serious as long as sulfamic acid is added promptly, for nitrite reacts with it more rapidly than with the other ions.

(3) Sulfamic acid slowly hydrolyzes in solutions to give sulfate:

$$HNH_2SO_3 + H_2O \rightarrow NH_4^+ + H^+ + SO_4^{--}$$

This can be avoided by using the solid acid which is stable.

d. Procedure. To a few drops of the Prepared Solution add $BaCl_2$ solution until precipitation is complete. Centrifuge and transfer the solution to a test tube. Add a few crystals of solid sulfamic acid and a drop of $BaCl_2$ solution. Flick the bottom of the tube with your finger to cause vigorous evolution of gas bubbles. The formation of both a white precipitate and gas bubbles indicates the *presence of nitrite*.

23-23. The Identification of Nitrate Ion, NO_3^-.

a. Preliminary Indication. ET-4, formation of a brown or black color. If this test is obtained and chromate and nitrite ions are absent, nitrate ion is almost certainly present. If this test is not obtained and reducing agents are also absent, it is unnecessary to test for nitrate.

b. Principle. Nitrate ion in alkaline solution is reduced to ammonia by active metals (Sec. 22-11e). Aluminum or zinc can be used as the reducing agent but Devarda's alloy (50% Cu, 45% Al, and 5% Zn) gives a smoother reaction. Ammonia gas may be detected by its action on red litmus or Nessler's reagent (Sec. 21-8).

c. Interferences.

(1) Nitrite ion gives the same reaction and must be removed with sulfamic acid.

(2) Thiocyanate ion is also reduced to ammonia and must be removed by precipitation as silver thiocyanate in acid solution.

(3) Ammonium salts will form ammonia in basic solution. The ammonium ion is removed by evaporation with sodium hydroxide before addition of the reducing agent.

(4) Nitrites are slowly oxidized by oxygen of the air to nitrate, and if nitrite ion is present, a small test for nitrate is almost inevitable.

d. Procedure.

(1) In the absence of interfering ions mix several drops of the Prepared Solution with an equal volume of 6 *M* NaOH. With a pipet transfer this mixture to a dry test tube in such a way as not to wet the upper walls of the tube with the basic solution. After withdrawing the pipet inspect the upper

walls of the tube to make sure that this critical requirement is satisfied. Have a piece of cotton and a strip of red litmus ready. Add a few granules of Devarda's alloy (or aluminum) and immediately push a loose cotton plug one-third of the way down the tube to filter out spray. Warm briefly in the water bath to induce a vigorous reaction. Withdraw the tube and insert in the top a piece of red litmus. Bend the strip into a V and moisten the fold only. The dry upper ends will support the litmus so that it does not touch the cotton (Fig. 23-1). Allow the tube to stand for several minutes. The *presence of nitrate* is indicated if the bottom tip of the litmus turns uniformly blue.

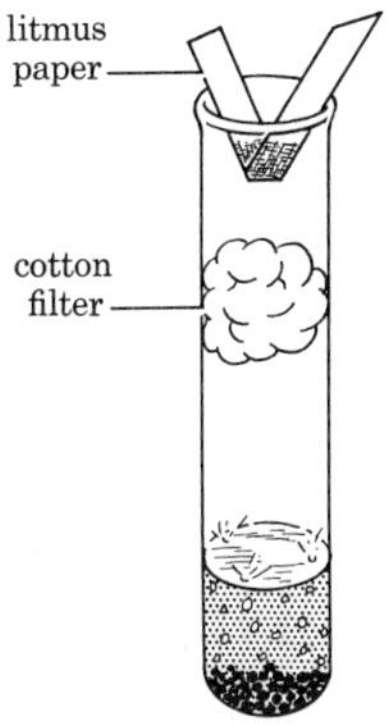

litmus paper

cotton filter

FIG. 23-1. The nitrate test.

(2) If interfering ions are present, some or all of the following eliminations must be done.

(a) If nitrite has been found to be present, add several crystals of sulfamic acid to 5 drops of the Prepared Solution in a test and warm until bubbles of nitrogen are no longer evolved. The solution should be acid. Add a little more sulfamic acid to check the completeness of the removal of nitrite. If thiocyanate is present, proceed to (b); if it is not, to (c).

(b) If thiocyanate has been found to be present, add one-half a spatula-full of solid Ag_2SO_4. Warm in the water bath and stir the mixture for several minutes to ensure precipitation of AgSCN and other silver salts. Centrifuge and withdraw 1 drop of solution to another tube. Test it with a drop of $AgNO_3$ reagent; if more precipitate forms, treat the remaining solution with more Ag_2SO_4. (Discard the side test which is now contaminated with nitrate. Silver sulfate reacts slowly with thiocyanate because the surfaces of its crystals become coated with the precipitate.) Transfer the clear thiocyanate-free solution to a casserole and proceed as in (c).

(c) Ammonium salts should have been removed in making the Prepared Solution, but small amounts may remain if boiling was not prolonged sufficiently, or they may be introduced by hydrolysis of sulfamic acid in acid solution. If the unknown was simply dissolved in water, ammonium salts may still be present. To the solution free of nitrite and thiocyanate add 10 drops of 6 M NaOH and check to make sure that it is strongly basic. Black silver oxide may form and can be removed by centrifugation. Transfer the clear solution to a casserole and evaporate it over a microflame to half the initial volume. Hold moist red litmus in the escaping vapors and, if it turns blue, add water and re-evaporate. Continue as long as ammonia is evolved. Centrifuge if necessary to remove silver sulfamate. Test the clear solution for nitrate as in (1).

23-24. The Identification of Phosphate Ion, PO_4^{---}.

a. Preliminary Indications.

(1) ET-1, strongly basic solution if phosphate ion is present in a soluble salt, but note that HPO_4^{--} is less strongly basic and $H_2PO_4^-$ is acidic.

(2) ET-6, formation of yellow Ag_3PO_4 momentarily as the ammoniacal silver nitrate-ammonium carbonate solution is acidified; Ag_3PO_4 is soluble in NH_3 and HNO_3. White $Ca_3(PO_4)_2$ precipitates upon addition of $Ca(NO_3)_2$. The freshly precipitated salt is soluble in acetic acid and reprecipitates when the solution is made alkaline again.

b. Principle. When an excess of ammonium molybdate is added to a solution of a phosphate that is 5-10% HNO_3 by volume, bright yellow ammonium molybdophosphate $(NH_4)_3[PMo_{12}O_{40}]\cdot6H_2O$ precipitates (Sec. 22-12f).

c. Interferences.

(1) Arsenate ion gives a similar precipitate and also retards the precipitation of the phosphorus compound. Arsenic is removed by precipitation as As_2S_3 in 6 M HCl solution.

(2) High concentrations of chloride or sulfate retard precipitation. Most of the chloride is destroyed by one evaporation with concentrated nitric acid.

(3) Reducing agents destroy the molybdate. They are also removed by evaporation with nitric acid.

(4) Some phosphates are not readily transposed by sodium carbonate. The test is best carried out on a nitric acid or aqua regia extract of the original sample.

d. Procedure. Treat 20-40 mg of the original sample with several drops of aqua regia (1 part of 16 M HNO_3 to 3 of 12 M HCl). Centrifuge and remove the solution to a casserole. Evaporate just to dryness. Dissolve the residue in several drops of 6 M HCl, transfer the solution to a centrifuge tube, and add 1-2 drops of 13% thioacetamide solution. Warm in the water bath to precipitate As_2S_3; remove the precipitate by centrifugation and discard it. Transfer the solution to a casserole, add 10 drops of 16 M HNO_3, and evaporate just to dryness. Add 2 drops of 6 M HNO_3, rub the acid against the walls and bottom of the casserole with a rod, dilute with 2 drops of water, and transfer the solution to a centrifuge tube. Warm for a minute in the water bath to make sure that any condensed phosphoric acids are converted to the ortho form. Withdraw the tube from the bath and add 2 drops of ammonium molybdate reagent. The solution should be acid. Allow it to stand for 5 minutes. The *presence of phosphate* is indicated by the formation of a bright yellow precipitate of $(NH_4)_3[PMo_{12}O_{40}]\cdot6H_2O$. A white precipitate of MoO_3 may form if phosphate is absent or if the solution is too hot (the temperature should be 40-50°, not too hot to hold, for fast reaction).

23-25. The Identification of Carbonate Ion, CO_3^{--}.

a. Preliminary Indications.

(1) ET-1, strongly basic solution because of hydrolysis of CO_3^{--}, but HCO_3^- gives only a weakly basic solution and

(2) ET-2, evolution of colorless, odorless CO_2.

b. Principle.
Acids stronger than carbonic acid liberate CO_2 from carbonates. When the gas is absorbed in barium hydroxide solution a white precipitate of $BaCO_3$ is obtained (Sec. 22-13b).

c. Interferences.

(1) Sulfites give the same reaction as carbonates (Sec. 22-8b). They are removed by oxidation to sulfates by hydrogen peroxide before addition of acid.

(2) Nitrites are decomposed by acid and the oxides of nitrogen neutralize barium hydroxide (Sec. 22-10b). Nitrite is also removed by hydrogen peroxide.

(3) Carbon dioxide is present to such an extent in laboratory air that the gradual formation of a turbidity in the barium hydroxide solution is inevitable. When a test is doubtful, the procedure should be carried out with distilled water in place of the sample, and the time required to produce a turbidity should be noted for this "blank" determination.

(4) Certain natural carbonates may be slow to react with acids. Warming is helpful.

d. Procedure.

(1) In the absence of interferences, add 1-2 drops of 6 M H_2SO_4 to 20-30 mg of the solid sample (*not* the Prepared Solution). Have a medicine dropper (not a capillary pipet) ready with a drop of $Ba(OH)_2$ in the tip. After adding the acid, quickly insert the dropper without squeezing the bulb (Fig. 23-2). The *presence of carbonate* is indicated by the formation of a white turbidity.

(2) In the presence of sulfite or nitrite, treat the sample first with several drops of 3% H_2O_2. Warm for several minutes in the water bath. Then carry out the test as in (1).

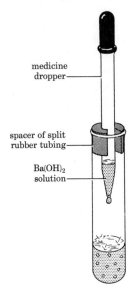

medicine
dropper

spacer of split
rubber tubing

$Ba(OH)_2$
solution

FIG. 23-2. The carbonate test.

23-26. The Identification of Oxalate Ion, $C_2O_4^{--}$.

a. Preliminary Indications. ET-6, $Ag_2C_2O_4$, white, may form during neutralization of the ammoniacal silver nitrate-ammonium carbonate solution; it is soluble in HNO_3 and NH_3. White CaC_2O_4 is precipitated in the next step and is insoluble in acetic acid.

b. Principle. Oxalic acid is oxidized by permanganate to carbon dioxide and decolorization of the permanganate results (Sec. 22-14e).

c. Interferences. Other reducing anions, e.g., SO_3^{--}, S^{--}, and NO_2^{-}, also decolorize permanganate. These can be eliminated by precipitation of calcium oxalate in acetic acid solution. The other anions do not form insoluble calcium salts in acid solution and are easily washed out of the precipitate. Calcium fluoride also precipitates, but fluoride is not oxidized by chemical agents. Such a separation of oxalate from other reducing anions is carried out as part of ET-6.

d. Procedure. Use the calcium oxalate precipitate of ET-6 or prepare one in the following way. Take several drops of Prepared Solution and determine the number of drops of 6 M $HC_2H_3O_2$ required to make it just acid. Add an equal number of drops again in excess. Add a drop of $Ca(NO_3)_2$ solution and allow the mixture to stand for a minute or so to ensure complete precipitation. Centrifuge and wash the precipitate three times with hot water.

To the calcium oxalate precipitate add 4 drops of H_2O and 1 drop of 18 M H_2SO_4. Warm briefly in the water bath. Have some freshly prepared 0.002 M $KMnO_4$ solution ready; make it by diluting the 0.02 M solution from your kit. Add the 0.002 M solution dropwise to the dissolved calcium oxalate. The *presence of oxalate* is indicated by decolorization of the permanganate. The first drop or two may be decolorized slowly; allow a minute. If only one or two drops of permanganate are consumed, it is advisable to do a "blank" determination with 5 drops of water and 1 drop of H_2SO_4.

23-27. The Identification of Acetate Ion, $C_2H_3O_2{}^-$.

a. Preliminary Indications. None unless large amounts are present and sulfite, nitrite, and sulfide are absent. Then a sharp, vinegar-like odor may be noted in ET-2.

b. Principle. There is no satisfactory simple test for acetate. It is usually identified by the odor of the free acid or the fragrant odor of the esters (Sec. 22-15b, f). Other organic acids such as propionic acid give similar results. They are not considered in this course.

c. Interferences. Other ions which give gases with pronounced odors must be removed. They are $NO_2{}^-$, $SO_3{}^{--}$, and S^{--} and are removed by warming an acid solution. Chlorate and permanganate must be absent in the ester test (see Sec. 23-12c).

d. Procedures.

(1) Liberation of acetic acid. To about 6 drops of Prepared Solution in a small beaker or casserole add one-half of a spatula-full of sulfamic acid and warm until bubbles of nitrogen cease to form. Then add 2 drops of 6 M H_2SO_4 and warm again. The *presence of acetate* is indicated by an odor resembling that of vinegar. Compare the odor with a control: warm several drops of the standard solution of acetate ion with sulfuric acid.

(2) Formation of ethyl acetate. Evaporate about 6 drops of Prepared Solution to a volume of about 1 drop in a casserole. Remove from the flame and manipulate the dish so that the remainder of the solution covers the bottom of the hot dish and gradually evaporates. Cool. Add several drops of 18 M H_2SO_4 and warm briefly on top of the water bath to destroy sulfite, nitrite, and sulfide. Add a few drops of ethyl alcohol and warm again on top of the water bath. The *presence of acetate* is indicated by the fragrant, pleasant odor of ethyl acetate. Compare the odor with those of authentic specimens of ethyl acetate and ethyl alcohol.

23-28. The Identification of Borate Ion, $B(OH)_4{}^-$.

a. Preliminary Indications.

(1) ET-1, strongly alkaline solution may be caused by hydrolysis of borate, but borax, the most common salt, has a pH of only a little over 9.

(2) ET-6, white silver borate may precipitate when the ammoniacal silver nitrate-ammonium carbonate solution is neutralized. It is soluble in nitric acid or ammonia. Neither of these indications is very definite or helpful.

b. Principles.   Boric acid can be esterified to give volatile methyl borate which burns with a green flame. Boric acid causes turmeric to turn pink in acid solution; the addition of alkali changes the color to dark green or blue (Sec. 22-16f).

c. Interferences.

(1) Barium and copper(II) salts also give a green flame but they are less volatile than the ester; thus the latter can be blown from the reaction mixture with a current of air.

(2) Oxidizing or reducing agents will destroy turmeric. Use the flame test if ET-3 and ET-4 show that they are present. Iron(III) and certain other metals turn turmeric red-brown but do not give the color change with sodium hydroxide.

d. Procedures.

(1) Flame test. Construct the apparatus shown in Fig. 23-3. The glass tubes are made by drawing out 8-mm tubing in the same way as pipets are made. Holes for the tubes through the cork can be bored with a hot wire.

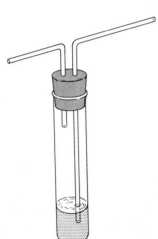

FIG. 23-3. Apparatus for the trimethyl borate flame test.

Place 20-30 mg of solid unknown in the dry test tube. Add a few drops of 18 M H_2SO_4 and several drops of methyl alcohol. Blow through the tube that reaches to the bottom of the test tube and point the other tube at a flame. The *presence of borate* is indicated by a green color in the flame.

(2) Turmeric test. Acidify several drops of Prepared Solution or 20 mg of unknown with 6 M HCl. Evaporate to dryness to destroy reducing anions.

Add 1-2 drops of 6 M HCl and with a stirring rod transfer some of the solution to a strip of turmeric paper. Put the paper on a watch glass and dry it on top of the water bath or under an infrared lamp. Make some 3 M NaOH by dilution of the 6 M reagent. Apply some of this with a stirring rod to the paper. The *presence of borate* is indicated by a pink spot that appears when the paper is dried and that turns dark green or blue upon addition of sodium hydroxide.

EXERCISES

23-1. Why is an alkaline, rather than an acid, solution of the unknown used for the tests?

23-2. Why are lead iodide and lead sulfate readily transposed to lead carbonate whereas lead sulfide is not?

23-3. If ammonium salts are not removed during the transposition with sodium carbonate, where will they cause difficulty?

23-4. Explain why a combination of silver nitrate, ammonia, and ammonium carbonate is used in ET-5. Reference should be made to the equilibria.

23-5. A certain sample contained arsenate ion. When a solution of the unknown in water was used in ET-5, a red precipitate was obtained. When the unknown was boiled with sodium carbonate and this Prepared Solution was used in ET-5, no precipitate was obtained. Account for the difference.

23-6. Why are Ag_2S and Ag_3AsO_3 the only silver salts of those obtained in ET-5 that dissolve in nitric acid?

23-7. A white precipitate, insoluble in 6 M HNO_3, is obtained in ET-7. Why is this not definite proof of the presence of SO_4^{--} ion?

23-8. A certain unknown was completely soluble in water and contained no heavy metals. In ET-1 the pH was found to be 11. In ET-2 a red-brown gas was evolved. In ET-3 a deep blue precipitate formed. In ET-4 there was no change in color. In ET-5 no precipitate was obtained. In ET-6 a white precipitate formed upon addition of $Ca(NO_3)_2$. An acetic acid solution withdrawn from above the precipitate gave no visible reaction when it was neutralized with ammonia. In ET-7 no precipitate was obtained. On the basis of these observations draw up an elimination chart for this unknown.

23-9. Which of the following are pairs of incompatible ions? For those that are incompatible write an equation for their reaction with each other in acid solution.

(a) NO_2^- — I^-, (b) $Cr_2O_7^{--}$ — S^{--}, (c) SCN^- — Cl^-, (d) S^{--} — SO_3^{--},
(e) $C_2O_4^{--}$ — NO_3^-, (f) SO_3^{--} — NO_2^-.

23-10. How would you dissolve silver sulfide (a) without destroying the silver ion, (b) without destroying the sulfide ion?

23-11. Why must sulfide ion be removed before the test for iodide?

23-12. Why are the barium salts precipitated in alkaline solution before testing for sulfite and sulfate?

23-13. Why in the borate flame test is methyl borate vapor blown into the flame?

23-14. What error would account for each of the following observations? (a) A yellow precipitate in the chloride test, (b) a white precipitate in the phosphate test, (c) a red color in the thiocyanate test although the ion was absent, (d) a turbidity in the carbonate test that dissolved in nitric acid and decolorized 0.002 M $KMnO_4$.

23-15. No test for sulfide was obtained on an acid solution of a certain sample, yet a black precipitate of lead sulfide was obtained from an alkaline solution. Suggest an explanation.

23-16. What is meant by a "blank" test? by a "control"?

23-17. Why are very small tests sometimes obtained for (a) Cl^-, (b) NO_3^-, (c) SO_4^{--}?

23-18. Write equations for the reactions used in the final identification of these ions: NO_2^-, I^-, $C_2H_3O_2^-$, Cl^-, CO_3^{--}, NO_3^-, $C_2O_4^{--}$, S^{--}, Br^-, SCN^-, and SO_3^{--}.

23-19. Which of the 18 anions (a) is colored? (b) forms a silver salt insoluble in sodium thiosulfate? (c) forms a barium salt insoluble in nitric acid?

23-20. Why is calcium fluoride insoluble in acetic acid but soluble in hydrochloric acid, whereas calcium phosphate is soluble in both acids?

23-21. What reagent or combination of reagents would you use to separate the ions of each pair in one step?

(a) SO_3^{--} — SO_4^{--} (b) AsO_4^{---} — $B(OH)_4^-$
(c) $C_2O_4^{--}$ — SO_3^{--} (d) CO_3^{--} — F^-
(e) NO_2^- — NO_3^- (f) AsO_3^{---} — F^-
(g) Cl^- — Br^- (h) Cl^- — SO_3^{--}
(i) S^{--} — Cl^- (j) I^- — Br^-

23-22. In each of the following pairs the second ion interferes with the test for the first. Explain why it does so and how the interference can be removed.

(a) CO_3^{--} — SO_3^{--} (b) $C_2O_4^{--}$ — SO_3^{--}
(c) Cl^- — I^- (d) NO_3^- — NO_2^-
(e) PO_4^{---} — AsO_4^{---} (f) I^- — CrO_4^{--}

23-23. A solid mixture contains some or all of the salts

$$BaSO_3, (NH_4)_2C_2O_4, AgNO_3, KBr, Ca(NO_3)_2$$

It is only partially soluble in water. When the mixture is acidified and treated with dilute permanganate solution, the color of the permanganate fades and no precipitate forms. This solution is warmed, and moistened starch-iodide paper is held over it. The paper changes color. Which substances are present and which are absent? For some there may be insufficient evidence to justify any conclusion.

23-24. A solid mixture may contain some or all of the following: Na_2CO_3, Na_2SO_3, KI, KBr, CaC_2O_4, $NaNO_2$. The material dissolves completely in water to give a basic solution. A portion of this solution was acidified with acetic acid and extracted with carbon tetrachloride. A violet lower layer was obtained. A second portion of the water solution did not effervesce when it was acidified with hydrochloric acid. Which substances are present and which are absent? For some there may be insufficient evidence to justify any conclusion.

23-25. A solid mixture contains one or more of the following salts: $NaCl$, $NaHCO_3$, $Na_2C_2O_4$, $KAl(SO_4)_2$, $BaCl_2$. It dissolves in water with the evolution of a gas. Which substances are present and which are absent? For some there may be insufficient evidence to justify any conclusion.

CHAPTER TWENTY-FOUR

The Analysis of Solids for Cations and Anions

24-1. Introduction. The analysis of solids presents special problems that require discussion. Sampling is the first such problem to be encountered. Solutions need only be shaken thoroughly to be homogeneous. Solids are more often than not heterogeneous, and the preparation of a representative sample is sometimes difficult. Much can be learned from preliminary examination of the solid before the more formal analysis is started. The preparation of solutions of the sample for use in analysis is sometimes more difficult and time-consuming than the analysis itself. The analysis for cations has been considered group by group in Chapters 17 to 21, and certain problems peculiar to a general analysis for all groups must be considered.

The analysis of three classes of solids is discussed in this chapter: simple substances containing one cation and one anion, alloys or mixtures of metals to be analyzed for cations alone, and salt mixtures or other nonmetallic substances containing several cations and anions.

24-2. The Analysis of Simple Substances. These include not only single salts but also acids, oxides, and basic hydroxides, so the cation may be H^+ and the anion O^{--} or OH^-.

Note first the physical appearance of the substance. Is it crystalline or apparently amorphous or finely powdered? Is it colored? The summary of common colored solids in Table 24-1 may be helpful in making a tentative identification. Further information on colors is given in Tables 6-5 and 18-1. Any such general summaries are imprecise in their description of colors. Not all the red-colored substances listed in the table are the same shade of red. Certainly the deep purplish red of silver chromate is easily distinguished from the orange-red of lead(II, IV) oxide or the brownish red of iron(III) oxide. The anhydrous and hydrated forms of a salt may differ profoundly in color; e.g., $CuSO_4$ is colorless and $CuSO_4 \cdot 5H_2O$ is blue, $NiSO_4$ is yellow and $NiSO_4 \cdot 6H_2O$ is green. Any identification based on color must be a tentative one to be supported by other evidence.

Flame tests are likewise helpful only in support of other tests. Some common flame colors are given in Table 24-2. Moisten a little of the solid with 12 M HCl. Dip a clean platinum or Nichrome wire in the mixture, and bring it into the oxidizing part of the flame above the inner cone.

TABLE 24-1.

Common Colored Solid Substances*

Color	Substances
Red	Hydrated Mn(II) salts (pink), hydrated Co(II) salts, HgI_2, HgO, HgS (cinnabar), Pb_3O_4, Ag_2CrO_4, AsI_3, Cu_2O, CrO_3, Fe_2O_3 (red-brown)
Orange	Sb_2S_3, SnI_2, many dichromates
Yellow	CdS, As_2S_3, SnS_2, PbO, HgO, many chromates, anhydrous Ni salts
Green	Hydrated Fe(II) and Ni salts, Cr_2O_3 (very dark, almost black), $CrCl_3·6H_2O$ (one form) and other Cr(III) salts, $CuCl_2·2H_2O$ (blue-green) and certain other Cu(II) salts, K_2MnO_4, anhydrous $CoBr_2$
Purple	$KMnO_4$ (very dark, almost black)
Violet	Many Cr(III) salts and certain Fe(III) salts such as $Fe(NO_3)_3·9H_2O$
Blue	Hydrated Cu(II) salts (sometimes yellowish or greenish), anhydrous $CoCl_2$
Brown	$FeCl_3·6H_2O$ (yellowish), anhydrous $CuCl_2$, PbO_2, CdO, Bi_2S_3 (dark), Bi_2O_3, SnS
Black	Fe_3O_4, CuO, NiO, MnO_2, CuS, Cu_2S, HgS, PbS, FeS, CoS, NiS, Ag_2S, BiI_3

*See also Tables 6-5 and 18-1.

Carry out the analysis for the anion next according to the procedures given in Chapter 23. Preparation of the solution is described in Sec. 23-2 Note that only one anion is to be detected; the test for it must be a strong one. Should one of the elimination tests indicate the presence of an ion, carry out a confirmatory test forthwith. For example, if a red-brown gas is obtained when 6 M H_2SO_4 is added to the sample (ET-2), nitrite is indicated and should be confirmed by reaction with sulfamic acid. Since only one anion is present, the interference of other anions need not be considered, and the simplified procedures that are given first for many of the anions can be used. But if a Prepared Solution of the sample is made, note that it contains carbonate in addition to the anion of the compound. This will need to be taken into account in the nitrite test. If no anion is found, the substance is an oxide or basic hydroxide.

A solution is next prepared for cation analysis. Test the solubility of very small amounts of the sample successively in water, 6 M HCl, and 6 M HNO_3. If no reaction occurs at room temperature, warm for several minutes in a water bath. Consult your instructor if none of these solvents dissolves the substance. The solubility or insolubility of a substance in one of these solvents when considered together with the result of the anion analysis is often an important clue as to its identity. Or it may equally well indicate what it cannot be. If the anion, for example is sulfate, and the substance is soluble in water, it cannot be $PbSO_4$, $BaSO_4$, $SrSO_4$, or $CaSO_4$ nor is it likely that the cation is Bi^{+++}, Sb^{+++}, or Hg^{++} which hydrolyze and precipitate basic sulfates. On the other hand, if the soluble sulfate is reddish, it may be hydrated $CoSO_4$.[1]

TABLE 24-2.

Common Flame Colors*

Element	Color
Na	Strong, persistent yellow
K	Weak violet, red through cobalt blue glass
Ca	Strong orange-red
Sr	Carmine
Ba	Yellow-green
Cu	Green
As	Bluish white
Sb	Bluish white
Pb	Pale blue

*The colors given by the salts moistened with 12 M HCl.

Analysis for the cations follows Outlines 1 to 7 (Chapters 17-21). Dissolve a small amount (about 10 mg) of the substance in the selected solvent. If a reducing anion is present, e.g., SO_3^{--} or NO_2^-, acidify with 6 M HCl and boil to destroy it. If iodide is present, remove it by evaporation with 16 M HNO_3. Carry out the group separations so that the cation is placed in its correct group. If it is a member of Cation Groups 2 or 3, the color of the group precipitate may be revealing: a yellow sulfide in Group 2 could be CdS, SnS_2, or As_2S_3; a gelatinous white precipitate in Group 3, $Al(OH)_3$. Note that a single cation is to be detected; the test should be a very positive one. If no cation is found, the substance may be an acid.

Summarize your results under these headings:

1. Ions tentatively eliminated or identified by the color of the sample.
2. Ions tentatively eliminated or identified by flame test.
3. The result of the anion analysis.

[1]This is a good time to make the acquaintance of chemical handbooks, e.g., Lange's *Handbook of Chemistry*, Handbook Publishers, or *Handbook of Chemistry and Physics*, Chemical Rubber Publishing Company. These books contain useful tables of the properties of inorganic compounds.

4. The solvent used to prepare the solution for cation analysis. Ions that were eliminated by consideration of the results of the anion analysis and solubility tests.

5. The result of the cation analysis.

6. Final identification of the substance.

24-3. Preparation of a Solution of an Alloy. Principles. Alloys are intimate mixtures of metals. The metals may actually combine to give a compound, one may dissolve in the other in variable amounts to give solid solutions, or they may give only a heterogeneous mixture of separate crystals. The properties of a metal may be considerably altered by alloying; even its chemical reactivity may change. Alloys also sometimes contain carbon, silicon, phosphorus, arsenic, and other nonmetals. The first two are often added to impart desirable properties to the alloy such as hardness or resistance to corrosion; the others are usually undesirable and are present as impurities.

Acids are the most commonly used solvents for metals and alloys. Hydrochloric acid is a satisfactory solvent only for the more active metals such as aluminum or magnesium, for the H^+ ion is not a powerful oxidizing agent ($\mathcal{E}^0 = 0.00$ volts). Even though it attacks aluminum and magnesium, it is not usually used to dissolve light metal alloys, for these may contain small amounts of an inactive metal that would then escape detection. Furthermore, if arsenic or antimony is present, it will be reduced to arsine or stibine and partially lost.

Dilute (6-8 M) nitric acid is the most generally satisfactory solvent for alloys. The nitrate ion in acid solution is a powerful oxidizing agent ($\mathcal{E}^0 = -0.96$ volts) and will therefore oxidize inactive metals such as copper ($\mathcal{E}^0 = -0.34$) or silver ($\mathcal{E}^0 = -0.80$). The dilute acid is usually preferred over the concentrated reagent for two reasons. (1) Several nitrates, e.g., $Pb(NO_3)_2$, are only slightly soluble in the concentrated acid and form surface coatings on the unreacted metal that slow down reaction. (2) Several metals, notably Cr, Al, and Fe, are passive towards the concentrated acid and virtually do not dissolve in it. This is attributed to the formation of an impervious oxide film on the surface of the metal that prevents further attack by the acid. The principal objection to the use of nitric acid as a solvent is its action on tin and antimony. These metals are converted to hydrated oxides, $SnO_2 \cdot xH_2O$ (metastannic acid, Sec. 18-6) and $Sb_2O_5 \cdot yH_2O$, which are difficult to bring into solution.

Aqua regia, next to dilute nitric acid, is the most satisfactory solvent for alloys. This combines the oxidizing action of nitric acid with the formation of chlorocomplexes and is also a more rapid oxidizing agent than nitric acid alone. The oxides of tin and antimony are not obtained, but silver and lead are converted to chlorocomplexes and insoluble chlorides. Mercury is oxidized to mercury(II) by either nitric acid or aqua regia. Typical reactions of metals with aqua regia are represented by

$$2H^+ + NO_3^- + Cl^- \quad + Ag \rightarrow AgCl\downarrow \; + \; NO_2\uparrow + H_2O$$

$$4H^+ + 2NO_3^- + 4Cl^- \quad + Hg \rightarrow HgCl_4^{--} + 2NO_2\uparrow + 2H_2O$$

$$5H^+ + 5NO_3^- \qquad\quad + As \rightarrow H_3AsO_4 + 5NO_2\uparrow + H_2O$$

$$8H^+ + 4NO_3^- + 6Cl^- \quad + Sn \rightarrow SnCl_6^{--} + 4NO_2\uparrow + 4H_2O$$

$$4H^+ + 2NO_3^- + 4Cl^- \quad + Cu \rightarrow CuCl_4^{--} + 2NO_2\uparrow + 2H_2O$$

24-4. Preparation of a Solution of an Alloy.   Procedure. The alloy must be in finely divided form: powder, shavings, turnings, drillings, or parings.

a. Preliminary Solubility Tests.   Test the solubility of a very small portion (5-10 mg) in 8 M HNO_3 (dilute the concentrated acid with an equal volume of water). Heat in the water bath until reaction appears to be complete. Centrifuge and examine any residue. A dark residue is unreacted metal or carbon; remove the solution and try to dissolve the residue in a fresh portion of nitric acid. If it does not dissolve, test the solubility of another very small portion of the alloy in aqua regia. White residues may form with either solvent; disregard these for the time being and look for dark particles of unreacted metal. If neither solvent appears to dissolve your alloy, consult your instructor. Other solvents such as a combination of bromine and hydrochloric acid are useful for particular types of alloys.

b. Dissolution of the Alloy.   Weigh 50 mg of alloy into a test tube or casserole and add a small amount of the solvent that has been selected. Heat the test tube in vigorously boiling water or the casserole over a microflame (do not boil). Stir frequently and break up clumps of particles or rub off surface coatings to expose fresh surfaces. Add more acid if vigorous reaction has ceased and dark particles of metal remain, but avoid a large excess of acid, for this must be removed by evaporation in a subsequent step. Bear in mind that *many alloys dissolve slowly at best* and allow plenty of time for reaction to occur. Centrifuge and withdraw the clear solution to a casserole; its treatment is described in step c. Examine the residue.

(1) If the residue is white, it may be the oxides of tin and antimony or the chlorides of silver and lead, depending on whether nitric acid or aqua regia was used as the solvent. Treat it according to step c.

(2) If the residue is dark, it may contain unreacted metal or it may be carbon. Try to dissolve it in a fresh portion of solvent. Should this fail, it may be carbon or a metal in a passive state. Wash the residue two or three times with water to remove nitrate and try to dissolve it in 6 M or 12 M HCl.

Ordinarily, any *small* black residue that resists nitric acid, aqua regia, and hydrochloric acid can be regarded as carbon and discarded.

   c. Preparation of the Solution for the Cation Analysis.   Transfer the solution together with any white residue to a casserole and evaporate it over a micro-flame to a volume of a few drops. Withdraw the flame and let the heat of the dish complete the evaporation. If there is a white residue of the oxides of tin and antimony, it is advisable to coagulate them further by a second evapora-tion with 6 M HNO_3. Dissolve the salts in 10 drops of 6 M HNO_3 and warm briefly to hasten their solution. Transfer the mixture to a centrifuge tube and centrifuge. Withdraw the solution to a test tube. Wash the residue twice with water containing a little HNO_3 and combine the washings with the solution. Mix thoroughly and use $\frac{1}{3}$ to $\frac{1}{2}$ of the solution for the systematic analysis (Sec. 24-5).

   d. Treatment of the White Residue from Step c.
   (1) If nitric acid was used as the solvent, the residue may contain hydrated forms of SnO_2, Sb_2O_5, and SiO_2 together with other occluded metal ions. Add 5 drops of 6 M NH_3 and 2 drops of 13% thioacetamide solution and warm in the hot water bath. Centrifuge and withdraw the solution to another test tube. Repeat the extraction of the residue. Acidify the combined extracts with 2 M HCl to reprecipitate the sulfides of antimony and tin. Dissolve these sulfides in 12 M HCl as indicated under Precipitate 4-1, Out-line 4, Chapter 18, and test for antimony and tin according to that procedure. If a black residue remains after the extraction of antimony and tin as thio-anions, it will be sulfides of other cations. Dissolve it in nitric acid and add the solution to that obtained in step c.
   (2) If aqua regia was used as the solvent, a white residue is probably AgCl or $PbCl_2$. Analyze it by Outline 1, Chapter 17.

   24-5. Analysis for Cations Only.   The sample may be a solution of an alloy (Sec. 24-4c) or a "general unknown" to be analyzed only for cations, the anions being nitrates or chlorides.
   If an alloy is being analyzed it will be unnecessary to test for NH_4^+, Fe^{++}, or Hg_2^{++} ions. Assume further, unless directed otherwise, that Na^+, K^+, Ca^{++}, Sr^{++}, and Ba^{++} are absent. Thus Mg^{++} ion is the only member of Groups 4 or 5 to be sought.
   a. Note the color of the solution and draw what conclusions you can from it (see Table 6-5 and Sec. 19-23 for the colors of ions in solution). Bear in mind that if the solution is colorless, certain ions are absent.
   b. Make a few crash precipitation tests. The simplicity of these makes them worth trying, but the results must be confirmed by other tests. Take 1 drop of the solution and dilute with a few drops of water for each test; then add the indicated reagent.

(1) Add excess 6 M NaOH. If no precipitate forms, these cations are absent: Ag^+, Hg_2^{++}, Hg^{++}, Bi^{+++}, Cu^{++}, Cd^{++}, Fe^{++}, Fe^{+++}, Mn^{++}, Co^{++}, Ni^{++}, and Mg^{++} (unless ammonium salts are present). If there is a precipitate, its color may be significant, e.g., blue $Co(OH)_2$ or $Cu(OH)_2$, red-brown $Fe(OH)_3$, yellow HgO, and brown Ag_2O (consult Chapters 17-19 for other hydroxides).

(2) Add excess 15 M NH_3. If no precipitate forms, all cations are absent but Ag^+, Cu^{++} (blue solution), Cd^{++}, Co^{++} (pink), Ni^{++} (blue), Zn^{++}, Ba^{++}, Sr^{++}, Ca^{++}, Na^+, K^+, and NH_4^+. [$Mg(OH)_2$ will not precipitate if ammonium salts are present.]

(3) Add a drop of 6 M H_2SO_4 and several drops of 95% ethyl alcohol and stir vigorously for a minute. If a precipitate forms, the presence of Pb^{++}, Ca^{++}, Sr^{++}, or Ba^{++} is indicated.

c. Tests for the following cations are made on the original solution: Fe^{++}, Fe^{+++}, Ni^{++}, Mn^{++}, Co^{++}, Zn^{++} (P-1 to -5, Cation Group 3), and NH_4^+ (Cation Group 5). Flame tests may also be done on this solution. All such tests should be confirmed by a systematic analysis.

d. To make a systematic analysis for the cations, follow the procedures in Outlines 1 through 7 (see the block outline of the whole scheme in Sec. 16-1). Three features of the general analysis for cations of all groups must be emphasized:

(1) Always test for completeness of precipitation. Failure to do this may lead not only to the loss of ions but also to confusion in later tests when foreign ions leak through and interfere.

(2) Wash precipitates thoroughly. Use a rod to disperse the precipitate in the wash water. Large gelatinous precipitates of hydroxides or sulfides are often contaminated with considerable amounts of unwanted ions.

(3) Adjust the volumes of reagents for precipitates or amounts of ions of abnormal size. Frequently in the analysis of alloys, a few metals will be present in large amounts, and the quantities of reagents must be increased accordingly.

e. An alternative separation of Cation Group 4[2] is advantageous, for these ions may be lost in a systematic analysis by precipitation with earlier groups. The slow oxidation of hydrogen sulfide or thioacetamide to sulfate by oxygen of air or nitric acid will result in the loss of barium and strontium. Because of this, thioacetamide and hydrogen sulfide are destroyed by evaporation with concentrated hydrochloric acid after the precipitation of Groups 2 and 3. Old solutions of thioacetamide should not be used as reagents unless they give no turbidity with barium chloride. The carbonates of Group 4 may prematurely precipitate with Group 3 if the ammonia reagent has absorbed carbon dioxide from the air. Other anions such as phosphate or fluoride also cause precipitation of Group 4 with Group 3. Even when such anions are absent, the ions of Group 4 may be coprecipitated by large

[2]This is a modification of the scheme proposed by L. Bark, *Mikrochim. Acta*, **1958**, 117.

gelatinous precipitates of aluminum or chromium(III) hydroxides. Should the precipitate of the carbonates of Group 4 be so small as a result of these losses that satisfactory tests cannot be obtained, it is desirable to use an alternative separation.

The precipitation of the sulfates of Group 4 is an attractive separation, for it can be made in acid solution before the precipitation of Group 2, in other words, before the losses occur. Lead sulfate, to be sure, will also precipitate, but this is easily separated. Calcium sulfate is only sparingly soluble, but its solubility can be decreased by the addition of ethyl alcohol which has a lower dielectric constant than water. Lead sulfate can be dissolved by forming the acetate or hydroxide complex of lead. The latter works better because sodium carbonate can be added with the excess of sodium hydroxide; thus the sulfates of calcium and strontium are transposed to the less soluble carbonates so they are not dissolved during extraction of the lead. Typical reactions are represented by

$$PbSO_4\downarrow \ + 3OH^- \ \rightarrow Pb(OH)_3^- + SO_4^{--}$$
$$CaSO_4\downarrow \ + CO_3^{--} \rightarrow CaCO_3\downarrow \ + SO_4^{--}$$

Transposition of barium sulfate to the carbonate is more difficult but usually occurs to a sufficient extent to permit the detection of barium. If a large residue remains untransposed, it can be fused with solid sodium carbonate for more effective reaction.

The procedure for the sulfate separation is given in Outline 9.

OUTLINE 9. The Sulfate Separation of Cation Group 4

Solution containing all cations but Ag$^+$ and Hg$_2^{++}$. Total vol should be 0.5 ml (10 drops); adjust by evapn or diln. Add 1 drop 18 M H_2SO_4 and 20 drops 95% C_2H_5OH. Stir vigorously for 1 minute.[1] Centrifuge and wash ppt twice with soln made by mixing 10 drops water, 1 drop 18 M H_2SO_4, and 10 drops C_2H_5OH.

Precipitate 9-1. PbSO$_4$, BaSO$_4$, SrSO$_4$, CaSO$_4$. Add 5 drops 6 M NaOH[2] and an equal vol of water. Dissolve a heaping spatula-full of Na_2CO_3 in the mixture. Stir and warm for several minutes in boiling water. Centrifuge.

Solution 9-1. Ions of later group

Precipitate 9-2. (PbSO$_4$), (BaSO$_4$), BaCO$_3$, SrCO$_3$, CaCO$_3$. Repeat the extraction and transposition with NaOH and Na_2CO_3 until the extract gives no more than a faint turbidity with K_2CrO_4.

Precipitate 9-3. BaCO$_3$, SrCO$_3$, CaCO$_3$. Treat it as if it were Precipitate 6-1, Outline 6, Cation Group 4.[3]

Solution 9-2. SO$_4^{--}$, Pb(OH)$_3^-$. Acidify wi 6 M HC$_2$H$_3$O$_2$. Add a few drops K$_2$CrO$_4$. Yello ppt, PbCrO$_4$: **presence of Pb.**

Notes on Outline 9

1. Calcium sulfate supersaturates, hence the vigorous stirring over a period of time. It is advisable to let Solution 9-1 stand for 5-10 minutes should more calcium sulfate precipitate.

2. If lead is known to be absent from the regular systematic analysis, the sodium hydroxide should be omitted.

3. Transposition of barium sulfate may be incomplete so that all of Precipitate 9-3 may not dissolve in acetic acid. Usually a sufficient amount of barium is brought into solution to give a precipitate with chromate. If there is a large residue insoluble in acetic acid, it should be dried and fused with Na_2CO_3 [Sec. 24-8c(3)].

24-6. Analysis of Nonmetallic Solids. Preliminary Work.

a. Note the obvious physical characteristics of the material. If it is colored, consider whether any deductions can be made with the aid of Table 24-1. If it is colorless, certain constituents are eliminated (Sec. 24-2). Examine it closely, preferably with a magnifying glass, for evidence of heterogeneity. It may be possible to estimate from this observation the minimum number of components of the mixture. Some of the crystals may be large enough to pick out by hand and analyze separately.

b. Prepare the sample. The sample taken for analysis must be representative of the entire lot of material. Since we use 100 mg or less for the analysis, sampling can be something of a problem when a large quantity of material is available. The formidable difficulties involved in sampling will probably not confront you in this introductory course. For a discussion of sampling refer to one of the larger textbooks of quantitative analysis.

The material to be analyzed must be finely powdered and intimately mixed. If it is not, i.e., if the particles of the separate components can be distinguished, grind it to an impalpable powder.

c. Make an ignition test. This is primarily a test for the presence of organic matter, but other useful information may also be obtained. Mixtures containing chlorates or other potentially dangerous substances must not be ignited. They should be excluded from consideration in this introductory course.

Place a few mg of sample (a spatula-full of solid is 100-150 mg; use less than a tenth of this) in a *dry* test tube of borosilicate glass (e.g., Pyrex or Kimax) and tap the tube until the sample collects at the bottom. Heat the tube cautiously at first, then strongly, with a microburner. Confine the flame to the closed end of the tube so the other end remains as cool as possible. Various things may be observed:

(1) Darkening or charring of the residue accompanied by evolution of a smoke with an odor reminiscent of burning hair, feathers, or other organic

matter or condensation of tarry oil near the cold, open end of the tube is an indication of the presence of organic matter.

(2) Change in color of the residue with or without evolution of water but without burnt odor or tarry deposit is characteristic of various hydrated salts or oxides, e.g., Cu(II), Co(II), and Ni salts or PbO.

(3) Formation of a deposit on the cool walls near the open end of the tube indicates the possible presence of various substances: (a) colorless liquid—water, (b) white solid—ammonium salts, As_2O_3, $HgCl_2$ (by sublimation of $HgCl_2$ or decomposition of Hg_2Cl_2), anhydrous chlorides of Sn, Fe, Al, or Sb, and certain volatile organic solids, (c) gray to black deposit—Hg or As, (d) yellow solid—As_2S_3 or S^0 from free sulfur or sulfides.

d. Test the solubility of the material in water and dilute acids. Try to dissolve a few mg of sample in cold and hot portions of water, 6 M HNO_3, and 6 M HCl. Watch for evolution of a gas with water or HCl. Consider your results in connection with the summary of solubilities in Table 24-3 and see if certain classes of substances or even specific substances can be eliminated or tentatively identified. If the unknown is completely soluble in water, for example, it may contain sodium, potassium, or ammonium salts of various anions or nitrates, acetates, or nitrites of various cations. If it is insoluble in water and hydrochloric acid but soluble in nitric acid, it does not contain insoluble sulfates but may contain sulfides or silver salts of weak acids. It is important to note that certain naturally occurring substances are less soluble than the same material freshly precipitated, and certain salts such as $PbCrO_4$ and various sulfates and oxides are much less soluble after they have been ignited, i.e., heated strongly.

c. Try the crash precipitations with NaOH, NH_3, and H_2SO_4 described in Sec. 24-5b on a solution of the sample.

f. Try flame tests on a few mg of sample moistened with 12 M HCl (Table 24-2).

24-7. Analysis of Nonmetallic Solids for Anions.   It is usually convenient to analyze for anions before cations although no rigid rule need be established. Some anions interfere in the separations of the cation analysis (Sec. 24-9c) and their presence should be known before the systematic analysis for cation is attempted. Certain anions and cations are also incompatible in solution, e.g., Ag^+ and Cl^- or Ba^{++} and SO_4^{--}, and if the presence of one ion is established, the other is necessarily absent from a solution of the sample.

Preparation of the solution for anion analysis is described in Sec. 23-2. If the solution is yellow, chromate or dichromate is probably present. Elimination tests ET-1 to -7 should be carried out and the elimination chart constructed. Then such individual tests can be performed as are indicated by the chart.

TABLE 24-3.

Summary of Solubilities

Class A. Almost all salts soluble in water.

1. Nitrates. All are soluble but certain basic nitrates, e.g., those of Bi and Hg(II), are only soluble in acids.
2. Nitrites. Silver nitrite is sparingly soluble in water, soluble in dilute HNO_3.
3. Acetates. The acetates of Ag, Hg(I), and Cr(II) are sparingly soluble in water; basic acetates such as that of Fe(III) are insoluble. All dissolve in dilute HNO_3.

Class B. Relative small number of salts insoluble in water.

1. Chlorides, bromides, iodides, and thiocyanates. Those of Ag, Hg(I), and Pb and also HgI_2 and $Hg(SCN)_2$ are insoluble. The salts of Pb are the most soluble of these. All are insoluble in dilute acids. Basic salts such as those of Bi, Sb, and Hg(II) are soluble in acids.
2. Sulfates. The sulfates of Ba, Sr, and Pb are insoluble; those of Ag, Ca, and Hg(I) sparingly soluble. All are only slightly soluble in acids. The ignited or dehydrated sulfates of Fe(III), Al, and Cr(III) are with difficulty soluble in water or acids. Basic sulfates are soluble in acids.

Class C. Almost all compounds insoluble in water.

The sodium, potassium, and ammonium salts of these are soluble; other exceptions are noted for each class of substance.
1. Fluorides. Somewhat soluble in acids; CaF_2 is least soluble. Soluble salts are those of Ag, Al, Hg, and Sn.
2. Sulfides. All soluble in HNO_3 but HgS; many soluble in HCl; HgS is soluble in aqua regia.
3. Sulfites, phosphates, arsenates, arsenites, carbonates, and borates are insoluble in water but usually soluble in dilute acids. Some phosphates found in nature are attacked with difficulty.
4. Oxalates. These are soluble in strong acids. Iron(III) oxalate is soluble, magnesium oxalate sparingly soluble in water.
5. Chromates. These are soluble in acids, but $PbCrO_4$ which has been ignited or fused is not attacked by acids. The chromates of Mg, Ca, and Cu(II) are soluble in water and $SrCrO_4$ is sparingly soluble. Dichromates are usually more soluble than chromates.
6. Oxides and hydroxides. The oxides of Ba, Sr, and Ca are moderately soluble in water. Most metal oxides are soluble in acids, preferably HCl, but As_2O_3 is best dissolved with NaOH. The oxides of Al, Cr(III), and Sn(IV) in some forms are virtually insoluble in acids.

24-8. Preparation of a Solution of a Nonmetallic Solid for the Cation Analysis.

a. If the solubility tests of Sec. 24-6 were inconclusive, test the solubility of separate small portions of the sample successively in cold and hot portions of

H_2O, 6 M HCl, 12 M HCl, 6 M HNO_3, 16 M HNO_3, and aqua regia

Use 5-10 drops of each solvent, stir it thoroughly with the sample, and allow time for reaction to occur. Centrifuge to determine if a small residue remains undissolved. When concentrated acids are used, dilute the mixture slowly with an equal volume of water after the reaction ceases. Certain salts are only sparingly soluble in the concentrated acids.

b. Weigh 100 mg of the sample and treat it with the solvent that has been selected. If no solvent dissolved the sample completely, use the one that had the most effect or, if there is little choice, use aqua regia. Treat any insoluble residue by step c. When the solution was obtained by use of one of the acid solvents, evaporate it to a volume of a few drops to remove excess acid. Do not evaporate to dryness, for this may cause decomposition or formation of basic salts that are difficult to redissolve. Add several drops of 6 M HCl and 1 ml (20 drops) of water. If a precipitate forms or persists in the presence of HCl, separate it, wash it carefully, and analyze it for Cation Group 1 according to Outline 1. Take one-fifth to one-fourth of the remaining solution (the equivalent of 20-25 mg of the original solid) for the systematic analysis of Groups 2 to 5 and save the rest for other tests and checking.

c. If there is a residue insoluble in acids, special treatment is required. The more common substances that it may contain are

$PbSO_4$, $BaSO_4$, $SrSO_4$, $CaSO_4$ (if a large amount is present), ignited sulfates of Fe(III), Al, or Cr(III), $PbCrO_4$ (fused),

AgCl, AgBr, AgI, AgSCN, CaF_2 (the mineral form),

Al_2O_3, Cr_2O_3, SnO_2, Sb_2O_4, SiO_2, or silicates,

C or S.

The residue is treated first with Na_2CO_3 solution to transpose the sulfates, then with Zn and H_2SO_4 to reduce the silver halides and thiocyanate, and finally it is fused with sodium and potassium carbonates.

(1) Wash the residue twice with a moderately dilute solution of the acid used to dissolve the sample. Then suspend it in 1 ml of water and add two heaping spatulas-full of Na_2CO_3. Heat in boiling water for ten minutes; stir frequently. Centrifuge, discard the solution, and wash the precipitate three times with hot water to remove sulfate. Add a few drops of 6 M HNO_3 to the residue and, after reaction ceases, dilute with several drops of water. Centrifuge and withdraw the solution; add it to the acid solution of the sample for the general analysis. If a residue remains, repeat the treatment with sodium carbonate solution.

(2) The residue from the transposition of the sulfates may be the silver salts, CaF_2, oxides, silicates, C, and S. Add 1 ml of water, 1 drop of 18 M H_2SO_4, and some granules of zinc to reduce the silver halides to free silver. Warm for several minutes and break apart clumps and disperse the residue with a rod. Centrifuge and discard the solution. Wash the precipitate twice.

Add several drops of 6 M HNO$_3$ to dissolve Ag and excess Zn. Identify silver in the solution by precipitating the chloride, dissolving it in ammonia, and reprecipitating it with HNO$_3$ as in Outline 1.

(3) If a residue still remains, a fusion is necessary. Wash the precipitate in the test tube twice with 95% ethyl alcohol and withdraw as much alcohol as possible. Heat the tube in boiling water to vaporize the remaining alcohol and then heat it over a microflame until the residue is dry. Cool. Scrape the residue into a depression of the spot plate and mix it with 3 to 4 times its bulk of a mixture of Na$_2$CO$_3$ and K$_2$CO$_3$. (The melting point of a mixture of equal parts of the two carbonates is lower than that of either one alone.) Fusion may be carried out in a small nickel crucible or on a charcoal block. Support the crucible in a triangle and heat strongly with a Bunsen or Meker burner. If the charcoal block method is used, make a torch from 8-mm glass tubing by drawing the end to a capillary tip and bending the tube to an L-shape (Fig. 24-1). Connect the torch to the gas outlet and direct the flame

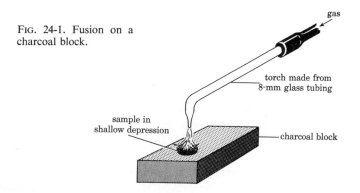

Fig. 24-1. Fusion on a charcoal block.

gas

torch made from 8-mm glass tubing

sample in shallow depression

charcoal block

at the mixture of carbonates and residue in a small hollow scooped out of the charcoal block. Practice first with some of the mixed carbonates to determine the proper size of flame and distance of the torch from the sample. It should be possible to fuse the mixture in less than a minute.[3]

Transfer the fused mass to a centrifuge tube. Add water and heat for several minutes in a water bath to disintegrate the solid and dissolve soluble salts. If a crucible was used, boil crucible and residue with water in a small beaker and after the mass has disintegrated, remove the crucible. Centrifuge the mixture and wash any residue with hot water.

The sodium carbonate solution may contain aluminate and silicate ions. Acidify it with hydrochloric acid and evaporate to dryness to dehydrate the silicon dioxide. Dissolve in a few drops of 6 M HCl and centrifuge to remove any precipitate. Look for aluminum in the solution according to the procedure in Outline 5 under Precipitate 5-5.

[3]See R. Belcher, R. Harrison, and W. Stephens, *Mikrochim. Acta*, **1958**, 201.

Acidify the residue from the sodium carbonate fusion with 6 M HNO_3 and analyze it for the cations. Note that nickel will necessarily be present if a nickel crucible is used for the fusion. If there is still a residue, insoluble in nitric acid, it may be SnO_2. It can be brought into solution by fusion with sodium carbonate and sulfur in a porcelain crucible. The thioanion of tin(IV) is obtained.

Typical reactions of sodium carbonate with constituents of the residue are represented by

$$4AgBr + 2Na_2CO_3 \xrightarrow{\Delta} 4Ag + 4NaBr + 2CO_2\uparrow + O_2\uparrow$$

$$Al_2O_3 + Na_2CO_3 \xrightarrow{\Delta} 2NaAlO_2 + CO_2\uparrow$$

$$Cr_2O_3 + 2Na_2CO_3 + \tfrac{3}{2}O_2 \xrightarrow{\Delta} 2Na_2CrO_4 + 2CO_2\uparrow$$

$$SiO_2 + Na_2CO_3 \xrightarrow{\Delta} Na_2SiO_3 + CO_2\uparrow$$

$$BaSO_4 + Na_2CO_3 \xrightarrow{\Delta} BaCO_3 + Na_2SO_4$$

$$PbCrO_4 + Na_2CO_3 \xrightarrow{\Delta} PbCO_3 + Na_2CrO_4$$

$$CaF_2 + Na_2CO_3 \xrightarrow{\Delta} CaCO_3 + 2NaF$$

$$2SnO_2 + 2Na_2CO_3 + 9S^0 \xrightarrow{\Delta} 2Na_2SnS_3 + 2CO_2\uparrow + 3SO_2\uparrow$$

The sodium salts are soluble in water, although the aluminate and silicate may partially hydrolyze to the insoluble oxides. The carbonates and silver are dissolved by nitric acid.

24-9. Analysis of a Nonmetallic Solid for Cations.

a. Carry out the analysis for cations on the solution prepared in Sec. 24-8. Refer to steps c, d, and e in Sec. 24-5 for suggestions.

b. Potassium can be sought in the Prepared Solution used for analysis of the anions. Acidify the solution with acetic acid and if iodide is present, remove it by adding sodium nitrite and evaporating almost to dryness. Then test for potassium with sodium cobaltinitrite. The ammonium ion should be absent if the Prepared Solution was boiled until the vapors did not turn litmus blue.

c. Account must be taken of interferences by anions:

(1) Oxidizing agents such as CrO_4^{--}, $Cr_2O_7^{--}$, MnO_4^-, NO_2^-, or SO_3^{--} will oxidize hydrogen sulfide or thioacetamide to sulfur or sulfate. Nitrite and sulfite are decomposed by acid. The oxyanions of chromium and manganese are reduced by hydrogen peroxide before the precipitation of Cation Group 2 (P-2 to Outline 2, Chapter 18).

(2) Fluoride and phosphate form precipitates with various cations such as those of Cation Group 4 when the solution is made alkaline. Borates can

also precipitate but not to any large extent if ammonium salts are present.[4] Phosphate can be precipitated as zirconyl phosphate in acid solution; fluoride can be removed by fuming with sulfuric acid.

(3) Organic anions such as oxalates and tartrates form soluble complexes with certain cations of Group 3, e.g., Fe^{+++}, Al^{+++}, and Cr^{+++}, and prevent their precipitation. The oxalates of Group 4 are precipitated with Group 3. Organic anions can be destroyed by evaporation with nitric and sulfuric acids.

(4) Iodide ion interferes with the test for potassium because it is oxidized by nitrite. It can be removed by evaporation of the solution with nitric acid.

The simplest way to get rid of unwanted anions is by ion-exchange. This method is described in Chapter 25.

EXERCISES

24-1. Outline the simplest scheme of analysis for each of these alloys. What solvent would be used for each? (a) Wood's metal: Bi, Pb, Sn, and Cd, (b) Dowmetal C: Al, Mg, and Zn, (c) nickel silver: Cu, Zn, and Ni, (d) Chromel: Ni, Fe, and Cr.

24-2. Why is it unnecessary to test for NH_4^+, Fe^{++}, or Hg_2^{++} ions in solutions of alloys?

24-3. Write equations for the action of nitric and hydrochloric acids separately on these metals: Al, Fe, Sn, Cu, Zn, As, Mg.

24-4. During the analysis of a simple salt, carbonate ion was found to be present. What cations can be present if the salt was soluble in water?

24-5. What conclusions can be drawn from these observations on simple substances? (a) A red compound dissolves in nitric acid to give an orange solution but hydrochloric acid changes it to a white precipitate, (b) A yellow compound is insoluble in 6 M HCl, (c) A green salt dissolves in water to give a blue-green solution which becomes more bluish as the solution is diluted, (d) A blue compound dissolves in water to give a pink solution, (e) A black solid is insoluble in dilute acids but dissolves in concentrated hydrochloric acid with the evolution of a gas that changes the color of starch-iodide paper.

24-6. Summarize the advantages and disadvantages of hydrochloric acid, nitric acid, and aqua regia for dissolving alloys.

24-7. How is the passivity of certain metals manifested?

24-8. Write equations for the reactions of tin with the following reagents in succession: HNO_3, NH_3 and thioacetamide, 2 M HCl.

24-9. What cations must be absent if the solution for the cation analysis (a) is colorless, (b) is strongly alkaline, (c) gives no precipitate with sodium carbonate solution?

24-10. Summarize the ways in which the ions of Group 4 can be lost during a systematic analysis and give the theoretical basis for the sulfate separation of Outline 9.

24-11. Explain the theoretical basis for separations in the cation analysis that depend on control of the concentration of (a) S^{--}, (b) OH^-, (c) CO_3^{--}, (d) CrO_4^{--}.

[4]See O. Hayes and J. Winterburn, *Mikrochim. Acta*, **1958,** 197.

24-12. Cite examples from the systematic analysis for cations, exclusive of group separations, of separation of ions by (a) chelation, (b) common ion effect, (c) formation of ammonia complexes, (d) amphoterism, (e) oxidation or reduction.

24-13. What is the best solvent for each of these: Ag^0, $BiCl_3$, $MgCa(CO_3)_2$, $BaSO_4$, $KAl(SO_4)_2 \cdot 12H_2O$, ZnS, CuS, $CaSO_4 \cdot 2H_2O$, $BaCrO_4$, HgS, $K_2Cr_2O_7$, $PbCO_3$, SnO_2, $AgBr$.

24-14. If a solution of an unknown contains Sr^{++}, Ag^+, and Al^{+++} ions, what anions must be absent?

24-15. If a solution of an unknown contains SO_4^{--}, $C_2H_3O_2^-$, and I^- ions, what cations must be absent?

24-16. If an unknown solution contains PO_4^{---}, NO_3^-, and OH^- ions, what cations must be absent?

24-17. Write equations for the reactions that occur when sodium carbonate is fused with: $SrSO_4$, $CaSiO_3$, AgI, Sb_2O_4, and SnO.

24-18. A green solid, which may be a single substance or a mixture, is insoluble in water, soluble in $6 M$ HCl with evolution of a colorless, odorless gas. When an excess of sodium hydroxide is added to the solution, a blue precipitate forms that turns black when the solution is boiled. What conclusions can be drawn as to the presence or absence of cations or anions?

24-19. A mixture of salts is readily soluble in cold water. A blue color is produced when an excess of ammonia is added to the solution. When sulfuric acid and ethyl alcohol are added to another portion of the aqueous solution, a white precipitate forms that is partially soluble in sodium hydroxide. What conclusions can you draw from these observations?

24-20. A white solid is soluble in water. When sodium nitrite is added to it, a red-brown color is produced. No precipitate is obtained when an excess of sodium hydroxide is added to a fresh portion of the aqueous solution, but a gelatinous white precipitate forms when excess ammonia is added to a third sample of the solution. What conclusions can you draw from these observations?

24-21. A solid mixture contains $AgCl$, $Sr(NO_3)_2$, $CoSO_4$, $Fe(NO_3)_3$, and CdS. Suppose that this were issued as an "unknown" and examined according to Secs. 24-6 to -9. Describe the observations that you would expect to be made during this analysis.

CHAPTER TWENTY-FIVE

Special Methods of Qualitative Analysis

25-1. Introduction. The analysis for cations and, to a lesser extent, anions has been based first on the separation of ions into groups by making use of one common property such as the formation of sulfides insoluble in 0.1 M hydrochloric acid. The subsequent analysis of each group called into play more and more specific properties of the ions. This general scheme of analysis was devised in the nineteenth century by Fresenius and others for the analysis of rocks. There are other methods of qualitative analysis, several of which are almost equally old. Some, such as spot testing, use familiar reactions between substances in solution in novel ways. Others, such as spectroscopy and polarography, are based on quite different properties of the ions. This chapter serves as an introduction to some of the methods. It cannot be more than an introduction, for an understanding of the potentialities and limitations of the methods sometimes will require more theoretical background and on occasion more experience with the techniques than a brief chapter can provide. But references to more extended treatments are given, and the student and teacher can do as much with these methods as time and inclination permit.

25-2. Spot Tests. In the most general sense a spot test is any test carried out on one or two drops of solution. The test may be done in a small test tube, and, from this point of view, many of the tests used in earlier chapters were spot tests. More commonly, we think of these tests as being done on a spot plate, on a slide subjected to microscopic examination, or on paper. This last technique was used in the dithizone test for zinc (Cation Group 3). The choice of a particular way of carrying out a test is determined by convenience and by the sensitivity that can be attained. A colored substance can frequently be seen at lower concentration against the white background of a spot plate than in a test tube. White turbidities can be viewed to advantage on a black spot plate. Dark flecks of precipitate can readily be viewed on the white background of paper after the solution from which the precipitate formed has diffused away through the pores of the paper. Paper does not always play merely a supporting role. Differences in adsorption of substances by paper fibers and in rate of diffusion through the pores can be exploited to separate ions and increase the sensitivity of tests. Paper is therefore widely used in spot testing.

An extensive collection of tests for both common and rare ions has been built up by the efforts of F. Feigl and many others. Few of these tests are based on a reaction that is *specific* for one ion. The better reagents are *selective;* i.e., they react with a limited number of ions. In order to identify one of this number, the interference of the others must be *masked*, whether by precipitation, complex formation, oxidation, or other methods. Organic reagents are frequently more selective than inorganic ones and are extensively used in spot testing. They may form, with the inorganic ion, complexes or chelates, colored lakes, colored or insoluble salts or addition compounds; or they may be oxidized or reduced by the inorganic ion or undergo a reaction that is catalyzed by it.

A spot test must be sensitive; i.e., it must detect small amounts or low concentrations of the ion. The *limit of identification* is the smallest quantity of material that can be detected. It is usually expressed in micrograms; the unit is represented by the Greek *gamma*, $1\gamma = 10^{-6}$ g. The concentration sensitivity is given by the *dilution limit*. If 1 part of the substance can be detected in not more than 100,000 parts of solution (10γ per milliliter for an aqueous solution), the dilution limit is $1:10^5$.

25-3. Some Experiments with Spot Testing. Since several of these tests are made on paper, the technique of spotting should be described. For best results the spot should not be too diffuse or waterlogged. Use a capillary pipet with a tip that is cut off squarely. Dip the tip in the solution that is to be transferred to the paper. If solution does not rise in the tip to the extent of 1-2 cm by capillary action, give the slightest of squeezes to the rubber bulb. Withdraw the pipet and touch the tip to the vessel to remove hanging drops. For best control grasp the pipet near the tip. Bring it down perpendicular to the paper and allow solution to flow out spontaneously until the spot is 4-8 mm in diameter.

EXPERIMENT 1. Test for Mn^{++} ion with benzidine. This is given to illustrate sensitivity under various conditions. In alkaline solution manganese(II) is oxidized by oxygen of air to manganese(III) (Sec. 19-7d) which in turn oxidizes benzidine to a blue colored compound. If we represent benzidine, $H_2NC_6H_4C_6H_4NH_2$, by BzH_2, the formation of the blue compound is indicated by

$$2BzH_2 \rightarrow Bz{\cdot}BzH_2 + 2H^+ + 2e^-$$

Other oxidizing agents such as chromate also bring this about. We shall not consider such interferences, although they are important in the practical application of the test. The dilution limit according to Feigl is 1:330,000.

Procedure.[1] Prepare some 0.05 M KOH by diluting the 0.5 M reagent. To make the test, mix a drop of solution under test with a drop of 0.05 M KOH and add a drop of benzidine solution. Carry out the test in a test tube, in a depression of the white spot plate, and on spot paper. Do it first with the standard solution of Mn^{++} ion (10 mg/ml) and then repeat with a solution prepared by diluting 1 drop of the standard solution with 200 ml of water. Mix this dilute solution thoroughly by pouring it back and forth between two beakers or flasks. Compare the sensitivity of the test under the various conditions. Calculate the dilution ratio (milligrams of solution per milligram of Mn^{++}) and compare with Feigl's dilution limit.

EXPERIMENT 2. Testing for Sr^{++} ion in the presence of Ba^{++}. The reactions of barium are so similar to those of strontium that it must be removed or masked if the test for strontium is to be valid. This is true whether the reagent is an inorganic ion such as sulfate or an organic ion such as the rhodizonate ion, $C_6O_6^{--}$. Many bivalent cations including Ba^{++} and Sr^{++} ions, but not Ca^{++} ion, react with this organic anion to give a brown-red precipitate in neutral solution. The dilution limit given by Feigl is 1:12,800 when Sr^{++} is to be detected in the presence of 80 times as much Ba^{++}. The reaction is more sensitive in the absence of barium.

Procedure.[2] Paint a piece of filter paper with saturated K_2CrO_4 solution. Dry the paper by holding it considerably above a flame or, more conveniently, by placing it under an infrared lamp. Spot this paper and an untreated piece in separate places with the standard solutions of Ba^{++} and Sr^{++} ions. After a minute add to each of the four spots a drop of 0.2% rhodizonate solution. Explain why the reaction of only one of the ions with rhodizonate is masked by the potassium chromate.

EXPERIMENT 3. Spot tests for Cl^-, Br^-, and I^- ions.[3] These tests can be used to identify the halide ions in the presence of each other or thiocyanate ion as, for example, on the solution prepared in Sec. 23-7b(3d) by the action of zinc and acetic acid on the silver halides.

a. Test for iodide ion. This is the only halide ion that is oxidized to free halogen by nitric acid at low concentration. The iodine is detected by the formation of its blue complex with starch (Sec. 22-5).

[1]Special materials: spot reaction paper (Whatman No. 120 or S. and S. No. 601) cut in 10–15 mm squares; 0.05% benzidine solution. To prepare the latter, dissolve 0.05 g of benzidine in 10 ml of glacial acetic acid and dilute to 100 ml with water. Filter if necessary to obtain a clear solution.

[2]Special materials: saturated solution of K_2CrO_4; 0.2% solution of potassium or sodium rhodizonate in water.

[3]H. Weisz, *Mikrochim. Acta,* **1956,** 1225; R. Belcher and H. Weisz, *Mikrochim. Acta,* **1956,** 1847; **1958,** 571.

Procedure.[4] Spot a drop of the solution to be tested on filter paper and hold it for a minute above a few drops of 16 M HNO_3 in a small beaker. Then add a drop of starch solution. A blue spot indicates the presence of iodide.

b. Test for bromide ion. Iodide is removed by oxidation to iodate with hydrogen peroxide. Bromide is then oxidized to bromine and reacts with fluorescein to give red eosin (Sec. 22-4f).

Procedure.[5] Spot the solution under test on filter paper (not spot paper; this is too thick) and add 1 drop of special hydrogen peroxide solution. Bring *nearly* to dryness by holding the paper high over a flame or under an infrared lamp. If a blue spot persists, repeat the treatment with hydrogen peroxide. Then spot with 2-3 drops of fluorescein solution and dry. A red ring around a yellow spot indicates the presence of bromide. Rinse the paper with water for a few seconds to make the red color more visible.

c. Test for chloride ion. Chloride is identified by precipitation of silver chloride, but the other ions must be removed or masked. Hydrogen peroxide will oxidize all but chloride to the free element, which reacts with oxine.

Procedure.[6] Place 2 drops of solution under test on a small watch glass and add successively 1 drop of special hydrogen peroxide, a small drop of 6 M HNO_3, and 1 drop of oxine solution. Place the watch glass over one of the openings of the water bath cover and warm for 4 minutes. Then add 1 drop of $AgNO_3$ solution. The formation of a white precipitate of AgCl indicates the presence of chloride. The precipitate often appears yellow because of the strong yellow color of the oxine solution. It can be confirmed in the usual way.

Suggestions for further work. Consult the references at the end of the chapter for other tests. See also the first suggestion in Sec. 19-24.

25-4. Electrographic Analysis. This technique was introduced in 1929 simultaneously by Fritz and Glazunov. It is essentially an electrical method of adding the ion under test to paper. Thereafter conventional spot test techniques are used to detect the ion.

When a metal is made the anode (positive electrode) of an electrolysis cell, one possible electrode reaction is for the metal to be oxidized to its ion, e.g., $Ni \rightarrow Ni^{++} + 2e^-$. The ion migrates into paper in contact with the metal surface. The simplest experimental arrangement is shown in Fig. 25-1. The

[4]Special reagent: starch solution. Triturate 2 g of soluble starch and 20 mg of HgI_2 with a little water and add to 1 liter of boiling water. Continue boiling for a minute or two or until the solution is clear. The concentrated nitric acid should contain some oxides of nitrogen.

[5]Special reagents: special hydrogen peroxide, 2 volumes of 20 volume H_2O_2 mixed with 1 volume of glacial acetic acid; 0.5% fluorescein in 95% ethyl alcohol.

[6]Special reagents: hydrogen peroxide, see footnote 5; oxine (8-quinolinol, 8-hydroxyquinoline), 2% solution in a mixture of 1 volume of glacial acetic acid to 4 of water.

cathode is usually a plate of aluminum or stainless steel. The sample under test may be a metal, a conducting mineral, or even a section of plant or animal tissue. Anions such as chloride or sulfate can be detected by making the sample the cathode.

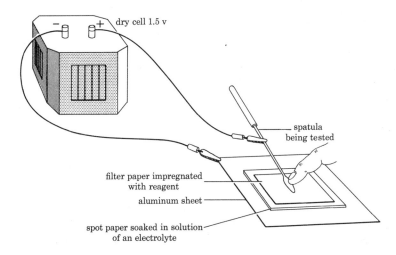

Fɪɢ. 25-1. Apparatus for electrographic analysis.

The product of the electrolysis operation is a "print" of the surface of the specimen. This is made visible by developing it with a reagent. Tiny pinholes in chrome-plated iron can be detected by electrolysis of the specimen in contact with paper impregnated with zinc ferrocyanide. Iron comes out through the pinholes and leaves blue spots of Prussian blue on the paper, a spot for every pinhole. Paper impregnated with insoluble reagents such as zinc ferrocyanide for iron or zinc sulfide for lead gives superior prints, for the ions have no chance to diffuse away from their point of entry to the paper. It is sometimes necessary because of the interference of other ions to electrolyze into plain paper. Interfering ions are then removed, and the color reaction for the ion being sought is carried out. The danger here is that the ions will diffuse away from the point of entry so that the print will no longer represent the distribution of the metal on the surface of the sample.

Procedure.[7] Add a few drops of dimethylglyoxime to a square of filter paper and allow the paper to dry. Set up the apparatus as pictured in Fig. 25-1. Use a square of spot reaction paper soaked in NaCl or Na_2SO_4 solution between the filter paper and the aluminum sheet. Use the blade of a spatula

[7]Special materials: 1 or more dry cells, scrap of aluminum sheet or foil, wires and two alligator clips, and spot reaction or photographic blotting paper. Ordinary smooth, not creped, filter paper can be used, but best results are obtained with hardened paper such as Whatman No. 50 or S. and S. No. 576.

or some other nickel object as the anode and press it down on the filter paper for a short length of time; a few seconds to a minute will usually suffice. When the surface is irregular, a better print can be obtained by using an aluminum foil cathode. To develop the red color of nickel dimethylglyoxime hold the filter paper over a few drops of 15 M NH_3 in a small beaker.

Suggestions for further work: identify metallic coatings, alloys, and minerals by the systematic procedures given by Hermance and Wadlow (reference at the end of the chapter). Many refinements in the experimental arrangement can be introduced. Several commercial instruments are on the market.

25-5. Chemical Microscopy. It is seldom easy to distinguish one white precipitate from another by superficial examination. Some grosser distinctions can be made; curdy $AgCl$, fine-grained $SrSO_4$, and gelatinous $Al(OH)_3$ are certainly different in appearance. But we would be hard put to distinguish fresh precipitates of barium, strontium, and calcium sulfates. When examined with a microscope, crystals of calcium sulfate are readily seen to differ from those of the other two: they form needles, often bundled into sheaves or rosettes, whereas the other two sulfates form fine granules.

The *habit* or external form of crystals depends on the pattern of arrangement of the ions or molecules in the crystal lattice. The faces of crystals generally correspond to densely populated planes of ions or molecules. Sodium chloride usually crystallizes in cubes, and inspection of Fig. 2-5 shows that these cubic faces contain ions of both kinds, each ion in the face being surrounded by four of the other kind. The habit of a crystal is not invariable but depends on the method of preparation and particularly on the presence of other ions or molecules. Sometimes such foreign ions promote the growth of more perfect crystals. Thus sodium chloride generally gives imperfect cubes unless a trace of lead(II) is present. Urea causes sodium chloride to crystallize in octahedra. This is not inconsistent with the cubic pattern of the ions. As Fig. 25-2 shows, the octahedral faces contain only ions of one kind in each layer. Normally these faces attract other ions more strongly than do the cubic faces. The octahedral faces usually grow more rapidly and tend to disappear; i.e., they grow out to a point or corner of the cube. Urea retards their growth and preserves the octahedral habit. It follows from this discussion that if crystals are to be identified by microscopic examination of their habit, they must be formed under carefully controlled conditions. The removal of interfering ions is fully as important in chemical microscopy as it is in other microchemical methods.

The most characteristic crystals are produced by slow growth. The solution must not be too supersaturated or the edges and corners of the crystal will grow too rapidly (see Sec. 8-8). If this happens, various irregularities form: hopper-shaped faces, dendrites (tree- or moss-like habits), and skeletal forms. Slow growth is most conveniently obtained by allowing the solvent to evaporate slowly from the solution.

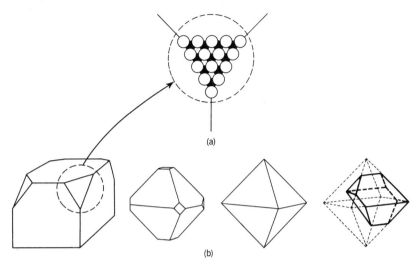

(a)

(b)

FIG. 25-2. Octahedral faces of sodium chloride crystals. (a) Two layers of ions in the octahedral face. (b) Octahedral faces in various stages of development.

25-6. Introductory Experiments in Chemical Microscopy.

EXPERIMENT 1. Rapid crystal growth. Place on a clean microscope slide a drop of $SnCl_2$ solution about 4-8 mm wide and 1 mm high. Place the slide on the stage of a microscope[8] and with forceps or spatula drop into the center of the drop *one* small granule of zinc metal. Immediately focus near the surface of the granule and watch the growth of the crystals of tin. Sketch representative examples in your notebook. Repeat the experiment with solutions of $AgNO_3$, $Pb(NO_3)_2$, and $Cu(NO_3)_2$ or $CuSO_4$ in place of the $SnCl_2$ solution.

EXPERIMENT 2. Modification of the crystal habit of sodium chloride. Prepare some saturated sodium chloride solution by boiling several milliliters of water with an excess of NaCl in a casserole. Pour off 1-2 ml of the solution into two test tubes. To one tube add a spatula-full of urea and stir until it is dissolved. Withdraw a drop of each solution to clean slides and allow them to stand until crystals begin to form. Then examine them under the microscope. Sketch representative crystals in the notebook. Follow the growth of the crystals for a short time. Note in interpreting what you see that

---

[8]A microscope with magnification of 50-100$\times$ is satisfactory. Even a simple toy microscope can be used for introductory work.

cubes usually rest on one face but sometimes are tilted. Perfect octahedra develop slowly (note the stages in Fig. 25-2). Usually the octahedron rests on an undeveloped cubic face, sometimes on an octahedral face. As the crystals grow larger, their imperfections become exaggerated, and little is gained by prolonged examination.

EXPERIMENT 3. Recrystallization of silver chromate. In a spot plate or test tube mix several drops of K_2CrO_4 solution with a drop of 6 M HNO_3. Spot one drop of the mixture on a slide, and a few millimeters away from it place a small drop of $AgNO_3$ solution. Draw a thin rod from the silver nitrate drop to the other and tilt the slide slightly so that the reagent flows into the acid chromate solution. This technique produces a more uniform and slower precipitation than direct addition of one drop to the other. Examine the precipitate under the microscope and sketch representative crystals. Then add a small drop of 6 M HNO_3 to the drop containing the precipitate. Warm cautiously over a microflame, holding the slide well above the flame and withdrawing it before the solution comes to a boil. Silver chromate should dissolve upon warming. Set the slide aside to cool and re-examine it when crystals appear. The formation of red platelets, usually diamond-shaped at first, is characteristic of silver chromate. Lead chromate forms only fine granules; strontium and barium chromates will not precipitate from nitric acid solution.

Repeat the precipitation of silver chromate, but this time dissolve it in a drop of 15 M NH_3. Sketch the somewhat different crystals of the ammine that separate on cooling.

EXPERIMENT 4. Differentiation of Ca^{++} ion from Sr^{++} and Ba^{++} ions. Clean three microscope slides carefully and spot them with small drops of the standard solutions of Ca^{++}, Sr^{++}, and Ba^{++} ions. Each drop should be about 5-7 mm wide and 1 mm deep; if it is larger, suck off the excess. Place a small drop of 6 M H_2SO_4 a few millimeters away from each of the three spots. Use the same technique for adding the reagent as was used in the precipitation of silver chromate. Observe the character of the precipitates through the microscope immediately after precipitation and after 5-10 minutes standing. The crystals of calcium sulfate often grow so slowly that the growth can be followed through the microscope. Sketch representative crystals in your notebook. The sensitivity of this test for calcium is much reduced if barium and strontium are present in the same solution.

Suggestions for further work. For any extensive work in this field the references at the end of the chapter should be consulted for more background, particularly on the design and use of microscopes, crystal systems, and techniques peculiar to microscopy. Among the many tests that can be studied are (1) differentiation of sodium and potassium with uranyl acetate, (2) precipitation of barium chromate, (3) precipitation of strontium nitrate, and (4) the reaction of tetrathiocyanatomercurate(II) ion with mixtures of Zn^{++} and Cu^{++} or Zn^{++} and Co^{++}.

25-7. Chromatographic Methods.   Tswett, a botanist at the University of Warsaw, was the first to exploit a chromatographic method (1903). He named the technique "chromatography" because of the colored zones that were obtained in the separation of plant pigments. Colorless substances of all kinds, such as amino acids, carbohydrates, and enzymes, as well as inorganic ions, can be separated by this powerful technique. It has been exceedingly popular since the synthesis of ion-exchange resins and the discovery of paper chromatography by Consden, Gordon, and Martin in 1944.

In chromatographic separations a bulk, mobile phase flows over another, thin phase held stationary on a supporting material such as a column of solid or a strip of paper. The mobile phase is usually a liquid, but in recent years gases have been used. Three types of chromatographic methods are usually distinguished according to the nature of the supporting material: adsorption, ion-exchange, and partition. The distinction is not always clearly defined.

a. Adsorption Chromatography.   The stationary phase is the surface of a solid adsorbent, such as alumina, charcoal, sugar, or chalk, packed into a column in a glass tube (Fig. 25-3). A solution of the mixture to be separated is added to the top of the column and is washed down the column with a liquid or succession of different liquids. During this *elution* the components of the mixture separate into zones which are slowly eluted from (washed down) the tube. With natural pigments such as the green coloring matter in leaves or many organic compounds, continual adsorption and desorption of solutes occur during elution. The rate at which a solute travels depends on a competition for it between adsorbent and solvent. Strongly bound solutes will stay near the top of the tube and travel slowly downward; lightly adsorbed solutes will be rapidly eluted. Separation of a mixture is thus achieved by exploiting differences in the degrees of adsorption and solubility of its components, and the choice of an adsorbent and solvent is critical for the success of the separation. In the separation of inorganic ions adsorption may not be the only process taking place; ion-exchange and complex formation are often involved.

b. Ion-exchange Chromatography.   This has as the supporting phase a solid that exchanges its own cations (or anions) for those in a solution that percolates through it. Certain silicates such as zeolites, clays, and fuller's earth are naturally occurring ion-exchangers. Synthetic organic solids with more reproducible and controllable properties are commonly used now; the first such ion-exchange resin was prepared in 1935. If we are content to ignore the complexities of their structures, we can represent two common types by $RSO_3^-Me^+$ and RN^+X^- where R stands for the organic framework of the resin. Actually each resin molecule contains many ionic groups but only one is represented in these formulas for simplicity. The Me^+ ions (or X^- ions) are counter ions (Sec. 8-19) attracted to the resin and held by the electrostatic force of the charges. Typical ion-exchange processes are represented by

$$\text{Cation exchange:} \quad RSO_3^-Me^+ + Na^+ \rightleftharpoons RSO_3^-Na^+ + Me^+$$
$$\text{Anion exchange:} \quad RN^+X^- \quad + Cl^- \rightleftharpoons RN^+Cl^- \quad + X^-$$

When an electrolytic solution and an ion-exchange resin are allowed to stand together, an equilibrium is established. The ratio of concentrations of the simple ions, e.g., $[Me^+]/[Na^+]$, is usually not far from unity, so exchange is seldom complete as a result of simply mixing resin and solution. The efficiency of the exchange is increased by allowing the solution of the electrolyte to percolate through a tube filled with the resin. True equilibrium is seldom attained and the rates of diffusion of ions into and out of the resin become important in determining the extent of exchange.

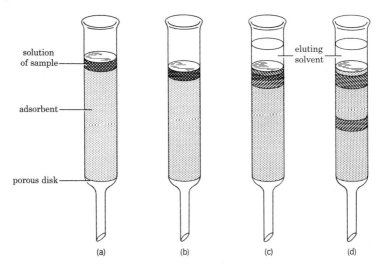

FIG. 25-3. Schematic representation of the separation of two solutes by adsorption chromatography.

Ion-exchange resins can be used to separate ions in various ways. The separation of cations from undesirable anions (Sec. 24-9c) can be carried out with a cation-exchange resin. The resin is used in its acid form, i.e., with $Me^+ = H^+$. A weakly acid solution of the sample is added to the top of the column. The cations of the solution are exchanged for the hydrogen ions of the resin. The anions and hydrogen ions are eluted from the column with water. Then 6 M HCl is passed through the column and the exchange reaction is reversed:

$$H^+ + RSO_3^-Me^+ \rightarrow RSO_3H + Me^+$$

because of the high concentration of hydrogen ion. The metal ions, chloride ions, and excess hydrochloric acid are eluted from the column, and after removal of excess water and acid the solution can be analyzed for the cations without fear of interference by anions such as phosphate and oxalate. The separation of interfering anions fails if a large excess of oxalate or fluoride is present, for these form anion complexes with cations such as Fe^{+++} ion.

Another type of separation is a simple variation of the foregoing one. If one cation can be converted to an anion complex, it can be separated from the other cations. Thus Fe^{+++} ion forms anion complexes with thiocyanate at high concentration whereas Al^{+++} ion does not. The iron is eluted and the aluminum stays behind on the resin.

When two cations must be separated as such, competing equilibria can be used to increase the difference in their rates of elution. Citrate ions form complexes with many cations to an extent that depends on the nature of the metal ion and on the pH. The competition between resin and citrate for metal ions can be regulated by controlling the acidity of the solution. Ions as closely similar to each other in chemical properties as those of the rare earth metals can be separated by elution with citrate solutions of controlled pH.

c. Paper Partition Chromatography.   The stationary phase is a liquid film adhering to the fibers of paper. The separation of ions is based on differences in their distribution between this largely aqueous film and the eluent, which is usually an organic solvent-water mixture. Adsorption of ions by the paper fibers may also be involved. The components of a mixture are separated into zones during elution which trail behind the solvent front at different rates. Three methods of carrying out paper chromatographic separations are illustrated in Fig. 25-4. The mixture to be separated is spotted on the paper at x. The end of the paper is dipped into the solvent, and the solvent advances through the paper and separates the mixture into a series of spots or rings. The circular technique introduced by Rutter requires the least time and is comparatively simple to do. It is used in the experiments of this text.

The qualitative identification of components of a mixture is based on the observation that the distance of travel of a component relative to that of the solvent front is constant for a given set of experimental conditions. The relative distance of travel is expressed by R_f (ratio of fronts) or R_{fc} when the circular technique is used:

$$R_{fc} = \frac{\text{distance from starting point to center of solute ring}}{\text{distance from starting point to solvent front}}$$

The determination of R_{fc} is illustrated in Fig. 25-5. The values of R_{fc} depend on the solvent, paper, manner of development, temperature, and other conditions. While values recorded in references can be used as rough guides in analysis, it is best to determine the R_{fc} values appropriate to the particular experimental conditions in use. The ratios of R_{fc} values for two ions are sometimes more nearly constant for different conditions than the separate values.

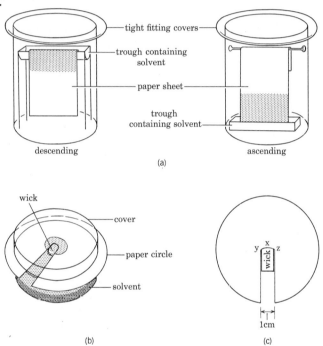

FIG. 25-4. Techniques of paper chromatography.

25-8. Introductory Experiments with Paper Chromatography.[9]

EXPERIMENT 1. Separation of Cations. Cut a circle of filter paper as shown in Fig. 25-4. Apply one small drop of standard solutions of Cu^{++}, Cd^{++}, Fe^{+++}, and Ni^{++} to the point marked x. Rest the paper on another circle of paper and use the technique for spotting described in the first paragraph of Sec. 25-3. Dry each spot by holding the paper high over a flame or by using an infrared lamp. Apply the next drop to the same spot. Continue until a spot centered on x is obtained which contains all 4 metal ions and has a diameter of not more than about 8 mm.

[9]Special equipment: two bottoms or two tops of a Petri dish (95–100 mm outside diameter, 15 mm inside depth); Whatman No. 1 filter paper (12.5 cm diameter), scissors, atomizer, source of H_2S (e.g., a lecture bottle), and infrared lamp or hair dryer (optional).

Place one part of the dish on the desk where it will not be disturbed and where it will be away from flames and direct sunlight. Pour in Solvent Mixture A[10] (CAUTION: inflammable) until the dish is about one-quarter filled. Rest the paper on the edges of the dish with the wick bent down into the solvent. Cover with the other part of the dish and leave undisturbed until the solvent has traveled almost to the inside edge of the dish; this should require about one-half to three-quarters of an hour.

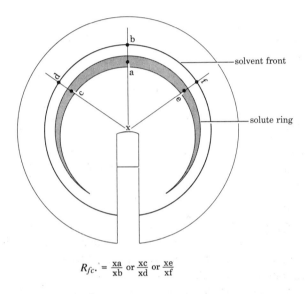

$$R_{fc.}' = \frac{xa}{xb} \text{ or } \frac{xc}{xd} \text{ or } \frac{xe}{xf}$$

FIG. 25-5. Determination of R_{fc}.

Remove the paper and, with a soft pencil, rapidly mark the extreme boundary of the solvent front. This is identical with the outer edge of the Fe^{+++} ring, and that may be used if the solvent evaporates too rapidly to determine the boundary directly. Hang the paper away from flames until the solvent evaporates completely. Pour a few milliliters of 15 M NH_3 into the empty half of the dish and rest the paper over it with the wick sticking up until fumes of ammonium salts no longer form and the blue ring of $Cu(NH_3)_4^{++}$ appears. The boundaries of this and the Fe^{+++} ring can be marked at this time if desired; nickel may be located near the center of the paper by streaking with dimethylglyoxime solution. Finally, spray the chromatogram with aqueous hydrogen sulfide using the atomizer (or pass the gas directly over the paper). The paper may be washed with water to remove excess H_2S and dried. Mark the rings and measure the distance from x to the center of each ring and to the solvent front (or outside edge of the

[10]Solvent Mixture A is 90% acetone, 5% 12 M HCl, and 5% water by volume.

Fe^{+++} ring). The zones are most readily seen by placing the chromatogram against a window pane. Calculate the R_{fc} values; they should be approximately 0.98 for Fe^{+++}, 0.9 for Cd^{++}, 0.7 for Cu^{++}, and 0.1 for Ni^{++}. Express your values to two decimal places.

If time permits, an unknown can be analyzed for these metals. Spot the unknown at y (Fig. 25-4) and a known mixture at z on either side of the wick.

EXPERIMENT 2. Separation of Anions. Prepare a paper and spot it as in Experiment 1 with a drop of each of the standard solutions of Cl$^-$, Br$^-$, I$^-$, SCN$^-$, and CrO$_4^{--}$ ions. Dry each spot before applying the next one. Use Solvent Mixture B.[11] After the solvent has spread to the edge of the dish, remove the paper and quickly mark the solvent front with a soft pencil. Dry the paper and then spray it with 0.02 M AgNO$_3$ solution. Note the red-brown ring of Ag$_2$CrO$_4$ and the yellow ring of AgI. Hold the paper vertically over the sink and rinse it thoroughly with water to remove excess silver ions. Spray it next in the hood with an aqueous solution of H$_2$S (or pass the gas briefly over the surface), rinse again to remove excess H$_2$S, and dry. Measure the R_{fc} values of the five rings; they should be approximately 0.2 to 0.3 for CrO$_4^{--}$, 0.4 for Cl$^-$, 0.5 for Br$^-$, 0.6 for I$^-$, and 0.7 for SCN$^-$. Analyze an unknown mixture if time permits.

Suggestions for further work:

1. If a Geiger-Müller counter is available, study the separation of RaDEF into isotopes of Pb, Bi, and Po.[12] The quantity of Bi^{210} is too small to detect chemically, and yet it is separated chromatographically and can be detected with photographic film or the Geiger-Müller counter.

2. Try the separation of the ions within the usual analytical groups by paper chromatography.[13]

3. Investigate the differential spray and chromatogram comparison methods of Pollard and McOmie (reference at the end of the chapter).

4. Investigate separations of inorganic ions by paper electrophoresis.

5. Try some separations of inorganic ions by adsorption chromatography on columns of activated alumina.[14]

25-9. Separation of Cations from Interfering Anions by Ion-Exchange. Prepare the apparatus illustrated in Fig. 25-6. Take about 5 g of a sulfonic acid type resin[15] in a small beaker and add enough water to give a thin slush. Invert the tube in the beaker, suck until the tube is filled, tighten the screw

[11]Solvent Mixture B is made by shaking together 80 ml of n-butanol, 40 ml of pyridine, 80 ml of water, and 5 ml of 15 M NH$_3$. Use the upper layer.

[12]See F. Lima, *J. Chem. Educ.*, **31**, 153 (1954) for details.

[13]See, for example, J. Surak and R. Martinovich, *J. Chem. Educ.*, **32**, 95 (1955).

[14]See, for example, H. Fillinger, *J. Chem. Educ.*, **24**, 444 (1947), and H. Fillinger and L. Trafton, *J. Chem. Educ.*, **29**, 285 (1952).

[15]Amberlite IR–120(H) or Dowex 50.

clamp, and invert quickly. Bend the rubber so that the glass tip points up, loosen the screw clamp slightly, and allow water to displace the air in the tip. Add more water to the top of the column if necessary. Never allow the water level to go down into the resin bed, for this results in air pockets in the bed which reduce its efficiency. The resin bed should occupy about two-thirds of the column.

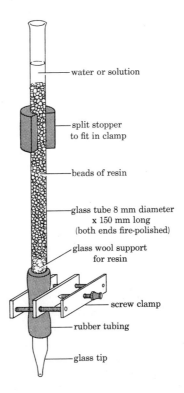

FIG. 25-6. Ion-exchange column.

water or solution

split stopper
to fit in clamp

beads of resin

glass tube 8 mm diameter
x 150 mm long
(both ends fire-polished)

glass wool support
for resin

screw clamp

rubber tubing

glass tip

It is convenient to know the free volume of the column, i.e., the volume of water required to fill the spaces between the resin beads. Draw off water until the level is just above the resin bed. Add 1 drop of K_2CrO_4 solution to the top of the column. Add water to the top and draw it out at the bottom into a graduated cylinder. Chromate is not taken up by the resin but the potassium ion is. Find the volume at which the yellow of chromate just begins to appear at the bottom. This is a measure of the free volume, which, for a column of the size indicated in Fig. 25-6, should be about 1.4 ml.

To illustrate the action of the column use a mixture of 2 drops each of the standard solutions of Fe^{+++}, Ni^{++}, Zn^{++}, and Ca^{++} ions with 1 drop each of Na_2HPO_4 solution, $(NH_4)_2C_2O_4$ solution, and 6 M HCl. Add the mixture to the top of the column and elute the anions with water. Test for the presence of oxalate and phosphate in the solution coming out of the bottom of the column by making a portion alkaline with 15 M NH_3 and adding $Ca(NO_3)_2$ solution to precipitate calcium phosphate and oxalate. After about 10 ml of water has been put through at a rate of about 1 to 2 seconds per drop, demonstrate that these anions are no longer present. Should they still be found, further elution with water is required. Elute the cations with 6 M HCl; the volume required will be 3 to 5 times the free volume of the column. Check for the presence of the cations by neutralizing some of the issuing solution with 15 M NH_3, adding thioacetamide, and warming to precipitate the sulfides.

The resin can be washed with water and reused or, since the amount required is so small, a fresh portion can be taken for each separation.

For the removal of unwanted ions before precipitation of Cation Group 3, use Solution 2-1 of Outline 2 after it has been evaporated with hydrochloric acid to remove hydrogen sulfide and thioacetamide. The hydrochloric acid solution of the eluted cations should be evaporated to a convenient volume before the precipitation of Cation Group 3.

25-10. Flame Spectra.   The outer electrons of certain atoms or ions (Secs. 20-12, 21-3, -4) absorb energy from flames and are excited to higher energies. In returning to lower, more stable states, they give off the excess energy as light. The frequency ν or wavelength λ of light emitted is given by the relation (Sec. 6-14)

$$\text{Change in energy} = h\nu = hc/\lambda$$

where h is Planck's constant and c is the velocity of light. Each transition from one energy level to another corresponds to light of a wavelength determined by this relation, and as the energy levels of atoms (or ions) differ, so do their flame spectra. Those of the alkali metals consist of a comparatively few wavelengths; a larger number of wavelengths is obtained when the atoms are excited more strongly, e.g., in an electric arc. The flame spectra of the alkaline earth salts contain bands of closely spaced lines characteristic of vapor molecules of salt or oxide. Typical flame spectra are shown in Fig. 25-7. The wavelength scale spreads as the violet end of the spectrum is approached because simple spectroscopes disperse violet light to a greater extent than red.

For qualitative analysis flame spectra can be examined with a simple hand spectroscope or one of the Bunsen type (Fig. 25-8). More elaborate and quantitative experiments can be carried out with a spectrograph or a flame photometer. Position the spectroscope so that the slit opening is several inches away from a colorless gas flame. The flame colors can be produced by holding in the flame a platinum wire that has been dipped in some of the salt under test moistened with 12 M HCl. A longer lasting flame is produced by bringing into the flame the edge of a piece of filter paper or porous porcelain that has been soaked in a solution of the salt. It is convenient to view the sodium flame first because its intensity makes adjustment of the instrument easy. Consult your instructor for any specific instructions. Adjust the width of the slit to give a narrow line, the image of the slit, as viewed through the telescope. For faint lines widen the slit opening to let in more light. The scale

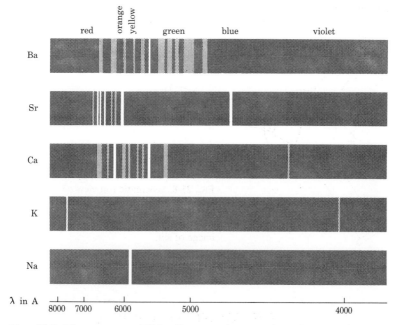

FIG. 25-7. Flame spectra. White lines are the most intense ones. The fine structure of the bands is not shown.

is an arbitrary one; adjust its position so that the sodium line is at some convenient point, e.g., 10 or 20. This line will probably be seen in all the spectra because of the presence of sodium as an impurity. View the spectra of the chlorides of potassium, calcium, strontium, and barium. Note the positions on the scale that correspond to bright lines or bands of color. The violet line of potassium and some of the others are difficult to see; it may be necessary to darken the room and turn off the scale light momentarily to locate them. An unknown sample can be analyzed by using the most prominent lines for identification.

25-11. Polarography. This is an electrical method admirably suited to the detection and approximate determination of traces of metals. An increasing voltage is applied to an electrolysis cell in which one electrode is large and the other is very small, usually a drop of mercury forming from a capillary tube. The discharge or plating out of a cation on the mercury drop is associated with a rapid increase in current. The increase is limited by the depletion of the ion in the neighborhood of the small electrode. Each ion has a characteristic potential, called the half-wave potential, at which half of the increase in current has occurred. When a solution is electrolyzed and the half-wave potentials are measured, the ions can be identified. For further details consult the references.

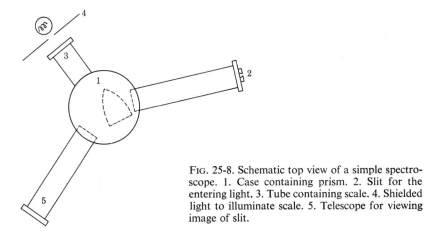

FIG. 25-8. Schematic top view of a simple spectroscope. 1. Case containing prism. 2. Slit for the entering light. 3. Tube containing scale. 4. Shielded light to illuminate scale. 5. Telescope for viewing image of slit.

SUPPLEMENTARY READING

Spot testing:

F. FEIGL, *Spot Tests*, vol. I, *Inorganic Applications*, 5th ed., Elsevier, New York, 1958.

P. WENGER and R. DUCKERT, eds., *Reagents for Qualitative Inorganic Analysis*, Elsevier, New York, 1948.

G. CHARLOT, *Qualitative Inorganic Analysis*, Wiley, New York, 1954.

H. WEISZ, *Mikrochim. Acta*, **1954**, 140, 376, 460, 785; see also a brief summary by P. West, *Anal. Chem.*, **28**, 758 (1956). The "ring-oven" technique described in these articles is an interesting new way of using classical analytical methods on a micro scale. The instrument is commercially available.

Electrographic Analysis:

H. HERMANCE and H. WADLOW, "Electrography and Electro-Spot Testing," in W. Berl, *Physical Methods of Chemical Analysis*, vol. II, Academic Press, New York, 1951, pp. 156–228.

J. LINGANE, *Electroanalytical Chemistry*, Interscience, New York, 1953, Chapter 16.

H. WILLARD, L. MERRITT, Jr., and J. DEAN, *Instrumental Methods of Analysis*, 3rd ed., Van Nostrand, New York, 1958, pp. 500–02, 504–05.

Chemical Microscopy:

E. CHAMOT and C. MASON, *Handbook of Chemical Microscopy*, 2nd ed., Wiley, New York, 1939–46, two vols., with useful photomicrographs in vol. II. A classic.

H. SCHAEFFER, *Microscopy for Chemists*, Van Nostrand, New York, 1953.

See also the book by Wenger and Duckert which contains useful photomicrographs.

Chromatography:

F. POLLARD and J. McOMIE, *Chromatographic Methods of Inorganic Analysis*, Academic Press, New York, 1953.

H. G. CASSIDY, "Fundamentals of Chromatography," in A. Weissberger, *Technique of Organic Chemistry*, vol. 10, Interscience, New York, 1957; see also by the same author, *J. Chem. Educ.*, **23**, 427 (1946); **33**, 482 (1956).

R. SAMUELSON, *Ion Exchangers in Analytical Chemistry*, Wiley, New York, 1953.

E. LEDERER and M. LEDERER, *Chromatography*, 2nd ed., Van Nostrand, New York, 1957.

R. BLOCK, E. DURRUM, and G. ZWEIG, *A Manual of Paper Chromatography and Paper Electrophoresis*, 2nd ed., Academic Press, New York, 1958.

Spectroscopy:

W. BRODE, *Chemical Spectroscopy*, 2nd ed., Wiley, New York., 1947.

G. HARRISON, R. LORD, and J. LOOFBOUROW, *Practical Spectroscopy*, Prentice-Hall, Englewood Cliffs, N.J., 1948.

N. NACHTRIEB, *Practice of Spectrochemical Analysis*, McGraw-Hill, New York, 1950.

B. McDUFFIE, "Qualitative Analysis with the 'Spectranal,'" *J. Chem. Educ.*, **30**, 454 (1953).

Polarography:

L. MEITES, *Polarographic Techniques*, Interscience, New York, 1955.

O. MÜLLER, *Polarographic Methods of Analysis*, 2nd ed., Chemical Education Publishing Co., Easton, Pa., 1956.

I. KOLTHOFF and J. LINGANE, *Polarography*, 2nd ed., Interscience, New York, 1952.

See also textbooks of quantitative and instrumental analysis for briefer discussions.

APPENDIXES

APPENDIX A

Answers to Numerical Problems

1-3. 35 times as large in dioxane; 1.6 times as strong at 100°
1-8. 3.1 A
1-19. 3×10^{12}
1-20. 6.10 debyes; 18% ionic character

2-1. Molecular weight 271, Al_2Cl_6
2-12. 435 ohms
2-20. $K_f = 1.864°$
2-21. i = 1.0, 2.8, 1.8
2-22. 3.2 times as much work in alcohol; 4 times as much for $MgSO_4$
2-32. 11.3 debyes; 2.79 A
2-33. 2.14 molar molecular HNO_3; 67.5% ionized

4-1. Equiv. wts.: (a) 68; (b) 49; (c) 17; (d) 37; (e) 32; (f) 53
4-2. (a) 2.0 mmoles; (b) 1 mmole; (c) 0.0024 g-atom; (d) 16 mg; (e) 17 mg; (f) 1.1 meq
4-3. (a) 3.7 M; (b) 0.84 M; (c) 1.34 $\times 10^{-5} M$; (d) 0.21 M; (e) 16 M; (f) 15 M
4-4. (a) 37 N; (b) 0.2 N; (c) 0.2 N; (d) 0.5 N
4-5. (a) 34 mmoles; (b) 5 mmoles; (c) 1 mmole Ba^{++}, 2 mmoles Cl^-; (d) 0.34 mmole Ni^{++}, 0.68 mmole NO_3^-; (e) 0.0075 mmole K^+ and Ba^{++}, 0.0225 mmole Cl^-
4-6. (a) 3.3 drops; (b) 4 drops; (c) 3.3 drops; (d) 2500 drops; (e) 133 drops
4-7. (a) 0.125 M; (b) 3 ml; (c) 3 drops; (d) 0.45 mg/ml; (e) 4 drops; (f) 0.02 M Cu^{++}, 0.016 M Na^+, 0.028 M SO_4^{--}
4-8. 5 mg Pb^{++}/ml, 2.0 mg Hg_2^{++}/ml, 2.5 mg Ag^+/ml, 0.21 M HNO_3
4-9. (a) 1.03 drops; (b) 0.2 drop; (c) 30 drops required; (d) 19 mg; (e) 3.6 mg; (f) 128 mg
4-10. (a) 0.043 M; (b) 0.008 M La^{+++}, 0.024 M Cl^-; (c) 0.078 M Mg^{++}, 0.156 M NO_3^-; (d) 0.04 M Na^+, 0.012 M Ba^{++}, 0.064 M Cl^-; (c) 0.1 M

K^+, 0.1 M NO_3^-, 10^{-7} M H^+; (f) both 0.04 M; (g) 0.035 M and 0.095 M; (h) 0.05 and 0.04 M
4-11. (a) (1) 0.0316 M, 0.65 g/100 ml; (2) 0.1020 M, 0.041 g; (3) 0.0186 M, 0.38 g; (b) 4.4 mg/ml; (c) 0.022 g/l
4-12. (a) 1.7 M HNO_3, 4.3 M H^+, 4.3 M NO_3^-; (b) 6×10^{-6} M H^+ or CN^-, 0.099994 or virtually 0.1 M HCN; (c) 0.0038 M HCO_3^-, 0.096 M CO_3^{--}, 0.0038 M OH^-; (d) 0.019 M Cl^-, 0.001 M $PbCl^+$, 0.009 M Pb^{++}

5-10. -164 kcal
5-13. 1.9779 ± 0.0009; 1.8754 ± 0.0156
5-14. 5.47×10^{-4}; 18,300 ohms
5-18. 390.8
5-19. 2.65%

7-7. (a) 8.1 times as fast at 98°; (b) 1.6 times as fast at 90°
7-10. (a) 10 times faster in 0.5 M solution; (b) 0.9 times as fast at 60°
7-25. First $K \times 10^5$: 2.33, 2.30, 2.54, 2.40, 2.38; Second $K \times 10^3$: 2.37, 2.76, 3.54, 4.87, 7.67
7-26. First K: 0.25, 0.19, 0.31, 0.22; Second K: 0.31, 0.20, 0.18, 0.11
7-29. 86
7-30. (a) 1.84 mg; (b) 1.95 mg
7-31. (a) 7.2 ml; (b) 1.3 ml
7-32. 0.37 ml
7-34. 2.6×10^{-22}
7-35 (a) 0.3 M; (b) 0.094 M

8-11. $2.00 \times 10^{-9} = K_{sp}$
8-12. $K_{sp} = 5.09 \times 10^{-13}$
8-13. $K_{sp} = 1.05 \times 10^{-10}$
8-15. (a) 0.06; (b) 0.06; (c) 0.01; (d) 0; (e) 0.06; (f) 0.05
8-16. 0.158
8-17. 0.697
8-18. 0.32

9-1. Values of K: (a) 2.1×10^{19}; (b) 4.5×10^4; (c) 1.0×10^{-8}; (d) 5.6×10^4; (e) 6.2×10^{-16}; (f) 1.1×10^3; (g) 5.6×10^3; (h) 7.7×10^8; (i) 3.9×10^{-5} (for formation of $HC_2O_4^-$); (j) 1.2

9-2. $(K/Q) = 3.4$ for $Mg(OH)_2$; 2.4×10^{-18} for $Al(OH)_3$

9-3. $(K/Q) = 2.6 \times 10^{-7}$

9-4. $(K/Q) = 1.9 \times 10^8$

9-5. $(K/Q) = 1.2 \times 10^{-12}$

9-6. $(K/Q) = 7.9 \times 10^{-4}$

9-16. -40.5 kcal

9-17. 8.5 kcal; -5.9 kcal

9-18. 54.2 kcal; -26.2 kcal

9-19. 15.9 kcal

9-20. $K = 9 \times 10^{-25}$

9-21. $K = 6 \times 10^{-7}$

9-22. $K = 29$

9-23. K: 6×10^{-7}; 4×10^3

9-24. K: 2.5×10^{-46}; 3×10^{27}

10-1. (a) $[H^+] = 0.5\,M$; $[OH^-] = 2 \times 10^{-14}\,M$; (b) $[H^+] = 4 \times 10^{-14}\,M$; (c) $[OH^-] = 1.7 \times 10^{-14}\,M$; (d) $[H^+] = 6.7 \times 10^{-13}\,M$

10-2. (a) 0.52; (b) 3.2; (c) 13.18; (d) -0.30; (e) 4.70; (f) 6.98; (g) 0.12

10-4. (a) $[H^+] = 5 \times 10^{-3}\,M$; $[OH^-] = 2 \times 10^{-12}\,M$; (b) $[H^+] = 2.5 \times 10^{-7}\,M$; (c) $[OH^-] = 2 \times 10^{-6}\,M$; (d) $[H^+] = 3.2 \times 10^{-12}\,M$

10-5. (a) 7.47; (b) 6.81; (c) 6.85

10-6. (a) $1.3 \times 10^{-21}\,M$; (b) $3.2 \times 10^{-20}M$; (c) $1.3 \times 10^{-19}\,M$; (d) $1.3 \times 10^{-7}\,M$

10-7. $1.4 \times 10^{-22}\,M$

10-8. $1.8 \times 10^{-15}\,M$

10-9. $1.4 \times 10^{-13}\,M$

10-10. 0.15 mg Sr/ml

10-11. 0.00015 mg Cd/ml

10-12. 2.9×10^{-9}

10-13. (a) 2.1×10^{-9}; (b) 0.041 g

10-14. 1.4×10^{-8}

10-15. 4×10^{-8}

10-16. 3.0×10^{-5}

10-17. 1.9×10^{-7} mg Ag/ml; 0.33 mg Pb/ml

10-18. (a) 6.1×10^{-13}; (b) 6.9×10^{-5} g/100 ml; (c) 3.4×10^{-9} g/100 ml

10-20. (b) 4.9×10^{-5}; $9.0 \times 10^{-9}\,M$; (c) $3.7 \times 10^{-6}\,M$; (d) 99.98%

10-21. (b) 8×10^{-23}; $8 \times 10^{-34}\,M$;

(c) $1 \times 10^{-13}\,M$; (d) $100 - 10^{-9}$ or virtually 100%

10-23. 2.26; 8.20; 9.52

10-24. 0.0015 M

10-25. 2.6×10^{-21}

10-26. 30, 0.30, 0.0030 mg Ca/ml

10-27. 74%

10-28. $1.6 \times 10^{-5}\,M$

10-29. $6.6 \times 10^{-9}\,M$

10-30. 6.80

10-36. $1.5 \times 10^{-5}\,M$

10-37. 6.94

10-38. 6.92; 6.92

10-40. Twice as soluble at depth of 9870 meters (6.1 statute miles)

10-41. 7.19

11-18. (a) $[H^+] = [C_2H_3O_2^-] = 1.9 \times 10^{-3}\,M$; $[HC_2H_3O_2] = 0.198$ or virtually 0.2 M; $[OH^-] = 5.3 \times 10^{-12}$; pH 2.73; (b) pH 5.70; [HCN] virtually 0.01 M; (c) pH 11.36; $[NH_4^+] = 2.3 \times 10^{-3}\,M$; (d) $[NO_2^-] = 2.0 \times 10^{-3}\,M$; pH 2.70; (e) pH 4.14; $[HCOOH] = 2.8 \times 10^{-5}\,M$; (f) $[OH^-] = 3.8 \times 10^{-6}\,M$; pH 8.58; (g) $[OH^-] = 6.3 \times 10^{-6}\,M$; pH 8.80; (h) $[Ca^{++}] = 0.02\,M$; $[C_2H_3O_2^-]$ virtually 0.04 M; $[OH^-] = 4.7 \times 10^{-6}\,M$; pH 8.68; (i) $[H_2S]$ virtually 0.05 M; $[S^{--}] = 1.3 \times 10^{-13}$; pH 4.15; (j) pH 4.18; $[CO_3^{--}] = 4.7 \times 10^{-11}\,M$; (k) $[CO_3^{--}] = 0.047\,M$; $[H_2CO_3 + CO_2] = 2.3 \times 10^{-8}\,M$; pH 11.51; (l) $[H_2SO_3 + SO_2] = 0.15\,M$; $[SO_3^{--}] = 6.2 \times 10^{-8}\,M$; pH 1.30; (m) pH 0.29; $[SO_4^{--}] = 0.0096\,M$; $[H^+] = 0.51\,M$

11-19. 5.62; $4.7 \times 10^{-11}\,M$

11-20. 4.87

11-21. $3.7 \times 10^{-2}\,M$; $2.7 \times 10^{-13}\,M$

11-22. $1.3 \times 10^{-3}\,M$

11-23. 2.9%

11-24. 1.2%; 11%

11-25. 5.7%, 2.9×10^{-10}

11-26. (a) 8.0%; 1.80; (b) 0.0034%; 4.77; (c) 0.011%; 5.27; (d) 1.0%; 2.98; (e) 0.007%, 5.45

11-27. (a) 0.9%, 11.27; (b) 1.6%; 11.2; (c) 58%, 12.76; (d) 0.001%, 8.3

11-28. (a) 9.12; (b) 8.88; (c) 1.64; (d) 1.89; (e) 8.87

11-35. (a) $[H^+] = [H_2PO_4^-] = 2.3 \times 10^{-2}$ M; $[H_3PO_4] = 0.077$ M; $[OH^-] = 4.3 \times 10^{-13}$ M; $[HPO_4^{--}] = 6.3 \times 10^{-8}$ M; $[PO_4^{---}] = 1.2 \times 10^{-18}$ M (b) $[H^+] = 8.2 \times 10^{-3}$ M; $[C_6H_5O_7^{---}] = 8.3 \times 10^{-10}$ M

11-37. 99.9999%; 99.4%; 0.57%

11-45. 5.92

11-46. 3.9×10^{-3} M

11-49. 1.89×10^{-3} M

11-50. 4.3×10^{-4} M

12-1. (a) 0.22; (b) 1.00; (c) 0.85; (d) 13.30; (e) 12.85; (f) 13.00

12-2. (a) $4.3 \times 10^{-5} M$; (b) $1.1 \times 10^{-5} M$; (c) 8.1×10^{-21} M; (d) 1.16×10^{-10} M

12-3. (a) 5.76; (b) 9.54; (c) 6.05; (d) 10.63; (e) 4.97; (f) 9.24

12-4. (a) 3.6×10^{-6} M; (b) 10.02; (c) 1.85×10^{-9} M; (d) 7.4×10^{-5} M; (e) 1.1×10^{-4} M; (f) 3.0×10^{-6} M; (g) 4.89; (h) 4.05

12-5. (a) change in pH 3.70; (b) 0.00; (c) 0.00

12-6. 7.18; 7.29

12-10. 6.6×10^{-5} M

12-14. 1.0×10^{-20} M; 3.2 M

12-15. 17.0 g

12-16. 1.7 to 1 up to 41,000 to 1

12-17. $[Cr^{+++}][OH^-]^3 = 7.5 \times 10^{-30}$; $[Mn^{++}][OH^-]^2 = 5.8 \times 10^{-19}$

12-18. 6×10^{-6} M

12-19. $[Fe^{++}][S^{--}] = 2 \times 10^{-12}$

12-22. 95%, 67%, 17%

12-25. 4.9

13-1. 2.80

13-2. 4.96

13-3. 0.059 moles

13-4. pH 3.36; $[S^{--}] = 6.8 \times 10^{-15}$ M

13-5. 3.48

13-7. pH 9.3; 53%

13-8. 7.06

13-9. pH 6.55; 0.2%

13-10. pH 4.73; 58%

13-11. pH 7.69; 1.1×10^{-6} M

13-15. pH 9.24; 2.3×10^{-6} M

13-16. pH 9.18; 1.4×10^{-5} M

13-17. 8.06

13-18. 4.59

13-19. pH 7.11; 0.01 M

13-20. 6.82

13-21. (a) 2.8×10^{-18} M; (b) 2.5×10^{-15} M

13-22. (a) 8.4×10^{-14} M; (b) 7.3×10^{-11} M

13-23. pH 8.34; 1.0×10^{-4} M

13-24. 9.82

13-25. 4.92; ratio $= 0.19$

13-26. 4.53; $[SO_3^{--}] = 2.1 \times 10^{-4}$ M

13-27. 3.66

13-28. 9.8 and 4.68

13-29. 6.06

13-31. 5.97

13-33. 0.001 M: pH 6.12; 0.076% and 0.00075%; 1 M: pH 5.14; 0.0079% and 0.0072%

14-1. 5.0×10^{-20} M

14-2. 1.0×10^{-29} and 6.2×10^{-18} M

14-3. 2.2×10^8

14-4. 0.004% as $HgCl_4^{--}$

14-5. 0.085 g/l

14-6. 5.5 g/l

14-7. (a) 0.67 g; (b) 1.67 g

14-8. $Q = 2.7 \times 10^{-14}$

14-9. 1.09 moles

14-11. 0.12 M

14-12. 1.5×10^{-33}

14-13. 1.2×10^{-5} M

14-14. 1.3×10^{-5} M

15-10. 2.9×10^9

15-11. 0.46

15-12. 2.7×10^3

15-13. 4×10^{19}

15-17. 2.12 v

15-18. 0.03 v for Cu; 0.06 v for Ag

15-20. (b) 1.7×10^{-10}

15-21. (a) 8×10^{40}; (b) 2.1×10^{12}; (c) 2×10^{21}; (d) 2×10^{-3}

15-22. 0.460 v

15-23. $Y = 0.85$

15-24. -0.39 v

15-25. 0.99; 7.75

Review Problems

B-1. If the concentration of hydroxide ion in a saturated solution of magnesium hydroxide is regulated at 9×10^{-6} M by a buffer mixture of ammonia and ammonium chloride, what is the molar concentration of magnesium ion?

B-2. The equivalent conductance of 0.1 N monochloroacetic acid is 43.3 units at 25°. The limiting equivalent conductances of the hydrogen and monochloroacetate ions are, respectively, 350 and 40 units. Calculate the approximate extent of ionization and ionization constant of the acid. Why is the answer only approximately correct?

B-3. Calculate the pH and concentrations of all ionic and molecular species in 0.001 M ammonium nitrate solution.

B-4. Calculate the equilibrium constants for two possible reactions between sodium hydrogen carbonate and potassium dihydrogen phosphate. Which is more likely to occur?

B-5. A saturated solution of calcium sulfate contains 0.208 g per 100 ml of solution. Calculate the solubility in moles per liter.

B-6. Calculate the pH of a mixture of 1 drop of 6 M potassium hydroxide and 10 ml of water.

B-7. Calculate the solubility of calcium iodate in 0.0107 M potassium hydroxide if the activity coefficient factor Y is 0.282 and $K_{sp}^0 = 7.119 \times 10^{-7}$ at 25°.

B-8. Calculate the molarity of iron(III) in a solution that contains 10 mg Fe^{+++} ml.

B-9. Three drops of a solution containing 5 mg Br^-/ml is warmed with hydrogen peroxide and acetic acid to oxidize the halide to free bromine. This solution, which has a total volume of 10 drops, is shaken with 4 drops of CCl_4. Calculate the percentage of the bromine in the lower layer. The distribution ratio $[Br_2]_{CCl_4}/[Br_2]_{H_2O}$ is 28.

B-10. Calculate $[FeOH^{++}]$ in a mixture that is 0.05 M in iron(III) perchlorate and 1 M in perchloric acid. What other ions containing iron may be present?

B-11. To what pH must a saturated solution of silver oxide be adjusted by addition of sodium hydroxide if it is to contain no more than 0.001 mg Ag^+/ml?

B-12. From the standard free energies of formation calculate the equilibrium constant for $2H^+ + ZnS(c) \rightleftharpoons Zn^{++} + H_2S(g)$.

B-13. Calculate the pH of a neutral solution at 100°C if $K_w = 5.5 \times 10^{-13}$.

B-14. What is the concentration of sulfide ion in a solution saturated with H_2S at 25° and 1 atm pressure if the pH is 3.0?

B-15. Calculate the ionic strength of a solution that contains 0.025 mole of both potassium dihydrogen phosphate and disodium hydrogen phosphate per liter.

B-16. The specific conductance of a saturated solution of silver chloride at 5° is 4.37×10^{-7} units; that of the water used to prepare the solution is 0.30×10^{-7} The limiting equivalent conductance of silver chloride is 86.3 at 5°. Calculate the solubility and solubility product.

B-17. Estimate the extent of ionization of 0.01 M acetic acid with allowance for the activity coefficient corrections.

B-18. Calculate the pH of a mixture that contains 0.05 mole of oxalic acid and 0.10 mole of $NaHC_2O_4$ per liter.

B-19. Solid silver nitrate is added gradually to a solution that contains 0.001 mole of thiocyanate ion and 0.02 mole of chloride ion per liter. Assume that the volume remains constant. (a) Which silver salt will precipitate first? (b) Calculate the concentration of silver ion when each precipitate first begins to form. (c) What will be the concentration of chloride ion when AgSCN begins to precipitate? What will be the concentration of thiocyanate ion when AgCl first begins to form?

B-20. Solid silver chromate is shaken with some 0.03 M potassium chromate solution to which a small amount of base has been added to suppress hydrolysis of the chromate ion. The concentration of silver ion in the saturated solution was found by an electrical method to be 9×10^{-6} M. Calculate the solubility product of silver chromate.

B-21. Calculate the pH of a solution prepared by adding 0.45 ml of 0.20 M NaOH to 68 mg of KH_2PO_4 and diluting to a final volume of 50 ml.

B-22. Calculate the extent of ionization of 0.1 M and of 0.001 M formic acid.

B-23. Find the approximate concentration of Co^{++} ion in mg/ml left unprecipitated when a solution of its salt is saturated with H_2S at 25° and 1 atm if the solution also contains 0.5 mole of sodium acetate and 1 mole of acetic acid per liter. Take the solubility product of freshly precipitated CoS to be 4×10^{-21}.

B-24. Calculate the pH and extent of reaction of the ions in 0.2 M ammonium cyanide.

B-25. The equivalent conductance of 0.0005 N $CaCl_2$ is 131.93 units. Calculate the specific conductance and the resistance of the solution when it is placed between plane electrodes having an area of 3 cm² and being 25 cm apart.

B-26. Calculate the pH of a solution prepared by dissolving 20 mg of succinic acid in sufficient water to give 40 drops of solution.

B-27. A cell equipped with hydrogen and silver–silver chloride electrodes contains a solution which is 0.02 M in sodium chloride. At 25° and a hydrogen pressure of 1 atm the e.m.f. of the cell is 1.000 v. Calculate the pH of the solution. Neglect activity coefficient corrections.

B-28. Calculate the pH and concentration of sulfide ion in 0.5 M ammonium sulfide.

B-29. Sufficient potassium cyanide is added to a suspension of silver chloride to give a solution that is 0.01 M in $Ag(CN)_2^-$ ion and 0.2 M in excess KCN. If enough KI is dissolved in the solution to make the concentration of iodide ion 0.01 M will any silver iodide precipitate?

B-30. Calculate the concentration of Ba^{++} ion in mg/ml left unprecipitated if precipitation of barium chromate is carried out in such a way that chromate is left in excess to the extent of 0.04 mole/l.

B-31. Calculate the pH and concentration of carbonate ion in 0.3 M ammonium carbonate.

B-32. Find the concentrations of hydrogen and hydroxide ions in a mixture of 2 drops of 0.1 M KOH and 3 drops of 0.05 M HCl.

B-33. Calculate the equilibrium constant for

$$2AgCl(c) + 2OH^- \rightleftharpoons Ag_2O(c) + H_2O(l) + 2Cl^-$$

from standard free energies of formation.

B-34. Calculate the pH and concentration of oxalate ion for 0.2 M $NaHC_2O_4$.

B-35. Calculate the number of milligrams of Na^+ required to give 50 mg of $Na(UO_2)_3Mg(C_2H_3O_2)_9 \cdot 9H_2O$.

B-36. Find the concentrations of hydrogen and hydroxide ions in 0.000005 M $Ca(OH)_2$ solution.

B-37. What is the molarity of chloride in water that contains 0.1 part of Cl^- per million parts of water? (Good distilled water should contain less than this.)

B-38. Calculate the pH of 0.1 M $Cu(NO_3)_2$ solution.

B-39. Calculate the concentrations of ions and molecules in 0.2 M oxalic acid.

B-40. Calculate the pH of a mixture that contains 0.02 mole of zinc nitrate and 0.3 mole of nitric acid per liter.

B-41. What is the minimum ratio of concentrations of ammonium nitrate to ammonia necessary to prevent the precipitation of $Mg(OH)_2$ from a solution that is 0.1 M in $Mg(NO_3)_2$?

B-42. Find from the standard oxidation potentials the equilibrium constant for $2Fe(CN)_6^{---} + 2I^- \rightarrow I_2 + 2Fe(CN)_6^{----}$.

B-43. Calculate the concentrations of sulfide ion and molecular hydrogen sulfide in 0.2 M KHS solution.

B-44. Calculate the concentration of hydrogen carbonate ion in a saturated solution of $CaCO_3$ in 0.2 M NaOH if the solubility of the salt is 8.3×10^{-5} moles/l.

B-45. Calculate the concentration of Hg^{++} ion in a mixture that is 0.01 M in $K_2Hg(CN)_4$ and 0.07 M in KCN if the instability constant of the complex at this ionic strength is 3×10^{-42}.

B-46. Concentrated hydrochloric acid varies from 36.5 to 38 % HCl by weight. The average density is 1.18 g/ml. Calculate the limits of its molarity.

B-47. Find the solubility product of silver chromate and its solubility in mg/ml at 50° if a saturated solution of it in pure water was found by a colorimetric method to contain 1.61×10^{-4} moles of chromate ion per liter.

B-48. Calculate the pH of a saturated solution of $CaCO_3$ in pure water if 100 ml of solution contain 1.4×10^{-3} g.

B-49. Calculate the concentration of Hg^{++} ion in a solution that is 0.01 M in $K_2Hg(SCN)_4$ and 0.2 M in KSCN.

B-50. The activity coefficient factor Y of acetic acid in a mixture that is 0.001 m in the acid and 2.01 m in KCl is 0.80. Calculate the hydrogen ion concentration of the mixture.

B-51. Calculate the solubility of silver cyanide in 10 M NH_3.

B-52. How many drops of 6 M HCl are required to neutralize 1 ml of 3 M NaOH?

B-53. The standard oxidation potential for $HgS \rightarrow Hg^{++} + S^0 + 2e^-$ is -1.07 v. Calculate the equilibrium constant for

$$3HgS + 8H^+ + 2NO_3^- \rightleftharpoons 3Hg^{++} + 3S^0 + 4H_2O + 2NO$$

B-54. Calculate the e.m.f. of the cell represented by

$$Zn \mid Zn(NO_3)_2 \ (0.02 \ M) \parallel AgNO_3 \ (0.06 \ M) \mid Ag$$

Neglect activity coefficient corrections.

B-55. Estimate the solubility of $PbCl_2$ in 0.001 M $Pb(NO_3)_2$.

B-56. Calculate the percentage conversion of silver chloride to silver carbonate if the chloride is equilibrated with 10 ml of 2 M Na_2CO_3 solution.

B-57. Calculate the pH of 0.0005 M barium acetate.

B-58. Find the number of millimoles of aluminum in 30 mg of $Al_2(SO_4)_3$.

B-59. Calculate the solubility of As_2S_3 in 0.5 M KOH if the equilibrium constant for $As_2S_3 \downarrow + 2OH^- \rightleftharpoons AsS_2^- + AsS(OH)_2^-$ is 7×10^{-3}.

B-60. Calculate the extent of ionization of H_2S in 0.03 M solution.

B-61. Calculate the solubility of CdS with allowance for the basic reaction of the sulfide ion with water.

B-62. Calculate the limiting equivalent conductance of benzoic acid if that of sodium benzoate is 82.4, that of nitric acid is 421.2, and that of sodium nitrate is 121.5.

B-63. Calculate the pH of a solution that contains 0.02 mole of calcium hydroxide and 0.1 mole of sodium nitrite per liter.

B-64. The standard oxidation potential for $Pb \rightarrow Pb^{++} + 2e^-$ is 0.126 v and that for $Pb + SO_4^{--} \rightarrow PbSO_4 + 2e^-$ is 0.356 v. Calculate the solubility product of lead sulfate.

B-65. Calculate the equilibrium constant for

$$SrCO_3 \downarrow + SO_4^{--} \rightleftharpoons SrSO_4 \downarrow + CO_3^{--}$$

from (a) standard free energies of formation and (b) solubility products.

B-66. Calculate the change in pH that results when 1 drop of 0.2 M NaOH is added to 10 ml of a buffer that is 0.1 M in acetic acid and 1 M in sodium acetate.

B-67. What is the molarity of Ni^{++} ion in a solution that was prepared by diluting 3 drops of a standard solution of the ion (10 mg Ni/ml) to a final volume of 2 ml?

B-68. What must the hydrogen ion concentration of a solution saturated with CO_2 at 25° and 132 mm pressure be to give a carbonate ion concentration of 3×10^{-17} M?

B-69. Calculate the pH of a solution prepared by mixing 1 drop of 0.1 M NaOH with 5 drops of 0.2 M H_3AsO_4.

B-70. A solution contains 1.8 g of $Hg(NO_3)_2$ and 4.56 g of $Bi(NO_3)_3 \cdot 5H_2O$ together with 50 ml of 8 M HNO_3 per liter. Calculate the number of mg of each metal ion per milliliter and the molarity of acid.

B-71. Calculate the pH of a mixture of 10 ml of 0.10 M H_3PO_4 and 1 ml of 0.2 M KOH.

B-72. Calculate the standard free energy changes for

$$2CrO_4^{--} + 2H^+ \rightarrow Cr_2O_7^{--} + H_2O$$
$$2CrO_4^{--} + H_2O \rightarrow Cr_2O_7^{--} + 2OH^-$$

What is the significance of these answers?

B-73. Calculate the pH of 5×10^{-8} M KOH.

B-74. Find the concentrations of hydrogen and hydroxide ions in a saturated solution of calcium hydroxide if the pH is 12.4.

B-75. Calculate the molarities of the ions in a mixture of 2 drops of 0.5 M $CaCl_2$ and 4 drops of 0.3 M KCl.

The Ionization Constants of Acids and Bases at 25°

All constants are for the loss or gain of a single proton.

Values of K_a are rounded off to two significant figures; some less accurate values are given to only one. Values of $pK_a = -\log K_a$ are given to two decimals when known with sufficient accuracy.

Values of K_b, the ionization constants of bases, are given only for certain molecular bases. Other values of K_b can be found from K_a of the conjugate acid by the relation $K_b = K_w/K_a$.

TABLE C-1.

Neutral and Anionic Acids

Name of acid	Formula of acid	Formula of conjugate base	K_a	pK_a
Acetic acid	$HC_2H_3O_2$	$C_2H_3O_2^-$	1.8×10^{-5}	4.76
Arsenic acid	H_3AsO_4	$H_2AsO_4^-$	6.0×10^{-3}	2.22
Dihydrogen arsenate ion	$H_2AsO_4^-$	$HAsO_4^{--}$	1.0×10^{-7}	6.98
Monohydrogen arsenate ion	$HAsO_4^{--}$	AsO_4^{---}	4×10^{-12}	11.4
Benzoic acid	$HC_7H_5O_2$	$C_7H_5O_2^-$	6.3×10^{-5}	4.20
Boric acid	H_3BO_3	$B(OH)_4^-$	5.8×10^{-10}	9.24
Carbonic acid	$H_2CO_3 + CO_2$	HCO_3^-	4.4×10^{-7}	6.35
Hydrogen carbonate ion	HCO_3^-	CO_3^{--}	4.7×10^{-11}	10.33
Hydrogen chromate ion	$HCrO_4^-$	CrO_4^{--}	3.0×10^{-7}	6.52
Citric acid	$H_3C_6H_5O_7$	$H_2C_6H_5O_7^-$	7.4×10^{-4}	3.13
Dihydrogen citrate ion	$H_2C_6H_5O_7^-$	$HC_6H_5O_7^{--}$	1.7×10^{-5}	4.76
Monohydrogen citrate ion	$HC_6H_5O_7^{--}$	$C_6H_5O_7^{---}$	4.0×10^{-7}	6.40
Formic acid	$HCHO_2$	CHO_2^-	1.8×10^{-4}	3.76
Glycine	$^+NH_3CH_2CO_2^-$	$NH_2CH_2CO_2^-$	1.7×10^{-10}	9.78
Hydrocyanic acid	HCN	CN^-	4×10^{-10}	9.4
Hydrofluoric acid	HF	F^-	6.7×10^{-4}	3.17
Hydrosulfuric acid	H_2S	HS^-	1.0×10^{-7}	7.0
Hydrogen sulfide ion	HS^-	S^{--}	1.3×10^{-13}	12.9
Lactic acid	$HC_3H_5O_3$	$C_3H_5O_3^-$	1.4×10^{-4}	3.86
Monochloroacetic acid	$HC_2H_2ClO_2$	$C_2H_2ClO_2^-$	1.4×10^{-3}	2.86
Nitrous acid	HNO_2	NO_2^-	5.1×10^{-4}	3.3
Oxalic acid	$H_2C_2O_4$	$HC_2O_4^-$	5.4×10^{-2}	1.3
Hydrogen oxalate ion	$HC_2O_4^-$	$C_2O_4^{--}$	5.4×10^{-5}	4.27
Phosphoric acid	H_3PO_4	$H_2PO_4^-$	7.1×10^{-3}	2.15
Dihydrogen phosphate ion	$H_2PO_4^-$	HPO_4^{--}	6.3×10^{-8}	7.20
Monohydrogen phosphate ion	HPO_4^{--}	PO_4^{---}	4.4×10^{-13}	12.4

TABLE C-1 (*continued*)

Neutral and Anionic Acids

Name of Acid	Formula of Acid	Formula of conjugate base	K_a	pK_a
Propionic acid	$HC_3H_5O_2$	$C_3H_5O_2^-$	1.3×10^{-5}	4.87
Succinic acid	$H_2C_4H_4O_4$	$HC_4H_4O_4^-$	6.2×10^{-5}	4.21
Hydrogen succinate ion	$HC_4H_4O_4^-$	$C_4H_4O_4^{--}$	2.3×10^{-6}	5.64
Sulfamic acid	HNH_2SO_3	$NH_2SO_3^-$	1.0×10^{-1}	1.0
Hydrogen sulfate ion	HSO_4^-	SO_4^{--}	1.0×10^{-2}	1.99
Sulfurous acid	$H_2SO_3 + SO_2$	HSO_3^-	1.7×10^{-2}	1.8
Hydrogen sulfite ion	HSO_3^-	SO_3^{--}	6.2×10^{-8}	7.20
Tartaric acid	$H_2C_4H_4O_6$	$HC_4H_4O_6^-$	1.1×10^{-3}	2.96
Hydrogen tartrate ion	$HC_4H_4O_6^-$	$C_4H_4O_6^{--}$	4.3×10^{-5}	4.37

TABLE C-2.

Cation Acids and Molecular Bases*

Cation acid and conjugate base	Formula	K_a	pK_a	K_b	pK_b
Ammonium ion	NH_4^+	5.7×10^{-10}	9.24		
Ammonia	NH_3			1.8×10^{-5}	4.76
Anilinium ion	$C_6H_5NH_3^+$	2.6×10^{-5}	4.59		
Aniline	$C_6H_5NH_2$			3.9×10^{-10}	9.41
Glycinium ion	$^+NH_3CH_2CO_2H$	4.5×10^{-3}	2.35		
Glycine	$^+NH_3CH_2CO_2^-$			2.2×10^{-12}	11.65
Methylammonium ion	$CH_3NH_3^+$	2.4×10^{-11}	10.62		
Methylamine	CH_3NH_2			4.2×10^{-4}	3.38
Pyridinium ion	$C_5H_5NH^+$	5.0×10^{-6}	5.30		
Pyridine	C_5H_5N			2.0×10^{-9}	8.70
Triethanolammonium ion	$(C_2H_4OH)_3NH^+$	1.7×10^{-8}	7.77		
Triethanolamine	$(C_2H_4OH)_3N$			5.9×10^{-7}	6.23
Trimethylammonium ion	$(CH_3)_3NH^+$	1.6×10^{-10}	9.80		
Trimethylamine	$(CH_3)_3N$			6.3×10^{-5}	4.20

*See also Table 11-3 for the acidity constants of hydrated metal ions.

TABLE C-3.

The Ion Product of Water at Various Temperatures

Temp, °C	K_w	pK_w
0	0.11×10^{-14}	14.94
20	0.68×10^{-14}	14.17
25	1.00×10^{-14}	14.00
30	1.47×10^{-14}	13.83
60	9.61×10^{-14}	13.02

Solubility Products at 25°

Substance	Formula	K_{sp}
Aluminum hydroxide	$Al(OH)_3$	1.4×10^{-34}
Barium carbonate	$BaCO_3$	1.6×10^{-9}
Barium chromate	$BaCrO_4$	1.2×10^{-10}
Barium fluoride	BaF_2	2.4×10^{-5}
Barium oxalate	$BaC_2O_4 \cdot 2H_2O$	1.5×10^{-8}
Barium sulfate	$BaSO_4$	1.0×10^{-10}
Bismuth sulfide	Bi_2S_3	1×10^{-96}
Calcium carbonate	$CaCO_3$	4.7×10^{-9}
Calcium chromate	$CaCrO_4$	7.1×10^{-4}
Calcium fluoride	CaF_2	1.7×10^{-10}
Calcium oxalate	$CaC_2O_4 \cdot H_2O$	2.1×10^{-9}
Calcium sulfate	$CaSO_4 \cdot 2H_2O$	2.4×10^{-5}
Cadmium hydroxide	$Cd(OH)_2$	2.8×10^{-14}
Cadmium oxalate	CdC_2O_4	2.8×10^{-8}
Cadmium sulfide	CdS	7×10^{-27}
Chromium(III) hydroxide	$Cr(OH)_3$	7×10^{-31}
Cobalt(II) hydroxide (pink)	$Co(OH)_2$	2×10^{-16}
Cobalt(III) hydroxide	$Co(OH)_3$	1×10^{-43}
Cobalt(II) sulfide	CoS	8×10^{-23}
Copper(I) chloride	$CuCl$	3.2×10^{-7}
Copper(II) chromate	$CuCrO_4$	3.6×10^{-6}
Copper(II) hydroxide	$Cu(OH)_2$	2.2×10^{-20}
Copper(I) iodide	CuI	1.1×10^{-12}
Copper(I) sulfide	Cu_2S	1×10^{-48}
Copper(II) sulfide	CuS	8×10^{-36}
Iron(II) hydroxide	$Fe(OH)_2$	8×10^{-16}
Iron(III) hydroxide	$Fe(OH)_3$	6×10^{-38}
Iron(II) sulfide	FeS	5×10^{-18}
Lead bromide	$PbBr_2$	4.6×10^{-6}
Lead carbonate	$PbCO_3$	1.5×10^{-13}
Lead chloride	$PbCl_2$	1.6×10^{-5}
Lead chromate	$PbCrO_4$	2×10^{-16}
Lead fluoride	PbF_2	2.7×10^{-8}
Lead hydroxide	$Pb(OH)_2$	4×10^{-15}
Lead iodide	PbI_2	7.1×10^{-9}
Lead oxalate	PbC_2O_4	8×10^{-12}
Lead sulfate	$PbSO_4$	1.7×10^{-8}
Lead sulfide	PbS	8×10^{-28}
Magnesium ammonium phosphate*	$MgNH_4PO_4 \cdot 6H_2O$	2.5×10^{-13}
Magnesium carbonate	$MgCO_3$	1×10^{-5}
Magnesium fluoride	MgF_2	6.4×10^{-9}
Magnesium hydroxide	$Mg(OH)_2$	1.1×10^{-11}
Magnesium oxalate	MgC_2O_4	8.6×10^{-5}
Manganese(II) carbonate	$MnCO_3$	8.8×10^{-11}

Substance	Formula	K_{sp}
Manganese(II) hydroxide	$Mn(OH)_2$	1.6×10^{-13}
Manganese(II) sulfide	MnS	1×10^{-11}
Mercury(I) chloride†	Hg_2Cl_2	1.3×10^{-18}
Mercury(I) chromate†	Hg_2CrO_4	2×10^{-9}
Mercury(I) iodide†	Hg_2I_2	4×10^{-29}
Mercury(II) oxide‡	HgO	3×10^{-26}
Mercury(I) sulfate†	Hg_2SO_4	6.8×10^{-7}
Mercury(II) sulfide (black)	HgS	3×10^{-52}
Nickel hydroxide	$Ni(OH)_2$	2×10^{-15}
Nickel sulfide	NiS	2×10^{-21}
Silver acetate	$AgC_2H_3O_2$	2.3×10^{-3}
Silver arsenate	Ag_3AsO_4	1×10^{-22}
Silver bromide	$AgBr$	5.2×10^{-13}
Silver carbonate	Ag_2CO_3	8.2×10^{-12}
Silver chloride	$AgCl$	1.8×10^{-10}
Silver chromate	Ag_2CrO_4	2.4×10^{-12}
Silver cyanide	$AgCN$	2×10^{-16}
Silver iodide	AgI	8.3×10^{-17}
Silver oxide‡	Ag_2O	2.6×10^{-8}
Silver phosphate	Ag_3PO_4	1×10^{-21}
Silver sulfate	Ag_2SO_4	1.7×10^{-5}
Silver sulfide	Ag_2S	7×10^{-50}
Strontium carbonate	$SrCO_3$	7×10^{-10}
Strontium chromate	$SrCrO_4$	5×10^{-6}
Strontium fluoride	SrF_2	7.9×10^{-10}
Strontium oxalate	$SrC_2O_4 \cdot H_2O$	5.6×10^{-8}
Strontium sulfate	$SrSO_4$	7.6×10^{-7}
Tin(II) hydroxide	$Sn(OH)_2$	1.6×10^{-27}
Zinc carbonate	$ZnCO_3$	2.1×10^{-11}
Zinc hydroxide	$Zn(OH)_2$	7×10^{-18}
Zinc oxalate	ZnC_2O_4	2.5×10^{-9}
Zinc sulfide	ZnS	8×10^{-25}

$*K_{sp} = [Mg^{++}][NH_4^+][PO_4^{---}]$

†The mercury(I) ion is Hg_2^{++}; hence $K_{sp} = [Hg_2^{++}][Cl^-]^2$, etc.

‡The oxide ion is hydrolyzed to hydroxide; hence $K_{sp} = [Hg^{++}][OH^-]^2$ and $K_{sp} = [Ag^+][OH^-]$.

Equilibrium Constants for Complex Ions at 25° *

Ligand	Equilibrium		K^0
Ammonia	$Ag(NH_3)_2{}^+$	$\rightleftharpoons Ag^+ + 2NH_3$	6.3×10^{-8}
	$Co(NH_3)_6{}^{++}$	$\rightleftharpoons Co^{++} + 6NH_3$	2.9×10^{-5}
	$Ni(NH_3)_6{}^{++}$	$\rightleftharpoons Ni^{++} + 6NH_3$	5.7×10^{-9}
	$Cu(NH_3)_4{}^{++}$	$\rightleftharpoons Cu^{++} + 4NH_3$	8.5×10^{-13}
	$Zn(NH_3)_4{}^{++}$	$\rightleftharpoons Zn^{++} + 4NH_3$	1.4×10^{-9}
	$Cd(NH_3)_4{}^{++}$	$\rightleftharpoons Cd^{++} + 4NH_3$	1.9×10^{-7}
Chloride	$HgCl_4{}^{--}$	$\rightleftharpoons Hg^{++} + 4Cl^-$	8.3×10^{-16}
Cyanide	$Ag(CN)_2{}^-$	$\rightleftharpoons Ag^+ + 2CN^-$	1×10^{-20}
	$Ni(CN)_4{}^{--}$	$\rightleftharpoons Ni^{++} + 4CN^-$	1×10^{-22}
	$Cu(CN)_3{}^{--}$	$\rightleftharpoons Cu^+ + 3CN^-$	2.6×10^{-29}
	$Cu(CN)_4{}^{--}$	$\rightleftharpoons Cu^+ + 4CN^-$	5×10^{-31}
	$Zn(CN)_4{}^{--}$	$\rightleftharpoons Zn^{++} + 4CN^-$	1×10^{-19}
	$Cd(CN)_4{}^{--}$	$\rightleftharpoons Cd^{++} + 4CN^-$	7.8×10^{-18}
	$Hg(CN)_4{}^{--}$	$\rightleftharpoons Hg^{++} + 4CN^-$	3×10^{-42}
Hydroxide	$Zn(OH)_4{}^{--}$	$\rightleftharpoons Zn^{++} + 4OH^-$	3.3×10^{-16}
	$Zn(OH)_2 \downarrow + 2OH^-$	$\rightleftharpoons Zn(OH)_4{}^{--}$	0.022
	$Al(OH)_4{}^-$	$\rightleftharpoons Al^{+++} + 4OH^-$	1×10^{-34}
	$Al(OH)_3 \downarrow + OH^-$	$\rightleftharpoons Al(OH)_4{}^-$	16
	$Sn(OH)_3{}^-$	$\rightleftharpoons Sn^{++} + 3OH^-$	4.1×10^{-26}
	$Sn(OH)_2 \downarrow + OH^-$	$\rightleftharpoons Sn(OH)_3{}^-$	0.38
	$Pb(OH)_3{}^-$	$\rightleftharpoons Pb^{++} + 3OH^-$	9.1×10^{-15}
	$Pb(OH)_2 \downarrow + OH^-$	$\rightleftharpoons Pb(OH)_3{}^-$	0.046
	$Sb_2O_3 \downarrow + 3H_2O + 2OH^- \rightleftharpoons 2Sb(OH)_4{}^-$		7.6×10^{-5}
Iodide	$HgI_4{}^{--}$	$\rightleftharpoons Hg^{++} + 4I^-$	5.3×10^{-31}
Thiocyanate	$FeSCN^{++}$	$\rightleftharpoons Fe^{+++} + SCN^-$	9.4×10^{-4}
	$Hg(SCN)_4{}^{--}$	$\rightleftharpoons Hg^{++} + 4SCN^-$	1.3×10^{-22}
Thiosulfate	$Ag(S_2O_3)_2{}^{---}$	$\rightleftharpoons Ag^+ + 2S_2O_3{}^{--}$	3.5×10^{-14}

*The constants include activity coefficient corrections. Without these, the values of K vary considerably with ionic strength. For the ammonia complexes in $2\ M$ NH_4NO_3 solutions the values of K are, respectively, 7×10^{-8}, 5.5×10^{-5}, 1.1×10^{-9}, 2.0×10^{-13}, 2.4×10^{-10}, and 5.2×10^{-8}. The value of K for the iron(III) thiocyanate complex, to cite another example, is 7.2×10^{-3} at $I = 0.5$.

Standard Oxidation Potentials at 25°

The couples are divided between two tables, one for acid solutions and one for basic solutions. In each table the reducing agent is on the left of the double arrows, and the oxidizing agent is on the right. The couples are listed in order from the one with the best reducing agent (most positive $\mathcal{E}^0$) first to the one with the best oxidizing agent last (most negative $\mathcal{E}^0$). An index of the couples by the element undergoing change in oxidation state is given at the end to facilitate finding the desired couple. Most of the values are from Wendell M. Latimer, *The Oxidation States of the Elements and Their Potentials in Aqueous Solutions*, 2nd ed. Copyright, 1938, 1952, by Prentice-Hall, Inc., Englewood Cliffs, N.J. Reproduced by permission of the publisher.

Acid Solutions

Index No.	Couple		$\mathcal{E}^0$, volts
1	Li	$\rightleftharpoons$ Li^+ + e^-	3.01
2	Rb	$\rightleftharpoons$ Rb^+ + e^-	2.92
3	K	$\rightleftharpoons$ K^+ + e^-	2.92
4	Cs	$\rightleftharpoons$ Cs^+ + e^-	2.92
5	Ba	$\rightleftharpoons$ Ba^{++} + $2e^-$	2.90
6	Sr	$\rightleftharpoons$ Sr^{++} + $2e^-$	2.89
7	Ca	$\rightleftharpoons$ Ca^{++} + $2e^-$	2.87
8	Na	$\rightleftharpoons$ Na^+ + e^-	2.71
9	Mg	$\rightleftharpoons$ Mg^{++} + $2e^-$	2.37
10	Al	$\rightleftharpoons$ Al^{+++} + $3e^-$	1.66
11	Mn	$\rightleftharpoons$ Mn^{++} + $2e^-$	1.18
12	Cr	$\rightleftharpoons$ Cr^{++} + $2e^-$	0.91
13	Zn	$\rightleftharpoons$ Zn^{++} + $2e^-$	0.76
14	AsH_3	$\rightleftharpoons$ As + $3H^+$ + $3e^-$	0.60
15	SbH_3	$\rightleftharpoons$ Sb + $3H^+$ + $3e^-$	0.51
16	Fe	$\rightleftharpoons$ Fe^{++} + $2e^-$	0.44
17	Cr^{++}	$\rightleftharpoons$ Cr^{+++} + e^-	0.41
18	Cd	$\rightleftharpoons$ Cd^{++} + $2e^-$	0.40
19	Pb + $2I^-$	$\rightleftharpoons$ $PbI_2 \downarrow$ + $2e^-$	0.365
20	Pb + SO_4^{--}	$\rightleftharpoons$ $PbSO_4 \downarrow$ + $2e^-$	0.356
21	Co	$\rightleftharpoons$ Co^{++} + $2e^-$	0.277
22	H_3PO_3 + H_2O	$\rightleftharpoons$ H_3PO_4 + $2H^+$ + $2e^-$	0.276
23	Pb + $2Cl^-$	$\rightleftharpoons$ $PbCl_2 \downarrow$ + $2e^-$	0.268
24	Ni	$\rightleftharpoons$ Ni^{++} + $2e^-$	0.250
25	Cu + I^-	$\rightleftharpoons$ $CuI \downarrow$ + e^-	0.185
26	Ag + I^-	$\rightleftharpoons$ $AgI \downarrow$ + e^-	0.152
27	Sn	$\rightleftharpoons$ Sn^{++} + $2e^-$	0.14
28	Pb	$\rightleftharpoons$ Pb^{++} + $2e^-$	0.126
29	Hg + $4I^-$	$\rightleftharpoons$ HgI_4^{--} + $2e^-$	0.04
30	H_2	$\rightleftharpoons$ $2H^+$ + $2e^-$	0.0000
31	Ag + $2S_2O_3^{--}$	$\rightleftharpoons$ $Ag(S_2O_3)_2^{---}$ + e^-	−0.01

Acid Solutions (*continued*)

Index No.	Couple		$\mathcal{E}^0$, volts
32	$Ag + Br^-$	$\rightleftharpoons$ $AgBr \downarrow + e^-$	-0.095
33	$Cu + Cl^-$	$\rightleftharpoons$ $CuCl \downarrow + e^-$	-0.137
34	H_2S	$\rightleftharpoons$ $S^0 \downarrow + 2H^+ + 2e^-$	-0.141
35	$Sn^{++} + 6Cl^-$	$\rightleftharpoons$ $SnCl_6^{--} + 2e^-$	-0.15
36	$2Sb + 3H_2O$	$\rightleftharpoons$ $Sb_2O_3 \downarrow + 6H^+ + 6e^-$	-0.152
37	Cu^+	$\rightleftharpoons$ $Cu^{++} + e^-$	-0.153
38	$Bi + H_2O + Cl^-$	$\rightleftharpoons$ $BiOCl \downarrow + 2H^+ + 3e^-$	-0.16
39	$SO_2 + 2H_2O$	$\rightleftharpoons$ $SO_4^{--} + 4H^+ + 2e^-$	-0.17
40	$Ag + Cl^-$	$\rightleftharpoons$ $AgCl \downarrow + e^-$	-0.223
41	$As + 3H_2O$	$\rightleftharpoons$ $H_3AsO_3 + 3H^+ + 3e^-$	-0.247
42	$Bi + H_2O$	$\rightleftharpoons$ $BiO^+ + 2H^+ + 3e^-$	-0.32
43	Cu	$\rightleftharpoons$ $Cu^{++} + 2e^-$	-0.34
44	$Fe(CN)_6^{----}$	$\rightleftharpoons$ $Fe(CN)_6^{---} + e^-$	-0.356
45	$2HCN$	$\rightleftharpoons$ $C_2N_2 + 2H^+ + 2e^-$	-0.37
46	$S_2O_3^{--} + 3H_2O$	$\rightleftharpoons$ $2H_2SO_3 + 2H^+ + 4e^-$	-0.40
47	$2Ag + CrO_4^{--}$	$\rightleftharpoons$ $Ag_2CrO_4 \downarrow + 2e^-$	-0.446
48	$S^0 + 3H_2O$	$\rightleftharpoons$ $H_2SO_3 + 4H^+ + 4e^-$	-0.45
49	$S_4O_6^{--} + 6H_2O$	$\rightleftharpoons$ $4H_2SO_3 + 4H^+ + 6e^-$	-0.51
50	Cu	$\rightleftharpoons$ $Cu^+ + e^-$	-0.52
51	$2I^-$	$\rightleftharpoons$ $I_2 + 2e^-$	-0.535
52	$3I^-$	$\rightleftharpoons$ $I_3^- + 2e^-$	-0.536
53	$CuCl \downarrow$	$\rightleftharpoons$ $Cu^{++} + Cl^- + e^-$	-0.538
54	$H_3AsO_3 + H_2O$	$\rightleftharpoons$ $H_3AsO_4 + 2H^+ + 2e^-$	-0.559
55	MnO_4^{--}	$\rightleftharpoons$ $MnO_4^- + e^-$	-0.564
56	$2Sb(OH)_2^+ + H_2O$	$\rightleftharpoons$ $Sb_2O_5 \downarrow + 6H^+ + 4e^-$	-0.581
57	$2Ag + SO_4^{--}$	$\rightleftharpoons$ $Ag_2SO_4 \downarrow + 2e^-$	-0.653
58	H_2O_2	$\rightleftharpoons$ $O_2 + 2H^+ + 2e^-$	-0.682
59	$2SCN^-$	$\rightleftharpoons$ $(SCN)_2 + 2e^-$	-0.77
60	Fe^{++}	$\rightleftharpoons$ $Fe^{+++} + e^-$	-0.771
61	$NO_2 + H_2O$	$\rightleftharpoons$ $NO_3^- + 2H^+ + e^-$	-0.775
62	$2Hg$	$\rightleftharpoons$ $Hg_2^{++} + 2e^-$	-0.789
63	Ag	$\rightleftharpoons$ $Ag^+ + e^-$	-0.799
64	$CuI \downarrow$	$\rightleftharpoons$ $Cu^{++} + I^- + e^-$	-0.86
65	Hg_2^{++}	$\rightleftharpoons$ $2Hg^{++} + 2e^-$	-0.92
66	$HNO_2 + H_2O$	$\rightleftharpoons$ $NO_3^- + 3H^+ + 2e^-$	-0.94
67	$NO + 2H_2O$	$\rightleftharpoons$ $NO_3^- + 4H^+ + 3e^-$	-0.96
68	$NO + H_2O$	$\rightleftharpoons$ $HNO_2 + H^+ + e^-$	-1.00
69	$2Br^-$	$\rightleftharpoons$ $Br_2 (liq) + 2e^-$	-1.065
70	$ClO_2 + H_2O$	$\rightleftharpoons$ $ClO_3^- + 2H^+ + e^-$	-1.15
71	$I_2 + 6H_2O$	$\rightleftharpoons$ $2IO_3^- + 12H^+ + 10e^-$	-1.195
72	$2H_2O$	$\rightleftharpoons$ $O_2 + 4H^+ + 4e^-$	-1.229
73	$Mn^{++} + 2H_2O$	$\rightleftharpoons$ $MnO_2 \downarrow + 4H^+ + 2e^-$	-1.23
74	$2Cr^{+++} + 7H_2O$	$\rightleftharpoons$ $Cr_2O_7^{--} + 14H^+ + 6e^-$	-1.33
75	$2Cl^-$	$\rightleftharpoons$ $Cl_2 + 2e^-$	-1.36
76	$Pb^{++} + 2H_2O$	$\rightleftharpoons$ $PbO_2 \downarrow + 4H^+ + 2e^-$	-1.456
77	Mn^{++}	$\rightleftharpoons$ $Mn^{+++} + e^-$	-1.51
78	$Mn^{++} + 4H_2O$	$\rightleftharpoons$ $MnO_4^- + 8H^+ + 5e^-$	-1.51
79	$Br_2 + 6H_2O$	$\rightleftharpoons$ $2BrO_3^- + 12H^+ + 10e^-$	-1.52

Acid Solutions (*continued*)

Index No.	Couple		$\mathcal{E}^0$, volts
80	$Br_2 + 2H_2O$	$\rightleftharpoons 2HBrO + 2H^+ + 2e^-$	-1.59
81	$Cl_2 + 2H_2O$	$\rightleftharpoons 2HClO + 2H^+ + 2e^-$	-1.63
82	$PbSO_4 \downarrow + 2H_2O$	$\rightleftharpoons PbO_2 \downarrow + SO_4^{--} + 4H^+ + 2e^-$	-1.685
83	$2H_2O$	$\rightleftharpoons H_2O_2 + 2H^+ + 2e^-$	-1.77
84	Co^{++}	$\rightleftharpoons Co^{+++} + e^-$	-1.84
85	Ag^+	$\rightleftharpoons Ag^{++} + e^-$	-1.98
86	$2F^-$	$\rightleftharpoons F_2 + 2e^-$	-2.65

Basic Solutions

Index No.	Couple		$\mathcal{E}^0$, volts
101	$Al + 4OH^-$	$\rightleftharpoons Al(OH)_4^- + 3e^-$	2.35
102	$Mn + 2OH^-$	$\rightleftharpoons Mn(OH)_2 \downarrow + 2e^-$	1.55
103	$Zn + S^{--}$	$\rightleftharpoons ZnS \downarrow + 2e^-$	1.44
104	$Zn + 4CN^-$	$\rightleftharpoons Zn(CN)_4^{--} + 2e^-$	1.26
105	$Zn + 4OH^-$	$\rightleftharpoons Zn(OH)_4^{--} + 2e^-$	1.22
106	$Cr + 4OH^-$	$\rightleftharpoons Cr(OH)_4^- + 3e^-$	1.2
107	$Cd + S^{--}$	$\rightleftharpoons CdS \downarrow + 2e^-$	1.2
108	$Cd + 4CN^-$	$\rightleftharpoons Cd(CN)_4^{--} + 2e^-$	1.03
109	$Zn + 4NH_3$	$\rightleftharpoons Zn(NH_3)_4^{++} + 2e^-$	1.03
110	$SO_3^{--} + 2OH^-$	$\rightleftharpoons SO_4^{--} + H_2O + 2e^-$	0.93
111	$Sn + 3OH^-$	$\rightleftharpoons Sn(OH)_3^- + 2e^-$	0.91
112	$Sn(OH)_3^- + 3OH^-$	$\rightleftharpoons Sn(OH)_6^{--} + 2e^-$	0.90
113	$H_2 + 2OH^-$	$\rightleftharpoons 2H_2O + 2e^-$	0.828
114	$Cd + 2OH^-$	$\rightleftharpoons Cd(OH)_2 \downarrow + 2e^-$	0.809
115	$Hg + S^{--}$	$\rightleftharpoons HgS \downarrow + 2e^-$	0.72
116	$2Ag + S^{--}$	$\rightleftharpoons Ag_2S \downarrow + 2e^-$	0.69
117	$AsO_3^{---} + 2OH^-$	$\rightleftharpoons AsO_4^{---} + H_2O + 2e^-$	0.67
118	$Cd + 4NH_3$	$\rightleftharpoons Cd(NH_3)_4^{++} + 2e^-$	0.597
119	$S_2O_4^{--} + 4NH_3 + 2H_2O$	$\rightleftharpoons 2SO_3^{--} + 4NH_4^+ + 2e^-$	0.56
120	$Fe(OH)_2 \downarrow + OH^-$	$\rightleftharpoons Fe(OH)_3 \downarrow + e^-$	0.56
121	$Pb + 3OH^-$	$\rightleftharpoons Pb(OH)_3^- + e^-$	0.54
122	S^{--}	$\rightleftharpoons S^0 + 2e^-$	0.48
123	$Ag + 2CN^-$	$\rightleftharpoons Ag(CN)_2^- + e^-$	0.31
124	$NH_3(g) + 7OH^-$	$\rightleftharpoons NO_2^- + 5H_2O + 6e^-$	0.18
125	$NH_3(g) + 9OH^-$	$\rightleftharpoons NO_3^- + 6H_2O + 8e^-$	0.13
126	$Cu + 4NH_3$	$\rightleftharpoons Cu(NH_3)_4^{++} + 2e^-$	0.11
127	$Mn(OH)_2 \downarrow + 2OH^-$	$\rightleftharpoons MnO_2 \downarrow + 2H_2O + 2e^-$	0.05
128	$NO_2^- + 2OH^-$	$\rightleftharpoons NO_3^- + H_2O + 2e^-$	-0.01
129	$Cr(OH)_4^- + 4OH^-$	$\rightleftharpoons CrO_4^{--} + 4H_2O + 3e^-$	-0.02
130	$Co(NH_3)_6^{++}$	$\rightleftharpoons Co(NH_3)_6^{+++} + e^-$	-0.1
131	$Mn(OH)_2 \downarrow + OH^-$	$\rightleftharpoons MnOOH \downarrow + H_2O + e^-$	-0.1
132	$Co(OH)_2 \downarrow + OH^-$	$\rightleftharpoons Co(OH)_3 \downarrow + e^-$	-0.17
133	$2Ag + 2OH^-$	$\rightleftharpoons Ag_2O \downarrow + H_2O + 2e^-$	-0.342
134	$Ag + 2NH_3$	$\rightleftharpoons Ag(NH_3)_2^+ + e^-$	-0.373
135	$4OH^-$	$\rightleftharpoons O_2 + 2H_2O + 4e^-$	-0.401
136	$Ag_2O + 2OH^-$	$\rightleftharpoons 2AgO + 2H_2O + 3e^-$	-0.57
137	$MnO_2 + 4OH^-$	$\rightleftharpoons MnO_4^- + 2H_2O + 3e^-$	-0.59
138	$4OH^-$	$\rightleftharpoons O_2^{--} + 2H_2O + 2e^-$	-0.88
139	$Cl^- + 2OH^-$	$\rightleftharpoons ClO^- + H_2O + 2e^-$	-0.89

Index of Couples

Element	Index numbers	Element	Index numbers
Li	1	Zn	13, 103, 104, 105, 109
Na	8	Cd	18, 107, 108, 114, 118
K	3	Hg	29, 62, 65, 115
Rb	2	C	45, 49
Cs	4	Sn	27, 35, 111, 112
Mg	9	Pb	19, 20, 23, 28, 76, 82, 121
Ca	7	N	45, 59, 61, 66, 67, 68, 124, 125, 128
Sr	6		
Ba	5	P	22
Al	10, 101	As	14, 41, 54, 117
Cr	12, 17, 47, 74, 106, 129	Sb	15, 36, 56
Mn	11, 55, 73, 77, 78, 102, 127, 131, 137	Bi	38, 42
		O	58, 72, 83, 135, 138
Fe	16, 44, 60, 120	S	34, 39, 46, 48, 49, 59, 110, 119, 122
Co	21, 84, 130, 132		
Ni	24	H	30, 113
Cu	25, 33, 37, 43, 50, 53, 64	F	86
Ag	26, 31, 32, 40, 47, 57, 63, 85, 116, 123, 133, 134, 136	Cl	74, 81, 139
		Br	69, 79, 80
		I	51, 52, 71

Standard Free Energies of Formation at 25°*

NOTES: (1) The standard free energy of formation is defined and used in Sec. 9-10. (2) The standard free energy of formation of the elements and of hydrogen ion are assigned the value zero. (3) All values of ΔF_f^0 in the table are in kcal/mole. (4) The symbols (c), (l), and (g) refer to stable crystalline, liquid, and gaseous states of substances at 25° and 1 atm pressure. All ions are at unit activity. (5) Substances are listed alphabetically by symbols (so CO_2 comes before Ca^{++} and Cd^{++}).

Substance	ΔF_f^0	Substance	ΔF_f^0	Substance	ΔF_f^0
Ag^+	18.43	Co^{++}	−12.3	I^-	−12.35
$AgBr(c)$	−22.39	Co^{+++}	+29.6	Mn^{++}	−53.4
$AgCN(c)$	+39.20	$Co(NH_3)_6{}^{++}$	−57.2	$MnO_2(c)$	−111.4
$Ag(CN)_2{}^-$	+72.05	$Co(NH_3)_6{}^{+++}$	−54.5	$MnO_4{}^-$	−101.6
$AgCl(c)$	−26.22	$CoS(c)$	−21.8	$Mn(OH)_2(ppt)$	−145.9
$AgI(c)$	−15.85	$CrO_4{}^{--}$	−168.8	$MnS(c)$	−47.6
$Ag_2O(c)$	−2.59	$Cr_2O_7{}^{--}$	−300.5	$NH_3(g)$	−3.98
$Ag_2S(c)$	−9.56	$HCrO_4{}^-$	−177.5	$NH_4{}^+$	−19.00
Al^{+++}	−115.0	Cu^+	+12.0	$NO(g)$	+20.72
$Al(OH)_3(c)$	−274.0	Cu^{++}	+15.53	$NO_2(g)$	12.39
Ba^{++}	−134.0	$CuCl(c)$	−28.2	$NO_3{}^-$	−49.37
$BaCO_3(c)$	−272.2	$CuCl_2{}^-$	−57.9	Ni^{++}	−11.1
$BaSO_4(c)$	−323.4	$CuI(c)$	−16.62	$NiS(c)$	−18.8
Br^-	−24.57	$CuS(c)$	−11.7	OH^-	−37.60
CN^-	+39.6	F^-	−66.08	Pb^{++}	−5.81
$CO_2(g)$	−94.26	Fe^{++}	−20.30	$PbCO_3(c)$	−149.7
$CO_3{}^{--}$	−126.22	Fe^{+++}	−2.52	$PbCl_2(c)$	−75.04
$HCO_3{}^-$	−140.31	$FeS(c)$	−23.32	$PbO_2(c)$	−52.34
Ca^{++}	−132.18	H^+ or H_3O^+	0.00	$PbS(c)$	−22.15
$CaCO_3(c)$	−269.78	HO^-	−37.60	$PbSO_4(c)$	−193.89
$CaF_2(c)$	−277.7	$H_2O(l)$	−56.69	S^{--}	+20.6
$CaSO_4·2H_2O(c)$	−429.19	$HCO_3{}^-$	−140.31	$SO_2(g)$	−71.79
Cd^{++}	−18.58	$HCrO_4{}^-$	−177.5	$SO_4{}^{--}$	−177.34
$CdS(c)$	−33.6	$H_2S(g)$	−7.89	Sr^{++}	−133.2
Cl^-	−31.35	Hg^{++}	+39.38	$SrCO_3(c)$	−271.9
$ClO_2(g)$	+29.5	$Hg_2{}^{++}$	+36.79	$SrSO_4(c)$	−318.9
$ClO_3{}^-$	−0.62	$HgI_4{}^{--}$	−51.15	Zn^{++}	−35.18
		HgS (black)	−10.22	$ZnS(c)$	−47.4

*Most of these values are from F. Rossini, D. Wagman, W. Evans, S. Levine, and I. Jaffe, "Selected Values of Chemical Thermodynamic Properties," *Natl. Bur. Standards Circ.*, 500 (1950) but those of the sulfides are from J. Goates, M. Gordon, and N. Faux, *J. Am. Chem. Soc.*, **74**, 835 (1952).

The Electronic Structure of Atoms

Atomic number	Symbol	Structure	Atomic number	Symbol	Structure
1	H	$1s^1$	41	Nb	(Kr core) $4d^45s^1$
2	He	$1s^2$	42	Mo	(Kr core) $4d^55s^1$
			43	Tc	(Kr core) $4d^65s^1$
3	Li	$1s^22s^1$	44	Ru	(Kr core) $4d^75s^1$
4	Be	$1s^22s^2$	45	Rh	(Kr core) $4d^85s^1$
5	B	$1s^22s^22p^1$	46	Pd	(Kr core) $4d^{10}$
6	C	$1s^22s^22p^2$	47	Ag	(Kr core) $4d^{10}5s^1$
7	N	$1s^22s^22p^3$	48	Cd	(Kr core) $4d^{10}5s^2$
8	O	$1s^22s^22p^4$	49	In	(Kr core) $4d^{10}5s^25p^1$
9	F	$1s^22s^22p^5$	50	Sn	(Kr core) $4d^{10}5s^25p^2$
10	Ne	$1s^22s^22p^6$	51	Sb	(Kr core) $4d^{10}5s^25p^3$
			52	Te	(Kr core) $4d^{10}5s^25p^4$
11	Na	(Ne core) $3s^1$	53	I	(Kr core) $4d^{10}5s^25p^5$
12	Mg	(Ne core) $3s^2$	54	Xe	(Kr core) $4d^{10}5s^25p^6$
13	Al	(Ne core) $3s^23p^1$			
14	Si	(Ne core) $3s^23p^2$	55	Cs	(Xe core) $6s^1$
15	P	(Ne core) $3s^23p^3$	56	Ba	(Xe core) $6s^2$
16	S	(Ne core) $3s^23p^4$	57	La	(Xe core) $5d^16s^2$
17	Cl	(Ne core) $3s^23p^5$	58	Ce	(Xe core) $4f^26s^2$
18	Ar	(Ne core) $3s^23p^6$	59	Pr	(Xe core) $4f^36s^2$
			60	Nd	(Xe core) $4f^46s^2$
19	K	(Ar core) $4s^1$	61	Pm	(Xe core) $4f^56s^2$
20	Ca	(Ar core) $4s^2$	62	Sm	(Xe core) $4f^66s^2$
21	Sc	(Ar core) $3d^14s^2$	63	Eu	(Xe core) $4f^76s^2$
22	Ti	(Ar core) $3d^24s^2$	64	Gd	(Xe core) $4f^75d^16s^2$
23	V	(Ar core) $3d^34s^2$	65	Tb	(Xe core) $4f^96s^2$
24	Cr	(Ar core) $3d^54s^1$	66	Dy	(Xe core) $4f^{10}6s^2$
25	Mn	(Ar core) $3d^54s^2$	67	Ho	(Xe core) $4f^{11}6s^2$
26	Fe	(Ar core) $3d^64s^2$	68	Er	(Xe core) $4f^{12}6s^2$
27	Co	(Ar core) $3d^74s^2$	69	Tm	(Xe core) $4f^{13}6s^2$
28	Ni	(Ar core) $3d^84s^2$	70	Yb	(Xe core) $4f^{14}6s^2$
29	Cu	(Ar core) $3d^{10}4s^1$	71	Lu	(Xe core) $4f^{14}5d^16s^2$
30	Zn	(Ar core) $3d^{10}4s^2$	72	Hf	(Xe core) $4f^{14}5d^26s^2$
31	Ga	(Ar core) $3d^{10}4s^24p^1$	73	Ta	(Xe core) $4f^{14}5d^36s^2$
32	Ge	(Ar core) $3d^{10}4s^24p^2$	74	W	(Xe core) $4f^{14}5d^46s^2$
33	As	(Ar core) $3d^{10}4s^24p^3$	75	Re	(Xe core) $4f^{14}5d^56s^2$
34	Se	(Ar core) $3d^{10}4s^24p^4$	76	Os	(Xe core) $4f^{14}5d^66s^2$
35	Br	(Ar core) $3d^{10}4s^24p^5$	77	Ir	(Xe core) $4f^{14}5d^9$
36	Kr	(Ar core) $3d^{10}4s^24p^6$	78	Pt	(Xe core) $4f^{14}5d^96s^1$
			79	Au	(Xe core) $4f^{14}5d^{10}6s^1$
37	Rb	(Kr core) $5s^1$	80	Hg	(Xe core) $4f^{14}5d^{10}6s^2$
38	Sr	(Kr core) $5s^2$	81	Tl	(Xe core) $4f^{14}5d^{10}6s^26p^1$
39	Y	(Kr core) $4d^15s^2$	82	Pb	(Xe core) $4f^{14}5d^{10}6s^26p^2$
40	Zr	(Kr core) $4d^25s^2$	83	Bi	(Xe core) $4f^{14}5d^{10}6s^26p^3$

Atomic number	Symbol	Structure	Atomic number	Symbol	Structure
84	Po	(Xe core) $4f^{14}5d^{10}6s^26p^4$	94	Pu	(Rn core) $5f^56d^17s^2$
85	At	(Xe core) $4f^{14}5d^{10}6s^26p^5$	95	Am	(Rn core) $5f^66d^17s^2$
86	Rn	(Xe core) $4f^{14}5d^{10}6s^26p^6$	96	Cm	(Rn core) $5f^76d^17s^2$
			97	Bk	(Rn core) $5f^86d^17s^2$
87	Fr	(Rn core) $7s^1$	98	Cf	(Rn core) $5f^96d^17s^2$
88	Ra	(Rn core) $7s^2$	99	Es*	(Rn core) $5f^{10}6d^17s^2$
89	Ac	(Rn core) $6d^17s^2$	100	Fm*	(Rn core) $5f^{11}6d^17s^2$
90	Th	(Rn core) $6d^27s^2$	101	Md*	(Rn core) $5f^{12}6d^14s^2$
91	Pa	(Rn core) $5f^26d^17s^2$	102	No*	(Rn core) $5f^{13}6d^17s^2$
92	U	(Rn core) $5f^36d^17s^2$	103		(Rn core) $5f^{14}6d^17s^2$
93	Np	(Rn core) $5f^46d^17s^2$			

*The structures of these atoms have not yet been definitely established.

APPENDIX I

Reagents

TABLE I-1.

Solutions

KEY: Solutions that are suggested for the reagent kit are marked with an asterisk. Under "Use," *A* indicates solutions used only in the anion analysis, *B* those used in both anion and cation analysis, *C* those used only in cation analysis, and *I* those used only in introductory experiments. Under "Bottle," 8 is for the 8-ml size, 30 for the 30-ml size, SS for side shelf reagent (250 ml); *am* stands for amber bottle, *gs* for glass stoppered, and *p* for polyethylene. Although 8 ml is an ample supply of most reagents, stock solutions should be available for refills. Like the side shelf reagents they may be kept in 250 ml bottles fitted with droppers. Reference is made to Table I-2 for more detailed directions or comments for certain solutions. Unless otherwise indicated, the weight in the last column of the table is dissolved in distilled water and made up to a final volume of 1 liter. This table does not include reagents for the special methods of Chapter 25; those are given in the chapter.

Reagent	Use	Bottle	Concn	Method of preparation
*Acid, acetic	B	30	6 M	Dilute the concd (17 M) acid
*Acid, hydrochloric	C	30	2 M	Dilute the concd (12 M) acid
*Acid, hydrochloric	B	30	6 M	Dilute the concd (12 M) acid
*Acid, hydrochloric	B	30gs	12 M	Use the concd reagent
*Acid, nitric	B	30	6 M	Dilute the concd (16 M) acid
*Acid, nitric	B	30gs	16 M	Use the concd reagent
*Acid, sulfuric	A	8	6 M	Dilute the concd (18 M) acid
*Acid, sulfuric	B	30gs	18 M	Use the concd reagent
*Aluminon	C	8	0.1%	1.0 g/l of ammonium salt of aurintricarboxylic acid
*Ammonia	B	30	6 M	Dilute the concd (15 M) reagent
*Ammonia	B	30	15 M	Use the concd reagent
*Ammonium acetate	C	8	3 M	231.2 g/l
*Ammonium carbonate	C	8		See Table I-2
*Ammonium chloride	C	8	satd	321 g/l
*Ammonium molybdate	A	8		See Table I-2
*Ammonium nitrate	C	8	0.2 M	16.0 g/l
*Ammonium oxalate	C	8	0.2 M	28.4 g $(NH_4)_2C_2O_4 \cdot H_2O$/l
*Ammonium sulfate	C	8	1 M	132 g/l
*Ammonium thiocyanate	C	8	satd	See Table I-2
*Barium chloride	B	8	0.2 M	48.8 g $BaCl_2 \cdot 2H_2O$/l. Store in bottle of borosilicate glass
*Barium hydroxide	A	8	0.2 M	Satd soln (approx 63 g $Ba(OH)_2 \cdot 8H_2O$/l)
*Barium nitrate	A	8	0.1 M	26.1 g/l
*Calcium nitrate	A	8	0.1 M	23.6 g $Ca(NO_3)_2 \cdot 4H_2O$/l
*Dimethylglyoxime	C	8	1%	10 g per liter of 95% ethyl alcohol

TABLE I-1 (*continued*)

Solutions

Reagent	Use	Bottle	Concn	Method of preparation
*Hydrogen peroxide	B	8am	3%	Use USP soln
*Iron(III) chloride	A	8	0.33 M	90 g $FeCl_3\cdot6H_2O$ to 20 ml 6 M HCl. Dil to 1 liter
*Lead acetate	C	8	0.2 M	76.0 g $Pb(C_2H_3O_2)_2\cdot3H_2O/l$
*Lead nitrate	A	8	0.1 M	33.1 g/l
*Magnesia mixture	C	8		See Table I-2
Magnesium chloride	I	SS	0.02 M	4.07 g $MgCl_2\cdot6H_2O/l$
*Magnesium uranyl acetate	C	8		See Table I-2
*Manganese chloride	A	8	satd	Sat 12 M HCl with $MnCl_2\cdot4H_2O$
*Mercury(II) chloride	C	8	0.1 M	27.2 g/l
Methyl orange	I	SS	0.1%	1.0 g/l
Methyl violet, modified	C	SS	0.06%	See Table I-2
Potassium bromate	I	SS	0.2 M	33.4 g/l
*Potassium chromate	C	8	0.5 M	97.1 g/l
*Potassium ferrocyanide	C	8	0.2 M	84.5 g $K_4Fe(CN)_6\cdot3H_2O/l$
*Potassium hydroxide	C	30p	0.5 M	28.0 g/l
Potassium iodide	I	SS	0.1 M	16.6 g/l
*Potassium permanganate	A	8am	0.02 M	3.2 g/l
*Silver nitrate	B	8am	0.2 M	34.0 g/l
*S. and O. reagent	C	8	0.05%	0.500 g of p-nitrobenzene-azoresorcinol in 1 liter of 0.025 M NaOH
Sodium chloride	I	SS	0.02 M	1.16 g/l
Sodium cobaltinitrite	C	SS	0.33 M	135 g/l. Keep cool
*Disodium hydrogen phosphate	C	8	0.5 M	Add 71.0 g anhyd Na_2HPO_4 gradually to water. Dilute to 1 liter
*Sodium hydroxide	B	30p	6 M	240 g/l
Solution A	A	SSam	3.3 M	170 g $AgNO_3$ in 300 ml H_2O
Solution B	A	SS		25 ml satd $(NH_4)_2CO_3$ + 10 ml 15 M NH_3 + 100 ml H_2O
Succinic acid	I	SS	0.5 M	59.0 g/l
*Thioacetamide	B	30	13%	See Table I-2
*Tin(II) chloride	C	8		See Table I-2
*Triethanolamine	C	8	20%	20% by volume with water

TABLE I-2.

Solutions. Directions and Comments

Ammonium carbonate: dissolve 192 g of powdered reagent in 500 ml of water and 80 ml 15 M NH_3. Dilute to 1 liter.

Ammonium molybdate: dissolve 90 g of $(NH_4)_6Mo_7O_{24}\cdot4H_2O$ in 100 ml of 6 M NH_3. Add 240 g of NH_4NO_3 and after it has dissolved dilute to 1 liter.

TABLE I-2 (*continued*)

Solutions. Directions and Comments

Ammonium thiocyanate: Saturate a mixture of equal volumes of diethyl ether and isoamyl alcohol with solid NH_4SCN.

Magnesia mixture: dissolve 130 g of $Mg(NO_3)_2 \cdot 6H_2O$ and 240 g of NH_4NO_3 in 500 ml of water. Add 150 ml 15 M NH_3 and dilute to 1 liter. Store in a polyethylene bottle.

Magnesium uranyl acetate: dissolve 30 g of $UO_2(C_2H_3O_2)_2 \cdot 2H_2O$ in a mixture of 120 ml of water and 100 ml of glacial acetic acid. Warm if necessary. Add 220 ml of glacial acetic acid. Prepare also a solution of magnesium acetate by adding slowly 148.5 g of $Mg(C_2H_3O_2)_2 \cdot 4H_2O$ to a hot mixture of 40 ml of water and 320 ml of glacial acetic acid. Mix the magnesium and uranyl solutions while they are still warm and allow the mixture to stand overnight. Filter through cotton or sintered glass.

Methyl violet, modified [H. G. Andrew, *Analyst*, **72**, 481 (1947)]: dissolve 3 g of haematoxylin and 0.60 g of methyl violet 6B in a mixture of 200 ml of isopropyl alcohol and 800 ml of water. The solution must age for several weeks before use; the fresh reagent is no improvement over methyl violet itself.

Thioacetamide: dissolve 130 g in a liter; the solution is almost saturated. An 8% solution can also be used, but reactions are more rapid with the more concentrated reagent. After being kept for more than a year in a clear glass bottle, the solution is still effective in precipitating sulfides. Decomposition occurs on standing as shown by the deposition of sulfur; this does no harm. More serious is the gradual formation of sulfate. If the reagent gives a precipitate with barium chloride, a fresh solution should be prepared.

Tin(II) chloride: let 45.0 g of $SnCl_2 \cdot 2H_2O$ stand with 170 ml of 12 M HCl until the lumps disintegrate. Dilute slowly to 1 liter. Keep tin shot in the solution.

Dithizone paper: dissolve 0.1 g of dithizone (diphenylthiocarbazone) in 100 ml of acetone. Transfer the solution to a cylinder. Cut Whatman Spot Reaction Paper (No. 120) into strips about 1 cm wide and dip the strips in the solution. Spread them over glass rods in the hood to dry. Then cut them into squares. Store the squares in a screw-capped vial; they will keep for six months or more if stored in this way.

TABLE I-3.

Solid and Pure Liquid Reagents

KEY: See Table I-1 for meaning of symbols under "Use." Asterisks mark reagents that can be issued in the reagent kit. Vials or 8-ml bottles with screw caps can be used. Reagents for the special methods of Chapter 25 are not included in this list.

Reagent	Use	Reagent	Use
*Aluminum wire, 5-mm lengths	C	Carborundum chips (boiling	
Ammonium chloride	I	stones)	A
Ammonium oxalate	I	Charcoal sticks	B
*Ammonium thiocyanate	C	Cotton	B
Arsenic(III) oxide	I	Copper, powder	I
Carbon tetrachloride	A	Copper(II) chloride	I

TABLE I-3 (*continued*)

Solid and Pure Liquid Reagents

Reagent	Use	Reagent	Use
*Devarda's alloy (Al can be used instead)	A	Silver sulfate	A
Ethyl acetate	A	*Sodium bismuthate	C
Ethyl alcohol, 95%	B	*Sodium carbonate	B
Iron(II) sulfate	I	Sodium carbonate–potassium carbonate, 1:1 mixture	B
Lead(II) oxide	I	Sodium chloride	I
Lead(II, IV) oxide	I	*Sodium dithionite	C
Mercury	I	*Sodium fluoride	C
Mercury(II) nitrate	I	*Sodium nitrite	B
Methyl alcohol	A	*Sulfamic acid	B
*Oxalic acid	C	Sulfur	C
*Potassium chlorate	C	Tin, 20 mesh	I
Potassium chloride	I	Urea	I
*Potassium dichromate	A	*Zinc, 20 mesh	B
*Potassium ferricyanide	B		

TABLE I-4.

Test Papers

Dithizone paper (Table I-2)

Indicator paper, wide range, e.g., Hydrion Vivid 1-11

Indicator paper, short range, e.g., Alkacid Paper, Range 1, pH 0.0 to 3.0 or impregnate filter paper with modified methyl violet (Table I-2).

Litmus paper, red and blue

Lead acetate paper

Starch-iodide paper

Turmeric paper

TABLE I-5.

Standard Solutions of the Ions*

Cations

Ion	Compound	Grams per liter	Solvent
Ag^+	$AgNO_3$	15.8	Water
Hg_2^{++}	$Hg_2(NO_3)_2 \cdot 2H_2O$	14.0	0.6 M HNO_3
Pb^{++}	$Pb(NO_3)_2$	16.0	Water
Hg^{++}	$Hg(NO_3)_2 \cdot \frac{1}{2}H_2O$	16.7	0.16 M HNO_3
Bi^{+++}	$Bi(NO_3)_3 \cdot 5H_2O$	23.2	3.0 M HNO_3
Cu^{++}	$Cu(NO_3)_2 \cdot 3H_2O$	38.0	Water
Cd^{++}	$Cd(NO_3)_2 \cdot 4H_2O$	27.5	Water

*10 mg of ion per milliliter.

TABLE I-5 (continued)

Standard Solutions of the Ions *

Cations

Ion	Compound	Grams per liter	Solvent
As^{III}	As_2O_3	13.2	4 M HCl
As^V	$Na_2HAsO_4 \cdot 7H_2O$	41.7	Water
Sb^{III}	$SbCl_3$	18.8	2.8 M HCl
Sn^{++}	$SnCl_2 \cdot 2H_2O$	19.0	2.8 M HCl
Sn^{IV}	$SnCl_4 \cdot 5H_2O$	29.6	2.4 M HCl
Al^{+++}	$Al(NO_3)_3 \cdot 9H_2O$	139.0	0.024 M HNO$_3$
Cr^{+++}	$Cr(NO_3)_3 \cdot 9H_2O$	77.0	0.024 M HNO$_3$
Fe^{+++}	$Fe(NO_3)_3 \cdot 9H_2O$	72.4	0.024 M HNO$_3$
Co^{++}	$Co(NO_3)_2 \cdot 6H_2O$	49.5	Water
Ni^{++}	$Ni(NO_3)_2 \cdot 6H_2O$	49.5	Water
Mn^{++}	$Mn(NO_3)_2 - 50\%$	42.4 ml	Water
Zn^{++}	$Zn(NO_3)_2 \cdot 6H_2O$	45.5	Water
Ca^{++}	$Ca(NO_3)_2 \cdot 4H_2O$	59.0	Water
Sr^{++}	$Sr(NO_3)_2 \cdot 4H_2O$	32.4	Water
Ba^{++}	$Ba(NO_3)_2$	19.0	Water
Mg^{++}	$Mg(NO_3)_2 \cdot 6H_2O$	106.0	Water
Na^+	$NaNO_3$	37.0	Water
K^+	KNO_3	25.9	Water
NH_4^+	NH_4NO_3	44.5	Water

Anions

Ion	Compound	Grams per liter	Ion	Compound	Grams per liter
F^-	NaF	22.1	NO_2^-	$NaNO_2$	15.0
Cl^-	NaCl	16.5	NO_3^-	KNO_3	16.3
Br^-	KBr	14.9	PO_4^{---}	Na_2HPO_4	14.8
I^-	KI	13.1	AsO_3^{---}	$NaAsO_2$	10.6
SCN^-	KSCN	16.7	AsO_4^{---}	$Na_2HAsO_4 \cdot 7H_2O$	22.5
S^{--}	$Na_2S \cdot 9H_2O$	75.2	CO_3^{--}	Na_2CO_3	17.6
SO_3^{--}	Na_2SO_3	15.7	$C_2O_4^{--}$	$(NH_4)_2C_2O_4 \cdot H_2O$	16.2
SO_4^{--}	$(NH_4)_2SO_4$	13.8	$C_2H_3O_2^-$	$NaC_2H_3O_2 \cdot 3H_2O$	23.0
CrO_4^{--}	K_2CrO_4	16.7	$B(OH)_4^-$	$Na_2B_4O_7 \cdot 10H_2O$	12.1

*10 mg of ion per milliliter.

Apparatus

The laboratory should be equipped with a centrifuge for every five or six students and should also have one or two triple-beam pan balances sensitive to 0.01 g. The following list of apparatus for student desks can be modified somewhat to suit the circumstances of the laboratory and the amount of laboratory work to be covered.

Apparatus List

 3 beakers, 250 ml
 1 each beakers, 5, 10, 50, 100 ml
14 bottles, 8 ml, with screw cap
28 bottles, 8 ml with droppers
 3 bottles, 8 ml, amber, with droppers
 7 bottles, 30 ml, with droppers
 2 bottles, 30 ml, polyethylene, with droppers
 3 bottles, 30 ml, glass stoppered
 1 casserole, 15 ml
 8 centrifuge tubes, 3 ml
 1 crucible, 1.5 ml
 1 flask, Erlenmeyer, 25 ml
 2 glass squares, blue
 1 graduated cylinder, 10 ml
 1 medicine dropper
 4 specimen vials
 1 spot plate, white
12 test tubes, 10 × 75 mm
 2 watch glasses, 25 mm
 1 wash bottle, polyethylene, 16 oz
 1 sponge
 1 towel
 1 burner, micro, with rubber tube
 1 burner, Bunsen, with rubber tube
 1 file or glass scorer
 1 forceps

 1 gas lighter or box of safety matches
 1 platinum or Nichrome wire
 1 ring
 1 ring stand
 1 spatula, monel or nickel
 1 screw clamp
 1 test tube holder
 1 tongs
 1 tripod
 1 water bath cover
 1 wing top
 2 wire gauzes
 1 wood block for test tubes
 1 wood block for specimen vials
 1 wood rack for 8 ml bottles
 1 wood tray for 30 ml bottles
 1 asbestos mat
 1 brush, tapered
12 corks, no. 1
 1 box labels
 1 pkg. pipecleaners
 4 rubber bulbs for pipets
12 rubber bands, $1\frac{1}{4}$ in. long
 4 ft glass tubing, 8 mm
 4 ft glass rod, 2 mm
 1 vial each of red and blue litmus, lead acetate paper, and turmeric paper

Index